D0991243

Engineering Manufacturing Methods

ENGINEERING
MANUFACTURING
METHODS

Gilbert S. Schaller

Professor of Mechanical Engineering
University of Washington

SECOND EDITION

McGRAW-HILL BOOK COMPANY, INC.

New York   Toronto   London   1959

ENGINEERING MANUFACTURING METHODS

THE MAPLE PRESS COMPANY, YORK, PA.

In memory of
John and Bertha
Oren and Susan

PREFACE

This edition has been thoroughly revised in order to bring to the student progressive manufacturing methods concepts. The first chapter keynotes the entire text. Herein new ideas and developments based upon research and scientific achievement indicate the direction as well as the pace of manufacturing development. There is small need to question the validity or potential for study in the engineering manufacturing methods area. Accomplishment is just as profound here as in other branches of engineering education. If this were not true, America's future would indeed be dismal.

A truth that is constantly overlooked in engineering education is that any design or concept must be translated or built into an acceptable end product at a profit if our way of life is to function successfully.

The text content is divided into five sections, each one depicting a definite area of engineering manufacture. Materials in manufacturing have been augmented by including those developed for high-temperature application. The light metals and carbides are given consideration commensurate with their importance. Recognized material and manufacturing standards are featured as a means of integrating manufacturing method with design.

The foundry section is a portrayal of the processing of molten metal through the cleaned casting. New developments, techniques, and equipment are included in this complete exposition. The importance of metal casting as a manufacturing method is too frequently overlooked or slighted because of a lack of comprehension of its economic and production potential.

The section devoted to shaping and treating gives special emphasis to the continuing improvements in the area of cold forming. However, developments in hot forming and heat-treating have been included for a well-rounded coverage of the subject.

In the machining section the addition of Chap. 18 on numerical control serves to give a thorough exposition of machine tool applications and potentialities. Machine tool revisions are emphasized in every chapter of this section.

Advancing techniques in the inert gas area are fully discussed in the welding section. This presentation is comprehensive and inclusive to the point of introducing numerical control of flame shaping. Heat-bending fundamentals are expanded so that the student can grasp the tremendous potential inherent in flame bending as applied in manufacturing.

The completion of this text revision is possible only because of the contributions of the many individuals and organizations who responded so graciously to requests for assistance. Credit for photographs is given in each individual case; yet the author acknowledges with profound thanks these essential contributions.

Especial appreciation is extended to Bert Forsman of Boeing Airplane Company for his critical suggestions on Numerical Control. Thanks are also extended to the Resistance Welders Association and to the American Welding Society for their helpful reviews and suggestions in the welding section.

The author's colleagues in the Mechanical Engineering Shops Division were all most helpful, as was Prof. B. T. McMinn, executive officer of Mechanical Engineering. The encouragement of Dean H. E. Wessman of the College of Engineering is gratefully acknowledged. The author's secretary, Cynthia Burnett, contributed immeasurably to the completion of this revision. Now that the manuscript is finished, the author expresses the wish that this revision will bring some measure of satisfaction to all those whose inspiration and encouragement have made it a fact.

Gilbert S. Schaller

CONTENTS

Preface vii

1. Engineered Manufacturing 1
2. Ferrous Metals 10
3. Nonferrous Metals and Plastics 29
4. Powder Metals and Cermets 52
5. Patterns for Metal Castings 62
6. Sands for the Foundry 82
7. Gating and Risering Metal Castings 101
8. Sand Casting 112
9. Sandless Casting Methods 129
10. The Melt Shop 150
11. Methods of Cleaning Castings 169
12. Cold Shaping 178
13. Hot Shaping 206
14. Heat-treating 231
15. Turning Lathes 265
16. Turret Lathes 292
17. Automatic Lathes, Chucking Machines, and Screw Machines 306
18. Numerical Control for Machine Tools 325
19. Screw Threads 341
20. Boring 359
21. Drilling 372
22. Planing, Shaping, and Slotting 391
23. Milling 403
24. Broaching 430
25. Gearing 443
26. Grinding and Finishes 465
27. Transfer and Special Machines 500
28. Machining and Cutting Tools 511
29. Measuring 530
30. Welding Basics 548
31. Arc Welding 561
32. Gas Welding 580
33. Brazing and Braze Welding 594
34. Resistance Welding 606
35. Automatic and Specialized Welding Arcs 627
36. Auxiliary Torch and Arc Applications 645

Index 675

Chapter 1

ENGINEERED MANUFACTURING

Manufacturing, in common with engineering sciences generally, is being subjected to profound changes. As the term is used here, manufacturing means the production of a satisfactory product from engineering materials by a systematized method or combination of methods. With increasing intensity of competition, manufacturing must be considered as a science rather than an art. The reasons for this are twofold: in the first place, demands being made by designers are extending into areas that were previously unknown and untouched; additionally, functional requirements of manufactured products are being revised continually (Fig. 1-1). As a result, manufacturing, to be successful, must be equal to these new requirements. New concepts and ideas are introduced into manufacturing as a means of meeting changing conditions. A survey of some of the more pertinent factors in this connection follows.

PRODUCIBILITY

The successful manufacturing organization is one in which all functions are coordinated. Lines of communication must be established, kept open, and cultivated, in order that the best abilities and thinking in every echelon can be brought to bear on the final product. Designs to be accepted in this new scheme must be "producible." It is disconcerting to note, in the face of available background and experience, how frequently designs that enter the manufacturing plant are impossible to produce or at best are most expensive.

In order to succeed with a manufactured product, design must concern itself with functionality, cost, and material and manufacturing requirements. A knowledge of engineering materials is fundamental. Demands are changing because of new service conditions and new knowledge. The developments in military aircraft serve as a sound example. Whereas aluminum alloys were considered the standard material for aircraft construction in the days of piston engines, that concept has now

1

undergone complete revision. The demands of jet-propelled craft on engineering materials have proved revolutionary.

If a definition were to be attempted, it could be stated that "producibility" is the attribute of a design which makes it suitable for efficient production at a rate commensurate with the demand. Manpower is a fundamental requirement to any manufacturing program; however, it has become mobile, and skills are no longer provincial in the sense that

Fig. 1-1. The first American jet transport prototype during a test flight. This plane is the Boeing 707. (Courtesy of Boeing Airplane Co., Seattle, Wash.)

they formerly were. This situation explains the phenomenal growth of the aircraft industry and subsequently the missile program on the west coast.

The decisions that must be made about the method of manufacture are basic. The correlations between the contributing areas and the co-operation necessary may well lead to an entirely new branch of engineering; it could be called *manufacturing engineering*. It would epitomize all of the functions that have been considered here. By way of example, analyze the problem of manufacture as between a component that is built by welding, or one that is cast, or again one that would be machined in its entirety.

AUTOMATION

Over the past several years the term "automation" has aroused great interest both in America and abroad. The meaning of this term has been given broad range. If the concept of mechanization is accepted, it can well be said that automation is nothing new. There are examples such as the newspaper printing industry or the manufacture of paper, both of which are completely mechanized and automatic in operation.

It seems best to regard automation as a two-part or dual development. The first aspect could be regarded as the introduction of the automatic mechanization that characterizes our mass-production industries. The second phase would include the newer developments of feedback controls, a feature that is being adapted in every area of manufacturing.

It is usually believed that automation lends itself solely to the large mass-production industries. Truth is that where large production obtains, the benefits to be derived from automation are greatest. Small shops with limited production just cannot afford the capital expenditure for automatic equipment and automatic controls on a scale commensurate with the larger enterprises. They can introduce automation if they will carefully survey potential markets and design their installations in keeping with present and future indicated demand.

Material handling is of basic importance in any manufacturing program. Competitors have equal equipment and materials available; they are equally well financed; the only increment that one can gain over the other then is obviously in the area of material handling. It has well been stated that the cheapest way to handle materials is "not to handle them." Automation is designed to eliminate manual effort in handling.

Some of the highly automated plants are already learning from experience that the rewards expected from such installation are not fully realized. Where large installations have been made it is found that product change has caused obsolescence well in advance of the anticipated life. In the light of this new experience, it seems that further thinking is necessary in order to arrive at a better solution. Among the solutions are those of product redesign with automated equipment in mind. Another approach is designing the automatic equipment so that it will prove more flexible. An example would be that of being able to change heads and similar devices while the bases and certain handling mechanisms could be continued in use.

The important social implication of automation has been summarized by stating that its adoption leads to "the human use of human beings." This statement means that the worker will be called upon for mental endeavor rather than mainly physical effort, a development which would be genuinely wholesome. With an expanding population and an increasing demand for more goods, automation may well prove to be of a significance that has not yet been comprehended. There is the further possibility that with lower production costs, which can follow correctly conceived and installed automation, lower priced goods will result, which will mean a higher standard of living for a substantial number of people throughout the world.

QUALITY CONTROL

The pressure for manufactured goods engendered by the demands of the last war focused attention on the subject of quality control. There just is no point in manufacturing components or entities that, upon completion, are unsatisfactory or fail to function. Such an activity spells inefficiency and a losing position for the producer. There is some difference of opinion as to the concept of the word *quality*. Sometimes it is believed that quality control is merely a type of inspection, or, stated another way, inspection means quality control; however, upon reflection, it must be realized that it is impossible to inspect quality into a product. *The only way that a satisfactory level of quality can be obtained in a product is to build that quality therein.* The competitive American market is growing more quality conscious; in consequence, no manufacturer will attempt to offer anything but a quality product. The problem remains, therefore, of establishing quality and of defining a unit as a means for its expression.

In engineering manufacture the term statistical quality control is becoming better known. The beginning of this development came with the work of Walter Shewhart,[1] who developed concepts that are currently being used and in many cases have been modified and expanded to suit individual situations. Fundamentally, this approach is that of using statistical methods of sampling in determining the quality level of a specific production lot. One of the most successful tools in this connection is the control chart technique, a device which makes it possible to check the output of a given machine tool or process at the source and plot the results so that production can be held within the acceptable quality limits. The limits on the control chart are established by the process itself, rather than in an arbitrary manner. Suffice it to say that with the introduction of statistical quality control, substantial savings have been achieved in many industries.

The importance of quality control is recognized in our forward-looking industrial companies by including a quality control engineer in their organization who heads a staff that is charged with maintaining

[1] "Economic Control of Quality of Manufacturing Product," D. Van Nostrand Company, Inc., Princeton, N.J., 1931.

the quality level in the company's product. It is a question just where the quality control engineer belongs in the manufacturing organization; in some instances he is placed above the chief engineer or the production manager. However, it would seem that a sounder solution could be found by equating the duties of the quality control engineer with those of the other important executives in the organization.

CYBERNETICS

In an earlier paragraph the possibility of the automatic factory was mentioned; in this connection, Dr. Norbert Weiner[2] has contributed some fundamental concepts. As a result of his activity in the field of automatic controls, he wrote a book entitled "Cybernetics." In this work he noted the similarity between the human brain and that of an automatic control. This is not exactly new since some of the oldest equipment, such as the flyball governor on a steam engine, is an example of a type of feedback. The control devices in our present regulating systems are a far cry from the old steam throttle governor control. This matter is mentioned because it is necessary, in considering any program of modern manufacturing methods, to recognize the potential of automatic control. A frequently quoted example of the behavior of the human control system, which includes the brain, the nerve system, and the muscles, can be expressed by citing the example of a baseball player. When the outfielder hears the crack of the bat he instantly starts moving in the direction in which the ball is flying; as he watches the ball, his brain continually controls his movement; and as his eye follows the ball, recalculations of the position of the ball with respect to his body are being made. Where an automatic feedback control[3] is installed a similar situation takes place, theoretically because these systems are self-regulating and fully automatic.

NUCLEONICS

In any discussion of engineered manufacturing it is necessary to consider the latest technological progress. In this connection, the influence of atomic developments cannot be overlooked. Aside from the military aspects of the subject, real interest is developing in the area of nuclear power. This is of importance for two reasons: the first being that here is a completely new device, and secondly that its successful application is based on the ability to manufacture requisite apparatus and equip-

[2] Weiner, Norbert: "Cybernetics; or, Control and Communication in the Animal and the Machine," John Wiley & Sons, Inc., New York, 1948.
[3] Chap. 18.

ment. Welding is the favorite method of joining in the construction of nuclear apparatus of whatever kind. At the turn of the century the prime movers installed in manufacturing plants were invariably of the steam type. These have now been superseded almost entirely by the use of electrical power. In the second half of the century it appears as though electrical power will be generated by the use of atomic energy. It is also reasonable to expect that atomic energy as such will be applied directly as a power source.

Another interesting possibility stemming from nuclear development is the use of radioisotopes. One aspect has been known to industry in connection with gamma ray inspection. However, newer techniques are being developed whereby radioisotopes are used in measurement as well

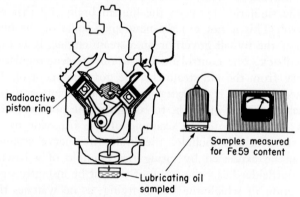

Radioactive piston ring

Samples measured for Fe 59 content

Lubricating oil sampled

Fig. 1-2. Radioactive iron, Fe^{59}, for friction and lubrication studies. Advantages:
1. Transfer of metal measured to 1/100,000 oz
2. Oil sampled during operation of motor
3. Rapid—simple—economical

as in tracing in connection with separation or movement of material. While these activities are not as yet too well defined, it is only a matter of research and time until manufacturing will be enabled to strike out on new horizons.

Radioisotopes have been used in the study of friction and lubrication. Experiments by Sackman, Burwell, and Irvine with samples of bronze, steel, glass, and lead sliding on a block of copper-beryllium, were simplified by radioactivating copper in the base of the cyclotron Cu^{64}. In another development Standard Oil of California has studied the extent of wear on engine piston rings (Fig. 1-2). The piston ring under study is radioactivated to Fe^{59} in a "pile" prior to installation in the test engine cylinder and samples of lubricating oil are drawn periodically in order to measure their radioactivity and consequent ring wear.

Measurements. Measurements in automatic control, such as strip mills, are now successfully made by the use of nucleonic gages. An example of such equipment is shown in Fig. 1-3. In this system of measurement, a comparison is made of the amount of radiation from a source received through the measured material against the amount received with no material in the line at all. The radiation in passing through the measured material loses part of its original intensity. The loss is dependent upon the thickness of the measured material. The radioactive source is mounted in the lower arm under the strip. The radiation detector, a metal ionization chamber, is mounted directly over the source in the upper arm.

Fig. 1-3. Radioisotope gage used for measuring and controlling strip thickness on continuous production lines. (Courtesy of Industrial Nucleonics, Columbus, Ohio.)

Current from the ionization chamber is directly proportional to the amount of radiation present. This current generates a measurable voltage across the resistor. Similar ideas have been developed into gaging of several types. Among these is the measurement of densities.

Radioactive isotopes are quicker and more reliable than any other method of rating the amount of diffusion in solids. In fact, they provide the only method specific enough to measure self-diffusion. Patches of radioactive paint on turbine blades make it possible to compare wear at various loads while the equipment is operating. Metallurgical research has also benefited from the use of isotopes in such areas as measuring vapor pressure on metals. Radioactivity has found considerable adoption in petroleum technology. Thus, tracers are used in refinery control as they are in products pipeline operation.

NUMERICAL CONTROL

The introduction of numerically controlled machine tools can well be compared in importance to the application of power in the Industrial Revolution. Chapter 18 is devoted to a survey of this significant accomplishment. It behooves the engineer to become familiar with the ramifications as well as the potentialities of programmed systems. While the

Fig. 1-4. Numerically controlled five-axis profile milling machine. (Courtesy of Giddings and Lewis Machine Tool Co., Fond du Lac, Wis.)

initial installations have been on machine tools primarily (Fig. 1-4), others have appeared in the area of resistance welding and flame shaping, to mention a few.

This concept is not limited to a single apparatus or machine tool; it is also applicable to a transfer line. It is now no longer necessary to think in terms of mass production in order to develop satisfactory manufacturing costs. Small lot sizes lend themselves to effective production by the use of computers and tape control equipment.

Numerical control will undoubtedly affect machine tools and equipment to the extent that entirely new design concepts will be forthcoming. Present equipment has always been designed with the idea of human control in mind. This traditional approach will prove inadequate for the complete utilization of numerical control. The impact on machine tool design will be profound and far-reaching.

SURVEY QUESTIONS

1-1. Why must manufacturing be considered a science?

1-2. The proposed term *manufacturing engineering* would include what areas?

1-3. Is the functionality of a design dependent upon its "producibility"?

1-4. What type of manufacturing activity should concern itself with automation?

1-5. In what specific industry is automation receiving greatest attention?

1-6. Is quality control of interest only in engineering manufacture?

1-7. Who pioneered the idea of statistical quality control?

1-8. In what ways does statistical quality control aid in lowering manufacturing costs?

1-9. Explain the term "feedback control."

1-10. Where has gamma ray inspection been used in the manufacturing industry?

1-11. How can radioisotopes be used in making wear studies?

1-12. Explain a method for measuring the thickness of steel strip being cold-rolled on a continuous mill.

1-13. Can numerical control be applied in areas other than machine tools?

1-14. What design trends are indicated for machine tools?

REFERENCES FOR CHAP. 1

"Airframe Manufacturing Equipment Committee Report," 1957, Aircraft Industries Association of America, Washington, D.C.

"Automation in Business and Industry," 1957, by Grabbe, John Wiley & Sons, Inc., New York.

"Electronic Digital Computers," 1959, by Smith, McGraw-Hill Book Company, Inc., New York.

"Industrial Engineering Handbook," 1956, by Maynard, McGraw-Hill Book Company, Inc., New York.

"Practical Automation," 1957, by Bittel, Melden, and Rice, McGraw-Hill Book Company, Inc., New York.

"Production Handbook," 1957, by Bangs, The Ronald Press Company, New York.

"Quality Control Handbook," 1951, by Juran, McGraw-Hill Book Company, Inc., New York.

"Radioisotope Laboratory Techniques," 1958, by Faires, Newnes, London.

Chapter 2

FERROUS METALS

The selection of an engineering material is usually approached either from the standpoint of functionality or from that of first cost of the chosen material. A close examination of any successful product which has been in continuous production over a period of time will show continual revision in the direction of lowered man-hour production time. Paralleling this favorable development will be found changes in the engineering materials providing for better manufacturing results.

Selection of Engineering Materials. The conclusion seems clear that engineering materials must be given a closer correlation with manufacturing methods. This need becomes more pressing as competition develops in industry. A pertinent and, for the most part, an overlooked development is the change in supply or availability as it applies to engineering materials. There are indications that some of the standard materials of the past will be forced to share their popularity with others that are developing and making their bid for recognition.

Gray cast iron is a manufacturing material that has been basic from the beginning of the building of machinery. In fact history proves the great antiquity of gray iron castings in almost every field of manufacturing. The concept of bulk and weight has been associated with this material, an idea that continues to persist in some areas even though it is no longer founded on fact. Recently, gray cast iron has been the beneficiary of research and re-evaluation. As a result of a program of research, gray cast iron is now being produced at a price and of a quality that place it in direct competition with steel as well as with other materials. In the continuing search for something better it repeatedly develops that what was considered commonplace has properties previously overlooked or underevaluated.

The practice of making changes in steel specifications from the commoner carbon steels to the complex alloy steels continues. The scarcities in certain alloying elements have focused attention on the necessity for conservation of these dwindling resources. This challenge was met by the development of the National Emergency (NE) series of steels. Once

10

the consumer became accustomed to these substitute steels, he was quick to note that here was a trend toward the use of lower amounts of alloying elements. This raised the question whether or not alloy steels were actually necessary in many of the applications where their use had become general.

When materials of engineering are discussed it is usual to consider only the metallic alloys. These in turn are divided into the general groupings of ferrous and nonferrous materials. It should be added, though, that there is some interest in the noble metals, especially silver, for use in manufacturing. However, no listing or consideration of the subject is complete unless the nonmetals are given their deserved place. The advances being made by ceramics, glass, plastics, synthetics, and processed woods are significant. Plastics have made great progress in engineering manufacture and must be considered.

CAST IRON

Pig Iron. A study of the materials in manufacture should start with the ferrous group, since they are most widely used and are produced in the greatest tonnage (Fig. 2-1). Pig iron is the basis of the far-reaching series of ferrous alloys. However, in a more restricted sense, pig iron is associated with the foundry as the base for cast iron. When considered from this standpoint the term pig iron, ASTM designation A 43, which is the specification for foundry pig iron, lists a total of 308 grades on the basis of chemical composition. These grades are arranged in the following groupings: low-phosphorus, intermediate low-phosphorus, Bessemer, malleable, Foundry Northern low-phosphorus, Foundry Northern high-phosphorus, Foundry Southern, silvery, and charcoal pig irons. These specifications establish accurate limits for silicon, sulfur, phosphorus, and manganese contents. Although carbon is a most important element, its percentages are not stated since it is not controllable within narrow limits.

Cast iron is defined in ASTM designation A 196 as:

Essentially an alloy of iron, carbon, and silicon in which the carbon is present in excess of the amount which can be retained in solid solution in austenite at the eutectic temperature. When cast iron contains a specially added element or elements in amounts sufficient to produce a measurable modification of the physical properties of the section under consideration, it is called alloy cast iron. Silicon, manganese, sulfur, and phosphorus as normally obtained from raw materials are not considered as alloy additions.

This definition of cast iron, in which alloy cast iron is specifically noted, covers the further modifications more familiarly known as chilled iron, inoculant, gray cast iron, ductile cast iron, white cast iron, mottled cast iron, malleable cast iron, and pearlitic malleable cast iron. Each of these is characterized by distinguishing chemical, physical, and mechanical properties.

Chilled Iron. Chilled iron is produced in the foundry in a manner similar to gray cast iron with the modification that the part of the casting

Fig. 2-1. Casting pig iron in a casting machine. (Courtesy of Hanna Furnace Corp., Buffalo, N.Y.)

to be chilled is subjected to accelerated cooling. This is accomplished by placing a metal adjunct, termed "chill," in such a position in the mold that the molten metal lying in contact with it is caused to cool at a greater rate than the remainder of the casting in the mold. The effect obtained is, in essence, a quenching action that prevents the precipitation of major amounts of graphitic carbon, with the result that combined carbon Fe_3C predominates. Since there is but little graphite present, the fracture is white and the section that was subjected to the chill is extremely hard. The purpose of chilling is to produce a very hard surface that is wear-resistant. The most widely used product whose manufacture includes the process of chilling is cast iron railroad car wheels (Fig. 2-2); the treads of these are chilled in order to withstand wear from the railroad rails as well as from brake-shoe action.

Gray Cast Iron. This most interesting and versatile material has been and continues to be the subject of study and research. An exhaustive treatment of gray cast iron in its engineering and metallurgical aspects has been written by John Bolton.[1] The interested student will find a study of this treatise most rewarding.

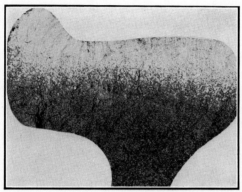

Fig. 2-2. Chilled section of a railroad car wheel tread. (Courtesy of Griffin Wheel Co., Chicago.)

It is the accepted practice to classify gray iron castings on the basis of minimum tensile strengths. The established classification, found in ASTM specification A 48, is shown in Table 2-1:

TABLE 2-1

Class no.	Tensile strength, minimum, psi
20	20,000
25	25,000
30	30,000
35	35,000
40	40,000
50	50,000
60	60,000

Even though the groupings show no. 60 as having the maximum tensile strength, higher values are regularly produced through the addition of

[1] "Gray Cast Iron," Penton Publishing Company, Cleveland, 1937.

alloying elements. It is not difficult to produce gray cast iron of 75,000 psi tensile strength. Some interesting research is under way in the direction of modification of structure by processing and alloying; this has already resulted in gray cast irons approaching 100,000 psi in tensile strength.

The classifications for minimum tensile strength do not include chemical compositions for the reason that the elements comprising gray cast iron vary widely in their effects on the final structure. These effects occur chiefly as the result of the combinations that are possible with such a wide range of variability.

Carbon and silicon exert the greatest influence on machinability; a highly graphitic structure is regarded as being easiest to machine, while a white cast iron possessing a structure in which iron carbide predominates is most difficult. The machinability of gray iron castings is predicted by a study of their structure. Structure has been recognized as of such importance that an ASTM specification A 247 has been developed in conjunction with the American Foundrymen's Society (AFS). The specification embodies two charts, one portraying graphite flake *size* and the other graphite flake *type*.

Any discussion of gray cast iron should refer to the fact that it can be cast into almost any conceivable shape. Moldenke in his "Principles of Iron Founding"[2] states that lace curtains were actually reproduced in cast iron in Belgium. Individual castings have been made in sizes weighing from a few ounces to hundreds of tons. They have been produced in such a wide range of application as to extend from cannon balls to the dome on the Capitol in Washington, D. C. It is little wonder that gray cast iron is so popular as a manufacturing material.

Cast iron can be successfully welded by any of the commonly used non-pressure-welding methods, but the oxyacetylene torch has been favored. The electric carbon arc process has been outmoded largely because of the development of suitable metal arc electrodes, which are gaining in favor. Braze welding remains a reliable method of joining broken cast-iron parts. It can be stated that the welding of cast iron is always for reclamation. Cast-iron weldments are scarce for the reason that a part can be cast as an entity to better advantage and with greater facility.

Nodular Cast Iron. Inoculated gray cast iron has taken many forms. Some of these, such as acicular cast iron, have proved their worth in critical applications as diesel crankshafts. A further development in inoculation has resulted in a group of cast irons wherein the graphite is of a nodular character in the "as cast" condition. Cerium additions were originally used to achieve the inoculating effect. Further progress has

[2] McGraw-Hill Book Company, Inc., New York, 1917.

featured magnesium or magnesium and nickel as the inoculating agency. An additional process develops the nodular reaction by adding a mixture of sodium and magnesium chlorides with calcium silicide as the reducing medium. Inoculants are added to the molten metal as ladle additions prior to pouring. The resultant structure is one that retains the graphite constituent in spherical shape and practically free of flakes.

Nodular cast iron, also termed spheroidal or ductile iron, includes a group of materials that are capable of wide variation in mechanical properties resulting from base iron composition and inoculating procedure.

Fig. 2-3. Nodular cast iron herringbone gear being assembled for 9 ft 0 in. rod mill drive. (Courtesy of Allis-Chalmers Manufacturing Co., Milwaukee.)

This series of cast irons is specified by ASTM designation A 339. Two general trends are noticeable. In one of these, high tensile strengths are secured in the as-cast condition; in the other, ductility is impressive although heat-treatment is generally required to develop its maximum values. It remains to be seen just where nodular cast iron will find its major field of utility (Fig. 2-3) and to what extent it will displace currently used ferrous castings.

Malleable Cast Iron. Malleable cast iron is divided technically into two classifications, viz., malleable iron castings, covered by ASTM specification A 47, and pearlitic malleable iron castings, specification A 220.

In specification A 47 the mechanical properties are as follows:

	Grade no. 32510	Grade no. 35018
Tensile strength, minimum, psi..........	50,000	53,000
Yield point, minimum, psi..............	32,500	35,000
Elongation in 2 in., minimum, per cent...	10	18

The castings covered by the above specification must be either poured from air-furnace, open-hearth, or electric-furnace metal. In addition to these, there is cupola malleable, which is covered by ASTM specification A 197. Malleable castings are generally small in size when compared to ferrous castings. They are used where shock resistance is important. Differential carriers, farm implements, and railway car components are standard applications for these materials.

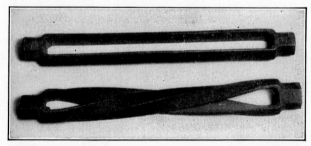

Fig. 2-4. Malleable iron casting for a turnbuckle. Note ductility exemplified by lower view.

Pearlitic Malleable Cast Iron. The products known as pearlitic malleable resulted from an interesting development in the field of malleable iron castings, which involves the use of alloying elements or a shorter annealing cycle, or a combination of both. As noted in ASTM specification A 220, the materials in this grouping exhibit higher strengths and lower ductility values than the standard malleable cast irons.

	Grade no. 43010	Grade no. 48005	Grade no. 60003	Grade no. 70002
Tensile strength, minimum, psi.........	60,000	70,000	80,000	90,000
Yield strength, minimum, psi..........	43,000	48,000	60,000	70,000
Elongation in 2 in., minimum, per cent..	10	5	3	2

Malleable cast irons have excellent machinability and ductility (Fig. 2-4). The superiority of the standard group in this connection over the pearlitic is due to the fact that in the latter there is some retained iron carbide, whereas in the former the total carbon content has been reduced to temper carbon of the characteristic globular form. Machining may be entirely eliminated for certain designs in standard malleable cast iron since the ductility of the material is such that it can be coinpressed. This method is limited to production runs because of the specialized tooling requirements.

All the ferrous materials discussed thus far in this chapter are produced or shaped by casting. This is important for the designer to remember since it gives him an economical and uncomplicated method for the production of ferrous components.

WROUGHT IRON

The ferrous material of antiquity is known to industry as wrought iron. Indications are that it was produced originally directly from iron ore in a hearth. The next development was the use of pig iron for the basic charge in the puddling process. The current production method is known in industry as the Aston or Byers process. The original work on this process was started in 1918; it was developed into a commercial operation in 1930.

In colonial America, as elsewhere at that time, the ferrous materials in common usage were cast iron and wrought iron. Since there have been many designs inspired by the work of the artisans of those early times, the term "wrought iron" has come to be very widely used; in fact it is not at all uncommon to encounter products being offered today under the name of wrought iron that are produced from steel or even gray cast iron. The point to note here is that the term wrought iron is used sometimes in the sense of a manufacturing method rather than in its proper province as the designation of a ferrous material.

The definition of wrought iron in ASTM designation A 81: "a ferrous material, aggregated from a solidifying mass of pasty particles of highly refined metallic iron, with which, without subsequent fusion, is incorporated a minutely and uniformly distributed quantity of slag."

It will be noted from this definition that wrought iron is never in a molten state during its production, a fact which readily explains that wrought iron is a material that can only appear in end-product form as the result of mechanical working.

Corrosion resistance is always associated with wrought iron. There is now cause to question whether wrought iron is not being pressed by steel in many applications, although it seems to be agreed that when it comes to resistance to corrosion of the pitting type, the fibrous slag content of wrought iron places it in a position of superiority. Its use in pipe, boiler stay bolts, and hold-down bolts as well as in some locomotive parts is traditional and constitutes an acknowledgment of the properties inherent in wrought iron.

STEEL

The beginning of the modern steel industry dates from the invention of the steel converter. This revolutionary method made its appearance around 1856. While Sir Henry Bessemer is generally acknowledged as the inventor, valid claims to priority on the converter have been advanced for William Kelly of Eddyville, Ky. It seems reasonable to assume that these men, working independently and in ignorance of each other's experiments, achieved the same results concurrently.

Cementation Steel. The earliest steels were made from wrought-iron bars by cementation. In that method, the iron bars were packed in a container along with a carbon-yielding agent. This sealed package was subjected to an elevated temperature for a considerable period of time, until the carbon had penetrated through the bar, thereby changing it into steel. Owing to a lack of control, coupled with the variability of the raw material used, cementation steel proved to be of erratic quality.

Crucible Steel. The lack of consistency in cementation steel led to a search for corrective measures that ended with an entirely new steel-making method. In the crucible process, as developed by Huntsman in England in 1742, bars of carefully selected cementation steel were cut into small pieces and placed in a crucible. When the latter was filled, a lid was luted into position and the crucible placed into a pit furnace, there to remain until its charge was melted. The molten metal was poured into ingots which, upon cooling, were forged into the desired shape. The processing has been revised in that pieces of wrought iron are used for the charge and carbonaceous material is added prior to melting. Crucible steel proved to be so homogeneous in quality that its manufacture has endured, in a measure at least, up to the present time. From the standpoint of quality, it shares its position only with electric-furnace steels.

Steel Making. The impressive steel-making industry was built on converter steel, even though the open-hearth process (Fig. 2-5) is now the leading tonnage producer. Recently the electric arc and still more recently the electrical induction furnace have added their influence to the steel-making industry, until production capacity has reached the imposing total of 120 million tons of ingots per year. All the ingot steel is destined for further processing and, therefore, represents a production exclusive of the steel-casting industry, which has also attained a heavy production volume.

Steel is shaped into end products by all manufacturing methods excepting only die casting. In order to meet this range of requirements, steels of widely varying chemical properties and microstructure are now regularly produced. Metallurgical control is of fundamental importance. The necessity of close control is strikingly portrayed by the requirements imposed through the recently developed cold strip mill (Fig. 2-6) whose operating speeds may exceed 4,000 fpm on the finishing pass.

Fig. 2-5. Charging floor of an open-hearth furnace battery at Great Lakes Steel Corporation, main plant, Ecorse, Mich. (Courtesy of Great Lakes Steel Corp., a unit of National Steel Corp.)

The methods of manufacture, some of which were mentioned earlier, can be summarized as follows:

Cementation steel
Crucible steel
Converter steel $\begin{cases} \text{Acid (American) Bessemer} \\ \text{Basic Bessemer} \end{cases}$
Open-hearth steel $\begin{cases} \text{Acid open-hearth} \\ \text{Basic open-hearth} \end{cases}$
Electric-furnace $\begin{cases} \text{Acid electric} \\ \text{Basic electric} \end{cases}$
Electric induction furnace steel
Duplexed steel $\begin{cases} \text{Cupola melted gray iron, refined in side blow converter} \\ \text{Molten pig partially refined in converter, finished in open-hearth} \end{cases}$

There is little point in detailing the above steel-making processes, since they are well known; instead a few of the newer processes under consideration or development will be mentioned briefly. The oxygen converter is being studied closely by the steel-making industry. In this method the oxygen is blown at supersonic speed onto the top of the molten metal bath. This is the reverse of the Bessemer process, wherein the air is blown from the bottom. The product resulting from this method is claimed to be a steel with properties resembling basic open-hearth. In addition small heats can be produced in a short time and of various grades, thereby offering a most flexible operation. Costs appear extremely favorable as judged from pilot-plant operation.

The Stora Powder Steel Process is a new method of steel making introduced in Domnarvet, Sweden. This is a steel-making method in which

Fig. 2-6. Continuous mill cold reducing strip steel from 0.100 to 0.035 in. (Courtesy of Republic Steel Co., Cleveland.)

the rolled steel is made directly from pig iron. Prerefined pig is granulated with the granules being packed into a sheet metal box, which is then placed in a furnace where the charge is decarburized. Following this, the box is heated to a temperature above 2000°F when the entire box with its contents is put through a rolling mill and rolled into final products.

The direct reduction of iron ore is of decided interest because of the cost potential as well as the favorable installation expenditure. In a process which produces a material known as H-iron, a stream of hydrogen is blown up through powdered ore. In this action it unites with the oxygen of the ore and produces iron sponge. The sponge then is used as a basis for further processing. Pilot-plant operation indicates that H-iron equipment can be installed for about 50 per cent of the cost of a blast furnace.

The classification of steel on the basis of its composition is important, inasmuch as end use is closely related to this characteristic. Any listing must consider both the wrought, or mechanically worked, steels as well as the cast steel categories. A simplified grouping follows:

Ingot iron: A highly refined open-hearth steel whose total impurities are 0.15% max.

Plain carbon steels
- Dead soft—C (0.10% max.)
- Low carbon (mild)—C (0.10–0.30%)
- Medium carbon—C (0.30–0.65%)
- High carbon—C (0.85–1.50%)

Alloy steels
- Low-alloy, high-strength structurals (total alloys range from 1–2%)
- Low-alloy steels (alloys total 8% max.)
- High-alloy steels (alloys total 8% min.)

Tool steels
- Carbon types
- Alloy types

In manufacturing, steels are processed either at room or at elevated temperatures. On that basis, the following grouping is obtained:

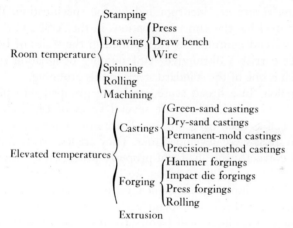

Perhaps there has been too much stress on the traditional approach when choosing a steel for a given design. The principal emphasis is placed on the mechanical properties of a given steel although the design may require only one or a combination of a few of these; the result is a program of trial-and-error selection. It is an established fact that the mechanical properties of steel are dependent primarily upon its microstructure. In consequence, the composition of a steel, which usually is given greatest emphasis, should be interpreted only in light of its effect on microstructure. The carbon content of a steel, coupled with phase transformations the steel may undergo during any heat-treatment, is the determinant of the microstructure.

Steel Compositions. The designer must specify an engineering material that is suitable for the projected component. His specification will serve best when it is confined to a recognized engineering standard. There are several such standards for steels, any one of which is satisfactory. American Society for Testing Materials (ASTM) specifications are fundamental. Society of Automotive Engineers (SAE) classifications afford a ready means of showing composition. Another specification of a similar nature is the American Iron and Steel Institute (AISI) classification. The designation numbers used by the SAE and AISI systems are identical. The point of difference is that the AISI employs a pattern of letter prefixes indicating the method of steel manufacture, as follows:

B—Acid Bessemer carbon steel
C—Basic open-hearth carbon steel
D—Acid open-hearth carbon steel
E—Electric-furnace steel
No prefix—Basic open-hearth alloy steel

When AISI designations are used, both the composition and the method of steel manufacture are incorporated in one specification. Basic open-hearth alloy steel has the same designations in the AISI and SAE classifications. This trend continues as exemplified in the series of boron steels, a group that carries a distinctive AISI number designation such as No. 42B35, which is one of the standard steels in this grouping.

Steel Selection. In a broad sense, steels are grouped into plain carbon and alloy classifications. There are several types of each, although carburizing as well as deep-hardening steels are available in each group. The plain carbon steels were developed first. They are less costly than the alloy steels and if correctly specified and properly processed are capable of satisfactory performance. Plain carbon steels are sometimes overlooked because of the more imposing mechanical properties possessed by most alloy steels. A careful evaluation of plain carbon steels, as to both properties and processing capabilities, will frequently result in a lower manufacturing cost for the end product. This situation is becoming increasingly important, since the supply of alloying elements is growing critical. It is impossible to generalize on the subject of plain carbon versus alloy steel. In each case the design should be studied and an economy survey made in order to arrive at the best solution.

Alloy Steels. The range of composition in this classification extends from the low-alloy high-strength structurals to the highly alloyed stainless and heat-resisting groups. An alloy steel is considered to be one in which manganese exceeds 1.65 per cent or silicon exceeds 0.60 per cent. Both elements are constituents of plain carbon steel and for that reason are considered as alloying elements only when present in the percentages given. In addition to these two, aluminum, boron, chromium, cobalt, copper, columbium, molybdenum, nickel, titanium, tungsten, vanadium, and zirconium are regarded as alloying elements. The content of any alloying element or elements can be found by reference to the specification of an individual alloy steel (Table 2-2). Compositions have been developed to impart specific properties. AISI specifications refer to wrought steel products and not to steel castings. Steel castings are specified under ASTM and, in some cases, SAE standards. Alloy Casting Institute (ACI)

TABLE 2-2. SAE-AISI ALLOY STEEL DESIGNATIONS

The first two digits of the series for the various grades of alloy steel and their meaning are as follows, while the last two digits give the C content in points.

Series designation	Types
13xx	Manganese 1.75%
23xx	Nickel 3.50%
25xx	Nickel 5.00%
31xx	Nickel 1.25%; chromium 0.65 or 0.80%
33xx	Nickel 3.50%; chromium 1.55%
40xx	Molybdenum 0.25%
41xx	Chromium 0.95%; molybdenum 0.20%
43xx	Nickel 1.80%; chromium 0.50 or 0.80%; molybdenum 0.25%
46xx	Nickel 1.80%; molybdenum 0.25%
48xx	Nickel 3.50%; molybdenum 0.25%
50xx	Chromium 0.30 or 0.60%
51xx	Chromium 0.80, 0.95, or 1.05%
50xxx	Carbon 1.00%; chromium 0.50%
51xxx	Carbon 1.00%; chromium 1.00%
52xxx	Carbon 1.00%; chromium 1.45%
61xx	Chromium 0.80 or 0.95%; vanadium 0.10 or 0.15% minimum
86xx	Nickel 0.55%; chromium 0.50%; molybdenum 0.20%
87xx	Nickel 0.55%; chromium 0.50%; molybdenum 0.25%
92xx	Manganese 0.85%; silicon 2.00%
93xx	Nickel 3.25%; chromium 1.20%; molybdenum 0.12%
94xx	Manganese 1.00%; nickel 0.45%; chromium 0.40%; molybdenum 0.12%
97xx	Nickel 0.55%; chromium 0.17%; molybdenum 0.20%
98xx	Nickel 1.00%; chromium 0.80%; molybdenum 0.25%

covers some grades of corrosion-resistant steels. There are other less known and less used standards, such as American Railroad Association, among others. The degree to which an alloying element is present in a steel varies within a given classification. The effect of each alloy or combination of alloying elements is well known and forms the basis of the property classifications of alloy steel.

The composition range for alloying elements as well as basic elements must be closely controlled within a given steel specification. Quality requirements are rigid. Special property and quality requirements have resulted in recognized classifications such as aircraft, axle shaft, bearing, cold heading, and hardenability, among others. Each of these types has its specific field of application and degree of utility.

Low-alloy High-strength Steels. This group of steels is produced with chemical compositions especially developed to impart higher mechanical property values and greater resistance to atmospheric corrosion than are obtainable from conventional carbon structural steels containing copper. High-strength low-alloy steels are produced to mechanical property requirements rather than to chemical composition limits. Minimum properties for these steels generally show yield point 50,000 psi and ultimate

Fig. 2-7. This shear-leg derrick, taller than a 20-story building, has lifted 800 tons dead load. The shear legs are fabricated from low-alloy high-strength steel. (Courtesy of Bethlehem Steel Co., Bethlehem, Pa.)

strength in the 70,000 psi range. These steels offer an interesting weight/strength ratio as compared to the better-known plain carbon steels; in consequence, where these steels are employed lighter structures result (Fig. 2-7). High-strength low-alloy steels are covered by ASTM designation A 242. They are readily adaptable to fabrication of the usual type found in structural shops, being especially well suited to welding in that no unusual precautions are necessary. Furthermore, optimum properties do not depend upon any thermal treatment by the fabricator.

H-Steels. Alloy steels are available whose hardenability can be specified within stated limits. The limits are referred to as hardenability bands and their values are given in Rockwell C points. H-steels are designated by numbers of the SAE-AISI classification with the letter H appearing in the suffix thus: 4340-H. There is some modification in analysis of these steels over their standard alloy steel counterparts so that the steel maker can meet the specified hardenability requirements. The development of H-steels is of significance since it affords a reliable means of meeting hardenability specifications. It is sound procedure to consult with the steel producer because of his records on every heat of steel. Precautions of this nature are valuable in eliminating variability in the end product.

Fig. 2-8. The supersonic Bomarc missile fired from a tactical launcher shelter. (Courtesy of Boeing Airplane Co., Seattle, Wash.)

Stainless and Heat-resisting Steels. Steels in these classifications are increasing in importance, paralleling the development of process-industry equipment and high-temperature applications. The application of these, the most highly alloyed types of steel, is in corrosion and/or heat resistance. The development of jet engines, gas turbines, and supersonic aircraft and missiles (Fig. 2-8) has intensified interest in these steels. Experience gained from exhaust stacks and similar aircraft engine components indicates that these are the most satisfactory steels for meeting corrosion and high-temperature conditions. Further research is necessary because the properties of the established stainless and heat-resisting steels are not entirely equal to the severity of jet and turbine requirements.

These steels are available in wrought form where they are, for the most

part, identified under trade names. Corrosion-resistant castings are produced for chemical plants, pulp and paper mills, oil refining, food processing, and other services that require resistance to corrosion or heat. Their classification is not identical with the wrought types. The latter are designated under the AISI classification as follows:

2xx—Cr-Ni-Mn steels, austenitic
3xx—Cr-Ni steels, austenitic
4xx—Cr steels, martensitic
4xx—Cr steels, ferritic
5xx—low Cr steels, heat-resisting

The range of properties inherent in this classification offers the designer an opportunity to select a steel that meets his needs. The martensitic steels are heat-treatable, while the others are susceptible to work hardening. Machinability is developed in these types by special chemical analysis and also through further alloying. A similar situation obtains for weldability, although low carbon content is especially desirable in order to avoid intergranular corrosion adjacent to the welds. Stabilized stainless steels are specified for welding where service conditions are severe; type no. 347 fits here.

Precipitation Hardenable Grades. With the advent of jet engines and supersonic flight, new materials for aircraft and missiles became imperative. The desired combination of properties was ease of formability, coupled with high strength capabilities at room as well as elevated temperatures. As a means of meeting these stringent requirements, a stainless type known as 17-7 PH was developed. This steel has a nominal composition of 0.07 per cent C, 17.00 per cent Cr, 7.0 per cent Ni, and 1.2 per cent Al. The composition limits of this particular steel are much more critical than the conventional AISI types. The reason for this exacting composition stems from the effect of unwanted elements and impurities upon the behavior of the martensitic transformation.

The thermal treatment of these steels is quite involved since mechanical properties are desired that will develop high strength in the range of 600 to 800°F operating temperatures. Another feature is the treatment by subnormal temperatures; by way of illustration, one such steel has this schedule:

1. Heat at 1750°F $\pm$ 15° for 10 min; air-cool.
2. Cool to 100°F and hold for 8 hr.
3. Heat at 950°F $\pm$ 10° for 60 min; air-cool.

The resulting properties show ultimate strength equaling 200,000 psi at room temperature. It seems certain that stainless steels in this category will find increasing use in aircraft structural components; other steels of similar classifications are under development.

Tool Steels. This group of steels are either carbon or alloy types of a composition that permits them to be hardened and tempered. For the most part they are produced from electric furnaces under rigid control in order to develop the required properties. These steels have a wide range of application such as hand tools, mechanical fixtures, cutting, shaping, blanking, etc., for use at either room as well as elevated temperatures. They are also used in the manufacture of precision gages and in some high-temperature components. Such steels are classified under six main types as follows: water-hardening, shock-resisting, cold-work, hot-work, high-speed, and special-purpose tool steels. In order to identify each of these types, the AISI has developed a series of symbols. Thus, for example, water-hardening steels are designated as "W," while shock-resisting ones are denoted with the letter "S." By way of example, a straight carbon water-hardening tool steel is designated as "W 1," whereas the same steel containing 0.50 per cent Va is designated as "W 3."

The increasing interest in these steels arises from their ability to perform satisfactorily at high temperature levels, and especially in supersonic craft. Their present use is on such components as landing gear parts and other designs requiring high strength at elevated temperatures. In the area of engineering manufacture, tool steels have a very significant assignment aside from their traditional usage in tool making. They are well known for their use in die work; however, other forms are available, among them being drill rod, which is traditional and basic to the toolroom.

Ultra-high-strength Alloy Steels. In searching for suitable high-strength materials for airframe construction, conventional high-hardenability alloy steels such as AISI 4340 have been investigated. While this particular steel had previously been tempered at 900°F to give an ultimate range of 180,000 to 200,000 psi, it is now being tempered at half that, or 450°F, resulting in an ultimate range of 260,000 to 280,000 psi. A modified 4340 with a higher silicon content, when tempered at 600°F, is capable of a tensile range of 280,000 to 300,000 psi. It can be noted from the above that meeting the new strength requirements is approached by using former steels but changing processing to lower tempering temperatures. Another development is that of modifying analysis in order to obtain improved properties.

SURVEY QUESTIONS

2-1. How do ferrous materials differ fundamentally from other engineering metals?

2-2. State two bases upon which engineering materials are selected.

2-3. To what extent is availability important in selecting engineering materials?

2-4. Are castings made wholly from pig iron?

2-5. Why are there several classifications of pig iron?

2-6. How does charcoal pig iron derive its name?

2-7. List at least five different types of cast iron.

2-8. Wherein does chilled iron differ from gray cast iron?

2-9. Is chilled cast iron used in the manufacture of machinery?

2-10. Explain the meaning of the specification A 48, class 30.

2-11. Should specification A 247 be consulted by the designer interested in machinability?

2-12. State any additional terms that would describe nodular cast iron.

2-13. Why is nodular cast iron replacing steel castings in some categories?

2-14. Do malleable castings compete with gray iron in function?

2-15. Is there any difference between the structure of nodular iron and that of malleable iron castings?

2-16. Do malleable iron castings require more processing than gray iron?

2-17. Do wrought iron end products resemble gray cast iron or steel castings?

2-18. What are the physical forms of wrought iron components?

2-19. Wherein does wrought iron have any superior application possibilities over other ferrous materials?

2-20. What is the oldest steel-making method of record?

2-21. Name three end products made from crucible steel.

2-22. Which steel-making process is the largest tonnage producer?

2-23. When should the designer consider plain carbon steels?

2-24. In what type of end products would alloy steels be predominant?

2-25. Recommend a type of steel to be used for aircraft landing-gear components.

2-26. What type of steel would be best for constructing welded steel bridges?

2-27. Does "stainless steel" refer to a single type material?

2-28. Suggest an engineering application for austenitic stainless steel.

2-29. Wherein does stainless steel differ from alloy steel?

2-30. Where do precipitation-hardening stainless steels belong in modern engineering design?

2-31. Why are tool steels being considered for components of modern aircraft and missiles?

Chapter 3

NONFERROUS METALS AND PLASTICS

Those engineering metals that contain no appreciable amounts of iron in their composition are classified as nonferrous metals or alloys. Obviously, this classification is extremely broad. It includes the alloys of such well-known metals as copper, aluminum, zinc, magnesium, nickel, tin, and lead. All these are processed similarly to the ferrous metals. Further, many metallic materials have been added to the nonferrous group by powder metallurgy (Chap. 4).

Cemented carbides, from the above process category, are best known for their excellent properties in connection with the machining of metals as well as nonmetals. Their first use, however, was for wire-drawing dies in which the chief composition component is tungsten carbide.

Heat-resistant Alloys. The heat-resistant casting alloys of cobalt base were introduced for the highly stressed gas turbine blading in 1941, and development and modifications have been rapid since then. Some of these alloys, especially of the stellite group, had been used for many years in other applications, such as tool-bit material and hard surfacing for abrasion resistance. These alloys are not confined to casting, since there are also wrought products of similar composition.

There are other alloys in the field of heat-resistant castings; prominent in this classification are many Ni-base alloys, especially of the Hastelloy group, whose compositions are primarily Ni, Mo with small percentages of Fe, and, in some cases, Cr and W. Other nickel-base alloys that are more widely used are known under trade names such as Inconel, Monel, and "K" Monel. These latter are especially noteworthy for resistance to corrosion both at normal and elevated temperatures.

COPPER

There is general agreement that copper and its principal alloys, brass and bronze, are the oldest metals known to civilization. They remain as the standard material for a multitude of engineering applications in the face of competition from many directions. Some of this competition was fostered during wartime when copper was in short supply; in other instances the scarcity of copper in the national economy, as in Germany, gave rise to the use of competitive metals.

Copper and its alloys are available to industry in wrought as well as cast form. Within the two classifications, these materials are shaped by every manufacturing method, with a wide range of products resulting. However, the high electrical conductivity of copper gives this metal its greatest field of application. Copper has also had wide application because of its inherent corrosion resistance.

The wrought alloys of copper are available in a complete range of physical forms. In addition to these end products, there are also copper and copper-base alloy forging rods, bars, and shapes, as can be noted in ASTM designation B 124. Forgings from the materials under this specification are used in valve bodies and similar equipment where the combination of strength, corrosion resistance, and pressure tightness dominate. Pressure regulators and cylinder valves for oxyacetylene welding and cutting equipment are familiar examples of the application of copper-base alloy forgings.

Copper-base Casting Alloys. The tonnage of copper-base alloy castings produced annually reaches an imposing total. Producing sound castings requires exacting control throughout the molding and core departments as well as in the melt shop. In fact, the raw materials, such as molding sand, core sands and binders, fuel, ingots, and, especially, scrap metal, must be given the closest attention if casting defects are to be avoided.

Casting design is an important matter, especially when such alloys as aluminum and manganese bronze are to be cast. Both liquid and solidification shrinkage must be understood by the foundry in order that correct gating and feeding methods will be employed. The melt shop needs to understand the affinity that the various alloys, in the molten state, have for gas. Hydrogen is especially difficult to control, since there are several sources from which this gas can enter the melt. That careful attention is given to every level in the process is evidenced by the fact that satisfactory copper-base alloy castings in a wide range, from those weighing but a few ounces to large ships' propellers weighing as much as 25 tons, are in regular production (Fig. 3-1).

Copper-base casting alloys are classified primarily as bronze and brass. In very general terms, bronze is an alloy of copper and tin while brass is an alloy of copper and zinc. The properties of both bronze and brass are modified by changing the ratio of the basic constituents and also by the addition of other metals such as lead. Consequently, there is an impressive number of bronze and brass compositions available. In order to standardize such a range, it is recommended that one of the several standard casting specifications available be used as reference. The leading specifications include ASTM, SAE, Federal Standard, and U.S. Navy Department.

The foundry shop, producing castings to specifications, can proceed in one of two ways: either it can make its own alloys by melting the constituents of the composition, or it can purchase specification metal in ingot form. Both of these methods are used; however, less alloy loss is experienced when purchased ingot is melted. This procedure is especially

Fig. 3-1. Cast bronze propeller, 9 ft 8 in. in diameter, for M.S. Kalakala. (Courtesy of Coolidge Propeller Co., Seattle, Wash.)

recommended for the smaller shops, since accurate alloying in a crucible requires extreme care both as to weights and in the technique of making the additions.

The designer should consistently use standard specifications as a guide rather than follow the loose practice of merely calling for brass or bronze for a given application; a better end product will result, and the manufacturing costs will be held to a minimum. A typical alloy is found in ASTM specification B 145, no. 4A, which is referred to as "85-three 5's." This alloy has high mechanical properties coupled with desirable characteristics for both the foundry and the machine shop.

Copper-base Wrought Alloys. Copper-base alloys are more familiar as castings than they are in wrought form. The reason for this is readily recognized by remembering that a small foundry operation for producing such castings is a relatively simple installation. On the other hand, where wrought products are produced, heavy capital expenditures for equipment are necessary. Whenever this is the case only large-volume operation can be undertaken to justify the original investment and continuing maintenance.

Copper and its alloys are available as wrought products in every conceivable form. Bars and rods were mentioned earlier; to this should be added tubing, extrusions, shapes, forgings, and especially sheet. The latter are obtainable in a wide variety of sizes, finishes, and tempers. It can be said that copper and its alloys form a series of engineering materials that will meet an extremely wide range of applications. However, because of the antiquity of these materials they have been subjected to an intensive amount of competition from other materials as they come into the market.

ALUMINUM ALLOYS

Metallurgical vocabulary has no counterpart to the terms steel, brass, or bronze that can be applied to aluminum alloys. There is some commercially pure aluminum used in the manufacturing industries, but by far the greatest field of application is for the aluminum alloys, which are available in both cast and wrought forms (Fig. 3-2). Since the expression, aluminum alloys, is cumbersome, it is becoming common practice to refer to aluminum alloys as "aluminum." There is so much interest in this branch of the light-metals field that too many applications are being made without the careful analysis that these materials deserve.

Aluminum-alloy Properties. The development of aluminum and its alloys, and its increasing importance as an engineering material, are most impressive when it is realized that the first commercial metal was produced only sixty years ago. A major contributing factor was the invention of Duralumin by Dr. Wilm in Germany in 1909. This alloy is more familiarly known in America as "dural" or 2017; it was the first of the heat-treatable aluminum alloys and also the first one to exhibit the property of natural age hardening.

The position of aluminum as an engineering material has been won through combinations of physical and mechanical properties that are peculiar to this metal. An important property is low specific gravity, the range of the established alloys lying between 2.52 and 2.87. This property is important when the combination of weight and mechanical properties is considered in the light of strength/weight ratio.

Another physical property of aluminum and its alloys is their high electrical conductivity; EC-O has a value of 62 per cent of the International annealed copper standard. When, however, this comparison is made with specific gravities considered, the EC-O alloy shows a mass conductivity of 201 per cent compared with copper. Thermal conductivity is high for the entire range of aluminum alloys; this fact is reflected in the use of these materials for food-processing equipment and for such parts as pistons and cylinder heads for internal-combustion engines.

The corrosion resistance of the aluminum alloys varies somewhat with their composition. Commercially pure aluminum 1100 has a high resistance to corrosion. Those alloys containing copper in substantial

Fig. 3-2. Final rolling operation on cold mill for aluminum alloy sheet coils. (Courtesy of Kaiser Aluminum & Chemical Co., Spokane, Wash.)

amounts are more susceptible to corrosive action and this susceptibility is influenced by the heat-treatment given them. The development of the clad sheet materials, which are, in effect, 3-ply composites wherein the two outer layers are usually commercially pure aluminum encasing an inner core of high-strength alloys, has proven to be an eminently satisfactory method of protecting the latter from corrosion. Other clad material is available wherein an aluminum alloy of a composition that is anodic to the core is used for the cladding or encasing material; Alclad 7075 is a leading example in this category.

It seems desirable before closing this discussion of the properties of aluminum alloys to call attention to the fact that as a class they actually show higher mechanical properties at subnormal than at normal temperatures. As more information is developed on this aspect of their properties, it seems reasonable to predict that these alloys will replace currently used materials which are susceptible to low-temperature embrittlement in certain applications.

Aluminum-alloy Designations. Aluminum alloys are designated differently than are the steels. This development originated when one company produced all aluminum alloys; in consequence, it adopted its own system of identification. When other producers entered the field they introduced distinctive designations suited to their own particular requirements, a situation which led to a rather confusing state of affairs. On October 1, 1954, the Aluminum Association sponsored a system of alloy designations for wrought aluminum alloys; this system was approved by the American Standards Association on May 9, 1957. Note, however, that this standard designation applies only to the wrought category of alloys; there is no standard as yet for the cast groups other than the established ASTM designations.

Now that a standard designation system is becoming known, exceptions are arising through the introduction of Al alloys produced by powder metallurgy. This latter group has been developed especially to meet higher temperature conditions. It is said that some of these powder metal alloys can withstand temperatures to 900°F. In consequence, these alloy types will find increasing application and their popularity will lead to further extension of designation standards.

Wrought Aluminum Alloys. The wrought aluminum alloys are divided into two categories, the strain-hardening and the heat-treatable. In the former type, increased strengths accompanied by decreased ductility can only be obtained by cold working. Heat-treatment is of no avail for improving strength; however, strain-hardened alloys can be annealed. Representative strain-hardening alloys and their temper designations are shown in Table 3-1.

TABLE 3-1. STRAIN-HARDENING WROUGHT ALUMINUM ALLOYS

Alloy no.	Temper	Condition
1100, 3003	H12, H14, H16, H18	Strain-hardened only, ranging from $\frac{1}{4}$ hard to full hard
3004, 5052	H32, H34, H36, H38	Strain-hardened and then stabilized
5056	H18, H38	Full strain-hardened
All of	"0"	Fully annealed

The heat-treatable alloys can be classified as those that age-harden naturally and the ones that require artificial aging. A further improvement in mechanical properties is possible through cold-working alloys that have previously been fully heat-treated; such processing is shown by a specific temper designation, viz., 2024-T36, as indicated in Table 3-2, an abbreviated listing of some of the more widely used wrought aluminum alloys. They are available as sheet, plate, wire, extrusions, rolled shapes, and forgings. All these different forms are of interest in manufacturing as evidenced by the continuing expansion of wrought

TABLE 3-2. TYPICAL TEMPER DESIGNATIONS FOR SOME WROUGHT ALUMINUM ALLOYS

Alloy no.	Temper	Condition
2011	T3 T8	Solution H.T. followed by strain hardening Solution H.T., strain hardening and then artificial aging
2014	T4 T6	Solution H.T. Solution plus precipitation H.T. (aging)
2018	T61	Solution plus precipitation
2024	T4 T36	Solution plus natural aging T4 plus cold working
2025	T6	Solution plus precipitation
4032	T6	Solution fully heat-treated
6151	T6	Solution fully heat-treated
6053	T6	Fully heat-treated
6061	T4 T6	Solution heat-treated Fully heat-treated
6063	F T6	As extruded Fully heat-treated
7075	T6	Fully heat-treated

aluminum products. Their favorable weight/strength ratio coupled with such properties as formability, machinability, and corrosion resistance recommends them to the designer.

Aluminum Casting Alloys. Castings are made exclusively from aluminum alloys, since commercially pure aluminum is not specified in cast form. The casting alloys are divided into two classifications, depending on the postcasting treatment. One type, which includes those sometimes referred to as the common casting alloys, does not require any heat-treatment; rather, these are used in the as-cast condition. The other classification refers to those alloys that are given some type of heat-treatment prior to end-use application. It should be strongly emphasized that in the interest of economy a heat-treatable casting alloy should not be used unless a heat-treatment is specified in conjunction with it.

Aluminum-alloy castings are made by every casting process common to the foundry. Sand castings, both green and dry, account for the bulk

Fig. 3-3. Pouring "squeezer" type molds with Al alloy metal on a loop conveyor. Temperature and metal control board in the background. (Courtesy of Aluminum Co. of America, Cleveland.)

of casting production (Fig. 3-3). Sound castings demand foundry knowledge peculiar to these alloys. Correct gating, along with proper melting and pouring temperatures, requires most careful attention. Such fundamentals as directional solidification, exclusion of oxides, and proper feeding must be included in the foundry control program.

MAGNESIUM

There was little interest in magnesium in the United States prior to World War I; the industry had its beginning here in 1915. The three distinguishing properties of magnesium are low specific gravity, a hexagonal lattice, and the fact that it is anodic to all the other common metals. This combination makes magnesium a unique metal and governs both its processing and applications. There is scant use for pure magnesium in engineering industry; its commercial alloys are the metals of importance. Aluminum is the chief alloying element, followed by zinc and manganese.

Designation of the commercial magnesium alloys is somewhat different from the aluminum ones. The ASTM specifications cover these alloys, as do others such as Federal and SAE. The trade name Dowmetal, established by the Dow Chemical Company, the first commercial producer, continues to be a popular designation. The Dow Company has abandoned its own system of designation in favor of the ASTM nomenclature. This development brings simplification in the understanding of magnesium alloys. For example, designation symbols are as follows:

A—Aluminum	K—Zirconium
E—Rare earth metals	M—Manganese
H—Thorium	Z—Zinc

Suffix letters represent variations in composition. The use of X denotes that the alloy is experimental and is not yet adopted by ASTM. Thus alloy AZ92A is from the (Mg-Al-Zn) series, whereas HM31XA is an experimental extrusion alloy of the thorium type. A study of Table 3-3 will show identifications and specifications of the most generally used commercial magnesium alloys.

Properties of Magnesium Alloys. The specific gravities of the magnesium alloys range from 1.76 to 1.87, which makes them the lightest common engineering materials. The chief interest in magnesium alloys arises from the weight-saving potential. Consequently, the aircraft and transportation industries have been pioneering with these alloys to the greatest extent. Processing and production machines possessing rapidly reciprocating or rotating members, for example, certain textile machines, have utilized magnesium alloys to good advantage. Hand tools and portable power tools, such as electric drills, are further examples. Recent applications of magnesium alloys include castings on portable chain saws, foundry flasks, bottom boards, and even falling and bucking wedges used in logging.

Physical Forms of Magnesium Alloys. Magnesium alloys are available in all the physical forms common to the nonferrous field. The classification of wrought and cast alloy forms is shown in Table 3-3. One important point to note about magnesium alloys is that they cannot as yet be rolled into sheets in as wide a range of sizes as can the aluminum alloys.

Wrought Magnesium Alloys. The use of magnesium alloy sheet for drawing operations has to be done at elevated temperatures. Generally both the blank and the dies are heated; the latter are rigged with either gas or electric heating devices so arranged as to maintain the required temperature. The depth of the draw as well as the alloy used determines the requisite temperature, which ranges from 100 to as high as 600°F. When proper temperatures and drawing speeds have been established, magnesium alloys are capable of very deep draws.

TABLE 3-3. MAGNESIUM ALLOYS: SPECIFICATIONS, FORMS, AND APPLICATIONS

ASTM specification	Alloy	Product form	Application
B 90	AZ31A MIA	Sheet and strip	Cold forming Deep drawing, low cost, weldable
B 107	AZ61A AZ80A MIA AZ31B	Extruded bar, rod and shapes	General purpose Highest strength Light stresses, weldable Cold forming
B 91	AZ61A AZ80A AZ31B	Forgings	Press forgings High strength, difficult to forge Forges readily
B 80	AZ63A AZ92A MIB	Sand castings	General purpose Weldable Pressure-tight
B 199	AZ92A AM100A	Permanent-mold castings	Strong, corrosion-resistant Casts readily, poor corrosion resistance
B 94	AZ91A	Die castings	Small castings

Pellet Magnesium Extrusions. Pellets are replacing ingots as the charge for an extrusion press in a development that indicates a profound step forward in the production of wrought magnesium alloys. The pellets are preheated, blown into the cylinder of the extrusion press, and then extruded directly. The operations of precompaction and sintering familiar to powder metallurgy are unnecessary in the pellet extrusion method.

The mechanical properties of magnesium extrusions are markedly improved by pellet fabrication. Strengths—and particularly compressive yield strength—are substantially increased without deleterious effect on shop and service characteristics. These remarkable improvements are attributed to the very small grain size of the pellet extrusion (Fig. 3-4).

The compressive yield strength of conventional extrusions is substantially lower than the tensile yield strength because of the twinning that occurs when the metal is compressed. As grain sizes decrease, twinning is increasingly inhibited, and the compressive yield strength is accordingly increased. Because of the small grain size of pellet extrusions, the compressive yield value is generally increased to the level of the tensile yield

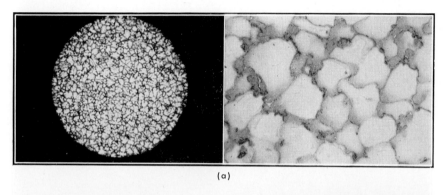

(a)

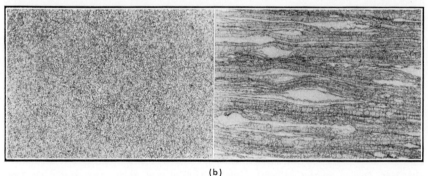

(b)

Fig. 3-4. Microstructure of cast and extruded ZK60A. (a) Cast. (b) Extruded. (Courtesy of The Dow Chemical Co., Midland, Mich.)

strength. The majority of work on pellet extrusions has been with alloy ZK60XB; this is essentially the same as ZK60A.

The pellet development is complemented by the installation of a 13,200T extrusion press (Chap. 13) for processing magnesium alloys. The extrusion press cylinder will accommodate a 32-in. diam ingot that can be worked at 33,000 psi. Lower extrusion temperatures are permitted which, in turn, will enhance the cys (comprehensive yield strength) noticeably.

Magnesium Alloy Castings. Magnesium alloy castings offer the widest field of application for this structural material, since green-sand (Fig.

3-4c), permanent mold, and die-casting processes are all practical. Castings of a wide range of sizes and of intricate shapes are in production. Gating and risering as well as the placement of chills demand careful attention. The low specific gravity of these alloys must be considered when gating and risering, since the head pressures of ferrous castings are not obtainable; risers must be larger and more numerous if sound castings are to be produced.

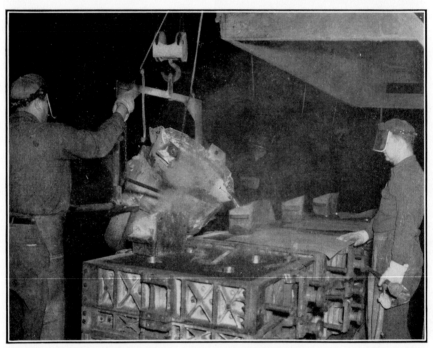

Fig. 3-4c. Pouring magnesium alloy castings in green-sand molds. Note ventilating hood above pouring station. (Courtesy of Dow Chemical Co., Midland, Mich.)

Magnesium alloys can be melted in steel pots that have been given an aluminum coating. The use of flux to protect the molten metal is a requirement of profound importance. The molten metal should be stirred with a steel rod to free impurities, which unite with the flux, thereby cleansing the metal. Following the melting operation, the metal is transferred to a superheating furnace where temperatures of 1650 to 1700°F are used for about 10 min in order to promote a fine grain size in the metal casting, which, in turn, improves the mechanical properties of the casting.

The flux is skimmed from the molten metal and the latter is then dusted with a protecting agent prior to pouring. The mold should always be made with a pouring basin wherein the metal and oxides can separate. This is necessary because the specific gravity of the oxide and of the metal are so close together that the mechanical separation afforded by a properly designed pouring basin is the only solution for obtaining clean metal. Pouring temperatures average around 1500°F, depending on the type of alloy as well as the casting section. The molding sand must be inhibited in order to prevent a reaction between molten Mg and sand moisture. Freshly poured castings should remain undisturbed for an appreciable period because of the hot-short character of the magnesium alloys.

Magnesium Alloy Casting Heat-treatment. Depending on the choice of the alloy, magnesium castings produced from either sand or permanent molds are generally given a heat-treatment. Solution heat-treatment is used for the purpose of increasing tensile strength, ductility, and toughness but it does not change the yield strength. For the highest values of tensile and yield strength, a solution heat-treatment followed by aging is recommended, although this treatment causes some deterioration in ductility. It is common practice to heat-treat castings prior to machining because of the fact that they are not subject to dimensional change following the heat-treat operation.

Machining Magnesium Alloys. The machinability of magnesium alloys is outstanding among the engineering metals. Actual operations using carbide-tipped tools have been performed at cutting speeds in excess of 2,000 fpm. Milling operations have been reported in which as much as 340 cu in./min have been removed.

In machining magnesium alloys, several precautions are necessary. Accurate clamping and chucking must be used in order to prevent distortion due to their lower modulus of elasticity. Further, because of that characteristic, the alloys cut closer to size, indicating that slightly oversize drills, taps, and reamers should be used. Most important in machining these alloys is the necessity for sharp, polished tools.

Corrosion Prevention. It is a fact that these alloys have not been readily accepted because when they were introduced their resistance to corrosion was considered low; however, development in purification and alloying has made possible alloys of good resistance to corrosion.

Along with improved composition, surface treatments have also undergone development. Magnesium alloy products are distinctive in appearance because of surface treatment. The resulting colors broadly range from yellow, brown, black, gray to iridescent blends of red to yellow. These surface treatments include chromate pickle and dichromate dip among others. There are, in fact, specifications governing the different surface treatments, and the purpose of each is to prevent tarnishing and to form a base for paint or for decoration, as through dyeing.

ZINC

Both as a major alloy and for its minor use in copper-base alloys, zinc ranks high in importance in engineering manufacture. Zinc is also rolled into sheet, plate, extruded, and drawn into rod and wire for engineering application. It is a principal alloying element along with nickel in the copper-nickel-zinc alloy series. Another important use is in brazing filler metal and kindred applications. ASTM designation B 6 covers slab zinc (spelter) while sheet and plates are specified in B 69.

Zinc Alloy Castings. Zinc-base die castings are used in many industries. In the automotive industry, a leading example, they are used for radiator grills, hub caps, body trim, door hardware, and instrument panel trim, as well as motor parts such as carburetors and gas pumps. Industrial applications are tool parts, building hardware, outboard motors, electric and gas motor components, and household appliances, to make a partial listing.

The popularity of zinc alloys for die casting is due to the fact that they take an excellent finish and are simple to make, since submerged-plunger die-casting machines are applicable (Chap. 9). Die castings have close dimensional limits. They can be chromium plated for pleasing appearance and lasting beauty. Other finishes such as electroplating with most metals, organic finishes, plastic and chemical treatment are also used. Zinc alloy castings tarnish unless they are given some surface treatment.

Sand casting is largely restricted to drop-hammer dies for fabricating aluminum, magnesium, stainless steel, and other sheet metal types. Detailed information on drop-hammer operation is given in Chap. 12. Dies of this type are readily machined and are economical especially where limited production runs obtain. Permanent-mold castings and slush castings are also produced from zinc alloys.

Zinc-base casting alloys contain aluminum as the major alloying element. Copper and magnesium are present in some alloys, in considerably lesser amounts than aluminum. There are relatively few zinc-base casting alloys in comparison with those of such other nonferrous metals as copper and aluminum.

TITANIUM

In the continuing program of the development of new engineering materials, titanium and its alloys are now receiving attention. The work that has so far been done is not sufficient to form the basis of a definite evaluation of the potentialities of titanium alloys. Some of the properties of these alloys are known. They lie about midway between aluminum alloys and steel so far as specific gravity is concerned. They offer unusual ductility and excellent corrosion resistance, especially in marine atmospheres, as well as good fatigue resistance. A high degree of surface hardness can be obtained. Strength properties at elevated temperatures, while unique, have not proven successful to the extent that was originally anticipated.

Some of the titanium alloys are heat-treatable; all can be advantageously cold-worked. There have been a host of alloys developed experimentally, and several producers are in the field. What can be expected in the way of mechanical properties is impossible to estimate accurately, but it can be said that these alloys will compare very favorably with and exceed most engineering metals on the basis of weight/strength ratio, especially at elevated temperatures.

At the present stage of development, their cost is so great as to preclude their general use. New methods of winning titanium from its ores must be found if costs are to be substantially reduced. There is no question about availability, since titanium is one of the most abundant elements. Titanium alloys can be shaped by most of the methods common to other metals used in engineering. They are now offered as sheet, strip, plate, bars, rods, wire, forgings, and tubing. It would appear as though titanium alloys will find their broadest applications in aircraft, missiles and similar directions where favorable weight/strength ratios are critical and elevated temperature conditions are encountered. Fabrication demands close control in order to prevent gas embrittlement, especially in welding. It is necessary to do most forming operations on heated material with heated dies.

NICKEL

This is one of the real basic alloying elements in engineering materials. It finds wide use in ferrous alloys where its fundamental influences on steel and cast iron are well known; furthermore, it is used with the nonferrous group, resulting in many important alloys. Nickel is one of the metals that is not found in our country, or at least not in commercial amounts; in consequence, dependence is placed upon imports principally from Canada and Cuba.

Nickel is used in anodes for electroplating and similar applications. Pure nickel is not generally employed as an engineering material; rather, it is the basic metal in a series of alloys. Among the better-known alloys of nickel are Monel and "K" Monel; others are Inconel and the Hastelloy series. Nickel alloys are fabricated by the usual methods of metal forming. These include casting, forging, rolling, machining, grinding, and extrusion. Some of the nickel alloys are gaining considerable importance in connection with the development of high-temperature-resistance materials that are needed in the programs for guided missiles and supersonic flight. Nickel has always been recognized as an excellent corrosion-resistant media. It continues to serve well in that category both by itself and in combination with other metals.

OTHER IMPORTANT METALS

There remain many metals which are pertinent in engineering materials but which have not reached production volume. Nonetheless many of these are extremely important; for example boron, which has already been mentioned as an alloying element in steel. It has the further important assignment of improving hot strength in some heat-resisting alloys. Lesser-known metals are coming into consideration as the search continues for materials that will serve in the high-temperature field or in an attempt to find new materials that can be processed by new methods. No attempt is made here to give an exhaustive portrayal; however, a few of the leaders will be surveyed.

Cobalt is a material of fundamental importance in engineering manufacture. It is the base for several high-temperature alloys that have proven themselves in service. This metal has found application as a binder in carbides, as it has in other fields such as high-speed tool steel, by way of example.

Another metal deserving of mention is zirconium; it is actually neither new nor rare. Zirconium metal is recovered from zircon sand which is found as beach sand in several locations. The atomic age has made zirconium a real giant among metals. There are several reasons for this sudden popularity, the main one being that it is the only commercially available structural metal that is impervious to nuclear radiation. In addition, it is almost as chemically inert as is glass; it also has high corrosion resistance, coupled with high strength. In addition to its contribution in the atomic field, zirconium is receiving attention from the chemical processing industry. High temperature, mechanical and corrosion properties can be improved considerably by alloying zirconium with tin and other elements. Zirconium is lighter than steel yet heavier than titanium.

In the continuing search for materials that will meet high-temperature operating conditions, some attention is being given to beryllium. Little has been known of this metal except for its beneficial effect as an alloying element in copper-base alloys. Attention has been focused on beryllium recently because of its density and possible high-temperature-resistant properties. Beryllium may prove to be the material that will succeed titanium in elevated temperature service. It is obvious that more research effort will be needed before beryllium becomes a metal of common usage.

Lithium is making significant contributions as an alloying element in aluminum. It is present in the Al alloys whose mechanical properties excel; furthermore Li-bearing alloys show to advantage in elevated temperature service. Li has also been used for controlled furnace atmospheres.

In order to improve mechanical properties of magnesium alloys, especially in the high-temperature region, thorium has served as a dependable alloying element. By way of example, experimental thorium bearing MG alloy HM21XA-T8 sheet can be satisfactorily used in the 200 to 800°F temperature range.

PLASTICS

ASTM designation D883-58T[1] carries the following definition: "A plastic is a material which contains as an essential ingredient an organic substance of large molecular weight, is solid in its finished state, and at some stage in its manufacture or in its processing into finished articles can be shaped by flow." In general, it can be stated that plastics are synthetic organic materials in which the binders are synthetic or natural resins, protein substances, or cellulose derivatives. Plastics can be formed by molding, casting, and extruding; another application for these materials is their use as coatings. They are also used as bonding agents in a variety of processes and products. The importance of plastics is evident from the ASTM Standards, 1958 which carry a total of 185 specifications, recommended practices, methods of tests, and other related information.

The most generally used classification for plastics is the one based on their thermal setting properties. Plastics which can be repeatedly softened by heating and hardened by cooling are known as *thermoplastics* or cold-set plastics. Since there is no chemical change involved in heating, it would be expected that this process could be repeated without limit; however, the heating temperatures must remain low, and for this reason thermoplastic materials are restricted in their applications. This group of plastic materials includes

Cellulose acetate	Polystyrene
Cellulose nitrate	Polyamide
Ethyl cellulose	Vinylidene chloride
Methyl methacrylate	Vinyl copolymers

Thermosetting plastics, on the other hand, undergo a chemical change during heating and assume a final shape that is retained on cooling. They are therefore designated as the hot-set plastics. They will not soften, by reheating, once they have been processed; when subjected to

[1] "ASTM Standards," American Society of Testing Materials, Philadelphia, 1958.

temperatures of 400°F they will char or burn. Representative materials in this classification include

Allyl alcohols   Phenol formaldehyde
Furfural formaldehyde   Polyesters
Melamine formaldehyde   Urea formaldehyde

Plastic Molding Compounds. The powders used for plastic molding are composed of a number of ingredients; of these, the binders exert the greatest influence on the end product. Next to the binders, filling materials are given the most attention. As in other products, fillers are used as a replacement for more costly materials. The choice of filler is also governed by the modification that it will exert on the final properties

Fig. 3-5. Express cruiser with hull and decking built from plastics re-enforced with Fiberglas. (Courtesy of Skagit Plastics, LaConner, Wash.)

of the plastic compound. Wood flour, made from soft wood, is a commonly used filler of considerable strength. Fillers also aid in promoting machinability. Other filler materials are fabrics, Fiberglas (Fig. 3-5), wood pulp, mica, and asbestos; the last two impart heat resistance to the plastic. Where hardness is more desirable than strength, inorganic binders such as China clay, infusorial earths, and gypsum are used.

To control the plastic mixture during and after processing, several other ingredients are added. These include such items as plasticizers, lubricants, catalysts, hardeners, solvents, and coloring materials; in each case the ones used are, necessarily, those most compatible with the basic mixture and best calculated to develop the desired properties in the end product. The function of the plasticizers is to increase the plasticity of the batch so that it will flow properly during processing.

In some cases lubricants are ingredients of the plastic formula, while in others they are applied directly to the mold surfaces by spraying or brushing. In either case the lubricants are present in order to prevent the plastic pieces from sticking in the molds. Experience with lubricants indicates that the choice is highly important; a given lubricant will prove successful with a given plastic when used in one mold but will prove unsuccessful in a different mold. Recognized lubricants are such materials as grease, fats, wax, oils, and various soaps.

The use of catalysts has the same function in connection with plastics as in other chemical processes. A catalyst is used to initiate or to alter the rate of a chemical reaction without becoming a part thereof. Under

Fig. 3-6. Gears and pulleys production-molded from nylon. (Courtesy of Barrett Division, Allied Chemical and Dye Corp., New York.)

certain conditions, where the formulation products are complex, the catalytic agents do exert profound influence on the nature of the final product. Catalysts are also referred to as accelerators and, under some circumstances, as hardeners.

The fact that plastic products can be produced in pleasing and even brilliant colors or color combinations is one of the chief reasons for their increasing popularity in manufactured items. Coloring of plastic end products is accomplished either by dissolving coloring matter in the plastic mixture at some stage of the processing or by applying dyestuffs to the finished product. Successful coloring requires the same careful attention to detail that characterizes the other features of the plastic-making process.

The majority of plastic parts are formed by molding (Fig. 3-6). The selection of the molding method is governed primarily by the basic type of plastic to be processed. The term molding as applied to plastics manufacture refers to the use of dies, heat, and pressure in combination.

Laminated Products. Laminated products are classified as plastics, since their composition and processing follow, in modified form, those familiar to molded plastics. They are of interest to engineering manufacture because they offer a combination of mechanical properties of a higher

Fig. 3-7. Laminated plastic components produced from phenolite laminated plastic. (Courtesy of National Vulcanized Fibre Co., Wilmington, Del.)

order than the general run of molded plastics (Fig. 3-7). The laminates are used in such mechanical components as gears, cams, bushings, housings, and washers. Laminated plastics are made from liquid binders and a filler in sheet form. The grading of the end product is based on the type of filler rather than on the resin binder used. The fillers are paper base of various types, fabric base, asbestos-paper base, asbestos-fabric base, and glass-fabric base; each of these bases modifies the finished product.

The processing of the laminates is relatively simple. The filler sheet is dipped into a plastic solution whose viscosity has been regulated by a previously added solvent. The sheet is then fed through squeeze rolls, much in the manner of hot-dipped tin-plate manufacture, and from the rolls through a drying oven for the purpose of curing. Following this operation, the sheet is rolled into coils or bolts for further processing. When laminated sheet is to be made, the previously processed material is cut into desired lengths of sheet and stacked between plates on the platens of a press. The surface of the plates is treated to the finish desired on the completed laminated sheet. The pressing operation combines a temperature of approximately 300°F with an operating pressure around 1,500 psi, which results in uniting the individual sheets and effecting the final set in the resin.

The single impregnated sheet is also used for producing laminated tubes and rods. In the former, the sheet is wound on a mandrel whose diameter corresponds to the internal diameter of the tube. After the tube wall has been built up to the requisite thickness, the tube can either be placed in an oven for setting or, for a stronger product, placed between split, heated dies for compacting and setting. The manufacture of rod stock of laminated material follows the same general scheme excepting for the fact that a small-diameter mandrel is used and is withdrawn prior to the final pressing operation. Laminated plastics are the basis of a limited number of molded parts—ignition distributor housings and shop safety helmets, among others.

Resin-bonded Plywood. The manufacture of resin-bonded plywood is a major industry. Wood sheets are used in place of the previously mentioned paper and fabric sheets in this product. An interesting development has been the use of high-frequency induction heating for curing plywood. There has also been a considerable amount of work done on molding plywood to specific shapes. The most noteworthy results have been achieved in connection with small boat hulls. Plywood is not usually classified under the heading of plastics; however, its properties offer alluring possibilities to engineering designers.

Plastics in Industry. The widest application of plastics in industry is found in nonstructural parts. One development for the machine shop is that of resin-bonded grinding wheels. These abrasive wheels have extended the scope of grinding because they possess mechanical strength superior to the better-known vitrified types. However, plastic products in themselves have received the best reception from the automotive and aircraft industries in the mechanical field. Plastic products are standard for many applications in electrical machines and equipment. In fact many major developments have come in plastics as an answer to the demands of the electrical industry.

Plastics are extending their applications in engineering manufacture both in the product field and in equipment (Fig. 3-8). Forming dies in automotive production are sometimes made from plastic materials. Artillery shell cases are another example where plastic materials are successfully replacing metal components. In one such instance the plastic shell case weighs 2.5 lb against 5.9 lb for the brass one it replaces. It is significant here that among other advantages strategic metal is conserved.

Novel Polymers. Continuing development work is showing up in the plastics area with an entirely new concept, whereby a polymer can be

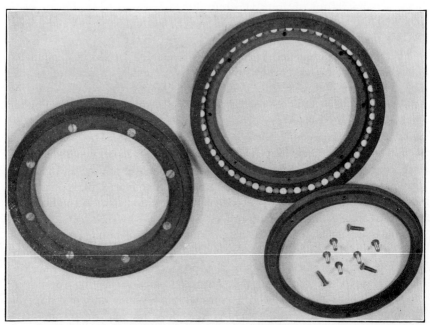

Fig. 3-8. Plastic pedestal bearing for 0.30 caliber machine-gun mount. The bearing balls are centerless, ground from cast phenolic rod. (Courtesy of Aircraft Armaments, Inc., Cockeysville, Md.)

given a distinct or predetermined molecular structure. As a result of this precise orientation a completely new set of values is obtainable, making it possible for the resulting plastics to compete with wood, glass, and even metal; in this respect they are of greater importance than nylon since costs are more favorable. Low costs stem from the invention in Germany by Professor Ziegler of a low-pressure polyethylene process. American industry is showing intense interest in this development and it can be expected, therefore, that new type plastics will make their appearance in engineering applications to a greater degree than has been the case in the past.

SURVEY QUESTIONS

3-1. Are nonferrous alloys generally more costly than ferrous ones on a poundage basis?

3-2. What application have cobalt-base alloys had in engineering manufacture?

3-3. Name at least three nickel-base alloys and give an engineering application for one of them.

3-4. What are the two basic copper alloys?

3-5. Give two examples of forged copper-base alloy components.

3-6. Mention a component on an automobile that would be made from "85-three 5's."

3-7. Give the numerical designation for Duralumin.

3-8. Are wrought aluminum alloys designated by ASTM or some other means?

3-9. Into what two classifications are wrought aluminum alloys divided?

3-10. How are wrought aluminum heat-treatable alloys distinguished by symbol?

3-11. Are die castings made from aluminum alloys?

3-12. In what industries do magnesium alloys receive greatest attention?

3-13. Are any innovations necessary in forming or stamping magnesium alloy sheet?

3-14. In what industry are zinc alloy die castings widely used?

3-15. Is there any application for zinc alloy sand castings?

3-16. What industry uses the major tonnage of titanium alloys?

3-17. Does titanium have any engineering application advantage over aluminum?

3-18. What are cold-setting plastics?

3-19. Of the two broad classifications of plastics, which one would be of primary interest in engineering manufacture?

3-20. Can plastics be machined the same as metals?

3-21. Are there such things as plastic castings?

3-22. List any advantages resulting from using plastics as engineering end products.

3-23. Is resin-bonded plywood classified as a plastic?

3-24. State some applications for laminated plastics.

Chapter 4

POWDER METALS AND CERMETS

Powder metallurgy is a method for the production of metal and semi-metal parts that is unique. Fundamentally the process consists of pressing, briquetting, or compacting a metal powder mixture under substantial pressure in a die and then sintering or heating this product, called the compact, so that the individual powder particles join together into a satisfactory end product (Fig. 4-1). This method has many favorable

Fig. 4-1. V-shaped wheel compacted from the two parts shown. Green compacts are assembled and then sintered; this is followed by impregnating the wheels with resin, after which they are plated. (Courtesy of National U.S. Radiator Corp., Johnstown, Pa.)

features; among them are the production of parts from metal powder blends whose components have widely differing melting points or characteristics; thus copper and silver, for example, can be combined with tungsten. Refractory metals such as tungsten, molybdenum, and tantalum can be successfully shaped by this method, whereas such a result would be impossible with casting or hot working. The combination of metal and nonmetal powders of wide variety makes possible the production of components that cannot be developed in any other way.

In common with other manufacturing methods the cost position is of utmost importance. Among the savings or advantages of powder metallurgy can be mentioned such items as surface finish, which means the elimination or certainly the reduction of the amount of necessary machinery. Since the parts are die-formed scrap or waste metal is eliminated.

Advantages and Limitations. It is possible to use powder metallurgy for the production of properties in end products that cannot be achieved in any other manner. A leading example of this development is oil im-

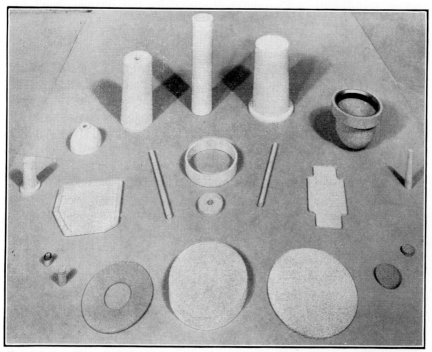

Fig. 4-2. Permanent powder metal filters. (Courtesy of Amplex Division, Chrysler Corp., Detroit.)

pregnation, which is used in the production of bearings. A corollary development is that of porous metal products such as filters, separators (Fig. 4-2), snubbers, metering elements, flame arresters, and sound deadeners. A further advantage is that of being able to obtain properties through alloying or processing or a combination of both that cannot be had by any other forming method.

Limitations on this method of metal forming arise from the factors of the method itself. Variability can be expected in the powders, in the pressure, and in the sintering operation. It is recognizable that since this is a die-formed product there will be a limitation on shape and size of the end product because of restrictions imposed by the die itself.

METAL POWDERS

The basic ingredient of this manufacturing method is the metal powder blend. The production of such metal powders takes a variety of forms. The choice is predicated upon the type of metal as well as upon the end product sought. It is possible to control chemical characteristics to a critical degree; the most widely used alloys are either copper base or iron base. The refractory carbides and metals form an increasingly important segment of end products produced by this method. Since the processing of the metal powder is similar to sand molding, obviously the characteristics of the latter could be applied to the former. This is quite true since a metal powder blend is critical as to particle size and distribution; density is also of importance. The flow rate of the metal powder governs the success of producing a given product.

The actual production of metal powders takes a variety of forms. Atomization is a favorite method for making powder from metal of relatively low melting point. The well-established method of milling that is applied in many industrial processes has also been applied to the production of metal powder. The nature of the metal as to degree of brittleness controls the particle shape and size to a major degree. A further method of producing metal powders is that of reducing metal oxides with hydrogen or in some cases carbon monoxide. Electrodeposition is also employed as a metal powder production method.

Compact Formation. The first operation in forming a powder metal component is that of mixing or blending the powder ingredients; this can be quite complex depending upon the requirements of the end product. For example, in making carbides the tungsten particles are mixed with cobalt for a considerable period of time until the cobalt has coated each tungsten particle. This procedure is necessary in order to obtain a proper cementing action during the sintering operation. It is during the mixing period that complete blending of the various powders and metallic or nonmetallic additions occurs. It is at this stage that volatilizing agencies are added when porosity in the end product is desired. Salicylic acid is a favorite additive for developing porous structures since it burns out during the sintering period. The mixing operation must be thoroughly controlled in order to promote homogeneity in the final product. This is not a simple requirement where powders of various specific gravities are included. Mixing time must be carefully controlled; if the batch is overmixed difficulties arise from destruction of particle size, or, with some metals, there can even be a degree of work hardening that can well prove troublesome.

The criteria for judging or accepting powdered metal parts are such attributes as density, hardness, tensile strength, and elongation. In addi-

tion such other mechanical properties as surface finish, dimensional tolerance, wear resistance, fatigue, and impact strength are also important.
The development of prealloyed powders is of significance since it has
been shown that parts using prealloyed powders are capable of unusually
high mechanical properties.

Powder Pressing. In processing powder metal parts the blended ingredients are introduced into a die which is mounted in a press. The

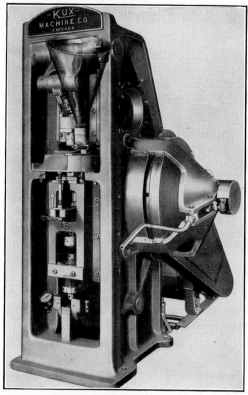

Fig. 4-3. Compacting press used for initial forming stage in powder metal components.
(Courtesy of Kux Machine Co., Chicago.)

following operation presses the powder into a form known as a compact. The presses must be designed for this particular application, the
reason being that operational requirements here are different than in
other metal pressing operations (Fig. 4-3). In the production of metal
stampings, die alignment determines the accuracy of the end product,
whereas in powder metal the accuracy of the machine determines the die
behavior and its influence on the end product. Presses must contain
design features that take into account characteristics of the blended metal
powders. The latter are frequently highly abrasive; because of their

fineness they work their way into the operating mechanism of the press unless restrained by proper construction. In some presses the operating mechanism is submerged in oil; others use bellows-type dust boots as well as telescoping metallic sleeves on exposed wearing surfaces. In short, every device is used to prevent metal powder from abrading wearing surfaces.

The multiple motion presses now available to the industry have provided a basic development in operating economy. Because of the potential that these presses have, much simpler dies and less expensive tooling can be used, which means that setup time is reduced and maintenance costs lowered. It is of interest to note that in these presses multiple motions are obtained in many cases through a combination of mechanical and hydraulic movements.

Press capacities have been increasing along with other design features. Whereas formerly 30 tons/sq in. was considered a maximum, presses now are capable of exceeding 75 tons/sq in. Insofar as capacities are concerned, presses range from $1\frac{1}{2}$ tons to well beyond 1,500 tons. It is well to remember that in pressing metal powder into the compact the flow behavior of the powder is not a hydraulic one; metal powders just do not flow in the die as would a liquid. Therefore, die design and filling techniques must be carefully developed. Density is higher at the surface of pressure application; thus a compact pressed from the top will have the greatest density at the top and the least density at the bottom. Likewise when pressure is applied from both sides the density is higher on the surfaces and lower in the center. This situation governs the design of the part as it does that of the tooling. It is well to remember, therefore, that in the end product diameters can be held more accurately than thicknesses or the dimension on the filling area. This phenomenon is being corrected with the introduction of automatic pressure equipment on modern presses.

Powder Metal Techniques. The operation routine for the production of simple powder metal components is actually divided into three parts. First is the blending of the powder, followed by pressing the green compact, which is then placed in a furnace for sintering as a final operation. Where high-density products are desired or where accuracy and surface finish are especially important, a somewhat different operation routine is followed. In this instance the sintering operation is followed by a coining operation or hot pressing, which is sometimes performed at the sintering temperature. There is still another method in which the sintering operation is followed by the infiltration routine, which is then followed by a cleaning operation to remove excess material. The actual blending within the compact is based upon the ingredients that are present and upon plastic behavior in the case of certain of the metals that are used. In other cases it is the fusion of mixture ingredients that accounts for the ultimate shaping of the product.

Furnaces are equipped with atmospheric control in order that requisite conditions can be maintained within the furnace that will produce the desired end product. Furnace maintenance is a definite problem because of volatilization of some given elements, such as lead for example. Other important items in connection with furnace are the necessity for uniform heating and the elimination of muffling effects. On some furnace designs it is desirable to have preheating in order to bring the green compact up to temperature gradually rather than subjecting it to final temperature upon introduction. In short, furnace operation and furnace design are an important and vital part of powder metal processing.

Powder Metal Developments. The idea of metal powder is spreading into broader and newer areas and markets. One far-reaching achievement has been the production of large magnesium alloy ingots that are designed for such further processing as rolling and extrusion. A similar development has come in the field of aluminum alloys. The objective is the production of alloys capable of operating at the elevated temperatures necessitated by supersonic flight requirements. Significant as these developments appear, there are others even more spectacular. The production of continuous strip from powder is a novel one; copper has been used in this connection. This achievement proves that strip or sheet can be rolled directly from powder.

The possibilities that iron powder processing is offering lead to many interesting opportunities. Some experimental work as early as 1940 indicated that iron powder produces acceptable sheet; based on this discovery development has proceeded to a point where continuous strip is possible. As this method has been worked out, the metal powder drops at an angle between rollers; the green strip resulting is not rolled to full density but passes through a sintering furnace. The sinter then can be treated in one of two ways, mainly by hot or by cold rolling in order to achieve the required densities and surface characteristics.

It can be said in summary that just about every area of metal production has been tried by some phase of the powder metal technique. In addition to metals already mentioned here, the list would include such others as brass, stainless steel, Monel, and even titanium. Truly powder metals are making significant additions to the materials of engineering now and in the future.

CERMETS

Further development of components for use in high-temperature service such as turbine parts will progress only in line with the ability of materials to care for operating temperatures and conditions (Fig. 4-4). Exploration in this field has been largely in the area of metals and alloys of every conceivable type. The investigations in this field have led to the examination of composite materials termed cermets and, in some instances, cermals. They include developments in which ceramics have been introduced along with other materials such as the so-called "hard metals." The end result achieved by these composite structures is in effect a hard refractory bonded to a more ductal metallic phase. Their production actually is not too far removed from the powder metal techniques. In their processing hot pressing is used, as is infiltration. Some

Fig. 4-4. Turbine wheel made from metal bonded Ti carbide (Kentanium grade K164B). (Courtesy Kennametal, Inc., Latrobe, Pa.)

degree of success has been achieved with cermets used as turbine blading. However, the operating requirements are so severe failures have occurred because of impact forces and fatigue.

The basic objective of the cermets is to combine the desirable properties of metals, ductility and impact strength, with those of ceramics, which have good high-temperature strength and stability. The chief cermet materials of interest are oxide base, carbide base, boride base, and intermetallic base. These different groupings each have some outstanding characteristics. By way of example, the oxide base CR-AL203 series are quite promising.

Carbides and Borides. In the carbide base area titanium carbide cermets are making genuine progress. They are being produced by several companies under various trade names in components such as turbine blading and nozzle and vane applications. In the boride base cermets, zirconium boride is one material proving quite satisfactory. There are some others in this group such as titanium boride, silicon boride, and manganese boride. The intermetallic base cermets seem to hold out great promise; among the developments in this area are molybdenum disilicide. The composition of this material is approximately 70 per cent molybdenum disilicide and 30 per cent alumina plus calcia. A further cermet in this classification is nickel aluminide, which appears to have exceptionally good oxidation resistance.

Graded Cermets. In order to meet the shortcomings of cermets, "graded" products are in production. In the graded components, the metal content varies in one or more directions, in order that the properties of any given section can meet imposed loading and requirements. It is possible with grading to develop ductility in regions where that property is necessary. It is presumed that throughout the length of the graded component varying load impositions can be met. The production of graded components can be achieved by making a skeleton. Skeletons are produced by sintering and are purposely made with considerable porosity. The pores in the skeleton are then infiltered with molten metal. The choice of materials that are used governs the results that can be obtained, which in turn are influenced by the operating

Fig. 4-5. A ramjet test nozzle made of slip-cast metal ceramic. (Courtesy of Haynes Stellite Co., Kokomo, Ind.)

requirements. Inasmuch as the resulting product will be intensely hard, it is common practice to machine these components prior to final sintering and infiltration. It is necessary to caution here that exacting control throughout this entire process is necessary in order to develop the type results that are wanted, and those that will produce a product that will function as desired.

Metal Ceramic. Inasmuch as nomenclature has not as yet been standardized in this area, the term metal ceramic is used sometimes in place of the word cermet. A typical example of a metal ceramic is the component shown in Fig. 4-5. This is made of chromium and aluminum oxide, which combines constituents with good high-temperature mechanical properties and high resistance to corrosion over a wide temperature range. The resistance is increased by the formation on the chromium of an oxide film, which is tightly bonded and highly stable. There is also a bonding mechanism between the chromium and aluminum oxide that contributes to the strength of the body at elevated temperature. Components have been made from this metal ceramic by casting to shape, sintering, and machining or grinding as required. The size and shape limitations lie in the furnacing facilities and in the problem of supporting the ware as it is sintered. Machining is done with tungsten carbide tipped tools; however, break-out at the end of the cut is a serious problem.

Ceramic Coatings. While ceramic coatings in the past have always been classified as enamels and not thought of particularly as engineering materials, there has been a complete change in this conception. Coatings that are capable of withstanding temperatures to 1200°F indefinitely, as well as some that are used for protection of stainless alloys at 1800°F, have helped greatly in meeting the problem of high-temperature protection. However, with continuing development of such coatings, changes in application techniques have similarly occurred. Whereas formerly processing was done at temperatures reaching 2000°F during the firing period, a new technique known as "Flame-Spray," which functions by melting the coating and spraying it upon the part to be protected, is now in operation. It is used for refractory oxides such as alumina and zirconia; both of these have been applied to metals and nonmetals such as plastics. There are no actual limitations to the shapes and sizes of parts that can be coated, whether large or small. While the coatings are somewhat porous, they exhibit good adherence, abrasion resistance, some flexibility, and they have low thermal conductivity. They provide short-period protection in high-temperature applications and are used on rocket nozzles and in ramjet engine components; in addition, such industrial applications as wear-resistant applications are developing. The trend in meeting high-temperature service conditions is turning more and more to the ceramic materials, either individually or as coatings.

SURVEY QUESTIONS

4-1. Wherein could a powder metal component differ from a metallic alloy component?

4-2. Why can certain types of powder metal components compete cost-wise with conventional manufacturing methods?

4-3. Why is quality control a problem in powder metal parts?

4-4. Why can the processing of powder metals be compared to foundry sand molding?

4-5. What is the common method of making metal powder?

4-6. State some of the criteria for judging the quality of powder metal parts.

4-7. List some of the mechanical properties that are outstanding in powder metal components.

4-8. Can presses for sheet metal be adapted to powder metallurgy satisfactorily?

4-9. What is a major source of deterioration of presses for metal powder?

4-10. Wherein does a multiple motion press differ from a mechanical press?

4-11. What is a distinguishing characteristic of furnaces used in powder metallurgy?

4-12. How has powder metallurgy invaded the field of supersonic flight?

4-13. Steel strip is produced on a continuous mill; has this equipment been adapted to powder metallurgy?

4-14. What is the meaning of cermet?

4-15. What has been the motivation for development of cermets?

4-16. Name some cermet end products.

4-17. Wherein are ceramic coatings of interest in engineering manufacture?

4-18. Mention two components of an automobile motor that have been successfully produced by powder metals.

REFERENCES FOR MATERIALS IN MANUFACTURING SECTION

Chaps. 2–4

"Aluminum Handbook," 1957, Aluminum Company of America, Pittsburgh.

"Applied Metallurgy for Engineers," 1956, by Burton, McGraw-Hill Book Company, Inc., New York.

"ASTM Standards," American Society of Testing Materials, Philadelphia.

"Basic Engineering Metallurgy," 1953, by Keyser, Prentice-Hall, Inc., Englewood Cliffs, N.J.

"Course in Powder Metallurgy," 1942, by Baeza, Reinhold Publishing Corporation, New York.

"The Making, Shaping and Treating of Steel," 7th ed., 1957, United States Steel Corporation, Pittsburgh.

"Materials and Processes," 1954, by Young, John Wiley & Sons, Inc., New York.

"Materials & Processes in Manufacturing," 1957, by DeGarmo, The Macmillan Company, New York.

"Materials for Nuclear Power Reactors," 1955, by Hausner and Roboff, Reinhold Publishing Corporation, New York.

"Metals Handbook" and Supplements, 1948 and later, American Society for Metals, Cleveland.

"Modern Plastics Encyclopedia," 1955, Breskin Publication,

"Modern Steels and Their Properties," 1955, Bethlehem Steel Company,

"Nonferrous Foundry Metallurgy," 1954, by Murphy, McGraw-Hill Book Company, Inc., New York.

"Plastics for Industrial Use," 1942, by Sasso, McGraw-Hill Book Company, Inc., New York.

"Powder Metallurgy," 1947, by Schwarzkopf, The Macmillan Company, New York.

"Steel Products Manual," American Iron & Steel Institute, New York.

Chapter 5

PATTERNS FOR METAL CASTINGS

In order to manufacture any machine or structure of an engineering design in which metal is used, a fundamental problem is that of producing the desired metal in the required shape or form. To this end, it is generally understood that engineering metals and alloys are shaped by two broad classes of manufacturing methods. These are known as castings and mechanically worked or wrought products, respectively. It is the purpose of this and the following several chapters to present the shaping of metals by casting.

Castings offer a relatively uncomplicated method of shaping metals. A well-known example is that of a V-8 motor block that is basic to the automobile industry. This motor block is an extremely complex structure, yet it is designed so that the metal can be readily shaped by the casting process. Furthermore, this process has been developed to the point where it is possible to produce castings entirely on mechanical equipment, as will be mentioned in subsequent chapters. In order to produce a casting, it is necessary to have a cavity that will receive the metal as it is poured. This cavity must represent the shape of the desired casting. It is well to comprehend that a casting is made by pouring or casting metal into a cavity or mold. This mold will take various forms, as noted further on in this chapter. Castings range in size from a few hundred tons to fractions of ounces. Housing for rolling mills are an example of the former, whereas dental inlays portray the latter. It should be realized, therefore, that castings can be of all conceivable shapes and can be made in most of the metals used in engineering. The majority of castings are produced in molds made from molding sand of some type.

In order to make a sand mold a pattern is necessary. Foundry patterns are made from a variety of materials such as wood, metal, plaster, or plastics. The patternmaker is given a drawing of the finished casting, which he uses in developing the pattern. It is rare indeed that the patternmaker is given a completely dimensioned drawing of the pattern itself; rather, he is given a drawing of the finished component. It then becomes the duty of the patternmaker to interpret the drawing into a foundry pattern.

Foundry patterns are extremely critical equipment to any successful manufacturing program. Their design must recognize metal behavior

Fig. 5-1a. Wooden pattern for manifold connection steel casting. Note core prints and parting line. (Courtesy of Washington Iron Works, Seattle, Wash.)

Fig. 5-1b. Manifold connection steel casting produced from pattern shown in Fig. 5-1a. (Courtesy of Washington Iron Works, Seattle, Wash.)

in solidification and contraction. Additionally, the patternmaker must provide allowances for any metal that is to be machined from the casting. He also must make provision for contraction of the metal from the time the casting is poured until it reaches room temperature.

The designer must know something of casting methods in order to provide a workable design that will result in an economical casting. The solution is to have the designer and the patternmaker consult on a given problem in order to develop a foundry pattern that will produce a satisfactory end product (Fig. 5-1a and 1b).

When a pilot run or experimental work is under way, castings are made from a single or "loose" pattern. The same idea is employed where a relatively few castings of one kind are wanted. The pattern is molded in a flask, also called a molding box, on an individual basis. However, as production increases, individual patterns become uneconomical and are abandoned in favor of multiple-mounted patterns.

PATTERN DETAILS

Importance of Pattern Ribs. When a drawing reaches the pattern shop it is analyzed with a view to the problems which may arise in the foundry when the part is cast. If the designer has failed to provide supplemental information such as the direction of stress application, the patternmaker will be in ignorance on this important matter and will not give it consideration in making the pattern. An example of this is the location of ribs on a pattern. The direction of load application will develop a major fiber stress normal to that direction. In consequence the pattern should be made with the major metal volume in such a position as to resist the force of load application; this will result in the lowest possible unit stress. Such a solution for lowered unit stress is found, for example, in rolled steel and extruded aluminum-alloy sections of bulb design. Bulbed sections of aluminum alloys are prominent in aircraft construction; similarly, steel bulbed sections are used for certain critically stressed members in shipbuilding. Examples of such sections are shown in Fig. 5-2.

In the matter of rib location in the construction of a pattern, where circumstances permit, the practice should be followed of placing the ribs in such a position that they will be in compression and the flat surface in tension, rather than the reverse. Ribs placed in tension will be more susceptible to cracking owing to the condition of loading. It can readily be seen in design B, Fig. 5-3, that the stress is distributed over a large area. This construction is referred to in the shop as "ribs in compression and flat surfaces in tension." Obviously the rib strength can be further improved by bulbing or beading (Fig. 5-2). However the use of a bead, whether on a rib or as a reinforcement on a thin section, should be held within the limits of practicality from the molding standpoint. A bead split along the parting line presents no molding difficulty, nor does one placed on a horizontal surface of a pattern made with vertical draft. When, however, beads are placed on vertical surfaces of

patterns where they may project in a way that will interfere with
drawing the pattern from the mold, a complicated core job results.

Locating Machined Surfaces. It is axiomatic that a pattern should be
made in such a way as to place the major machined surfaces on the
bottom, or drag, side of the casting as it is molded. This practice is
followed wherever possible in order to take advantage of the fact that
the metal at the bottom of the casting is sound, since slag and loose sand
tend to float and will come to rest against the upper, or cope, side of
the casting, so that any unsound metal will be in that area.

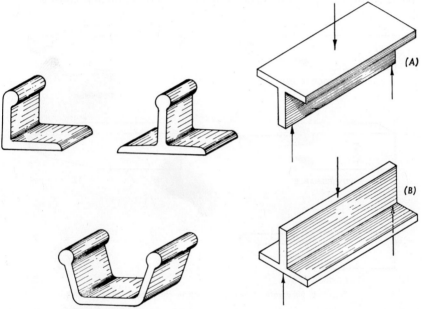

Fig. 5-2. Sketches of rolled and extruded bulbed
sections.

Fig. 5-3. A, rib in tension. B, rib in
compression, flat surface in tension
—preferred design.

Filleting. A very common error made by the draftsman in the design
room is neglecting the proper use of fillets on a pattern. This drafting
room error is frequently corrected by the patternmaker; he is, however,
limited in his choice, since placing an inside fillet and disregarding the
outside corner may result in a mass concentration making the casting
unsound at that location. The omission of the fillet, on the other hand,
will result in undesirable stresses from cooling and may form the basis
for a crack. The extent of such defects will vary with the type of metal
being cast; those of high hot-short characteristics prove especially troublesome.

Filleting is important at the junction of section changes. An even better solution, however, is a gradual taper. The available methods of designing junctions of section changes are shown in Fig. 5-4 with appropriate notations.

Pattern Draft. Draft on a pattern facilitates its molding since, once the pattern is loosened in the mold, it can be readily withdrawn; the draft provides for a clean and easy lift. The amount of draft, sometimes spoken of as taper, is actually a variable quantity although it is usually taken to mean one degree. The designer should consider the amount of permissible draft when he is establishing design dimensions in order to avoid scant sections and surfaces at critical points on the casting.

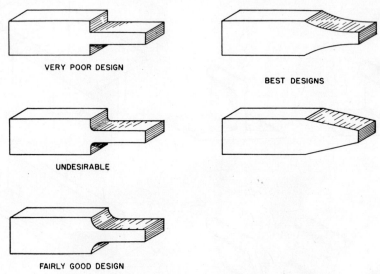

VERY POOR DESIGN

BEST DESIGNS

UNDESIRABLE

FAIRLY GOOD DESIGN

Fig. 5-4. Schematic drawing of section changes in casting iron.

Careful attention should be given to the possibility of avoiding undercutting, which is in reality reverse draft, or back-draft. There are complicated designs in which this undesirable condition cannot be avoided; where back-draft does occur, molding the pattern becomes complicated and necessitates the use of cheeks or cores or both.

Pattern Parting Line. It is frequently possible to design patterns in such a way that they can be made in one piece and molded entirely in the drag flask. In such instances the draft is in one direction from the pattern face and there is no problem of locating the parting line on the pattern. When a more complicated pattern shape is encountered the pattern must be made in sections or parts—the "split" pattern. The junction line is referred to as the *parting line*, and since the pattern will then be molded in both the cope and the drag flask, the pattern draft will be divergent from the parting line. The location of the parting line calls for consideration of previously mentioned factors such as location of ribs and machined surfaces as well as of the problem of molding the pattern. It is sometimes possible to locate a parting line or split the pattern in such a way as to overcome back-draft. There is no single feature of pattern-making that requires more exacting study than does the location of the parting line (Fig. 5-5).

It is not always possible to develop a straight parting line because of the inherent shape of the casting. Every effort, up to and including rede-

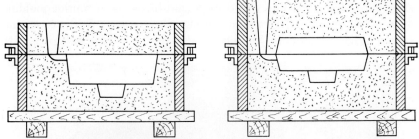

Fig. 5-5. Example of a single-piece pattern (left) and a split pattern for the same casting (right). Draft is exaggerated in both patterns.

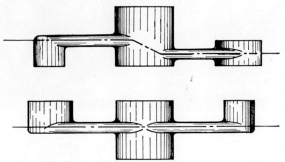

Fig. 5-6. Example of a pattern redesigned for production. Top, irregular parting line; bottom, redesign permits a straight parting line.

sign, should be made to achieve a straight parting surface since an irregular parting line requires more molding time or additional pattern rigging. The principle of redesign from an irregular to a straight parting line is sketched in Fig. 5-6. The discussion here has been based on the idea of a single pattern. When production attains a considerable volume, regularity of parting lines is not so important because more elaborate pattern equipment can be justified.

Follow-boards. One standard method for simplifying the molding of a pattern with an irregular parting line is the use of the follow-board. The follow-board is made to the contour of the pattern parting line. It is built up from wood which is recessed to receive the pattern to its parting line. Another method of making a follow-board, or "match," is to pour a plaster of Paris mixture to the desired shape; a mixture of sharp sand, binder, and hardener can be used in the same way. Patterns of irregular parting line are on occasion molded with a follow-block or fill-in piece for economy in pattern equipment.

Follow-boards are not used exclusively as a device for simplifying the molding of irregular parting lines; they also serve to facilitate the molding of patterns of thin section where splitting on the parting line would result in a fragile pattern section. Such sections are likely to warp and at best are subject to damage and breakage in routine molding practice. Figure 5-7 illustrates a steering-wheel pattern with its accompanying follow-board. In this design the rim section is I-shaped, with

Fig. 5-7. Follow-board shown at left fits one-piece steering-wheel pattern at right.

a web thickness of $\frac{1}{8}$ in.; obviously if this pattern were to be split through the web it would be too fragile for foundry use.

Match Plates and Mounted Patterns. The accepted method for the production molding of irregular-parting-line patterns is to mount them on "match plates"; regular-parting-line patterns are given like treatment. The manner of constructing the match plate is determined by the amount of production to be obtained from the patterns. Where production runs are to be extensive it is common practice to cast the pattern parts and the plate as an integral unit; the casting is generally some type of aluminum alloy. The match plates for regular-parting-line patterns are frequently built up by mounting the mating pattern parts on opposite sides of a hardwood board or metal pattern plate. Obviously the term match plate is derived from the fact that the pattern parts mounted on each side of the plate will match perfectly. The term mounted pattern refers to one or more patterns that have been fastened to a plate or board, usually a series of patterns on a single board (Fig. 5-8). This series may consist of duplicates or of different parts with a similarity in volume and section. Patterns so mounted are provided with necessary runners and ingates arranged so that the entire group can be poured at the same time.

In the foundry the mounting of patterns is comparable in importance to tooling in the machine shop; consequently, imagination and understanding of the casting process and foundry equipment are required of the patternmaker. It is customary in production work to mount every pattern that can possibly be adapted to this form of treatment. Such complex castings as V-type motor blocks are in production using mounted patterns (Fig. 5-9a and 9b). Molding single or "loose" patterns

Fig. 5-8. Mounted sheave pattern that serves for molding both cope and drag. Note unusual spoke treatment to eliminate cracking in spokes. Casting is poured with manganese steel. (Courtesy of Skagit Steel & Iron Works, Sedro-Woolley, Wash.)

is not a production method; rather, such procedure belongs to the job shop, pilot plant, or experimental category.

SOLIDIFICATION BEHAVIOR OF CASTINGS

Solidification Phenomena. The design of a sound casting requires a knowledge of the behavior of cast metal from pouring to cooling at room temperature. As the mold fills with molten metal a temperature gradient is established between the mold interface and the casting. Obviously the influence of the mold temperature will be exerted first on the metal which lies in contact with the mold face and a cooling action will be started there. A given casting section then will be solidifying from all bounding surfaces toward the center. If the casting has been designed with a uniform section throughout, its solidification rate will be uniform. However, when sections of varying thickness are present in

Fig. 5-9a. Mounted drag pattern for molding two V-8 motor blocks in a single mold. (Courtesy of Dodge Division, Chrysler Corp., Detroit.)

Fig. 5-9b. Drag mold for two V-8 motor blocks made from the pattern shown in Fig. 5-9a. (Courtesy of Dodge Division, Chrysler Corp., Detroit.)

a casting, differential solidification rates will develop within the casting. This condition is a major cause of unsound castings. In the process known as slush casting, the mold is inverted immediately after pouring in order to drain the still liquid metal from the casting interior; thereby a casting is left that is merely a shell of metal. Such castings are used for making small metal toys and some types of plumbing fixtures.

The first metal to solidify is actually chilled, since the mold surface has not had sufficient time to become heated. The casting will exhibit

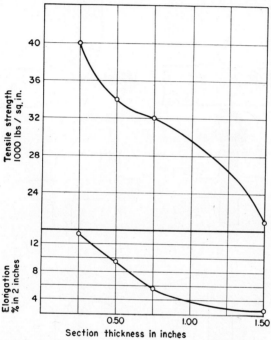

Fig. 5-10. Effect of section thickness on tensile strength and elongation for aluminum-alloy casting 195-T6. (Courtesy of Aluminum Co. of America, Pittsburgh.)

a fine, close-grained structure at this surface but a coarser texture toward the center of the section. However, actual porosity—or what is even worse, a cavity—will not occur if provision is made for a continuing supply of liquid metal through some feeding device. This "feeding" is necessitated by the behavior of the solidifying mass, which draws upon the liquid portion of the casting, or melt, until solidification is complete. An understanding of the phenomena of solidification is necessary if the designer is to obtain maximum strength from a cast section. The thinner the casting section within practical limits, the greater will be its strength per unit area. The graphs in Fig. 5-10 applying to Alcoa alloy 195-T6 show the effect of section thickness.

To ensure the production of a casting free of porosity the casting must be designed, or the pattern made, in such a way as to avoid large concentrations of metal. The design must be studied from the viewpoint of the actual solidification behavior of the liquid metal within the mold. It is obvious that the last part filled will be the hottest and that it will be in a liquid state while the part of the mold filled first is solidifying. When the problem of *directional solidification* has been solved—*i.e.*, the

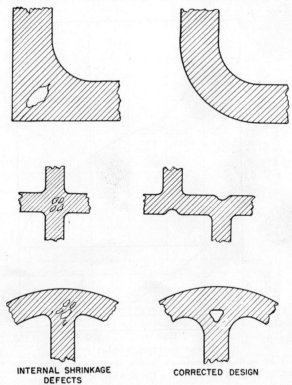

INTERNAL SHRINKAGE   CORRECTED DESIGN
DEFECTS

Fig. 5-11. Effect of improper design, together with corrective design.

progressive feeding of molten metal in the direction of solidification has been attained—castings will be sound. The final part of the casting to cool will receive molten metal from the sprue, or riser, to compensate for any solidification shrinkage that might tend to develop there.

Hot Spots. Unsound sections in castings can frequently be attributed to the fact that "hot spots," or metal concentrations, occur at locations where they cannot receive adequate liquid metal to compensate for solidification shrinkage. Typical examples of such difficulties are shown in Fig. 5-11, together with suggested corrective measures. It is impossible to overemphasize this very basic factor of casting design. Traditionally, castings have always been of great bulk or mass; close analysis of the phenomena of solidification, however, indicates that mass in itself does not mean much from the viewpoint of strength. Limitation on minimum section thickness must be observed if mis-runs are to be avoided in the casting. The data in Table 5-1 are recommended by the American

TABLE 5-1

Casting alloys	Recommended minimum section thickness, in.
Aluminum	$\frac{1}{8}$
Brass and bronze	$\frac{3}{32}$
Gray cast iron (soft)	$\frac{1}{8}$
Magnesium	$\frac{5}{32}$
Malleable cast iron	$\frac{3}{32}$
Steel	$\frac{3}{16}$
White cast iron	$\frac{1}{8}$

Foundrymen's Society. The use of these values must be tempered by the judgment of the patternmaker, who will take into account the fact that small surface areas are more readily poured, or run, than large ones.

Contraction and Shrinkage. Castings permitted to remain in a sand mold will cool slowly because of the insulating nature of the sand. When metal molds are used, as in die or permanent-mold casting, the cooling rate is accelerated. During the cooling period the casting is contracting in size. If, then, the pattern is made exactly to design dimensions, the resulting casting will be too small by the amount of its contraction. Each classification of the cast metals has a different set of values in this regard. Further, the same metal yields varying results in accordance with the size and shape of the casting as well as the position in which it is molded. In order to compensate for normal contraction, or shrinkage, to use a shop term, pattern dimensions are increased. This is accomplished by using a shrinkage rule graduated so as to increase dimensions in the amount of the contraction characteristics of the metal in question. Shrinkage rules are available for all cast metals; a notation of shrinkage value is marked on them. The data in Table 5-2 are offered as a general guide for contraction allowances.

TABLE 5-2

Casting alloy	Contraction, in./ft
Aluminum	$\frac{1}{8}$ –$\frac{5}{32}$
Brass	$\frac{3}{16}$
Bronze	$\frac{1}{8}$ –$\frac{1}{4}$
Gray cast iron	$\frac{1}{10}$–$\frac{1}{8}$
Magnesium	$\frac{1}{8}$ –$\frac{5}{32}$
Malleable cast iron	$\frac{1}{8}$ –$\frac{3}{16}$
Steel	$\frac{3}{16}$–$\frac{1}{4}$

Distortion in Castings. Slight distortion of a finished casting may be traceable to any one of several causes; an unyielding mold or carelessness in handling immediately after solidification may be responsible. However, a more serious distortion is traceable to the casting shape (Fig. 5-12). An expedient used to overcome such distortion is that of "faking" the pattern in a direction opposite to the one in which the casting will

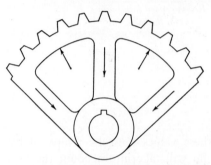

distort. It will shed some light on the behavior of a casting during cooling to observe that a bushing stock casting will contract diametrically, whereas a half-bushing casting will contract along its arc.

Effect of Design on Machining. Consideration given to machining problems by a designer will be helpful in subsequent processing. Locating points should be shown on the drawing; they are useful for checking both the pattern and the resultant casting. The locating

Fig. 5-12. Diagrammatic sketch of forces acting on a casting during cooling period owing to heavy metal concentration at the hub.

points are preferably placed on a part of the casting that is not subject to such variations as those caused by parting-line shifts. It is always necessary to remember that layout for machining a casting must be done from some base point or points.

CORING CONSIDERATIONS

The core work on a casting is another essential feature that calls for careful analysis when the pattern is being made. Cores are used to form desired depressions, recesses, or contours in the casting. The largest single use of cores is for forming cast holes of a desired size, shape, and location. Cores are broadly classified as green-sand or dry-sand, depending on their method of manufacture. Green-sand cores are made from the same molding sand as that used in the molds; in most instances they are an integral part of the mold. There are jobs, such as soil pipe, where the green-sand cores are made separately and then placed in the mold. Green-sand cores are the most economical to use, since they require no additional materials or processing and since they are returned to the system sand in the same way as molding sand from the molds.

Dry-sand Cores. Dry-sand cores are made from materials and by processes different from those used in the mold in which they are placed. An exception occurs in some complicated jobs where the entire mold is made up of a series of dry-sand cores, for example, the cast-aluminum cylinder heads for air-cooled radial aircraft motors. A dry-sand core is composed of some type or types of sharp sand mixed with a binding material selected on the basis of its imparting desirable mechanical properties to the core. The core mix is molded in a core box; there may be several of these for a single casting. The next operation consists of placing the core into a core oven for baking, or subjecting it to gassings (Chap. 6).

Dry-sand cores require a means of anchoring them into position in the mold to prevent shifting during the casting operation. The usual method is that of adding core prints to the pattern. A core print forms an imprint or depression in the sand mold of a shape and size corresponding to the print on the core. Size and location of core prints are usually left to the patternmaker's judgment. Core prints serve the dual purpose of providing core support and vents for gas escapement. When a core extends through the casting, a core print can be placed at its ends. There are situations, though, in which the core is almost entirely surrounded by metal and there is a total lack of openings in the casting, where core prints could be placed.

The patternmaker has to choose between two alternatives in solving this problem; he can arbitrarily place a core print or prints at desired locations, or he can use available core print locations and metal core supports, known as core *chaplets*. A *false core print* is one used at some point other than a designed opening in the casting. The cored hole resulting must then be closed with a threaded plug or by pressing in a metal stamping, depending on the design requirements. Core chaplets are obtainable in about every conceivable shape and size. They are made of steel stampings that have been tinned to aid in fusing into the casting and prevent their rusting in storage or the mold.

Cores frequently require the use of metal rods, arbors, or wires as reinforcement to give the necessary strength to withstand the pressures developed by the metal filling the mold. These metal pieces are withdrawn from the casting at the time the cores are removed. This is another reason for having cored holes situated to permit easy rod removal.

Core boxes are made concurrently with the pattern. In many cases there is the necessity for making several core boxes to accommodate a single pattern. This work can be reduced, sometimes, by fitting loose stop-offs, or removable pieces, into a core box in an arrangement that will permit one core box to be used for making several different cores. Core boxes are often built to produce a segment of a core; these segments are fitted and pasted together to form the large final core.

Pattern and Core Box Colors. Standardization of the painting of wooden patterns and core boxes has been adopted to aid the foundry in understanding the various features of this equipment. This color code

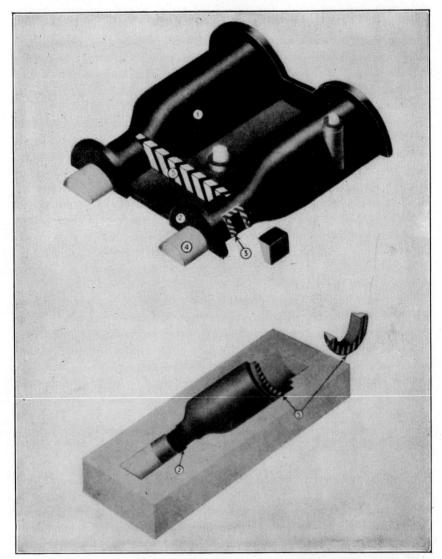

Fig. 5-13. Standard pattern colors. Pattern shown at top and core box below.

1. Surfaces to be left unfinished are painted black.

2. Surfaces to be machined are painted red.

3. Seats of and for loose pieces are to be marked by red stripes on a yellow background.

4. Core prints and seats for loose core prints are to be painted yellow.

5. Stop-offs are to be shown by diagonal black stripes on a yellow background.

has been approved as American Recommended Practice B45.1—1932 under the Procedure of the American Standards Association. Figure 5-13 shows the standardized color scheme applied to a wooden pattern and its core box. Note the color code explanation at the bottom of Fig. 5-13.

PATTERN CONSTRUCTION

Materials for Patterns. The selection of a satisfactory species of wood for the pattern is determined by the service expected of the pattern and also by the amount of shaping needed to make the pattern. Such soft woods as white pine, sugar pine, and western cedar are most popular, since they are relatively light in weight and can be fashioned easily. Philippine mahogany is common for patterns that are to have a long service life in the foundry. Patterns for extended production runs are made from metal. Aluminum alloys are most useful because of favorable weight and ease of finishing. Metal patterns are cast from a master pattern that, in turn, is made with double shrinkage allowance. In order to gain a fuller appreciation of the many problems facing the pattern-maker and his solutions for them, it is suggested that a modern treatise on patternmaking be consulted. An outstanding text is "The Pattern Maker's Manual," by McAfee and Wagner.[1]

Plaster in Patternmaking. Among several procedures for the use of plaster, perhaps the best-known one is that of starting with a wooden counterpart of the core. This is mounted inside an open-top knockdown wood box of a size which will give the desired wall thickness for the plaster core box that it is intended to produce. That part of the box which will be in contact with the plaster mix must be treated with a parting compound such as petroleum jelly or grease.

The batch is prepared by sifting the plaster into water. Large volumes of plaster must not be added or lumps will develop in the mix. Two volumes of water to three of plaster of Paris is regarded as a satisfactory ratio. The acceptable viscosity is one approaching that of thick cream. The chief source of trouble in casting plaster arises from the inclusion of air bubbles which produce porosity or voids in the cast.

As the cast sets, it will begin to develop temperature, accompanied by expansion; all wood parts must be withdrawn immediately when there is evidence of heating. The cast can then be set aside for a day, during which time it will develop hardness and strength. The working surfaces are given several coats of shellac prior to the use of the cast in the foundry.

The above operation will produce the core box, since the cast was made against a wood replica of the desired core. The wood replica is

[1] An official publication of the Pattern Makers' League of North America, 1947.

then used as the foundation for the pattern. It need only be built up for the requisite metal thicknesses; flanges or bosses may be added by applying some material, such as sheet wax, which forms easily. When this building-up process is completed, the newly finished piece can in turn be used as a pattern for a plaster cast. Upon completion, these two casts will provide pattern and core box for several castings.

Gypsum Cement Patterns. Gypsum cement is another material of interest for the patternmaker. It is not cast by the method described for plaster of Paris, which is poured in liquid form. Gypsum cement is mixed with water to form a liquid that soon reaches a stage of plasticity. When in this condition, it is "screeded," or worked to contour, by means of a metal template.

Fig. 5-14a. Drag half of plastic matched-plate pattern for P trap. Note cast plastic at left, mounted pattern at right.

Patterns from Plastics. The development of foundry patterns made from plastics has been moving forward rapidly; with the introduction of new type plastics, interest in patterns has been markedly increased. There are inherent advantages to plastic patterns and, of course, also some disadvantages; however, they compete quite well with metal patterns insofar as foundry service is concerned, and they can be produced at considerably less cost. This situation has been brought about through the introduction of the epoxies, a series of resins that has many attributes. They offer good mechanical properties and lower shrinkage values; generally, as is true of these plastic materials, they have high dimensional stability and a good degree of flexibility since they are available both as casting and laminating resin types.

In the production of plastic patterns, two different procedures are employed. In one case the pattern is poured in a mold, whereas in the other method the pattern is built up by laminations. In the latter tech-

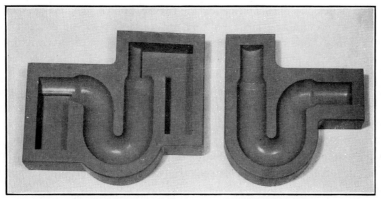

Fig. 5-14b. Plastic core boxes for both cope and drag pattern for P tray casting in Fig. 5-14c.

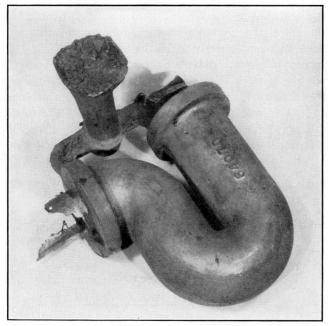

Fig. 5-14c. Casting of P trap molded from plastic matched-plate pattern with cores made in plastic core boxes.

nique, glass fiber is built up with a resin binder; obviously such procedure is time-consuming, and, therefore, of high cost. The other method whereby patterns are cast is relatively simple. Here a mold is used for casting both the pattern and the core boxes (Fig. 5-14a, 14b, and 14c). Molds are generally made from plaster and some of them are faced with a low-fusion alloy. One problem in connection with casting patterns arises from the tendency of plastic bodies to shrink, especially where they occur as a large volume. In consequence, the pattern has to be developed with either a filler or a core of some type, over which the plastic is introduced. By such means the volume of plastic is reduced and the cracking tendency is overcome.

The interesting development is that the epoxy resins can be cured or hardened very simply. In most cases they are cured at room temperature in a time range of several hours; however, the development of the maximum strength potential may require as much as a week. This time can be materially reduced by subjecting the pattern to a temperature in the range of 120 to 150°F, an operation that follows room-temperature curing.

Plastic patterns are not limited to individual units, but on the contrary they are also used as match plate or gated patterns wherein several are mounted on a board for use in machine molding. Their surface finish, being a natural one, remains in good condition over a long service life. Furthermore, the surface is smooth, thereby ensuring an excellent mold surface and consequently a fine casting.

Other types of plastics and plastic formulations are being used satisfactorily in the pattern shop. It is well to remember, however, that a great deal of knowledge and skill is required for achieving successful results. There seems to be little question but that with the further expansion of this type of patternmaking, plastic patterns and core boxes will come into far more general use than is now the case.

SURVEY QUESTIONS

5-1. Is the usual drawing that comes from the designing room that of a machine end product or of the pattern for that product?

5-2. Mention one important detail wherein a drawing for a casting would vary from the pattern drawing.

5-3. Why is a foundry pattern necessary and what is its function?

5-4. What materials are used for making production patterns as opposed to single-piece patterns?

5-5. What are the two broad classifications applying to the manufacture of a metal component?

5-6. Why is the casting method considered the most flexible metal forming method?

5-7. What limitation, if any, is placed upon casting size?

5-8. Can all engineering metals be produced as castings?

5-9. Why are ribs used on castings?

5-10. Are rib locations of significance?

5-11. Are any of the bulbed sections shown in Fig. 5-2 of a design that could not readily be cast?

5-12. Why are machine surfaces on castings placed in the drag or bottom side when possible?

5-13. Why are fillets important to promotion of sound castings?

5-14. What is meant by the "parting line" on a pattern?

5-15. Is the parting line always a straight line?

5-16. Why are follow-boards used in the foundry?

5-17. Is a match plate the same thing as a mounted pattern?

5-18. List three advantages to using mounted patterns.

5-19. Explain the term "directional solidification."

5-20. Does increasing thickness in a casting indicate increased strength? Explain.

5-21. What are hot spots in a casting?

5-22. Is the contraction shrinkage value the same for all types of metal castings?

5-23. Can distortion in castings be controlled?

5-24. What is the function of a core in a casting?

5-25. Why are green-sand cores generally more economical than any other type?

5-26. Why is the use of core chaplets usually undesirable?

5-27. What is the function of a core box?

5-28. List materials other than wood and metal suited to making patterns.

5-29. Do plastic patterns have any advantages over metal patterns?

Chapter 6

SANDS FOR THE FOUNDRY

Sand is the basic foundry material. It is used, in some form, in every major foundry activity, from molding to the cleaning room and melt shop. These diverse applications require a variety of physical as well as mechanical properties. Foundry sands include such materials as pit sand, beach sand, bank sand, sharp sand, and blended sand, to mention some of the more common types.

Molding sand is the most important one since it is the investment material used for sand castings. The phrase "naturally bonded molding sands" has become the accepted term for molding sands that are used in the foundry in the condition in which they are quarried. They are tempered by water additions until their properties are satisfactory for molding use. As the demands of the foundry became more diversified, it developed that naturally bonded sands could not meet all necessary molding and casting requirements. Research uncovered the shortcomings of these sands and led to investigations that have resulted in the development of "synthetic sands." Synthetic molding sands are compounded of refractory grains, buffers, atmosphere agents, and bonding agents, together with tempering water. These sands were formerly peculiar to steel foundries but are now used throughout the foundry industry.

Natural Molding Sand. Naturally bonded molding sand is composed of grains of refractory material held together by a bonding agent that is primarily a clay; impurities may be present, in varying amounts. Sand deposits are found in many parts of the country, and it is the accepted practice to name a sand for the region of its origin; thus Albany sand comes from the vicinity of Albany, N.Y. The cost of transporting molding sand is critical to the foundry and accounts for the effort to use local sand, with its attendant difficulties. The geological nature of a deposit can be such that a considerable variation in the sand will occur. This situation is met by suppliers of molding sand through the use of blending or mixing equipment which ensures a degree of uniformity in the final product.

The lack of uniformity of performance by molding sands has been the subject of scientific investigations going back to the beginning of this century. Among the pioneering efforts in this direction was the work of Dr. H. Ries, professor of geology at Cornell University, in testing some Michigan and Wisconsin sands prior to and during 1904.[1] Dr. Richard Moldenke was another early student of molding sand.[2] These researches in molding sand are being continued by other investigators, notably Dietert, Dunbeck, and Snyder. Research work on foundry sands has led to the establishment of both adopted and tentative standards that form the basis of sand control. Methods of testing are published in the "Foundry Sand Testing Handbook" issued by the American Foundrymen's Society.

Synthetic Molding Sands. The synthetic molding sands mentioned earlier are compounded to meet specific requirements within a foundry. Where a wide range of casting requirements must be met, several different types of synthetic sand will be used by a foundry in order to obtain the best results. Synthetic molding sands are generally prepared by using a refractory base material and bonding it with some type of clay, although such additives as silica flour, iron oxide, and corn flour are sometimes included.

Silica sand, SiO_2, has become established over the years as a satisfactory material capable of meeting the requirements imposed by every type of casting. There are, however, some other geological materials that are satisfactory for use as base sands.

Olivine, a natural combination of forsterite ($2MgO \cdot SiO_2$) and fayalite ($2FeO \cdot SiO_2$), is a satisfactory base sand. Its expansion characteristics are more favorable than those of silica: expansion is less and remains constant throughout the casting temperature range. Olivine, composed of 90 per cent forsterite and 10 per cent fayalite, has a fusion temperature in the range of $3100°F$.

Olivine is proving itself increasingly as an outstanding refractory material in commercial foundries. It is preeminent in manganese steel shops since it does not react with the molten metal; the result is that the castings have better surface finish and require much less cleaning. Because of its favorable heat capacity olivine is proving to be a decided help in eliminating many casting defects. By way of example, in casting steel ship propellers, the tendency of the blades to crack at the hub is eliminated by using this type of sand base; similar favorable results are obtained in the casting of aluminum alloys.

The physical and mechanical properties of Twin Sisters olivine,

[1] The Laboratory Examination of Molding Sand, *Trans. AFA*, Vol. 15, pp. 63–79, 1906.

[2] Molding Sand Tests, *Trans. AFA*, Vol. 21, pp. 17–126, 1912.

which is found in massive form in the Cascade Mountains of Washington state, have been studied in the foundry laboratories at the University of Washington. Olivine rock is crushed and graded; it does not occur in the form of sand. This gives it a distinctively angular shape rather than a spherical grain shape.

Because of its many favorable properties olivine is also finding application as mold wash and refractory linings. Norwegian foundries are using olivine exclusively in the manufacture of steel castings while in the last few years its use has spread to Sweden. In these European countries interest in olivine arises from its hygienic properties. It has been proved that where olivine sand has been introduced there have been no cases of silicosis. When olivine becomes better known and evaluated its acceptance in American foundries will be widespread.

Another material that is used as a base for synthetic molding sand is known as zirconite, or more familiarly as zircon. The richest grades of this material are imported from Australia; however, some zircon sand enters the market from Florida. It is a competitor to silica because it has a more favorable expansion rate and also a higher fusion point. Zircon and olivine serve somewhat the same market.

In European practice there are other materials used for molding, among them one known as shamotte. This is a formulation consisting of calcined and granulated aluminous clay suitably bonded with fire clay. Yet another molding material is known as compo, which is a composition of various materials such as crushed graphite crucibles and high-alumina brick bonded with plastic clay. This mixture is used for very heavy steel castings or for sections where sand would not be capable of withstanding enormous heat and pressure. On some large molding operations, loam is used as a molding media; however, its use is no longer widespread.

MOLDING-SAND CONTROL TESTS

Molding-sand Grains. Grain shape, size, composition, and distribution determine the suitability of a given molding sand for a particular use. Grain shape is observed by microscopic examination. Grains are classified as rounded, subangular, angular, and compound. Compound grains consist of two or more grains so firmly joined that the standard AFS clay and fineness tests fail to separate them. The four AFS grain-shape standards appear in Fig. 6-1.

Grain size is determined by a standard AFS test. This test procedure is applied to new sands, which fall into three main types:

1. Sands containing appreciable clay percentages as mined, termed naturally bonded sands.

2. Sands containing 2 to 3 per cent of clay bond as mined, known as crude silica sands.

3. Sands free of clay bonding material, called washed sands.

The standard fineness test can be applied to all three classifications. In the case of the first two, however, the clay or bonding agent must be removed by a standardized washing procedure.

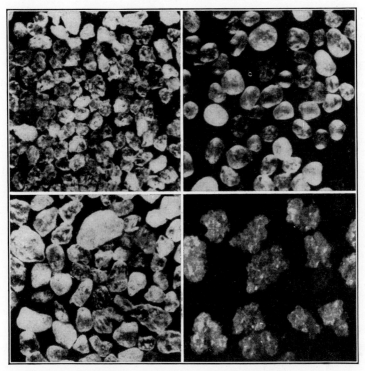

Fig. 6-1. Upper left—Angular sand grains. Lower left—Subangular sand grains. Upper right—Rounded sand grains. Lower right—Compound sand grains.

Grain-fineness Test. The apparatus for the fineness test consists of a set of eleven nesting sieves 8 in. in diameter, mounted in a mechanical shaker device, together with a top lid and bottom pan. Sieve openings used are the U.S. Series equivalent nos. 6, 12, 20, 30, 40, 50, 70, 100, 140, 200, and 270.

The test is made with a 50-gram dried sample. The sample is placed in the upper sieve, the lid is put in place, and the sample is shaken for 15 min. The weight of sand grains retained by each sieve after this shaking is multiplied by 2. This product will express the weight of grains of the various sizes as percentages of the original 50-gram sample and will also show the percentage distribution of the various sizes of grains in the sample.

The grain-fineness number is calculated by multiplying the above percentage figures by a factor termed a multiplier. The products of this multiplication are added to obtain a total product.

The AFS grain-fineness number is then calculated from the formula

$$\frac{\text{Total product}}{\text{Total \% retained on screen}}$$

A typical calculation is given in Table 6-1.

TABLE 6-1. TYPICAL CALCULATION OF AFS GRAIN-FINENESS NUMBER*
(Cedar Mountain, Wash., sand. Size of sample: 50 grams. AFS clay content: 17.4 grams or 34.8%. Sand grains: 32.6 grams or 65.2%.)

U.S. Series equivalent no.	Amount of 50-gram sample retained on each sieve		Multiplier	Product
	Grams	Per cent		
6	None		3	0
12	0.2	0.4	5	2
20	0.2	0.4	10	4
30	0.2	0.4	20	8
40	0.3	0.6	30	18
50	0.7	1.4	40	56
70	1.7	3.4	50	170
100	7.4	14.8	70	1,036
140	8.8	17.6	100	1,760
200	5.3	10.6	140	1,484
270	1.9	3.8	200	760
Pan	5.9	11.8	300	3,540
	32.6	65.2		8,838

$$\text{AFS grain-fineness number} = \frac{\text{total product}}{\text{total \% retained on screen}} = \frac{8,838}{65.2} = 136$$

* Analysis made in Foundry Sand Control Laboratory, Department of Mechanical Engineering, University of Washington, Seattle.

Permeability Test. The venting property of molding sand is determined by the particular combination of grain size, shape, and distribution, plus the type and amount of binders included. This characteristic is termed permeability; it is defined as that physical property of the molded mass of sand which allows gas to pass through it. For molding-sand control purposes, green permeability is determined, since the tempered molding sand as used in the foundry sand system is under test. The unit for expressing permeability is an arbitrary one that is referred to as the permeability number. It is calculated from the formula

$$P = \frac{vh}{pat}$$

where P = permeability number
$\quad\quad v$ = volume of air passing through standard specimen, cc
$\quad\quad h$ = height of standard specimen, cm
$\quad\quad p$ = pressure of air, gram/sq cm
$\quad\quad a$ = cross-sectional area of standard specimen, sq cm
$\quad\quad t$ = time, min

Instruments are available for making direct permeability readings (Fig. 6-2).

Fig. 6-2. Permmeter used for making standard AFS permeability test. (Courtesy of Harry W. Dietert Co., Detroit.)

The permeability of tempered molding sand is chiefly dependent on grain size, the larger sizes generally yielding higher permeability values; grain distribution is also important. Table 6-2 gives typical test values that have been taken from actual production foundries.

Green Compression Strength. Green compression strength is another quality of tempered molding sand that is regularly determined in the sand control laboratory. It is measured in pounds per square inch (psi) and is determined by the load a standard rammed specimen can sustain before fracture. This property is dependent upon the amount and type of bond present in the molding sand as well as grain shape, size, and distribution. Moisture content in the form of tempering water also exerts an influence on green compression strength.

TABLE 6-2. MOLDING SAND SPECIFICATIONS*

Kind of casting	Type of ramming	Per cent moisture, approx.	Shear strength		Compression strength		Permeability
			Green	Dry	Green	Dry	
Stove plate......	Squeeze	7.5–8.5	1.3	6.0	7.0	19	9
8-lb plate........	Jolt squeeze	7.0–7.0	1.4	6.0	7.0	33	15
15-lb plate.......	Jolt squeeze	6.0–8.7	1.4	6.5	7.0	40	25
20-lb jobbing....	Hand	7 –8	1.8	7.0	8.0	40	35
Radiators........	Hand	6 –7	1.2	7.0	6.5	52	35
Radiators........	Machine	6 –7	1.4	7.0	7.0	52	35
Bath tubs........	Sand slinger	5.0–6.0	1.1	7.0	6.0	46	70
Cylinder blocks..	Sand slinger	5.5–6.5	1.5	7.0	7.5	42	80
Cylinder blocks..	Jolt	6 –7	1.5	7.0	8.5	44	80
Car wheels......	Jolt	7.5–8.5	1.4	7.0	6.2	40	130
Boiler sections...	Jolt	6 –7	1.3	7.0	7.0	40	80
Boiler sections...	Sand slinger	5.5–6.5	1.2	7.0	6.5	40	80
Pipe............	Jolt	8–9	1.3	8.0	7.0	48	300
Pipe............	Pneumatic	6 –7	1.3	8.0	7.0	48	300
Plow...........	Jolt	6 –7	1.4	8.0	7.5	47	30
Steel...........	Jolt	3.0–4.0	1.5	10.0	7.5	52	160
Steel plate.......	Jolt squeeze	3.0–4.0	1.5	10.0	7.5	50	110
Flywheels.......	Jolt	6.3–7.3	1.3	7.0	7.5	40	90
Flywheels.......	Sand slinger	6.0–7.0	1.2	7.0	7.0	40	100
Bronze bushings..	Jolt	6.0–7.0	1.2	6.0	7.5	39	35
Aluminum plate..	Jolt squeeze	6.0–7.0	1.2	6.0	7.0	20	20
Aluminum large..	Jolt	6.0–7.0	1.2	6.0	7.5	32	37
Brass...........	Jolt squeeze	7.5–8.5	1.4	6.0	7.5	30	13
Malleable.......	Jolt squeeze	6.0–7.0	1.4	8.0	7.5	40	45
Magnesium......	Hand or machine	3.8–4.2			6.5		60–75

* Data from Harry W. Dietert and American Foundrymen's Society sources.

SAND CONDITIONING

Tempering Molding Sand. Moisture is an important factor in the control of molding sand. Its primary function is that of coating, or wetting, each sand particle. The amount of water necessary for this purpose is in direct relation to the extent of surface areas. Since synthetic sands are usually compounded from silica grains and a bonding clay, they do not require the high moisture content of the naturally bonded molding sands. The latter frequently are burdened with large amounts of silt in the clay bond and as a result require high moisture content for acceptable temper. When moisture is too high, excessive volumes of steam may be forced into the casting, causing blows and other defects such as rough surfaces and porosity. Too low a moisture content results in improper dry bond strength, which may lead to cuts, washes, and dirty castings.

Bonding Agents. There are several types of materials that impart bond to sand. Clay minerals are most prevalent, since they are a constituent part of the naturally bonded molding sands. However, they vary in nature and may be of complex composition. When sand undergoes the casting cycle, some part of the bond may be affected adversely by high temperatures; it may be vitrified or burned so that it can no longer function as a bonding material. This condition is counteracted by the addition of new naturally bonded sand, where the base sand is of that type, or, as is the practice in some foundries, bonding clay is added to revive the sand.

The choice of bonding clays and their behavior have been the subject of considerable study. These investigations indicate that desirable results can be gained only through careful analysis of the requirements for a given casting sand. Bonding clays for molding sand are divided into four categories.

Class I. Montmorillonite clays, which are more familiarly known as bentonites. Chemical composition $(OH)_4 \cdot Al_4 \cdot Si_8 \cdot O_{20} NH_2O$
    Class IA. Western bentonites
    Class IB. Southern bentonites
Class II. Halloysite clays. $(OH)_8 \cdot Al_4 \cdot Si_4 \cdot O_{10}$ and $(OH)_{16} \cdot Al_4 \cdot Si_4 \cdot O_6$
    White clays from Eureka district, Utah
Class III. Illite bonding clays. $(OH)_4 \cdot K_y (Al_4 \cdot Fe_4 \cdot Mg_4 \cdot Mg_6)(Si_{8-y} \cdot Al_y)O_{20}$
    "Grundite" from Grundy County, Ill.
Class IV. Kaolinite bonding clays. $(OH)_8 \cdot Al_4 \cdot Si_4 \cdot O_{10}$
    Ohio and Illinois fire clays

Actual foundry application of bonding clays has pointed to the bentonites as being of greatest interest. The general practice is to use Western bentonite for high dry strength and Southern bentonite for high green strength. A mixture in which these are both used is, theoretically, an ideal sand.

Bond strength is improved also by additives other than clays. In fact the use of a cereal binder, such as corn flour, is routine in many foundries. It air-dries rapidly and also increases the dry strength of the sand. Cement is sometimes used for bond in large molds. One such formulation consists of 100 parts of river sand and 10 parts of high-early strength Portland cement tempered with 7 parts of water.

Plastic resin binders are developing very rapidly in both molding and core making. Hot and cold mulled sands are replacing dry resin sand mixtures to the point where phenol formaldehyde organic binder is taking the lead in this area.

The addition of silica flour to steel foundry sands is another practice aimed at improving the functioning of these sands. Such additions exert a profound effect by increasing hot strength, at the same time making the sand more workable. The drawback is lowered permeability—a condition that can affect the quality of the castings adversely.

Facing Sand. Facing sand, the sand used against the pattern, is specially prepared in order to ensure a clean, smooth surface on the casting. Sea coal has, over the years, been the accepted additive material for facing sand. Opinion is divided as to the effect of sea coal on molding-sand properties. Residual sea coal and resulting ash have the effect of increasing the fines in the sand, thereby necessitating a higher moisture content if the sand is to be workable. The functioning of sea coal is explained by the reducing-type gas that it generates when affected by casting temperatures.

Tempering water has not escaped the attention of the advocates of higher sand strengths. There have been recommendations suggesting molasses, dextrin, and lignins as beneficial additions to tempering water. There are some instances where tempering water has been replaced either wholly or in part by light fuel oils. This practice is confined, primarily, to those areas where climatic conditions are such as to cause rapid evaporation of the moisture in tempered molding sand.

System Sand. Prepared molding sand is used directly on the pattern in some foundries to eliminate the labor involved in the placement of facing sand. Where facing sand is used, backing sand is required to fill the remainder of the flask. System sand may consist solely of backing sand, depending on the operation routine; backing sand does not require the degree of control necessary for facing sand.

Molding-sand Preparation. The preparation of molding sand for foundry use is of more than routine importance. Methods employed for this purpose run the gamut from hand shoveling, termed "cutting," to elaborate installations including washers, dryers, and completely mechanized mulling and handling equipment. In the smaller jobbing shops, where sand is "heaped," either hand shoveling or a mechanical sand cutter is used. The sand cutter travels over the shaken-out molding sand, from which the castings and tramp metal have been removed and over which water and new bonding material have been spread, stirring and turning the sand by its reel-like action (Fig. 6-3).

The larger jobbing and production foundries have muller installations for their sand-conditioning equipment. Some of these installations are quite elaborate, since the volume of sand passing through them is enormous. Sand mullers vary in design, but the principal feature is that of wheel-like elements that are arranged to press and turn the sand passing under them (Fig. 6-4). Sand aeration devices are built into

Fig. 6-3. Reel-type motive sand cutter. Note new light-colored molding sand added for rebonding heap. (Courtesy of Wheelabrator Corp., Mishawaka, Ind.)

modern mulling equipment as a further means of improving the quality of molding sand. The mulling time, or cycle, is dependent upon the type of bonding clay in the system sand. Bonds of the fire-clay type require longer mulling time to develop their properties than the bentonites.

Control of Molding-sand Quality. Any program of quality control in the foundry should begin with the molding sand. Sand control laboratories are becoming more numerous in foundries of all categories. Their rate of growth has been sensational and is in direct proportion to the appreciation of the fundamental importance of properly prepared sand in the production of salable castings.

Flowability, deformation, durability, and collapsibility are properties of molding sand that affect the molding and casting process. Correctly conditioned molding sand is the major factor in any program pointed toward the elimination of defective castings. Information on this subject can be found in "Analysis of Casting Defects,"[3] in which case studies are discussed and remedial suggestions given.

Sand Reclamation. The system sand in the foundry gradually loses its effectiveness because of the dilution from cores and accumulated burned clay, silica flour, and carbonaceous residues. Such sand requires more

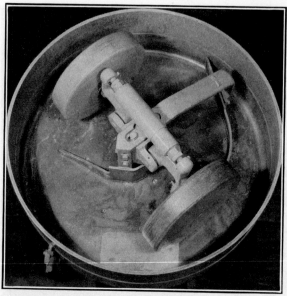

Fig. 6-4. A portable sand muller showing mulling wheels, plows, and sand discharge port. (Courtesy of National Engineering Co., Chicago.)

careful attention and exacting work in tempering because of these inclusions. The time finally arrives, however, when the sand is considered impossible to work and is relegated to the dump—obviously a waste that can seriously affect cost. Sand reclamation has been introduced as a remedy for this costly and time-consuming practice.

System sand is always dark in color, even though it may have started with white silica or even olivine as the sand aggregate. The reason for this discoloration arises from the burning effect and additives that appear in the molding sand during the preparation and casting cycles. Such coloration can be removed in a correctly installed and operated sand reclamation system. Sand reclamation takes two forms, the wet type or the dry type. In the wet type the sand is actually washed and

[3] American Foundrymen's Association, Chicago, 1947.

scrubbed, residual material is settled out and the aggregate sand grains reclaimed as new.

In the system of dry reclamation, two objectives are in the forefront; one is to loosen and peel off coatings by impact and attrition resulting from high-velocity air. The second is to eliminate coating debris by entraining it in slow-moving air and trapping it in the dust collector. Equipment designed for this type of work is illustrated in Fig. 6-5. It

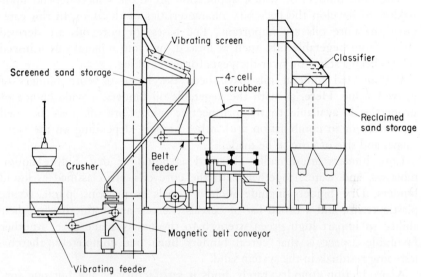

Fig. 6-5. Arrangement of a dry reclamation unit for foundry sand. (Courtesy of National Engineering Co., Chicago.)

is interesting to note that commercial foundries generally are paying more attention to sand reclamation and that this equipment is receiving acceptance throughout the industry where it is serving admirably.

THE CORE ROOM

Foundry Cores. Core sands do not have the wide geographical distribution of molding sands. Local deposits are tapped for this material, although silica sand from the Ottawa, Ill., district is widely accepted as the standard sand for cores. Olivine has also proved its suitability as a dry-sand core material.

Foundry cores are classified, as was mentioned in Chap. 5, as green-sand and dry-sand cores. Dry-sand cores are made from sand that is usually free of, or low in, natural bond. It is mixed with a binder; the resultant batch is rammed into a core box for shaping and then placed on a core plate or dryer for baking in a core oven.

Dry-sand Core Binders. There are certain essential requirements for a satisfactory core binder. It should (*a*) hold core to shape while green, (*b*) impart sufficient mechanical strength to withstand casting conditions, (*c*) generate little or no gas during casting, (*d*) cause the baked core to be nonhygroscopic, (*e*) offer sufficient strength to withstand necessary handling, (*f*) burn out for easy removal from the casting, and (*g*) be economical to use.

The core binders of widest application are those which depend upon baking to develop the necessary characteristics of the core. In this category the core oils are important. The bases for core oils are derived either from vegetable oils, such as linseed, or from mineral oils. Linseed oil has been a stand-by over the years for coremaking.

Polymerized mineral oils have been developed as core binders of proved value. Here, as with the vegetable-oil binders, a wide choice of properties is available to the prospective user. Core oils may be used separately or in combination with other binders, depending on the type, shape, and size of core to be made.

Core binders are broadly classified as liquid or dry. Sulfite liquor, molasses, and water, together with the core oils, are classified as liquid binders. Dry binders include such materials as proteins, pitch, resins, plastic resins, and a broad list of cereals. Cereals are distinctive for their ability to impart high green strength to the newly made core. Another favorable aspect is that cereal binders burn out completely, thereby lessening residuals in the system sand.

A production foundry rarely finds it satisfactory to use but one formula for all its core requirements. The danger of the substitution of one mix for another can be avoided by adding dyes of distinctive colors to the batches as they are mixed. Preparation of core-sand mixes is performed by mulling equipment of the same type as that used for molding sand.

Dry-sand Core Making. Making cores for limited production is largely a manual operation. Adaptations of various molding machines for ramming, rolling over, and drawing the core boxes are common practice. There are, in addition, stock core machines used for making cores of uniform cross section and lengths up to 24 in. The cross section of the core is determined by a die through which the core mix is forced by a screw feed device. The latter is equipped with a spindle end that forms a vent on the axis of the core.

The one machine that is peculiar to core making is the core blower (Fig. 6-6). The core-blowing machine fills and rams the core simultaneously. Core-box equipment must be specially designed for core blowing, since filling and venting the core box introduces a novel requirement. The reservoir of the blower is filled with the core-sand mix, and air pressure approximating 100 lb is applied to cause the mix to flow at a high velocity through the openings in the blow plate into the core box. Core blowing is confined to small and medium-sized cores.

Core Baking. Cores are baked at varying temperatures, depending upon core binders and core sizes. Core ovens employing all common fuels, as well as electricity, are in use. The newest development in core drying is the introduction of electronics; Figure 6-7 shows a dielectric oven

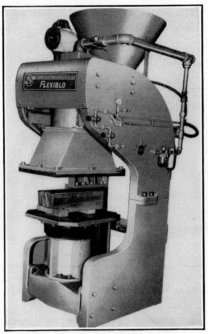

Fig. 6-6. Core-blowing machine shown with core box in blowing position. (Courtesy of Beardsley & Piper Division, Pettibone Mulliken Corp., Chicago.)

equipped with generator and centralized controls. The larger ovens feature circulation of forced air from an external heat source. Conveyors are common in ovens where large production is demanded; many ovens are built with conveyors traveling vertically as a means of saving floor space.

The baked cores may be given a coating or wash by spraying, dipping, or painting; this is done to improve casting finish by eliminating burnt-on sand. Core wash is selected on the basis of the casting temperatures and metal specification. Olivine flour is providing a most acceptable base for such washes.

Carbon Dioxide Process. In common with many other developments, the CO_2 process is really not new since it was described in a British patent issued in 1898. Current formulation employs about a 4 per cent sodium silicate binder mixed with the sand aggregate; however, other materials such as pitch, wood flour, and iron oxide may be present in order to develop special properties. This sand mixture is tempered with water to a moldable consistency. The mold or core is made in the usual manner and as a final procedure it is treated with CO_2 gas to the desired degree of hardness.

CO_2 *Cores*—There are numerous advantages to be gained from this type of core. The core need not be baked; instead as soon as the core has been made or blown it is treated with CO_2 gas for a matter of seconds, during which time the chemical reaction between the gassing and the binder develops a bond that sets the core. Since the core is hardened

Fig. 6-7. Core baking in dielectric oven. Note cores passing through oven on conveyor. (Courtesy of Allis-Chalmers Co., Milwaukee.)

in its box, neither core plates nor core dryers are needed. Cores made by this process can be stored indefinitely with reasonable care. Another real advantage is the fact that a uniform sand can be used for both cores and the molding floor; when this is done the entire foundry operation is greatly simplified. A further advantage of the process results from the very small capital outlay needed. The installation consists of a source of CO_2 gas equipped with a flowmeter and a hose leading to a cup or tubes which can be inserted or placed over the core to be hardened (Fig. 6-8).

Among the disadvantages of the process is the fact that the sand mixture tends to air-dry rather rapidly and for this reason must be stored carefully. A very real disadvantage, especially in the use of a CO_2 core with gray iron, is the difficulty with which the core is removed. Investigation on this type of core has shown conclusively that the core strength increases with increasing temperature. In order to develop collapsability, wood flour is added to the core mixture. The addition of oil, specifically core oil, to the mix will aid in core collapsability as a result of its burn-out behavior during casting; the property of collapsability has not been completely solved.

CO_2 *Molds*—A genuine advantage of the CO_2 development is the ability to make molds with extreme accuracy. In the ordinary procedure a sand mix is prepared and molded in the usual manner; then it is gassed

Fig. 6-8. CO_2 core gassing operation showing gas cyclinder at right equipped with regulator, hose gassing valve, and tube inserted in core being hardened.

prior to the removal of the pattern. There is some difference of opinion as to whether the pattern should be rapped prior to or after gassing. It is necessary, however, to design the equipment and rigging carefully so that the gassing cycle can be effective. Sometimes patterns are made hollow or equipped with tubing so that the gas can reach the mold from inside the pattern. By way of example, cast-iron gears as much as 8 ft in diameter are made this way with outstanding results.

In summary, the CO_2 process has brought to the foundry a new method for making cores and molds which may make possible considerable savings. It is claimed that the residual sand may cause trouble; however, this development is lacking in established proof. It might be well to consider the possibility of making shell cores and molds by this process, and especially so if an angular grain sand such as olivine, capable of producing high strength, is used. The European foundries have introduced CO_2 processing to a greater extent than in America. There are foundries in England that have abandoned core ovens entirely. Others are using a combination of CO_2 gassing and some slight amount of heat in order to expedite the core setting and improve its mechanical properties. Yet another development suggests mixing air with CO_2 as a gassing media. Hot air has been substituted for CO_2 with indifferent results.

Gas-less Binders. A wide variety of silicate base binders has been developed here as in Europe. Each modification is expected to produce some distinct property in the core or mold where it is used. They all need CO_2 gassing as a complement process. However, development work has led to the formulation of silicate type binders that do not require CO_2 gassing. Such binders develop their final properties by air-setting in a relatively short time. They have found broader acceptance in Germany than in this country.

Shell Cores. In a preceding paragraph shell cores and molds were mentioned; the former will be discussed here, whereas the latter is detailed in Chap. 8. About the time that CO_2 cores were beginning to be known in the foundry, the development of shell cores began to move into the forefront. Such cores are made from a sand mixture that varies from job to job and from one type of sand to another. In one operation an AFS 80 fineness sand is used for both applications, whereby a typical mixture consists of 400 lb of sand placed in a muller to which 16 lb of plastic resin is added. After mulling for 1 min, 58 oz of alcohol and 19 oz of water are poured in the mix; it is then mulled for an additional 2 min when a heated blower comes on which delivers air at 140°F through the sand mix for a total mulling cycle of 20 min. The resulting mixture is a sand in which each grain is coated with suitable bond for the ensuing operation.

Shell cores are produced on equipment especially built for that purpose (Fig. 6-9). Some of these machines are extremely simple in construction and operation, since on many designs the sand mix is introduced into the core box by gravity. The core box is heated to a temperature suitable for the type of sand mix under operation. At the instant that sand mix is introduced into the heated core box, a shell starts to take form upon contact of the mix with the heated core-box surface.

One striking feature is that the core box can then be tilted and the un-affected or unheated mix dumped from the center of the core, leaving a shell in the box. There are also core blowers on the market which blow the resin-coated sand into electrically heated core boxes. Some of these boxes have multiple cavities and are capable of producing as many as

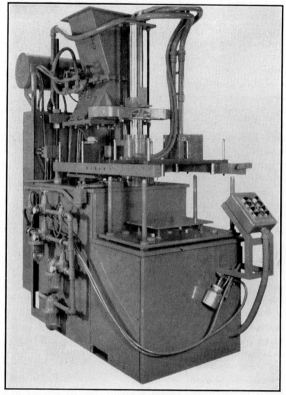

Fig. 6-9. Two-station rotary automatic shell core blowing machine. (Courtesy of C & S Products Co., Detroit.)

250 cores/hr. A curing cycle of 10 to 30 sec is generally necessary to produce a shell core.

The outstanding advantages of shell cores include a high degree of accuracy coupled with a very smooth surface. Shell cores offer extreme ease of removal from the casting and, for that reason, are more favor-ably received in many classes of castings than are CO_2 cores. Since they are cured in the core box no baking or dryers are needed. They are light in weight and easy to handle and "set" in the mold. They are destined to increase in popularity and adoption in foundries of all categories.

SURVEY QUESTIONS

6-1. Is sand used in a foundry only for molding?

6-2. What is meant by the term "naturally bonded" molding sand?

6-3. What materials are present in synthetic molding sands?

6-4. Name several types of refractory grains that are used in synthetic sand.

6-5. Does olivine offer any advantages over silica?

6-6. Is olivine of interest beyond the usual foundry sand applications?

6-7. When is zircon sand used?

6-8. What is the importance of the AFS standard grain size test?

6-9. Are permeability and grain size related?

6-10. Why is dry compression strength of molding sand substantially higher than green compression strength?

6-11. How is molding sand tempered?

6-12. Give the general term applying to montmorillonite clays.

6-13. Do both Western and Southern bentonite impart the same properties to molding sands?

6-14. If Portland cement were ever used as a bonding agent, to what class of work would it be suited?

6-15. Wherein do system and facing sands differ?

6-16. How is backing sand used properly?

6-17. What is the function of a sand muller?

6-18. Can synthetic molding sand be prepared properly without the use of a muller?

6-19. Why are atmosphere agents added to facing sands on occasion?

6-20. Is molding sand re-used or re-cycled?

6-21. What is the function of a foundry core?

6-22. Are core binders and molding-sand binders the same material?

6-23. What is the physical state, shape, or characteristic of a core binder?

6-24. Are all dry-sand cores made in core blowers?

6-25. What is the purpose of a core oven?

6-26. How are core ovens heated?

6-27. How does a core vent function?

6-28. Do core dryers and core ovens serve the same purpose?

6-29. Why are cores washed?

6-30. Can core rods be re-used?

6-31. In casting a motor block, would a single core or a series of cores be used for a single casting?

6-32. When a core is made in several parts, how are these parts joined?

6-33. Basically, wherein do CO_2 cores differ from oil cores?

6-34. What is necessary to harden CO_2 cores?

6-35. Are CO_2 cores ever heated or baked?

6-36. What is meant by gas-less binders?

6-37. Would there be any major difference in weight between a shell core and an oil core of exactly the same type?

6-38. What are some of the outstanding advantages of shell cores?

6-39. What binders are used in shell cores?

6-40. Would it be advantageous to use shell cores for the bores in automobile cylinder blocks?

Chapter 7

GATING AND RISERING METAL CASTINGS

The gating system on a casting is the means of channeling molten metal from the ladle into the mold cavity. Obviously there are many different ways of arranging the gating. Further, functions other than merely providing a passage for the molten metal are included in the gating system. The type of metal being poured has a marked influence on the gating details, since the light metals are more susceptible to oxidation and are not capable of the head pressures that the ferrous ones exert. The gating system also requires correlation with the design of the casting which it is to serve from the viewpoint of metal distribution as well as of solidification. A summation of these demands on the gating system shows the critical role that gating plays in producing sound castings.

Gating Terminology. The absence of standardization in gating systems carries over into their terminology, and there is no assurance that the terms employed here are accorded general acceptance. The basis for this apparent disagreement seems to be traditional or, in some cases, provincial, since molding is a process dating from antiquity and its development has been shared by many nations.

The simplest gating system is the one in which metal is poured through a vertical opening that leads directly to the mold cavity; the opening is known either as a sprue or as a riser, depending upon the details of its functioning and, again, upon local terminology. The more generally used gating system is designed to lead the metal into the side rather than the top of the mold cavity. For some types of castings—especially where side surfaces must be preserved, as in a cast gear, for example—the metal is introduced into the mold cavity at the bottom, the openings being known as gates or ingates. A typical gating system is sketched in Fig. 7-1. In this example a sprue circular in cross section is shown, since that shape is most general; however, square, oblong, and oval sprues have also been used successfully. The use of a square-cross-sectioned sprue is popular for casting light metals; this contour is believed to cause less turbulence in the molten metal, thereby eliminating one source of the inclusion of oxides in the metal stream.

Control of Metal Velocity. It is necessary to make the cross-sectional area of the sprue proportional with that of the runner and, in turn, with that of the gates, as a means of controlling the metal stream entering the mold cavity. Control, as used here, refers to the velocity of the entering metal; it also is aimed at arresting the flow of oxides and inclusions into the mold cavity. A high entering velocity gives the same effect as a nozzle does to the flow of water through a hose. The jets of metal will have a tendency to impinge against the surface of the mold cavity with

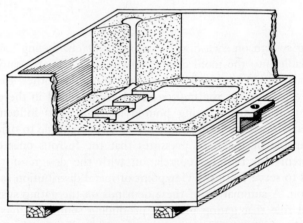

Fig. 7-1. One arrangement of sprues, runners, and gates.

a force that will cause washing at those points, resulting in sand inclusions in the casting. Another difficulty arising from high-velocity metal streams is the turbulence that results in the mold cavity, which is filled with air that must be forced out through the sand by the oncoming metal; however, air remaining above the metal will cause oxidation under the condition of extreme turbulence.

Design of gating systems is under continuing scrutiny because of the known effect gating can have on the quality of the casting. Reduction in metal turbulence is of prime importance. Turbulence can be reduced to the vanishing point by regulating the flow of the metal stream. Sharp corners are especially troublesome. They should be replaced by gradual curves—a change which amounts to a streamlining of the runner system. The sprue should also be given its deserved attention. When metal is flowing down the sprue, proper pressure conditions must be maintained within that sprue; otherwise an aspirating action can develop. This is especially true when the sprue takes the shape of an inverted truncated cone. A similar condition occurs, but to a lesser degree, when the sprue is a cylinder. The best condition results from a tapering sprue with the large diameter at the top and the small diameter at the bottom where the sprue joins the runner. It has been proved experimentally that the latter type of sprue is not subject to aspiration troubles.

The type of metal being poured, the volume of the mold cavity, as well as its area, all offer variables to the gating system design. In some instances it is desirable to introduce chokes in the runners, both for slag entrapment and to regulate flow velocity. Directional solidification of the casting is another matter of decided importance. There still remains a great amount of trial and error to be gone through in developing a properly functioning gating system for a given casting. Much experimentation can be eliminated through an understanding of gating fundamentals; yet this does not remove the necessity for the individual attention required by a particular mold.

Gating Nonferrous Castings. Among the cast metals, nonferrous alloys present the most difficult gating problems. They always require attention because of the necessity of restraining dross and oxides from entering the mold cavity. The general plan of attack for solving this problem includes either a skimming or a choking technique. Skimming refers to holding back the dross, which being lighter, floats on the surface of the molten metal. Strainer cores are placed in the sprue to act as a filter. Magnesium alloy castings are frequently gated with a pad of steel wool placed at the top or the bottom of the sprue in such a position as to strain the molten metal that passes through on its path into the mold cavity.

Skim Gate Types. Another method of separating slag and oxides from the molten metal makes use of a runner box, which is a reservoir on top of the mold. The sprue connects with one end of the runner box cavity; however, the sprue opening is covered with a small metal disk whose thickness is such that by the time the runner box is full of molten metal with its slag afloat, the disk will have melted, permitting the metal to enter the sprue. Pouring must continue at such a rate that the runner box is kept filled with metal in order to prevent the floating slag from entering the sprue. A stopper rod is used in place of the disk in some gating systems. The rod is removed the instant the runner box is sufficiently filled with molten metal.

The use of runner boxes is confined to relatively large castings. Smaller molds are poured directly into the sprue; or, on occasion, a cup acting similarly to a funnel, is placed on the sprue. In this gating method the cleansing of the metal is done at some point between the bottom of the sprue and the gate. There are, broadly speaking, two devices employed to accomplish the skimming action, one known as a choke gate and the other as a whirl gate. A choke gate is one in which either the runner or the gate is constricted at some point. The constriction acts to hold back the upper portion of the metal stream so that the clean metal from the bottom portion can flow into the mold cavity. The arbitration test bar casting in Fig. 7-2 illustrates the use of choke gates.

Whirl gates are not very commonly used although they have proved successful with some types of castings. They are designed to function

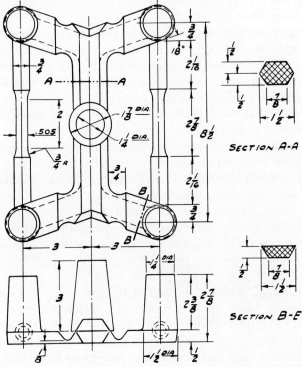

Fig. 7-2. Drawing of pattern equipment for casting arbitration test bar. Note choke gates at each end of bar.

by imparting a whirling action to the metal in the runner. Centripetal action on the molten metal forces the lighter slag to the center of a vertical cylindrical opening. Solid metal at the periphery of the whirl-gate cylinder is gated into the mold cavity.

Pouring Rate. In a setup in which the gating system is designed to restrain slag from entering the mold, the rate of pouring is extremely critical. When pouring is too slow, none of the slag-restraining measures described above will function as intended. It is considered good practice always to keep the sprue filled while pouring a mold. One resulting drawback is the likelihood of spilling metal over the top of the mold through failure to stop pouring at the instant the mold is filled. Experience in pouring and accurate timing are safeguards against this difficulty. Failure to keep a full stream in the sprue causes an injector action on the part of the flowing metal that results in drawing air down into the mold, thereby setting up additional oxidation difficulties. Pouring a mold correctly requires skill and judgment.

Improper shape, size, or location of the gates will cause turbulence of the metal in the mold cavity. Molten metal should fill the mold without undue agitation: in foundry parlance, "The metal should lie quietly."

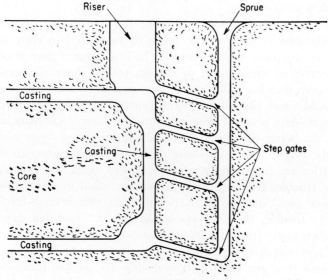

Fig. 7-3. Step gate.

If the mold cavity is of some depth and is gated from the side cascading and splashing of the metal will result—a condition that will promote dirty castings. On molds of considerable depth, the practice of using step gates is usual (Fig. 7-3); there are several modifications, such as staggering, gating horizontally, and gating at an upward inclination from the sprue. Johnson and Baker have concluded that only the type of step gate in which the bottom step inclines upward at an angle of 60° and the remaining steps are horizontal will actually feed the casting in the desired sequence. Another conclusion of these investigators is that no gating system will prevent turbulence.[1]

Solidification. Solidification characteristics of cast metal tend to cause

[1] Johnson, W. H., and W. O. Baker: Gating Systems for Metal Castings, *The Foundry*, Vol. 76, No. 10, pp. 68–73, 252, October, 1948.

cavities or porosity in the casting. Some relief can be expected from proper casting design; yet despite corrective measures the foundry must be prepared to meet the shrinkage[2] problem that is present with any heavy metal section. Two devices, viz., the use of risers and the use of chills—or both in combination—are the foundryman's methods of combating shrinkage. Reversing the idea of chills is done sometimes on thin sections by ramming anti-chiller pads, which retard the solidification rate by acting as insulators, against such sections. Since chills are of doubtful utility on heavy masses of metal, they find little favor except in the casting of light metals, since these rarely have heavy sections. Risering or heading a casting to compensate for shrinkage is accepted practice where heavy sections exist.

Theory of Riser Behavior. Concepts of the functioning of risers have lately undergone revision as the result of research into their behavior. Until rather recently it was generally believed that a riser should be a large reservoir of metal, open to the air, placed above the section that was showing shrinkage defects. It was presumed that this weight of metal would cause the solidifying section to be fed by the pressure it would exert. As a result of this concept, the feeling grew that the bigger the riser, the better the result. Risers of fantastic proportions came to be used; their weight was so imposing that the ratio of casting to riser was disproportionate. Surprisingly, though, larger risers did not solve the shrinkage trouble; frequently the defects increased in direct proportion to the riser size. Analysis uncovered the fact that reverse feeding was causing the trouble; the riser was solidifying at a rate that caused it to draw molten metal from the adjacent casting area.

Risers function as expected so long as they remain open—*i.e.*, do not freeze across their top surface; several ideas are used to bring about the desired result. Unique among these is the device used by some foundries in Germany of placing electrodes over the risers on steel castings and striking an arc; in effect the functioning is the same as that of an electric arc furnace. The use of proprietary compounds that are placed over the riser surface is accepted practice in American foundries. Some of these are compositions designed to develop an exothermic reaction when in contact with the molten metal, thereby increasing its temperature and prolonging its period of fluidity. Other compounds are used on the surface of risers as insulators against early freezing. Charcoal has been used for this purpose over the years, as has asbestos. These devices have been of some value; but they have all fallen short of keeping the metal in the riser molten until after the casting has solidified.

Insulating Risers. Experimental work on insulating risers has been in progress at the Puget Sound Naval Shipyard wherein diatomaceous

---

[2] The generic term used for describing solidification defects.

earth as well as perlite are used for the basic insulating material in this work. The proprietary material Sil-O-Cel, which is sintered diatomaceous earth, is ground in a muller to a no. 8 sieve. The ground material is then used in powdered form to cover the top of a riser. For other applications the ground material is mixed with such bonding agents as bentonite, synthetic resins, and water, forming a plastic mass that can be shaped for neck-down riser collars, contour anti-chiller pads, blind riser hoods, and other similar devices. These shaped parts are dried at 400°F for a period of from 1 to 4 hr prior to setting in the mold.

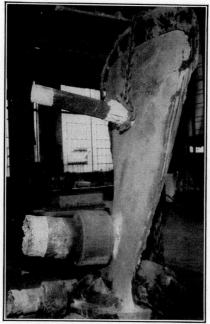

Fig. 7-4. Propeller blade casting, showing risers and gating. (Courtesy of Puget Sound Naval Shipyard, Bremerton, Wash.)

Results obtained from using this insulating material when casting stainless steel, copper-nickel alloys, manganese and other bronzes, steel, cast iron, and aluminum have been very gratifying. An indication of the potential saving possible in metal when such insulated risers are used can be seen from the data obtained from a manganese bronze propeller blade casting (Fig. 7-4):

	Pounds
Gross weight as cast	12,800
Weight of risers	1,500
Net weight of casting	11,300

On this job the ratio of risers to casting weight is but 13.3 per cent. Figure 7-5 shows insulated risers as well as blind risers on a typical steel casting.

Blind Risers. Open risers are easily placed and do not substantially increase molding labor. Risers which do not open to the top of the mold, termed blind risers, are also used. Blind risers are placed in the runner with a very short gate leading to the mold cavity. A modification of the blind riser known as the shrink-bob is frequently used in the malleable foundry.

Fig. 7-5. Steel casting showing an adequate riser and gating system.

Blind risers are incapable of doing much feeding, since the gate or the riser freezes prior to complete casting solidification. Investigation of the action of such risers has led to a new theory on the mechanics of riser behavior. It is now understood that as the molten metal leaves the riser it creates a vacuum therein which precludes further metal flow. By inserting a dry-sand core that extends from the riser cavity into the molding sand backing, atmospheric pressure is exerted on the molten metal within the riser, causing the metal to flow and thus feeding the casting. Graphite or carbon rods have been used in place of a dry-sand core with good results on the feeding characteristics of the riser.

A series of experiments with graphite and carbon rods inserted in semiblind risers was conducted at the Lebanon Steel Foundry and reported by Vosburgh and Larson of the National Carbon Co., who were connected with this study.[3] Results indicate that a graphite rod inserted in a riser is consumed by the contacting molten metal. This action in turn has a dual effect on the metal in the riser, since the absorbed carbon lowers the melting point and the combustion of some of the carbon tends to increase the metal temperature. Both these factors have a favorable action on the fluidity of the metal in the riser. The shrink cavity in such a riser (Fig. 7-6) tends toward flatness across its bottom, in con-

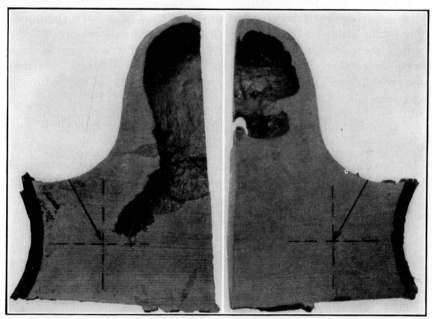

Fig. 7-6. Standard type blind riser at left. Graphite-equipped rod blind riser on right. Note difference in shrinkage from the common gated center line. (Courtesy of National Carbon Co., Cleveland.)

trast to the piping-type cavity of the usual riser; this permits the use of shorter risers, with an attendant saving of metal.

The success gained by the use of graphite rods in semiblind risers was followed by experimental work with these rods in open risers. Early tests with this method of causing risers to feed was done at the Farrell-Cheek Steel Co., Sandusky, Ohio. Conclusions reached there indicate that the end shaping of the rods, together with their size, is a critical consideration for optimum results.

[3] Vosburgh, F. J., and H. L. Larson: Tests Graphite Rods in Producing Steel, *The Foundry*, Part 1, pp. 108–111, 194, January, 1944; Part 2, pp. 128–129, 187–188, February, 1944.

THEORETICAL CONSIDERATIONS

The American Foundrymen's Society, through its Committee on Gating and Risering, has contributed significantly toward standardization of nomenclature and procedures. There have been many empirical solutions of gating offered, and, in addition, some elaborate motion pictures have been developed by the committee in the area of gating design. However, the subject has not been completely resolved, since additions, revisions, and modifications are continually being suggested.

The liquid flow proceeds either in laminar fashion or with a turbulent behavior. Many variables enter into this situation, since such conditions as velocity and viscosity, coupled with the cross-sectional area of the gating, are contributing causes. The flow behavior is expressed as a Reynolds number. Berger and Locke[4] have made a pertinent contribution in this area. The Reynolds number is expressed by the following equation:

$$R_n = \frac{\text{mean liquid flow velocity} \times \text{tube diameter} \times \text{liquid density}}{\text{liquid kinematic viscosity}}$$

The above calculations indicate that when the Reynolds number exceeds 3,500, turbulent flow causes such difficulties as aspiration, erosion, etc.

Riser Size. Calculation of riser sizes has been developed by Caine,[5] as expressed by the formula

$$x = \frac{a}{y - b} + c$$

where $x = (SA_c/V_c)/(SA_r/V_r)$
SA_c = casting surface area
SA_r = riser surface area
V_c = casting volume
V_r = riser volume
$y = V_r/V_c$
b, c = constants determined experimentally

A formula for the freezing time of steel as related to these factors is given below:

$$x = \frac{0.10}{y - 0.03} + 1.0$$

Problem: Calculate the size of a cylindrical riser whose height and diameter are equal and which is necessary to feed a slab casting 10 by 10

[4] A Theoretical Basis for the Design of Gates, *Foundry*, Vol. 79, February, 1951.
[5] Risering Castings, *Trans. AFS*, Vol. 57, 1949, p. 66.

by 2 in. with a side riser, casting poured horizontally in the mold.

$$V_c = 10 \times 10 \times 2 = 200 \text{ cu in.}$$
$$SA_c = (10 \times 10) \times 2 + (2 \times 10) \times 4$$
$$= 200 + 80 = 280 \text{ sq in.}$$
$$\frac{SA_c}{V_c} = \frac{280}{200} = 1.40$$

Assume that a freezing ratio x of 1.60 and a volume ratio y of 0.50 are to be employed in order to develop soundness in the casting:

$$\frac{SA_c}{V_c} \div \frac{SA_r}{V_r} = 1.60$$

$$1.60 \times \frac{SA_r}{V_r} = \frac{SA_c}{V_c} = 1.40$$

$$\frac{SA_r}{V_r} = \frac{1.40}{1.60} = 0.875$$

and

$$\frac{V_r}{V_c} = 0.50 = \frac{\pi D^3/4}{200}$$

$$D^3 = \frac{200 \times 0.50 \times 4}{\pi} = 127.2$$

$$D = 5.07 \text{ in.}$$

This solution indicates that a riser 5 in. in diameter and 5 in. high would properly feed the casting. A basic assumption is that all feeders remain open.

SURVEY QUESTIONS

7-1. What is the primary function of a gating system?

7-2. What part of the system is known as the sprue?

7-3. Are sprue cross sections always of the same geometry?

7-4. Is a high entering metal velocity injurious to a mold?

7-5. Why is choking applied in gating?

7-6. Why is steel wool used in magnesium gating systems but never in cast iron?

7-7. What is the function of a whirl gate?

7-8. Explain why risers are not used on all castings.

7-9. Describe at least three types of risers.

7-10. Why are blind risers used?

7-11. Do insulating risers offer any cost advantage?

7-12. Do different types of metal castings require different riser sizes?

7-13. Can riser sizes be calculated mathematically?

7-14. Why are "necked-down" risers used?

7-15. Assuming the casting size and shape to be identical, would gray iron or an aluminum-alloy casting have the greater metal volume in the riser system?

7-16. Why are exothermic compounds used on steel risers?

7-17. What is the purpose of churning a riser on a gray iron casting?

Chapter 8
SAND CASTING

Metal castings are produced from sand molds predominantly because of the flexibility and economy of this method. There is no other method for shaping metal that offers as much latitude and freedom of expression to the designer. Other methods of producing castings are explained in Chap. 9; these are largely confined to small or intermediate sizes. Casting tonnage is produced chiefly by gray iron, steel, and malleable iron foundries, which, with but minor exceptions, cast in sand molds.

Hand Molding. Hand molding is divided into bench and floor types. The former is restricted to small work where flask sizes are such that the molder can care for the entire routine. Molding is done on a bench designed to facilitate the work and conserve the molder's energy. All molding operations are performed manually in bench molding, the exception being the occasional use of a bench-type air rammer. It is customary for the molder to pour off his own work. However, this practice is not invariably followed; in some foundries pouring crews are employed.

Snap Molding. The pattern equipment and rigging used for bench molding is designed for production. Match plates and gated patterns are much in evidence, although loose patterns are common where small lots are scheduled. Although pattern equipment is of a diversified nature, flask equipment for bench molding is generally of the snap-flask type. Snap flasks, of either metal or wooden construction, are built to be removed from the finished mold for continuing re-use. The construction either has a lock on one corner with hinges on the opposite corner so the flask can be opened for removal (Fig. 8-1) or there is a metal sand strip, located at the parting, which can be withdrawn to permit the flask to be lifted upward from the finished mold.

Snap molds are strengthened to withstand casting pressure by a tight-fitting jacket that is pushed onto them prior to pouring. Tapered snaps have the advantage of tight-fitting jackets, since the latter are brought to tightness by pressing them downward. Snap molds are weighted to prevent the pouring pressure from floating the copes.

112

Floor and Pit Molding. Floor molding is the term applied to the large work that is rammed up in flasks on the foundry floor. Exceptionally large castings of substantial tonnage are molded in a pit. The molding pit is bounded by strong concrete walls designed to resist the pressures generated during pouring. Castings weighing hundreds of tons have been molded in pits.

There is little difference between bench molding and floor molding insofar as the fundamental molding operations are concerned. The

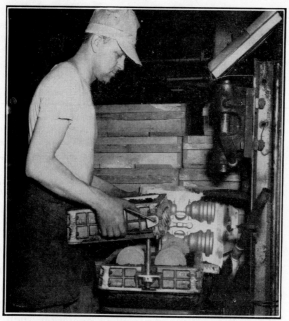

Fig. 8-1. Snap-flask operation on production line molding. Note flask lock being held by thumb. (Courtesy of The Fremont Flask Co., Fremont, Ohio.)

latter is done on a larger scale, with larger patterns and flasks and greater volumes of sand. Flask equipment is generally made of pressed steel or cast iron, since wooden flasks lack stiffness and are inflammable. Complicated patterns frequently require molding to be done in multiple-part flasks where, in addition to the cope and drag, intermediate flask parts known as cheeks are necessary. Cheeks are designated by number; for example, a four-part mold would be built up of a drag, a no. 1 cheek, a no. 2 cheek, and a cope. Floor molds are clamped prior to the pouring, and on occasion clamping is supplemented by weights for further security. The floor molder may use an air rammer but otherwise his work is chiefly manual. On large flasks he may call the crane for roll-over and lifting; too, some help in filling the mold with sand may be available

Fig. 8-2. Steps in the manufacture of 1½-in. bronze high-pressure globe valve, front row left. Back row (left to right) shows plastic core-box halves, core rods, finished core, and cope and drag pattern boards. Front row shows valve casting and cope and drag sections of sand mold. (Courtesy of Puget Sound Naval Shipyard, Bremerton, Wash.)

from the crane. Figure 8-2 shows the complete pattern, core, and mold for casting a 1½-in. high-pressure bronze globe valve body.

MOLDING MACHINES

Molding machines may be described as the machine tools of the foundry. They are the means by which manual skill is transferred into mechanical equipment. They offer several methods of compacting sand and may mechanically perform some allied operation, such as roll-over, pattern draw, strike-off, clamping, flask handling, and mold handling. These machines are designed to ram sand and to form molds by one of three basic mechanical actions—squeezing, jolting, or slinging. There are also machines in which several of these ideas are combined into one piece of equipment. It can well be said that a molding machine, in comparison with hand molding, will not only produce a better mold but a less expensive one as well.

Plain Squeezer. The operating principle of a squeezer is simple. A flask is placed on the pattern board and filled with sand; the operator then tucks the sand around the edges. A squeezer board, of a size to fit exactly inside the flask, is placed on the leveled sand and air pressure brings the flask assembly against the stationary head of the machine. Continued upward travel of the mold against the head causes the squeezer board to be pressed into the sand, thereby firming it. Mold hardness is controlled by regulating air pressure. A regulating, or unloading, valve in the air line is adjustable to desired pressure settings. The operating cycle is completed when the cylinder has exhausted its operating air and the table of the machine has returned to the starting position.

The squeezer is limited in its function to ramming; all other operations necessary to making a mold remain to be done manually. Limitations as to size and shape of pattern that can be successfully molded on a squeezer confine its use to small, uniform-sectioned castings. A flat pattern is ideal for the squeezer. If, on the other hand, a pattern has pronounced projections there will be but a shallow layer of sand above them, and, by the nature of the squeezing operation, that volume of sand will be firmed more than the balance of the mold, resulting in nonuniform hardness.

Fig. 8-3. Plain jolter molding machine. (Courtesy of Wm. H. Nicholls Co., Long Island, N.Y.)

Plain Jolter. A second basic design for ramming a mold is termed a jolter or, less frequently, a jarrer or bumper. Molding machines embodying this design ram the sand in the mold by a combination of inertia and impact. The jolter table is fixed to a piston that travels vertically in an air cylinder (Fig. 8-3). The pattern board is mounted on the jolter table and the flask clamped into position. As the flask is being filled with sand, air is turned into the cylinder, causing the table to move upward; the valve arrangement on the cylinder cuts off the air at the end of the upward stroke, allowing the table assembly to drop. The downward motion is stopped abruptly when the table strikes a stationary bumping pad. This sudden jar causes the sand to be packed.

The top layer of sand in the mold is not completely rammed, which means that a hand ramming operation, generally called butting-off, must be done. There are few limitations to the size of the molds that can be jolt-rammed. Portable machines as well as some mounted with the table at floor level are used.

Jolt-squeeze Machines. The plain squeezer as well as the plain jolter require some degree of hand ramming to complete the mold. In order to eliminate hand ramming entirely the squeezer and jolter principles are combined into one machine, appropriately termed the jolt-squeeze. Machines of this design are capable of a broader range of work than can be done on the plain squeezer; however, they do not reach the capacity of the plain jolter. Jolt-squeezers are built in both portable and stationary models (Fig. 8-4).

Drawing a Loose Pattern from Its Mold. The molder of a loose pattern precedes the pattern-drawing operation by swabbing around the edges

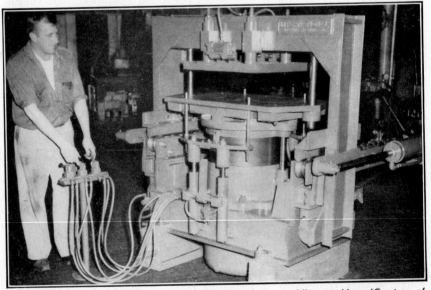

Fig. 8-4. Stationary model of a jolt-squeeze-stripper type molding machine. (Courtesy of International Molding Machine Co., LaGrange Park, Ill.)

of the pattern, reinforcing the sand to prevent its crumbling. However, this operation is superfluous in machine molding, especially where proper sand control is observed. A draw spike is next driven into the pattern, if it is made of wood, or a draw screw is threaded into a metal drawplate attached to the pattern. Sometimes a rapping plate is present so that a rapping pin can be inserted therein. The molder strikes the rapping pin with sharp blows in order to loosen the pattern in the mold. It is also common practice to use a rubber mallet for rapping directly against the pattern. In either event, the pattern is rapped in all directions until it is free in the mold. An air or electric vibrator fastened to the pattern plate replaces this routine for machine molding. The vibrator is built into the table in some designs of molding machines.

Mechanical Pattern Draw. There are but two methods of removing a pattern from the mold, viz., (1) drawing the pattern from the mold and (2) drawing the mold from the pattern. Drawing the pattern from the mold can be done by the stripper principle. Stripper machines are built with a metal stripper plate that is cut out to fit the exact contour of the pattern at its parting line. The pattern is mounted so that it can be raised through the stripper plate until its parting line is on a plane with the plate. It is only necessary to move a lever in order to strip the

Fig. 8-5. Portable pin-lift molding machine of jolt-squeeze design. (Courtesy of SPO, Inc., Cleveland.)

pattern downward through the stripper plate. The mold is supported by the plate, so that there is no likelihood of a cracked mold resulting from drawing the pattern. Stripper machines are available with mechanical ramming; the machine with this added feature is known as a jolt-squeeze stripper. A modification of the stripper principle is the pin-lift, in which stationary pins contact the pattern plate as the completed mold moves vertically. The pin-lift design is not confined to a distinctive type molding machine as such; rather it is generally included with squeeze or jolt types (Fig. 8-5). The term pin-lift refers to the mechanical action whereby pins contact the pattern plate, lifting or drawing it free of the mold. A modification of the pin-lift machine is known as the bar or rail lift type. This design is intended for larger application than the pin lift, which means that flasks of much larger size can be handled. The flask is lifted by means of rails rather than pins as in the former type.

Roll-over Draw Molding Machines. Adding the roll-over feature to a jolt-squeeze machine provides for mechanical pattern removal and, thereby, fully automatic molding. The molding machine shown in Fig. 8-6 is equipped with a single set of controls by means of which one man performs the entire molding operation. The attendant jobs of placing the flask and bottom board and filling the flask with sand are considered here as being extraneous to mechanical molding proper.

Fig. 8-6. Portable shockless jar roll-over and pattern draw molding machine. (Courtesy of The Tabor Manufacturing Co., Lansdale, Pa.)

Sand Slinger. The sand slinger embodies one of the oldest principles in molding, in that it impels or throws parcels of molding sand into the mold. These parcels travel at a high rate of speed and follow each other in rapid succession. Their velocity is arrested upon contact with the pattern and pattern board; this results in a compacting action that imparts a rammed finish to the mold. Ramming effects develop in directions both normal and transverse to the path of the impelled sand. It will clarify this result to note how a snowball, thrown against any solid surface, behaves on impact with that surface.

The sand slinger fills and rams the mold but performs no other molding function. Sand slingers are preferred for installation where molds are larger than bench size and especially where volumes of sand are needed for a single mold. Sand slingers are used in both jobbing and production-type foundries. Production foundries combine some type of pattern-drawing equipment with the sand slinger in order to eliminate manual molding operations entirely. There are many different types of installations of this combined equipment (Fig. 8-7).

The head of the sand slinger, from which the molding sand is impelled, must be guided over the flask area for uniform sand distribution and ramming. Several designs have been developed in order to meet differing requirements. Hand-guided head designs were followed, on large

Fig. 8-7. Motive type sand slinger ramming large mold. Note operator seated at ramming head. (Courtesy of Beardsley and Piper Division, Pettibone Mulliken Corp., Chicago.)

models, by a single control lever in the hands of the operator who was seated above the head. A design intended for repetitive work has automatic operational control to the point of eliminating the operator. Other design modifications of the sand slinger center around the method of handling the molding sand.

HIGH-PRESSURE MOLDING

The concept of making molds under extremely high pressure has been before the industry for some time. In the original concept a briquetting

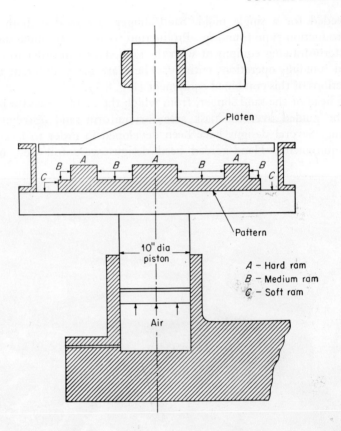

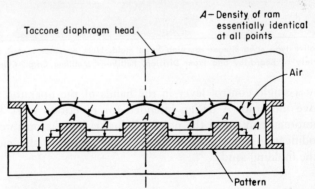

Fig. 8-8a. Operating principle of conventional squeezer above, while diaphragm high-pressure system is detailed below.

press was used, which operated at 600 psi. In order to function properly it was necessary to develop a waterless sand to prevent water from being squeezed out during the molding cycle. The chief problem here was to develop flowability in the molding sand. Continuing development has resulted in a sand, somewhat similar to the usual molding sand, in

Fig. 8-8b. High-pressure diaphragm-type molding machine. (Courtesy of Eastern Clay Products, Chicago.)

which moisture and bond both occur. It is now possible to use sand of any reasonable moisture content that may be required for the job that is to be done; however, an additive is incorporated in this sand formulation.

The molding is done with a modification of the squeeze principle; a diaphragm squeeze head serves as the ramming element (Fig. 8-8a). A flask is placed over the pattern and is then filled with sand in the usual manner; it is then placed under the diaphragm squeeze head. When air is admitted to the diaphragm it proceeds to expand so that it follows the contour of the pattern, inasmuch as it is working against a solid head on the opposite side. The obvious advantage of this type of ramming is equal pressure and uniform density throughout the mold, resulting in precision and weight-controlled castings. Under present equipment conditions it is possible to operate in a range of 60 to 300 psi. However, an operating pressure of 100 psi is quite common now with

Fig. 8-9. San-Blo mold blowing machine equipped with three-station turntable. Unit is tooled to eliminate manual operations. (Courtesy of Archer-Daniels-Midland Co., Cleveland.)

the diaphragm principle. The complete high-pressure molding system combines the use of a sand and a machine designed for this application (Fig. 8-8b). Larger sizes are built with the roll-on, roll-off principle that enables molds to be made on a conveyor. In another design modification the diaphragm head is stationary while the traverse car, carrying the mold, moves under the head like a drawer.

Research is under way on a combination of high-pressure diaphragm molding with treated silicate-CO_2 sand for the production of cured molds at high speeds.

Mold Blowers. Yet another principle of machine molding uses the idea of ramming by blowing sand into the mold (Fig. 8-9). This is not to be confused with sand blasting as used for casting cleaning. Instead, in this development the blowing machine is equipped with a low-pressure sand prefill device that places the first molding sand without any danger of undue wear on the pattern. Following this operation, the machine automatically fills the mold by blowing sand therein, and then finish rams it by squeezing. The entire unit operates automatically, including the handling of the flasks and the closing of the stack mold.

PLASTIC RESIN SAND CASTINGS

Molding sand compounded from a base sand with the addition of a resin-type binder has been introduced for producing sand castings. There is no noteworthy change in molding routine prerequisite to its use in the foundry. Sand preparation requires specialized treatment that is, for the most part, governed by patents. Claims for improved casting results have been advanced in behalf of this material, yet widespread adoption has not come about.

Croning Process. In contrast to molding with a resin-bonded synthetic sand, the Croning Process introduces a new concept. Shell molding was originated by Johannes Croning in Hamburg, Germany. It was developed sometime during World War II, and was first revealed to the American foundry industry in 1947 by the U.S. Department of Commerce in the publication of FIAP Report No. 1168, "The C Process for Making Molds and Cores for Foundry Use." The process has enjoyed a remarkable tonnage increase from 1951, when 3 tons of castings were produced by this method, through 1956, when over 100,000 tons were produced. These castings are of all types but the automotive industry has especially used the method for casting camshafts as well as crankshafts. The inherent advantages are less stock removal by machining, the elimination of machining operations, and wider latitude in design.

The basic requirements for the C process consist of a prepared sand, coupled with the machinery for making and curing the mold. The sand is a refractory sand, usually silica or similar material, that is coated with plastic resin, of which many types are available. Precoated sand can be purchased from suppliers or the sand can be prepared in a muller at the foundry. The operation of the shell-making equipment varies among the different designs. Most generally the sand is dumped or blown onto the metal pattern equipment, which has been heated to approximately 400°F, the patterns being mounted on the machine (Fig. 8-10). The mix spreads rather evenly over the pattern and is cured by the heated pattern mount. At the end of that cycle the unaffected sand is removed, leaving the shell behind. A release agent is sprayed on the pattern periodically in order to prevent the shell from sticking to the pattern. After the shell, which is in effect a half mold of about ⅛-in. thickness, has been cured, it is lifted from the pattern equipment mechanically. This shell (Fig. 8-11) contains all necessary gating. Shells are assembled in a variety of

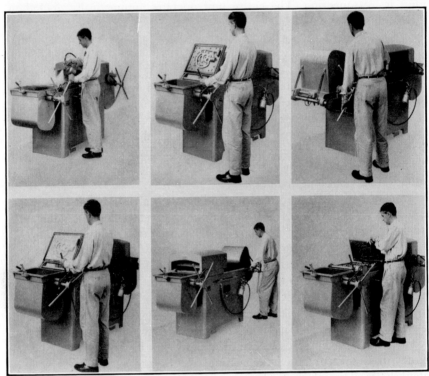

Fig. 8-10. Shell molding machine in operation. Upper row left to right shows spraying parting liquid on pattern, placing pattern, investing heated pattern with shell molding sand; lower row left to right: shell mold after investing, curing shell mold, shell mold removed from pattern. (Courtesy of Shalco Corp., Palo Alto, Calif.)

ways: they may be glued together or they may be mechanically clamped. Sometimes they are assembled in containers with backing, usually shot; however, this idea is no longer popular.

Switching from green sand to shell molds is not an easy matter. One difficulty arises from runner and gating design. Usually they are too large and trial and error must be used in cutting them down to correct size. Sometimes shell molds crack immediately after pouring, with run-outs resulting. This can be remedied by properly adjusting the shell molding cycle and pattern temperatures. Pilot-line operation is indicated in order to work out all the difficulties whenever a new job in shell molding is set up.

D Process for Precision Castings. This process, now familiarly known as the D method, was developed by H. W. Dietert, starting in 1952. It employs an accurately machined metal pattern mounted, complete with gates, on a metal blow plate, which in turn is bolted to the blow chamber of a core blower. A warm metal dryer is placed under the

Fig. 8-11. Shell mold half capable of casting two automotive crankshafts simultaneously. A machined crankshaft poured in such a mold is in the foreground. (Courtesy of Reichold Chemicals, Inc., White Plains, N.Y.)

pattern and contoured around the pattern surface, leaving a small space of approximately ⅜ in. for the core-sand shell. The two are clamped together by the core blower and the core-sand mix is blown through the blowholes in the pattern plate into the aforementioned space. The pattern is cold though the dryer is heated. The dryer with the blown shell mold is placed in a core oven and baked. After baking the core is removed and two such cores are clamped together to form a complete mold. Molds are poured either vertically or horizontally; they are allowed to cool from ½ to 3 min; then the casting is removed. The burned sand can be reclaimed. The reverse operation of heating the core box and keeping the contour or dryer plate cool has also been successfully used. The sand used in this process ranges from 90 to 150 AFS fineness number.

The binders used are generally some special core oil. However, developments in using resin-bonded sands are increasing. Precoated sands are available as they are for shell molding, mentioned previously. If, however, the sands are to be coated within the foundry, two processes are possible, namely, the hot or the cold process. In the latter, a liquid resin and a catalyst are added to the sand at room temperature and mixed in a standard muller. The hot process requires heating the sand to 600°F, then adding dry powdered resin, followed by mulling.

Frozen Molds. Research on the possibility of casting metal in frozen green-sand molds was undertaken by the author in 1939. Additional work has been done by Prof. W. A. Snyder. In these investigations, green-sand molds were poured at temperatures as low as —20°F. It developed that permeability increased with freezing, along with mold strength. Such molds withstand rough handling and do not require strengthening against casting pressures. Cores need no rodding. Since steam is not generated at the beginning of pouring, gas inclusions are at a minimum. Excellent surface finish is obtained on the castings.

The investigations were conducted primarily with aluminum alloys, although some gray-iron castings were also produced successfully. Close-grained castings were obtained because of the chilling action of the mold. It appears that this method of sand casting has considerable merit.

AUTOMATION IN MOLDING

Even though the major publicity for automation has been in the metal machining area and, to less extent, in metal forming, the same trend is developing in the foundry industry. Although something similar to automation has been in existence through a combination of molding machine units aligned in a sequence, there is now new equipment available that does the entire job. Such progress is not confined to our country but also appears in Europe. An example is seen in the molding unit shown in Fig. 8-12. It represents a complete molding system wherein the molds are rammed individually as cope and drag and then closed into the complete mold, which is poured as it moves to the shake-out. From that station the mold boxes are returned to the molding unit and the castings are conveyed to the cleaning room. The entire operation is automatic and is controlled from a single station. With this sort of equipment it is possible to mold as many as 500 sections/hr, or 250 complete molds. Its capacity is such that it will accommodate patterns for two automotive cylinder heads in a single mold; obviously the production potential of such a molding system is substantial.

Fig. 8-12. Automated molding equipment. Molds are rammed in the center area and moved mechanically in a rectangular path. Note molding-sand hopper above molding station. (Courtesy of Badishe Maschinenfabrick, Karlsruhe-Durlach, West Germany.)

Automated molding lines are also built in America. Although somewhat different designs are used, the ultimate objective is identical with European concepts.

SUMMARY

Hand molding has disappeared from the foundry except in jobbing shops, pilot operations, or experimental facilities. It is uneconomic to produce castings for the manufacturing industry by hand molding because of the low production potential in relation to the high labor costs. It is impossible to offer proof of this by precise mathematical or empirical formulas; however, it is accepted practice that when casting requirements run to double figures, hand molding cannot compete with a machine.

In line with the trend in industry generally, automation is now established in the foundry. The best-known domestic examples are found in automobile motor block production, although other areas have also been similarly tooled.

Shell molding and the other developments presented in this chapter are all aimed toward more accurate castings, with better finish at a lower price. This objective will continue to be sought with new equipment and tooling ideas.

SURVEY QUESTIONS

8-1. Why do sand castings account for the major foundry tonnage?

8-2. What is meant by hand molding?

8-3. Primarily what type of patterns are used for snap molding?

8-4. On what class of work are pits used for molding?

8-5. In foundry terminology, what is a "cheek"?

8-6. Can hand molding be regarded as a manufacturing production method?

8-7. Do molding machines function only to ram molds?

8-8. What type of patterns would be molded on a squeezer?

8-9. Are loose patterns generally used with molding machines?

8-10. What type of molding machines are designed for drawing the pattern?

8-11. Are a pin-lift and a stripper the same type molding machine?

8-12. What is the function of a sand slinger?

8-13. On what class of work would a slinger show to best economic advantage?

8-14. Would a squeezer or a diaphragm machine produce the more uniformly rammed mold?

8-15. What type machine or system offers the best possibility for weight-controlled casting?

8-16. Does a mold blowing machine ram sand in the mold by blowing?

8-17. Describe any advantages to a stack mold.

8-18. Who is credited with the invention of the resin-bonded shell mold?

8-19. What advantages do shell molds offer over the usual sand molds?

8-20. Are shell molds re-usable?

8-21. Is the D process similar to the Croning?

8-22. Are there any advantages to the use of frozen molds?

8-23. Is complete automation an accomplished fact in sand molding?

8-24. Can sand castings ever compete with sandless types on a cost basis?

Chapter 9

SANDLESS CASTING METHODS

The concept of making castings by pouring molten metal into molds of a composition other than sand has its roots in antiquity. Sand molds are, except in extremely rare cases, capable of but one casting operation. Pouring the mold destroys it—the only salvage is the recovered molding sand. The important cost item of molding labor cannot be salvaged.

Despite the fact that sand molds, and their resulting castings, are being produced at favorable cost rates, they are encountering increasing competition from other casting methods. The supplier of castings must be alert to merchandising his product, since his industry has passed the day when the customer was tractable. Specifications extend beyond purely metallurgical considerations and include such other items as dimensional accuracy, trueness to pattern, and, especially, surface finish.

Sandless Castings. There are several casting methods available to industry in which molding sand plays no part. Each of these offers some distinguishing property; at the same time, all are hampered by limitations insofar as versatility is concerned. Sandless castings are credited with the following advantages over sand castings:

1. Better surface finish—degree of smoothness and absence of inclusions

2. Closer dimensional accuracy—true to design dimension

3. Greater possible speed of production—molds are made but once and have a long life

4. Reduction of scrap losses—variability is less than in sand molding

5. Conservation of raw material—less metal in gating system

6. Lower machining costs—true to design, true surface, requires less metal removal

7. Lower finishing costs—in many instances, no machining necessary

8. Better mechanical properties in the casting—finer grain structure

CENTRIFUGAL CASTINGS

Castings of cylindrical shape lend themselves admirably to the centrifugal process (Fig. 9-1). There are modifications attendant upon the centrifugal casting process. The distinction between centrifugal castings and centrifuged castings should be understood. Centrifuged castings are produced in sand molds which are arranged in such a position on the casting machine that they can be rotated about a central axis. The sprue is located concentrically with the axis in order that pouring can be done while the molds are rotated about the sprue.

Centrifugal castings, on the other hand, are produced in molds rotating about their own axis (Fig. 9-2). The mold axis may be horizontal, vertical, or inclined, depending on the dimensions of the casting, or, as in the

Fig. 9-1. Centrifugally cast gray-iron cylinder liner at left. Macrograph of cylinder section showing absence of chill at right. (Courtesy of Centrifugal Casting Machine Co., Tulsa, Okla.)

case of the inclined axis, the internal shape desired in the casting. External shape is generated by the internal mold surface. Hollow cylinders are the most common forms of centrifugal castings, but fluted and hexagonal exteriors are also cast.

Metal molds are general for centrifugal castings. Other designs include such innovations as carbon molds, baked sand molds, and clay-lined molds. A development used in German foundries for casting steel gun tubes during World War II consisted of sprinkling the bore of the metal mold with refractory sand. Centrifugal force caused this sand to cling to the mold wall so satisfactorily that no binder was needed with the sand; the lining was renewed for each casting.

Heat generated in the mold during the casting process must be considered, since a relation exists between mold temperature and required speed of mold rotation. D. S. deLauvaud, a Brazilian engineer, invented the method of centrifugally casting pipe in metal molds. This method was introduced and developed in America by the U.S. Cast Iron Pipe and Foundry Company about 1925.

Centrifugal casting can be traced in the patent office to the beginning of the nineteenth century. Superiority is claimed for centrifugal castings because the casting action assures sound metal and fine grained structure, with any slag or inclusions appearing at the inside of the casting where they can be removed by a subsequent machining operation. Gun tubes, liners, brake drums, bushing stock, and gear blanks, together with

Fig. 9-2. Hydrocentrifugal casting machine showing control panel, hydraulic drive unit, and casting machine. (Courtesy of Herman Pneumatic Machine Co., Pittsburgh.)

cast-iron pipe, constitute the bulk of the castings produced by the centrifugal method.

PERMANENT-MOLD CASTINGS

Permanent-mold castings are also termed gravity die castings because they are produced in metal molds that are poured directly from the ladle. A distinction exists in this casting method between *permanent molds*, where mold and components are made of metal, and *semipermanent molds*, wherein dry-sand cores are used in conjunction with metal molds. Permanent molds are used for casting both ferrous and nonferrous metals, the greater part of production being in the latter classification.

Permanent-mold castings have a finer-grained structure and in consequence are of higher strength than sand castings of the same metal. They have good surface finish, since they are cast against a machined surface. All the usual metals are satisfactorily cast in permanent molds, but the aluminum alloys predominate. Automotive pistons are largely cast by this method. There are many other applications, including vacuum cleaner housings, valve bodies, and gear laps. This method is economical for production runs of a wide range.

A permanent mold is made from a fine-grained cast iron. The mold can be cast to approximate shape, requiring only a finishing operation, or the mold can be machined from a solid block of cast iron. Larger molds are built up, as are molds of complicated shape, for economy in manufacturing cost.

While production-type molds are built from cast iron, other mold materials have proved satisfactory. Graphite molds are successfully used in the production of railroad car wheels. The author has used a permanent mold of aluminum alloy no. 43 for casting lead ducks used in the drafting room since 1937. This mold has produced several hundred castings and has shown no deterioration other than the normal wear resulting from handling.

A development in England known as the Parlanti Casting Process[1] features permanent molds made from aluminum-alloy castings. They use the British alloy L33 primarily. The process is a patented one and includes such developments as an anodized mold face which is sprayed with sillimanite for a refractory coating. Ferrous metals such as cast iron, steel, and heat-resisting steels have been poured successfully. A cast ring 5 ft in diameter, weighing 450 lb, is cast successfully from aluminum alloys by Parlanti.

Another innovation in permanent-mold construction made by the author is that of using steel-reinforced cement-bonded silica-sand molds. These cement molds are poured from a mixture of cement, silica sand, and water. The mold face is given a graphite wash as the refractory coating. These molds have been satisfactory for casting aluminum alloys; one such mold produced 25 consecutive castings in 30 min.

Parting lines on permanent molds are in a vertical plane, with sprue and risers located so that they are bisected by this plane, for ease of removal when the mold is opened. Parting-line locations require careful study, since the mold is rigid and does not yield to the casting, which is contracting as it cools.

Castings must be designed for suitability to the permanent-mold process. Such items as undercuts, drawbacks, and coring can be suc-

[1] Developments in the Parlanti Casting Process, *Machinery* (London), Vol. 78, No. 1990, pp. 3–8, Jan. 4, 1951.

cessfully cared for to a degree but the flexibility of the sand mold is impossible to achieve. Permanent-mold castings are generally of thin section; mass concentrations are avoided since they cause difficulty in cooling, with subsequent slowing of production.

Permanent-mold Design and Operation. Mold design and gating systems require fundamental knowledge of the permanent-mold process. Mechanical details of mold operation vary from hinged molds to sliding types. Closing mechanisms are also varied as to design; most depend on a mechanical action, but pneumatic as well as hydraulic systems are used for this purpose. The latter are especially well suited to permanent-mold production machines. Where production requirements are sufficiently high, permanent molds can be installed on a continuous casting machine. Such an installation permits continuous pouring that results in a high output rate.

Two important requirements of permanent-mold operation for proper casting results are temperature control and venting. Temperature control includes both heating and cooling. Molds in a continuous pouring system are made with radiating fins so placed that a stream of air can be blown over them for controlled cooling. Individual molds are also made with cooling fins located opposite heavy, or slow-freezing, casting sections. Another device used for local chilling is that of a copper stud screwed into the mold just short of the mold face, with a considerable part of the threaded stud protruding from the outer mold surface. Where casting sections are thin and premature cooling starts, the mold can be insulated locally with asbestos or other material.

The problem of venting the mold must also be solved, since the mold is impervious to air. An easy solution is at hand when the gating system is open to the top of the mold cavity. Slanting the mold while pouring is one expedient for venting. Using a sectional construction in a part of the mold in an arrangement whereby venting space is permitted between sections is another solution of the venting problem.

Metal cores are a featured part of permanent-mold construction. Cores are always given draft of about 1 per cent of their length. Suitable provisions must be made for pulling the cores, which is a critical item. Cores are sometimes made in sections so that they can be removed. For example, in aluminum-alloy pistons where a three-sectioned core is used, the center section is pulled first and then the remaining sections can be withdrawn by a combined sidewise and upward motion. Metal cores must be protected by a coating such as a graphite-water paint, chalk, or a rouge-graphite mixture.

A permanent mold is usually gated in such a way that the metal enters from the bottom in order to eliminate splashing and minimize turbulence. A helpful device used for checking gating and mold design is that of pouring the newly made mold by using successively colder metal. The resulting mis-run castings will show the behavior of the metal as it filled the mold.

Semipermanent molds feature the use of dry-sand cores as a replacement for metal ones. Such design permits more intricate internal cavities (Fig. 9-3). The cores are set into the mold much as in sand casting

Fig. 9-3. Pouring Al alloy automotive transmission housing in a permanent mold. (Courtesy of Rapidcast Corp., Grand Rapids, Mich.)

practice. Since dry sand is permeable, they aid in solving the mold venting problem.

Permanent molds must be coated with a refractory lining to prevent castings from sticking to the mold and also as a protection against metal erosion. There may be a base lining that is given a subsequent wash, as is common practice where gray iron is cast. A simple method for producing a uniform and effective coating is to smoke the mold with an acetylene gas flame.

Slush casting is a modification of permanent-mold casting. A mold is filled with molten metal and after a crust or shell has formed the remainder of the molten metal is poured out of the casting. The resultant casting has a satisfactory exterior although the interior is rough. Small toys are frequently produced by this process, which eliminates the necessity for using internal cores.

Continuous Casting. There have been several successful attempts with continuous casting processes, especially in Europe. Such developments

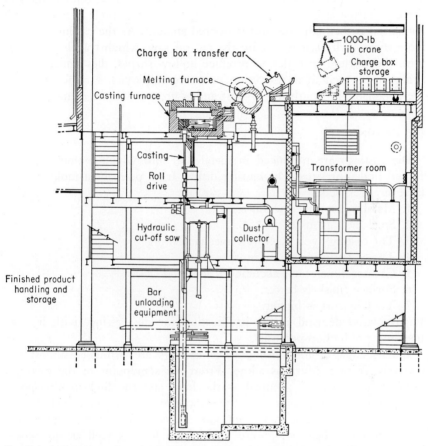

Fig. 9-4. Arrangement of equipment for the continuous casting of copper alloy products by the Asarco process. (Courtesy of the American Smelting and Refining Co., Barber, N.J.)

have applied to ferrous and nonferrous metals alike. An installation of this type in America is designed for the production of copper-base bushings and similar components. As this layout has been engineered, the production line is vertical and four stories high (Fig. 9-4), as opposed to the usual horizontal line. The molds are made from relatively inexpensive high-density graphite whose life is comparatively short, although some dies operate for as much as a week or more. The dies are assembled inside a jacket. Prior to starting the casting operation, a plug of the same material as the metal to be cast is inserted in the die. The lower end of this plug is attached to an aluminum starting rod of the same diameter, which in turn is strung through power-driven rolls where it is firmly gripped. Molten metal is then introduced into the mold. When the metal welds itself to the previously installed plug and begins to solidify, the roll drive is started at a given speed; this sets the casting cycle in motion and roll speed is then adjusted to the desired amount. As the casting emerges from the roll drive it is met by the cut-off saw, which travels vertically with the casting. In order to produce hollow shapes, dies similar to the bridge type used in an extrusion press are employed. Finished castings are obtainable in lengths up to 16 ft and as great as 9 in. in diameter.

DIE CASTING

Die castings are produced in metal dies into which molten metal is forced under pressure. Die casting differs from permanent-mold casting in several respects:

1. Metal is cast under pressure.
2. Steel dies are used.
3. The casting cycle is entirely mechanical.
4. The operating cycle is faster.
5. Greater dimensional accuracy is achieved.
6. Surface finish is better.
7. Tooling cost is higher.

High-volume demand is the justification for die casting, with its tremendous production potential.

Classification of Die Castings. Die castings are produced almost exclusively from nonferrous alloys. From the standpoint of die castings, nonferrous alloys are grouped as the low- and the high-melting-point types. Low-melting-point types are those which are cast well below 1000°F. From a volume standpoint, zinc alloys are of greatest importance, although some die castings are made from lead as well as tin alloys. Aluminum alloys lead in the field of high-melting-point types on a production-volume basis; the copper-base alloys and those of magnesium are also in the high-melting-point category. It is well to remember these distinctions, since a die-casting machine is designed for one or the other and not for both. Some machines can be changed over by modifications on the casting end.

Die Casting Production. This method of casting is so named because dies are used instead of molds. These dies must be composed of at least two parts, so that they can be opened for casting removal. As soon as the molten metal has solidified after the casting operation, the die is unlocked and opened and the casting ejected. Following this sequence the cycle is repeated; the die is closed and locked and metal again is injected. Necessary pressure for casting is provided either by a hydraulic system or by compressed air. In addition to these features the die casting machine is equipped with some type of attached or auxiliary furnace. It also provides the necessary means for supporting and closing the die.

It is of decided importance that the dies be equipped with locking devices of such a nature as to withstand the tremendous casting pressures. Some of these locking systems are quite complex in that interlocks are used as safety devices against opening the die prematurely; if this were not done there would be a spatter of molten metal issuing from the die parting line. Insofar as die casting machines types are concerned, they are usually classified on the basis of the method of metal injection as follows:

1. Plunger type
2. Cold chamber type   } Vacuum system
3. Direct air injection type

Plunger-type Machines. This particular type is suited best to low-melting-point metals, an area in which the zinc alloys are dominant. A furnace holding molten metal is attached to the die casting equipment. A fixed cylinder equipped with a plunger is immersed in this molten-metal reservoir. As the plunger is raised, a port in the cylinder opens, thereby permitting the molten metal to flow in to the level of the opening. When the plunger travels downward, it forces the molten metal contained in the cylinder out through the nozzle into the die. Just as soon as the metal in the die has solidified the plunger is withdrawn, permitting the die to be opened and the casting ejected.

This type of machine is capable of high production and is of considerable flexibility (Fig. 9-5). The pressure applied ranges from 1,500 to 2,000 psi. Necessary working pressure is obtained either from air or from a hydraulic source. The operating mechanisms that are submerged in the molten metal need to be made of a material that does not dissolve or alloy itself with that metal.

Cold-chamber Machine. The operation of this design follows closely upon that of the plunger type previously described; however, there are some basic differences (Fig. 9-6). In the cold-chamber machine the cylinder and plunger are not submerged in the molten metal; rather the molten metal is ladled into the cylinder through a suitable port. This means that a furnace is needed in connection with the installation of such equipment. A revised design (Fig. 9-7) combines a melting and holding furnace in a manner whereby molten metal can be pumped from the furnace in just the precise amount needed for each "shot." As soon as

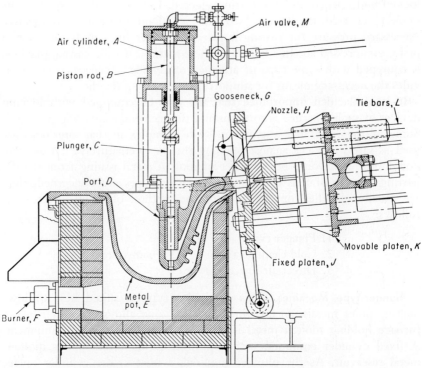

Fig. 9-5. Plunger-type die casting machine for zinc alloys; vertical ram is air-operated. (Courtesy of American Die Casting Institute, New York.)

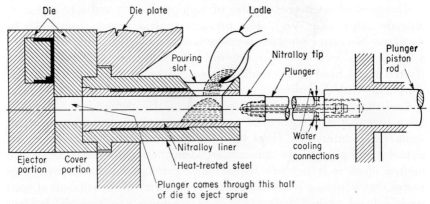

Fig. 9-6. Sectioned diagram showing die, cold chamber, and horizontal ram or plunger (in charging position) of a modern cold-chamber type die casting machine. (Courtesy of American Die Casting Institute, New York.)

the correct amount of molten metal has been introduced into the cylinder, its plunger moves forward under high pressure in the casting operation. The general pressures range from 3,000 to 8,000 psi for copper-base alloys. The selection of materials of construction for the casting mechanisms is important; frequently Nitralloy is used in the plunger construction as a means of combating operating temperatures and erosion difficulties. The term "cold chamber" has been derived from the basic design, since the cylinder is not submerged in molten metal.

Fig. 9-7. Globar reverberatory holding furnace equipped with automatic ladling unit for aluminum alloys. (Courtesy of Lindberg Engineering Co., Chicago.)

These machines do not operate as rapidly as the plunger type, and for that reason are generally not used with the low-melting-point alloys.

Direct Air Injection Machines. In this type of machine, which is used for casting aluminum alloys and in some instances the lower-melting-point alloys, pressure for casting comes from an air source (Fig. 9-8). The pivotal operating mechanism is known as a "gooseneck," which usually is suspended above a reservoir or pot of molten metal. When it is lowered therein, a measured quantity of molten metal enters the gooseneck, which is then connected to the die and is locked into position. Air pressure in the range of 300 to 600 psi is then admitted in order to force the molten metal into the die. Upon solidification of the casting the die is unlocked and the casting ejected. This is followed by closing the die and locking it, and the cycle can then be repeated.

Vacuum Die Casting. In keeping with the advance in die casting, a new innovation is receiving deserved attention. This development is known as vacuum die casting and its use has resulted in profound benefits to the die casting industry. It is said that zinc-base castings are now free from porosity. Low-silicon aluminum alloys are not only cast success-fully but can be treated by anodizing with a full range of color finishes. In this vacuum system all that is needed is the introduction of a vacuum

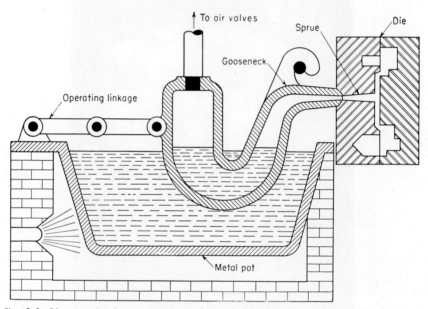

Fig. 9-8. Diagram showing arrangement of an air injection die casting machine having a horizontal nozzle positioned for filling the die by air pressure and without the use of a plunger. (Courtesy of American Die Casting Institute, New York.)

into practically any of the present type of die-casting machines. The vacuum equipment consists essentially of three parts: a vacuum pump, a large accumulator storage tank, and finally a hood enclosing the die plate area (Fig. 9-9). This hood is in two sections, one surrounds the movable plate and the other covers the fixed platen. Vacuum casting is supposedly faster than the conventional type of die casting by as much as 30 per cent. Among the reasons are that the die is exhausted during its closing cycle and, further, that the casting solidification period is shortened because the casting contains no trapped air. Not the least of the advantages is the absence of inspection, since castings produced in vacuum are uniformly of acceptable grade.

Dies and Die Operation. Dies are made by sinking the desired die impression into steel blocks or steel forgings. An innovation in die making is that of casting the dies by a precision casting method. Dies consist of at least two parts, since they must open for removal of the die casting. Where the die casting is of intricate design, the die will need additional parts to provide for undercutting and similar features on the casting.

The part of the die through which the molten metal is injected is fastened to the fixed platen of the machine. The other part of the die

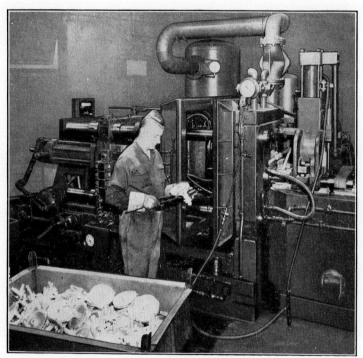

Fig. 9-9. 400-ton die casting machine equipped with vacuum unit for producing zinc-base die castings. (Courtesy of Reed-Prentice Corp., Worcester, Mass.)

is fastened to the moving platen, which also carries the ejector plates. Guide or dowel pins are a necessary construction feature in order to ensure the correct alignment or registry between the die halves. Ejector pins move through this part of the die in such a way as to free the casting from the die for removal. These pins must function with correct timing and must be so located that they do not indent the casting unduly to the point of marring its surface by dimpling.

Some die casting designs require the use of cores. Most cores are of the movable type and are "pulled" from the casting mechanically. Since the cores are of metal and precision-machined, cored holes of extreme accuracy are made in die castings. Die inserts are placed in the die when it is desirable to cast a part into the die casting. There are occasions when the insert takes the form of a die casting of a dissimilar metal.

While most dies are of single-cavity design, there are others in which multiple impressions are used. In that type of construction all cavities are cast from a common sprue simultaneously. It is not necessary that the cavities be duplicates; rather varying designs that may balance production schedules are included. A further innovation is that of making

Fig. 9-10. 600-ton H-P-M die casting machine casting the well for the Dormeyer Friwell at Midwestern Die Casting Co., Chicago, Ill. (Courtesy of The Hydraulic Press Manufacturing Co., Mount Gilead, Ohio.)

the cavities as individual parts and grouping them together into one whole, known as a unit die. All dies that are intended for use with high-melting-point alloys are hardened.

Other die features include such items as venting and overflow wells. Most dies are water-cooled for temperature control under high-production operating cycles. Die life varies primarily with the type of metal cast. Zinc alloys are associated with long die life; production as high as 1 million shots has been recorded. Aluminum alloys tend to erode dies, and higher casting temperatures contribute to shortening useful die life to about one-quarter of this figure; with copper-base alloys, die life is even shorter. A die casting machine is shown in operation in Fig. 9-10.

It is difficult to give an exact production rate for die castings, since casting design and required metal volume are never alike in any two cases. However, an average maximum rate for low-melting-point alloys can be stated as 550 shots/hr, with high-melting-point alloys reaching somewhat less than half that rate.

Research and development continue to show new possibilities in the die-casting method of production. An adaptation of the cold-chamber design has been used for producing die castings of steel. Innovations consist of using tungsten carbide for injection elements and silicone lubricants

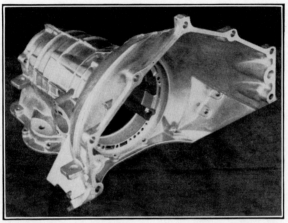

Fig. 9-11. Aluminum-alloy die casting of the Turboglide transmission case. (Courtesy of Chevrolet Motor Division, General Motors Corp., Toledo, Ohio.)

to prevent premature die burning. A large aluminum-alloy die casting is shown in Fig. 9-11.

PRECISION CASTINGS

Renewed interest in methods for producing castings of a degree of accuracy sufficient to eliminate the necessity for machining developed during World War II. Dentists and jewelers have used the investment casting technique for many years. This trend in casting production has been so pronounced and its development so rapid that terminology has failed to keep pace. The basic idea is not new; there is a record of precision casting in plaster by Benvenuto Cellini in the sixteenth century. Undoubtedly similar work had an even earlier beginning.

Terms employed for describing this general method include precision casting, precision refractory casting, plaster molding, precision investment casting, microcasting, and lost-wax casting. Not all these terms refer to exactly the same thing, since a distinction is made between the method in which the pattern is expended with each molding operation and the one in which a permanent pattern is used.

Predominant interest attaches to the method using expendable patterns. Castings of a high degree of precision are made from a wide range of metal alloys and, in the case of some of the complex high-temperature-resistant alloys, this is the only economical manufacturing method available. Examples of castings made by this method are shown in Fig. 9-12. While the castings shown are intricate, the method is not confined to

Fig. 9-12. A group of 119 miscellaneous precision castings. (Courtesy of Misco Casting Co., Whitehall, Mich.)

small sizes; aluminum-alloy castings weighing approximately 24 lb are in production.

Precision Investment Castings. For the sake of uniformity the term precision investment castings will be employed here, since this usage is sponsored by the American Foundrymen's Society. Precision investment castings are made by casting metal into a mold from which an expendable pattern has been removed by melting, combustion, evaporation, or solution. For a more detailed description, it seems best to start with the pattern and follow the production sequences through to the final casting.

A master pattern is machined to a size that makes provision for process shrinkage to the finally desired dimensions of the casting. *It is here that the precision of the casting is established.* Extreme care must be given to making the master pattern because it in turn is used for making the die, or mold, in which the expendable patterns are produced. No compromise with accuracy can be permitted in making the master pattern.

The molds in which the expendable patterns are produced are made from a variety of materials including soft metals, light metals, vulcanized rubber, carbon steels, plastics, alloy steels, and gray cast iron.

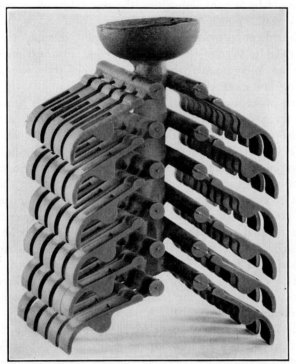

Fig. 9-13. "Tree" of precision castings containing 60 turbine buckets cast from high-temperature-resistant alloy.

Patterns in turn are made by injecting the expendable material into the mold. Pattern material is generally selected from among beeswax, carnauba wax, petroleum wax, plastics, mercury, and fusible alloys. Molten wax is injected at pressures of 400 psi into water-cooled molds for some classes of patterns; in others, fusible alloys are poured into the mold under gravity. A freshly filled mold is permitted to stand for a period of time sufficiently long to ensure solidification of the pattern.

Upon removal from the mold the pattern is checked for accuracy and any slight imperfections are corrected. Patterns passing inspection are then mounted or clustered on requisite gating and sprue systems—assemblies frequently referred to as trees (Fig. 9-13). Wax patterns are readily joined by heating abutting surfaces until they flow together. Careful handling is called for in placing patterns; they must be arranged in a manner that will facilitate their removal from the investment mold.

The completed pattern assembly is then invested as the next operation. Investment materials are of many kinds; included are such substances as olivine, silica flour, quartz, cristobalite, sillimanite, bauxite, gypsum, and plaster of Paris. A point to remember in choosing the investment material is that it should be free of impurities; the possibility of its reacting with the casting metal at pouring temperatures must also be kept in mind. Proprietary investment compounds, which simplify manufacturing operations, are available. Water is used as the vehicle, although chemical compounds are not uncommon for developing special properties in binding, rate of setting, and modifying mold permeability.

Investment procedures are varied; the choice depends primarily upon the casting finish desired. For a very smooth casting surface the pattern is dipped into a silica-flour solution—a practice termed "coating." When the first coat has set, the pattern may be dipped into a second solution of coarser material and then be placed in a flask for final investing. It is more common practice, however, to place the pattern in the flask and pour in the investment without regard to a preliminary surface coating. Investing a pattern requires control; segregation in the investment material must be avoided and at the same time the patterns must be accurately covered. Some investment techniques employ vibration, while in others the mold is slanted for desired results; tamping is also used. The major objective is to eliminate air bubbles from the solidifying investment. A vacuum process of treating the freshly invested pattern has proved successful for eliminating air pockets.

In some investing operations asbestos sheet is used to line the inside of the flask as an aid toward developing mold permeability. Vacuuming promotes mold permeability, since air bubbles are drawn along the path of least resistance, *i.e.*, away from the pattern and toward the outside of the mold. Evaporation of water in the investment while the mold is being processed is another source of mold permeability.

Upon completion of the investment operation the molds are permitted to harden for a period, the length of time depending upon the composition of the investment. Molds are then placed in a furnace, in an inverted position, for the burn-out operation. Temperature ranges are such that the pattern material will soften and flow out of the mold through the gating system; this may be done in one furnace or by a differential treatment using two furnaces. In the latter case the mold is brought to a relatively high temperature, approximately 1600°F for pouring heat-resistant alloys.

Most casting is done by gravity in a heated mold, although some casts are poured at room temperature. Some molds are poured on a vacuum table while in other cases a centrifugal casting machine is used. Conditions governing procedure are flowability of the casting metal, intricateness of casting design, and the need to prevent moisture accumulation within the mold cavity.

Molds are permitted to cool prior to breaking out the castings. No effort is made to salvage the used investment material; on the contrary, a disposal problem is created by this spent material. The final operation in precision investment casting is that of removing the gates. Grinding

Fig. 9-14. Frozen-mercury precision patterns are dipped in cold refractory mix and hung up to dry in icebox at —60°C (—76°F). (Courtesy of Sperry Gyroscope Co., Great Neck, N.Y.)

the gates is generally the only machine or mechanical work necessary on the castings.

Plaster Casting. A sizable number of castings are produced using plaster of Paris as the investment material. This method, as described here, differs from the previously presented precision investment casting technique in that *a metal pattern is used*. To be sure, various plasters and compounds are used for investment material, which is mixed dry and introduced into the flask with water as a vehicle. The molding operation is similar to sand practice, since the mold is jolted and, after the plaster has started to harden, is drawn off the pattern.

Molds are immediately placed in a conveyor-type furnace, where both free water and water of hydration are driven off with temperatures reaching 1650°F. Cooling of the mold follows in the same furnace. Any necessary cores are made of the same material as the investment. These are processed and placed in the molds just prior to pouring. Pouring is done over the lip and generally through an asbestos paper tube that is inserted into the sprue. Tube height aids in developing hydrostatic pressure within the mold cavity.

Mercury-pattern Precision Castings. A further development in precision casting introduces the novel idea of making the expendable patterns

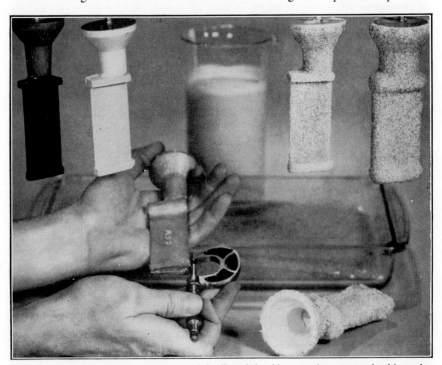

Fig. 9-15. Disposable wax pattern at left dipped in Glascast slurry, coated with grains until mold is built up (extreme right). Finished mold and casting at bottom. (Courtesy of Corning Glass Works, Corning, N.Y.)

of mercury, which is poured into the master mold and then frozen. Following this operation, the frozen-mercury pattern is invested at subnormal temperatures (Fig. 9-14). Upon reaching room temperature, the now fluid mercury is poured from the mold for re-use. Salvaging the pattern material is an economical aspect of the process, which is one capable of producing extremely accurate castings.

Investment Innovations. An investment process developed in England uses a different approach to the wax pattern removal operation. In this system one-piece shells are made by spraying or dip-coating a wax pattern with a permeable refractory slurry, backed by a packing investment of large particle size. Following the formation of the shell, the wax pattern is removed by immersing the shell with its wax pattern in nontoxic trichlorethylene vapor. The shells are then poured, some of them even without support, by both ferrous as well as nonferrous metals.

Another successful achievement in novel investment material is the use of low-thermal-expansion silica glass. This is quite different from the investment methods previously discussed. In this instance a cope and drag mold are used. The molds are formed by pouring an aqueous slip of the Glascast powder into a porous metal mold. The mold absorbs water, thereby building up a shell of the glass material inside the mold; when proper shell thickness has been reached, the excess material is poured out and the shell dried. After removal from the mold the shell is placed in an oven and fired at temperatures as high as 1,900°F. The mold then is assembled (Fig. 9-15) in the usual manner and used for casting such things as stellite, Rexalloy, and other alloys, together with stainless steels. This process is of definite interest in connection with the production of gas turbine buckets and similar high-temperature-requirement components.

SURVEY QUESTIONS

9-1. Wherein do sandless castings differ from other foundry types?

9-2. Give some specific examples of centrifugal castings.

9-3. What is another term for permanent-mold castings?

9-4. Wherein do semipermanent and permanent-mold castings differ?

9-5. Would automobile motor blocks be adapted to permanent-mold casting?

9-6. Can all engineering metals be produced by permanent-mold casting methods?

9-7. Wherein does the Parlanti method differ from the usual permanent molds?

9-8. What products are produced by slush casting?

9-9. Would automotive pistons lend themselves to the continuous casting process?

9-10. Is die casting faster than permanent-mold casting?

9-11. Are all metals die-cast by the same method?

9-12. Why is automotive trim zinc base rather than aluminum base die casting?

9-13. What type of metals are cast in a cold-chamber machine?

9-14. Why is vacuum die casting used?

9-15. What is an investment casting?

9-16. Mention some automotive castings that are produced by this method.

9-17. What is the lost-wax process?

9-18. Is there any advantage to using mercury in precision casting?

9-19. What type of castings are produced in Glascast molds?

9-20. If machining is to be eliminated, what metal and what casting method should be used?

9-21. Aluminum-alloy auto pistons are die-cast to some extent. Does this also apply to gray iron ones?

9-22. Is it possible to die-cast alloy steel differential pinions?

9-23. A domestic vacuum cleaner housing is under design as a casting. Would equipment and tooling costs be greater for permanent-mold or die casting?

Chapter 10

THE MELT SHOP

Molten metal is required for the production of castings. The function of the melt shop is to produce the necessary molten metal in a suitable condition and quality. The melting range of an alloy is the spread of temperature in which complete fusion occurs. In general, the melting points of the ferrous alloys are higher than those of the nonferrous ones, but the melting range in both classifications is dependent upon the specific composition of the alloy. Cast iron cannot be said to have a definite melting point because of the varied compositions and structural components included in this category. When a gray cast iron contains the phosphorus-rich component Steadite, it will start to melt near 1750°F, whereas gray cast irons melt in the range of 2000 to 2400°F. Aluminum alloy AN-A-33 (10 per cent mg) has a solidus temperature of 840°F and its liquidus is 1150°F, which gives a melting range of 310°F. These examples serve to show that the spread in melting range is similar in ferrous and nonferrous alloys.

The function of the melt shop is that of remelting, in contradistinction to smelting or refining, the metal charge. The chief exception occurs in the case of duplexing in the steel foundry, where the furnace is given a molten charge. Many melting operations include some type of alloying for analysis adjustment, but here again the furnace is operating on the remelting principle. Variations of the procedures in the melt shop include such innovations as ladle treatment of the melt as well as duplexing and even triplexing, wherein several furnaces are used in a supplementary routine to produce the requisite metal.

Furnaces and Fuels. The cost of melting a pound of metal is the leading consideration, while the chemistry of the melting process, as it affects a given metal, acts to limit the choice of melting equipment in any given case. The first cost of the melting equipment and installation charges also serve as modifying factors. There have been instances where such items as hazards and zoning ordinances have dictated the choice of melting equipment.

Regardless of type of furnace or fuel used, the fundamental of converting the potential energy of the fuel into heat units effective for melting the charge should receive first consideration. Transferring heat units into metal in order to bring about its fusion is the basis of foundry melting furnace design.

Fuels most generally used in foundry melting furnaces together with their calorific values in Btu are shown in Table 10-1.

TABLE 10-1

Fuel	Average gross calorific value, Btu	Unit
Coke................	13,000	lb
Natural gas.........	950	cu ft
Coal gas............	500	cu ft
Fuel oil............	140,000	gal
Electricity.........	3,415	kwhr

Costs of the fuels listed vary widely with geography—coke shows a low price in the Midwest while electricity is cheapest in the Pacific Northwest, natural gas and fuel oil in the Southwest and other oil-producing areas. The point to note here is that fuel costs and availability must be studied for each locality in order to reach an intelligent decision on a given projected installation.

Furnace Heat Losses. Heat losses vary considerably with different furnace types. The crucible furnace has an over-all efficiency of 5 per cent maximum, whereas the coke-fired cupola will use up to 35 per cent of the total heat potential. Open-hearth practice indicates about 20 per cent of the heat used for molten steel with an additional increment being consumed by the slag. Electric arc furnaces show a 10 to 15 per cent over-all efficiency, the variation being accounted for largely in design and operation.

Waste gases account for the major part of the heat loss. There are installations, such as checkers on open-hearths, waste heat boilers on large reverberatory furnaces, and hot stoves on blast furnaces, that improve the over-all operating efficiency. The only major attempt at salvaging heat from furnace gases in the melt shop is the installation of the hot blast cupola.

Radiation heat losses also cut down the efficiency of the melting furnace. It is not always desirable to insulate a furnace against radiation losses since such insulation may have adverse effects on the life of the furnace lining.

The selection of the type of melting furnace is rather clearly defined as between ferrous and nonferrous metals. Since the former run to tonnage capacities, they are melted in furnaces of the direct-flame type for the most part. Nonferrous metals are poured in smaller-volume castings, with the result that their melting equipment is generally of the indirect-flame type. Exceptions are found in the case of the copper-base alloys, which are melted in such a wide variety of furnaces as the crucible, the indirect-arc, the direct-flame and, on occasion, the cupola furnace. The most versatile piece of melting equipment is the induction furnace, which is used for melting all foundry metals.

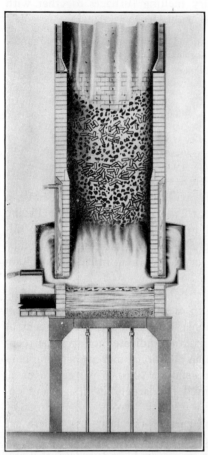

Fig. 10-1. Schematic view of a water-cooled cupola showing charges, blast flame, and molten cast iron on hearth. Note cooling water entrance and discharge at left. (Courtesy of Whiting Corp., Harvey, Ill.)

Cupola Furnace. The cupola furnace, or cupola, as it is termed in the industry, derives its name from the old Germanic word *Kuppel*, meaning stack (Fig. 10-1). The construction of the cupola is simple; it consists of a cylindrical steel shell open at the top, equipped with hinged doors at the bottom which can be swung into position for closing the bottom of the shell.

An opening in the shell just above the mantle is the location for the breast; here the tap hole is located, being built in with a clay-base mixture. Opposite to the breast and at a somewhat higher level is another opening through the shell, which is used for the slag notch. Circumscribing the shell at its lower end is the wind box; it is connected to the blower through suitable blast piping. Openings between the wind box and the furnace are known as tuyères; these may be a single row situated in a radial plane or there may be more than one row arranged in echelon. There is an opening equipped with a hinged door located several feet above the slag notch, through which the charges enter the furnace.

Cupolas are usually lined with fire-clay brick. However, cupola blocks are available and when these are used, there are fewer lining joints, which are points of weakness and the location for the start of lining failures.

Plastic refractory compounds are available from which monolithic linings can be rammed, thereby entirely eliminating brick or blocks. When being prepared for operation, the cupola lining is given a protective coating of daubing made up of fire sand and refractory clay moistened to the consistency of stiff mud. After each heat, the daubing and its adhering slag are chipped off preparatory to the next daubing treatment.

Metallurgical coke is universally used for fueling the cupola. Coke quality has been improved in order to develop more efficient melting operations. Coke developed for this purpose is characterized by low internal porosity and has a more uniform structure. With this dense coke, cupola melting rates are substantially increased as is metal fluidity. Another important property is that the coke raises the carbon content of the melt yet at the same time retains its mechanical strength. When charging the cupola, coke is placed on the bottom sand, which has previously been rammed over the bottom doors to protect them and also to direct the molten metal so that it will drain toward the tap hole. Coke is ignited by a torch flame impinging through the breast or by dry kindling placed ahead of the coke. As the first coke becomes fully ignited, additional coke is added, until the desired depth of coke bed has been laid. Bed height is an important consideration for achieving proper melting results.

When the bed charge has been fully ignited, the first metal charge is placed, with heavy material preceding the smaller pieces. The metal charge is followed by a coke charge, or split, until the cupola is filled to the level of the charging door. The metal charges and coke splits are held to a constant weight, in a range from 7:1 to as high as 12:1. These so-termed melting ratios refer to the number of pounds of metal that can be melted with 1 lb of coke in the split charges. If, then, the coke split weighs 40 lb, the metal charge will weigh 400 lb when a 1:10 melting ratio is being used. For sustained melting, flux—such as limestone, marble chips, or other calcium material—is charged on the coke layer to slag off coke ash and impurities introduced with the metal charge.

The cupola is tapped intermittently in the smaller operations; in the case of furnaces of larger capacity it may deliver molten metal continuously. At the conclusion of the heat, the prop holding the bottom doors in place is knocked out, thereby releasing the remaining coke and slag through the bottom, with a spectacular display resulting.

Cupola Design—Innovations in cupola design are many and varied. A noteworthy example is that of using the heat of the escaping gases for heating the incoming blast in order to improve operation and increase the melting ratio efficiency. Installations in which the blast is dried by freezing to eliminate moisture are an important feature in controlling cupola melting. In order to meet the increasing regulations about smoke and dust from industrial operations, cupolas are now constructed with closed tops to prevent the emission of gases and dust. There are several such designs, not all of which have closed tops. They do scrub the cupola gases, however, in order to cleanse them.

Metallurgical Blast Cupola—A cupola designed along the lines of a blast furnace has made its entry into the industry. It is capable of continuous tapping while it does not require the shutdowns demanded by the standardized type cupola. A difference in construction is that carbon blocks are used in the hearth and permanent bottom. Because of the material used, they are not attacked chemically or wetted by liquid iron or slag; in consequence, they show excellent refractory life and are highly abrasion resistant. This cupola design is destined to increase in popularity because it takes a 100 per cent steel scrap charge and delivers metal of blast-furnace quality.

Cupola operation is not a simple matter if quality metal of correct temperature is to be produced.[1]

Cast irons constitute the bulk of the metals melted in the cupola furnace. Gray cast iron, alloyed cast iron, and white cast iron are melted in the cupola. Copper is on occasion melted in the cupola, with ladle additions for making copper-base alloys.

Basic-lined Cupola—Interest in basic-lined cupolas is increasing as the potential of this melting equipment becomes better understood. The construction of this cupola follows generally that of the acid-lined type. Here, however, the basic lining in the wall and melting zone is made up of unburned magnesite key blocks. It is also possible to ram the lining from granular refractory of dead-burned dolomite. This lining serves acceptably although the chief source of deterioration is that of silica; in consequence, extreme care must be exercised in order to prevent the entrance of silica sand into the cupola charge.

While in acid practice the slag is more or less tolerated as a nuisance, basic slag can be controlled somewhat and made to refine several elements of the melt. Desulfurization, carbon pickup, and a limited amount of dephosphorization depend on the quality of the slag and its volume. In acid practice the slag adheres to the coke, thereby preventing carburization; the final carbon content of the tap depends upon the carbon in the charge. In basic practice, however, the slag cleanses the coke, allowing the molten iron to dissolve large percentages of carbon. A 100 per cent steel charge can be melted in the basic cupola with a final carbon above 3 per cent. A booster charge of coke is added occasionally in order to develop and maintain the proper carbon percentages. It can be realized from these features that basic cupola operation offers possibilities of improved metal melted more economically.

[1] For detailed information see "Cupola Operations Handbook," American Foundrymen's Association, Chicago, 1944.

Converter. The side-blow converter, also known as the Tropenas, is a modification of the better known bottom-blow Bessemer type. Side-blow converters are employed for making foundry steel by a duplexing process (Fig. 10-2). The converter metal is melted in a cupola and is then charged into the converter for refining into steel. This method of duplexing played an important role during World War II as a rapid means of producing steel for castings.

Fig. 10-2. One ton side-blow converter in operation, as evidenced by flame issuing from converter mouth. (Courtesy of Whiting Corp., Harvey, Ill.)

A shallow bath of molten metal is used for the converter charge. An air blast approximating 4 lb in pressure is turned onto the molten bath. The converter steel-making process is one of oxidation. The reaction of the oxygen in the blast with the oxidizable elements of the charge is an exothermic one that supplies all necessary heat for steel making. The reactions within the converter are gaged by both the appearance and the volume of the flame issuing from the mouth of the converter. Formerly the operator depended upon visual observation entirely; however, accurate operation is now obtained through electronic control equipment.

After the "blow," which is of 15 to 20 min duration, the steel is recarburized in the vessel; the converter is then turned down and its contents are discharged into a ladle containing any necessary deoxidizers. Low sulfur and phosphorous pig iron must be charged into the cupola for producing converter metal, although sulfur can be reduced by a soda-ash treatment in the cupola receiving ladle. Low equipment and installation costs, economy in melting and refining, coupled with rapid processing time, form a combination that makes the converter a competitor of any melting equipment installation in the steel melt shop.

Air Furnace. In the malleable iron foundry the melt shop is equipped for air-furnace operation where tonnage is required. Metal for malleable cast iron in smaller quantities is produced in the cupola or the electric arc furnace. There are some large-tonnage installations where duplexing is

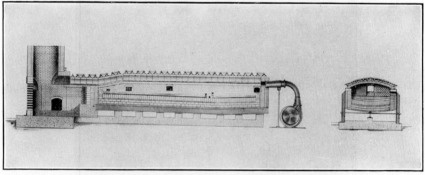

Fig. 10-3. Cross-sectional views of a pulverized coal-fired, ventilated bottom duplexing air furnace for producing molten iron on a continuous basis for malleable foundries. (Courtesy of Whiting Corp., Harvey, Ill.)

practiced—cupola melted metal is charged into the air furnace for subsequent refining.

An air furnace is large, with a long narrow hearth that has a firing area at one end and a stack at the opposite end (Fig. 10-3). Construction is primarily of fire-clay brick with a steel framework that provides the requisite stability for hearth, side walls, and roof. The hearth is built of fire-clay brick or silica sand or both. Roof sections of an arch shape, known as bungs, are designed to reflect heat downward upon the metal charge. This contoured roof design, resulting in reflected heat, gives rise to the application of the term *reverberatory* to the air furnace.

An air furnace is usually charged through the roof after removal of some of the bungs. Heat for melting and refining is generated by powdered coal or oil firing. The combustion gases flow over the charge to the stack, thereby heating both the furnace lining and the charged metal. Melting results from the action of the hot gases in combination with reflected heat from the furnace lining. In a furnace with a 25-ton charge the melting time will approximate 6 hr. Increased efficiency results from using preheated air obtained through a recuperator that is a part of the furnace installation. Direct-flame action, or contact between the fuel and the charge, does not occur in the air furnace.

When the charge is completely melted, it has become covered with slag formed from bottom material and adhering sand on the charged

Fig. 10-4. Stack melt reverberatory furnace tilted for tapping. (Courtesy of Foundry Laboratory, Mechanical Engineering Department, University of Washington, Seattle, Wash.)

scrap. Refining action is accomplished after slag removal by maintaining an oxidizing flame above the molten bath on the hearth. Since the refining time is of some duration, it is possible to take samples and thereby to adjust the composition of the bath to desired specifications.

Stack Melt Reverberatory Furnace. An extremely flexible furnace fired by either gas or oil has been introduced into the iron foundry (Fig. 10-4). In this particular type, charging is done through the stack where the melting also occurs. The molten metal flows onto a hearth where it accumulates. The furnace is built on rockers so that it can be tilted for emptying the molten charge into ladles. Interest in this type of furnace arises from the small charges and the rapidity with which they can be melted, as well as its much lower maintenance cost as compared to the cupola. Foundries are installing this type of equipment increasingly.

Crucible Furnace. A crucible furnace has a cylindrical steel shell built with a rammed or bricked lining. It has a cover that is either tilted, lifted, or swung clear to afford access to the crucible. Heat is supplied through burners from either oil or gas as fuel; solid fuel is obsolete in current furnace designs. Furnaces are built for tilting on trunnions or they may

Fig. 10-5. Battery of gear tilting crucible-type melting furnaces equipped with no. 275 crucible capable of an 800-lb brass charge. (Courtesy of The Campbell-Hausfeld Co., Harrison, Ohio.)

be stationary, in which case the crucible must be lifted out of the furnace (Fig. 10-5).

Crucibles are refractory containers, more or less barrel-shaped, open at the top where the pouring lip is located. After forming, crucibles are baked and finally treated at a temperature sufficiently high to drive off the water of hydration. Since the firing is not sufficiently intense to vitrify the clay, crucibles are susceptible to moisture pickup; consequently, crucibles should be heated to drive off absorbed moisture prior to installation in the furnace. Crucibles are made from a variety of refractory materials; among them are magnesia, silica, silicon carbide, fire clay, and graphite. Capacities are indicated by number. Crucibles are used primarily for melting nonferrous metals, especially copper-base alloys.

The so-named pot furnace, in which a cast-iron pot replaces the ceramic crucible, is popular for remelting aluminum alloys. Similar furnaces are used for remelting and superheating magnesium alloys, although here pots fabricated from steel plate are used in place of cast-iron ones. This difference in melting containers, as between aluminum and magnesium alloys, is a vital requirement.

Open-flame Furnace. Where large melting capacities are necessary for copper-base alloys, a tilting furnace somewhat similar to the crucible

Fig. 10-6. Fisher oil-fired melting furnace remelting scrap brass. (Courtesy of Lindberg Engineering Co., Chicago.)

type is used (Fig. 10-6). In this furnace, however, there is no crucible; instead the metal is charged directly into the furnace, where it is subjected to direct flame action. The melting operations of the open-flame furnace can be controlled to provide specification metal, as is evidenced by such castings as large ship propellers (Fig. 3-1) by way of example.

Electric Arc Melting Furnace. The general appearance of an electric arc melting furnace with top electrodes can be noted in Fig. 10-7. A cylindrical steel shell is integral with a concave bottom. The top is separate and is constructed so as to open for charging or to be removed for repair; in either event, the top consists of a ring into which silica bricks are fitted. Suitable openings for electrode passage are provided by water-cooled castings. The charging door is in one side of the furnace shell with the tap hole located opposite. Trunnions are provided for tilting the furnace when tapping the molten metal or as an aid in charging through the furnace door.

Furnace linings require careful attention since they have a short life at best. Linings follow one of two types, depending on whether basic or acid operation is used. In the basic-lined arc furnace the bottom courses are laid with fire-clay brick; magnesite brick is placed on these and up the side walls to a distance above the slag line. The remainder of the lining, as well as the roof, is of silica brick. Magnesite is rammed in to com-

Fig. 10-7. Lectromelt three-phase arc melting furnace installation of 10—12T heat capacity. (Courtesy of Pittsburgh Lectromelt Furnace Corp., Pittsburgh.)

plete the bottom. Brick are laid dry with allowance for expansion to prevent bulging and lining failure. Numerous designs for water-cooling the lining, above the hearth, are installed to increase its life. Acid-lined furnaces are lined throughout with silica brick, the bottom being made by sintering ganister and silica sand.

There are some single-phase arc furnace installations; however, the great majority are three-phase for reasons of both power-line load and melting speed. Single-phase design has a bottom electrode and conducting bath, the charge forming a part of the electrical circuit. Three-phase arc furnaces have three electrodes in triangular arrangements entering through the roof. The charge is melted and refined by heat radiated from the arcs between the electrodes as well as resistance due to current flow through the bath. The bath is not a part of the circuit but it carries current because its resistance to current flow is lower than the air path between the electrodes.

Arc furnaces are used in foundries primarily for the production of steel, although there are some exceptions where cast iron of controlled

Fig. 10-8. A 200-T top charge Herault electric furnace of 24.5 ft shell diameter equipped with 24 in. diameter electrodes and 25,000/33,333 kva transformer capacity. Installed at McLouth Steel Corporation. (Courtesy of American Bridge Co., Pittsburgh.)

quality is desired. Occasionally some malleable iron is also melted in the electric arc furnace. The capacity of these furnaces is steadily increasing, one reason being the flexibility of the unit and another the control of smoke and dust previously referred to. A recent 200-ton installation for steel making is shown in Fig. 10-8. It is obvious that the electrical equipment for this installation is of truly imposing capacity and size.

Rocking-type Arc Furnaces. These are designed with the electrodes entering the ends of the furnace. This design prevents arc impingement on the charge, thereby providing means for melting in which there will be no carbon pickup from the electrodes (Fig. 10-9). A second distinctive feature is that the rocking action of the furnace, which is controlled automatically, continually stirs the bath, thereby promoting homogeneity. These furnaces are employed for melting copper-base alloys, nickel alloys, gray and white cast iron, stainless and alloy steels in a capacity range from 10 lb to 2 tons per charge.

Fig. 10-9. Tapping a Detroit electric furnace. Note end electrode location. (Courtesy of Kuhlman Electric Co., Bay City, Mich.)

Induction Furnace. An induction furnace is in effect a transformer in which the charge forms the secondary. The primary coil is copper tubing with circulating water acting as a coolant. The charge is held in a crucible that is placed within the primary coil. The heating energy is transferred by electromagnetic induction from the cold exterior portion of the furnace into the charge. When high-frequency current is applied to the terminals of the primary coil, all the space within the coil is subjected to a rapidly alternating electromagnetic field. Any electrical conductor within this field has currents induced in it, which cause rapid heating. Figure 10-10 is a diagrammatic sketch of a core type induction furnace. It has a laminated silicon steel transformer coil that is surrounded by the primary coil, which induces the melting control in a secondary loop formed by the molten metal.

The choice of electrical equipment for providing the necessary high-frequency current is governed by the capacity of the furnace. For use where input requirements do not exceed 40 kw, a spark-gap converter is available. This equipment, which uses single-phase, 220/440 volt, 60-cycle current, consists of a high-reactance transformer, a discharge

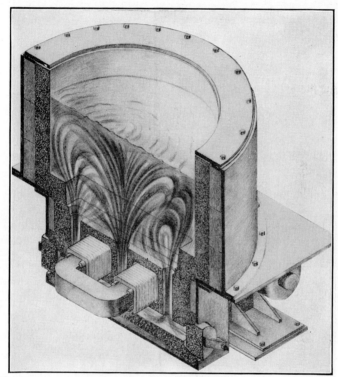

Fig. 10-10. Diagram of a core type induction melting furnace. (Courtesy of Ajax Engineering Corp., Trenton, N.J.)

gap composed of a mercury pool and two copper electrodes operating in an atmosphere of hydrogen, and a bank of capacitors connected to the furnace primary. Frequencies available from this equipment vary between 20,000 and 40,000 cycles, depending on the furnace size and requirements.

On larger furnaces, a motor-generator set is used for producing currents with frequencies that fall in the range of from 1,000 to 3,000 cycles. These are not fixed values, since melting requirements dictate the choice of current frequencies. There is also mercury arc frequency-changing equipment built that converts three-phase arc power into single-phase power at a frequency of about 1,000 cycles.

The advantage of induction melting is that the charge can be melted entirely free of contamination. There is no fuel burned and no flame impingement or gas contamination. Induction melting can be carried on

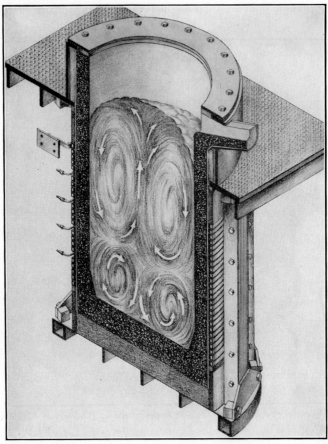

Fig. 10-11. Diagram of a coreless type induction melting furnace for operation with 60-cycle current. (Courtesy of Ajax Engineering Corp., Trenton, N.J.)

in vacuum or under controlled atmospheric conditions. Molten metal can be produced under exact control in the induction furnace; hence this is regarded as the best method for melting quality metal.

Low-frequency Induction Furnace. The principle of melting by the induction furnace as previously described is that of inducing an electrical current in the metal itself. These furnaces all operate on some type of high-frequency current. A design development whereby a 60-cycle current can be used is now available (Fig. 10-11). There is a design revision here since this furnace carries a cylindrical primary coil backed by magnetic flux-returning yokes which surround the lower portion of a cylindrical melting hearth. The application of a 60-cycle current to this primary coil induces a secondary current of high amperage in the metal charge, thereby generating the necessary heat for melting. Another feature is that the resulting electromagnetic pressure causes a strong stirring action in the melt. This action tends to maintain uniform temperatures and prevents layering of the charge. This furnace is known as a coreless type and is used for the melting of various types of cast irons. It is also successful in melting aluminum in all physical forms, such

Fig. 10-12. Electric crucible transformer melting furnace. (Courtesy of Manufacturing Instrument & Tool Corp., Clifton, N.J.)

as turnings and foil, among others. Copper-base alloys are also readily melted in this type of furnace, which obviously is a very flexible one.

Resistance Type Furnace. An entirely new design in melting equipment has been developed in Germany under the name of Linder, a resistance furnace. This one uses a 220-volt current and carbon contactors which clamp on the crucible. With this type design temperatures as high as 6000°F are achieved in about 6 min. The crucibles are made of carbon or graphitic clay or numerous other common refractories. The entire furnace is mounted on trunnions and, as a result, it can be tapped either from the bottom or the top (Fig. 10-12). The furnace is mounted inside a steel shell where the intervening space is filled with carbon pellets that act as insulators and also prevent undue oxidation. While present models are small in size, there seem to be no reasons that would prevent production models from being successfully introduced. This furnace is especially useful where high-temperature metals are to be melted.

Vacuum Melting. Where the requirements for metal quality are critical, vacuum melting is an answer. This principle has been applied to induction furnaces of various types. Actually there are two basic designs: in one, where extreme purity is desired, the melting is done in a furnace equipped with a consumable electrode; this equipment is used in making titanium ingots from sponge, by way of example (Fig. 10-13). In the

Fig. 10-13. Placing a copper crucible into a vacuum consumable-electrode melting furnace. This crucible serves as the ingot mold. Ingots are 26 in. in diameter and weigh to 12,000 lb. (Courtesy of Watervleit, N.Y., Works, Allegheny Ludlum Steel Corp.)

other development (Fig. 10-14), a vacuum is applied to induction type furnaces primarily. Since this application is not too expensive it is applied to many engineering materials. The resulting products are stronger and have a higher density than those melted in air.

Vacuum melting is accompanied by vacuum pouring in order to ensure desired results. Another approach to this idea comes from the vacuum degassing of metal. The objective is to improve metal quality by the

Fig. 10-14. Vacuum melting furnace of 400 lb capacity for producing iron, nickel, and cobalt-base alloys. (Courtesy of Cannon-Muskegon Co., Muskegon, Mich.)

elimination of porosity. In addition to improving the mechanical properties this treatment also has an effect upon the surface appearance. The field of vacuum metal treatment is a rapidly growing one and it is destined for increasing acceptance because of the quality of product of which it is capable.

SURVEY QUESTIONS

10-1. How does the melt shop serve the foundry?

10-2. Do metals for casting have a fixed or a constant melting point?

10-3. What is the basic principle of a furnace used in a foundry?

10-4. To what extent does geography dictate foundry melting equipment?

10-5. Are furnace heat losses the same among the different types of furnaces?

10-6. What furnace is used predominantly for melting cast iron?

10-7. Can white cast iron, gray cast iron, and malleable cast iron all be melted in the same furnace?

10-8. What type fuel is used for melting gray cast iron?

10-9. Give an advantage for a basic-lined cupola over the acid type.

10-10. When a converter is used as the metal source, what type of castings are being poured?

10-11. Give an advantage for a stack melt reverberatory furnace.

10-12. In what type foundries are crucible furnaces used?

10-13. What two main types of electric furnaces are installed in foundries?

10-14. Are electric furnaces ever used for melting nonferrous metals?

10-15. From what material are the electrodes in an arc furnace made?

10-16. What is the benefit to be derived from a vacuum furnace?

10-17. How is molten metal transported from the furnace to the mold?

10-18. Are melt shops connected with die casting installations?

10-19. Is it possible to melt steel for castings in a cupola furnace?

10-20. What metal does duplexing provide for the foundry?

Chapter 11

METHODS OF
CLEANING CASTINGS

Castings are routed from the pouring floor through the cleaning room for process finishing. The amount of cleaning required, as well as the method employed, is a function of the casting process. Sand castings require more processing than do those produced from permanent molds. There are additional factors that require consideration before a casting cleaning program can be established. Among these are the composition of the casting, the end use, and the type or class of finish desired.

After the casting has been poured, an interval sufficiently long to permit necessary solidification elapses prior to the removal of the casting from the sand mold. "Shaking out" is the generic term applied to this foundry operation. In small foundries, shaking out is a tedious and rather unpleasant manual operation. Production foundries shake out with mechanical devices so designed that the molding sand and flasks are separated from the casting. The former two are recycled into their respective systems and the casting is conveyed to the cleaning operation (Fig. 11-1).

Removal of Gates and Risers. Gates and risers are removed from iron castings by a sharp blow with a hammer. In order to prevent breakage or having the gate break into the casting, the hammer blow should be struck against the sprue in a direction toward the casting. Gates should be lightened at the junction with the casting in order to give a clean break at that point.

Steel castings pose a more difficult problem of gate and riser removal. Some risers can be knocked off, but the majority cannot, because of the nature of the material and also because of the fact that they are generally of large cross section. Torch or arc-cutting of risers is the universally accepted practice in the steel foundry.

A sprue-cutting machine similar in design to a small power shear is used in brass and bronze foundries for sprue cutting. Other types of nonferrous castings are separated from gates and risers by band-sawing. Greatest economy results from using a band saw of correct tooth pitch for the metal being cut. Accurate sawing will save subsequent grinding time; care should be exercised to prevent sawing into the casting when removing gates and risers.

Tumbling Mills. Small and intermediate-sized ferrous castings are cleaned of adhering sand in tumbling mills. These mills, or rattlers, as they are known in the foundry, are hollow cylinders equipped with

Fig. 11-1. Mold shakeout in operation receiving sand and castings from conveyor. (Courtesy of Jeffrey Manufacturing Co., Columbus, Ohio.)

removable staves that form the outside wall. At the center of each end are placed trunnions on which the mill rotates. Castings that have had their sprues removed are packed into the mill through the side opening created by the removal of adjacent staves. Care should be taken to avoid an admixture of heavy and light castings in a load as a precaution against breakage. Small pieces such as rattler stars, steel slugs, gate scrap, sprues, and risers are included with each load. Cleaning results when the mill is rotated, causing the castings to rub against each other and the smaller pieces to ride over casting surfaces.

Tumbled castings have a bright and clean surface finish. It is only in cases of severely fused sand that additional cleaning is necessary. Adhering sand that is removed in tumbling is carried from the mill by a connected exhaust system. Figure 11-2 shows a tumbling mill equipped with exhaust systems.

Tilted mills, open at the top or small end, are used for cleaning some copper-base castings. Abrasives, sawdust, or cereal products are charged with the castings to impart a polish. Mills of this type are operated with either a wet or dry load, depending on the surface finish desired on the work. Some horizontal mills are also operated with a wet load, but polishing rather than sand removal is the objective. Mills in which polished balls are charged with the load are used for burnishing.

Fig. 11-2. Standard type tumbling mill equipped with gear-head motor drive. (Courtesy of the W. W. Sly Manufacturing Co., Cleveland.)

Blast Cleaning. Impact cleaning, as originally practiced, consisted of directing a stream of sand of high velocity against the surface to be cleaned. The cleaned surface has a pleasing appearance, and adhering sand can be completely removed no matter how tenaciously it may cling to the casting. The use of sand for impact cleaning has all but disappeared because of the introduction of metal abrasives. Sand grains shatter rather easily, thereby losing their efficiency and at the same time creating a dust problem.

Metal abrasives have been developed that are now used as the material for blast cleaning. These are made from cupola melted metal by causing the fine metal streams leaving the cupola spout to be blown by an air stream or steam jet. The blowing action is such that the resulting metal globules are directed into a water quench which gives them a high degree of hardness. The globules, or shot, are then screened for sizing and grading in accordance with standard specifications.

Metal abrasive shot are spherical; consequently, when used for impact cleaning, they give the effect of peening with a multitude of miniature ball-peen hammers. The resulting surface is not satisfactory for enameling, plating, or galvanizing; however, the process of shot peening is also useful for increasing fatigue resistance of stressed members.

Metal shot that fail to meet specifications are further processed by a crushing operation that shatters them into sharp-edged and -angled particles. These particles, known as angular grit, are used in blast cleaning and produce a mat finish on the blasted surface. The cleaning action of grit can be likened to the effect of using many minute chisels. Surface imperfections are exposed by these sharp-edged cutting abrasives. The

Fig. 11-3. Phantom view of an air-blast cleaning room equipped with completely mechanical abrasive handling and reclamation system. (Courtesy of Pangborn Corp., Hagerstown, Md.)

choice of metal abrasives as between shot or grit is governed both by the nature of the surface to be cleaned and the type of surface finish desired. Blast cleaning as a method for surface preparation cannot be handled in a haphazard manner.

Air-blast abrasives, whether sand or metal, must strike with a high impact value if their action is to be effective. Compressed air, as the vehicle for carrying abrasives, is well known. In air blasting, the abrasive is stored in a container and is introduced into the air stream at a regulated rate. Methods of accomplishing this are the direct pressure principle, the gravity feed system (where gravitational forces act only to introduce the abrasive into the air stream), and the suction system, in which the abrasive is lifted from its container by static vacuum developed in the blast gun. An example of an air-blast cleaning room is shown in Fig. 11-3.

The air stream carrying the abrasive is directed against the surface through a nozzle. The latter is subjected to a high degree of wear and must be renewed frequently if top performance is to be maintained. Nozzles are available in diverse designs and various materials, ranging from iron pipe to hard alloys. Positioning the nozzle with respect to the work is another modifying factor in air-blast cleaning, since the cross-sectional area of the blast stream increases as it lengthens. A larger pattern

Fig. 11-4. Hydraulic principle blast cleaning room. Sand is mixed with the water stream for more effective operation. (Courtesy of Pangborn Corp., Hagerstown, Md.)

results when the nozzle is moved farther from the work, but at the same time abrasive velocities are slowed.

Water-blast Systems. Water is used as the vehicle for carrying the abrasive in water-blast cleaning. This design has been in successful operation for several years. Stream velocities of 20,000 fpm are used with this equipment, which is capable of removing cores as well as adhering sand. Water-blast systems are economical to use, since both water and sand can be reclaimed for re-use. A water-blast room installation is pictured in Fig. 11-4. All types of metal castings can be cleaned with water blast.

Mud Blasting. Mud blasting is a system in which a very fine abrasive is used for delicate cleaning operations. Polishing discolored machined surfaces can also be done by mud blasting. Mud-blast systems for polishing employ abrasives of widely differing character extending from extremely fine silica powder to cereals. Equipment is not on the large scale that is characteristic of water blasting.

Airless Blast Methods. The idea of propelling abrasives by centrifugal force rather than by air velocity is almost as old as blast cleaning itself. The development of suitable propelling wheels has resulted in three recognized systems, known respectively as (*a*) batter type, (*b*) slider type, and (*c*) valveless type wheels. The principal differences between

Fig. 11-5. Wheelabrator Super Tumblast emptying cleaned castings on a conveyor. (Courtesy of Wheelabrator Corp., Mishawaka, Ind.)

them stem from the method of introducing the abrasive to the wheel and, further, from the action of the abrasive while in contact with the wheel.

Design trends have been in this direction to the extent that modern production equipment is mainly of the centrifugal type. Casting handling equipment has been built around the centrifugal unit to the point of eliminating a substantial amount of the labor formerly necessary to the casting cleaning operation.

In the case of smaller castings and in those instances where batch operation is satisfactory, cleaning is best done in equipment that combines the action of the tumbling mill (Fig. 11-2) with the centrifugal blast device. In fact, the tumbling mill design is modified somewhat in that a moving element within the mill causes the castings to roll in a manner that will bring all their surfaces into the abrasive stream. One such design is shown in Fig. 11-5. This equipment provides satisfactory low-cost cleaning for castings and other metal products such as forgings. Surface finish is pleasing and of good quality.

Grinding and Chipping. Castings whose surfaces have been cleaned by any of the previously mentioned methods require further processing for the removal of fins, gate stubs, riser bases, and casting imperfections. The amount of time needed is, as a general rule, directly proportional to the metal used in the casting. Accordingly, steel castings require more grinding and chipping than is necessary for gray cast iron.

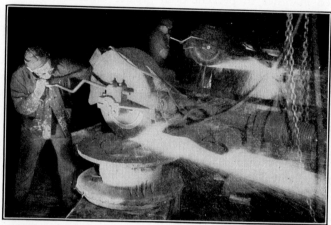

Fig. 11-6. Grinding a riser base on a steel casting with a swing frame grinder. (Courtesy of Norton Co., Worcester, Mass.)

Grinding requires attention to such matters as selection of correct abrasive wheels. Care in wheel selection, coupled with correct peripheral wheel speed, is the combination that will yield best results. Casting grinding is performed by portable, swing, or stationary grinding machines (Fig. 11-6). Proper protection of the worker is necessary against such hazards as flying abrasive particles and wheel breakage. Eye protection in grinding as in chipping is of decided importance. Goggles and face shields equipped with shatterproof lenses are required equipment. Ventilation and good housekeeping are further items of importance to the modern foundry cleaning room.

CASTING SALVAGE

It is impossible to produce perfect castings continually. Imperfections can result from a variety of causes, such as loose sand, slag inclusions, core shifts, shrinks, blows, rattails, corrugations, and many others. In addition, careless or accidental handling of castings can cause breakage. Another source of imperfection comes from riser and gate removal, especially where they are knocked off, resulting in breaking into the casting. Defects of this nature are frequently salvaged in the cleaning room.

Casting repair and also the decision as to which ones can be repaired require both skill and judgment. The electric arc with its many accompanying types of electrodes has become a recognized method of repairing ferrous castings. Torch welding requires prolonged heat input over a larger area, causing expansion and contraction problems that must be recognized in order to prevent even greater difficulty. It is suggested that Chap. 36 be studied prior to attempting the repair on castings, in order to avoid distortion and breakage that can result from improper heat application.

Entirely satisfactory and permanent repairs can be made in the cleaning room by welding minor casting defects. This is the best way to resolve the problem. Holes in castings which are not critical, insofar as load-carrying applications are concerned, may be repaired by filling them with some form of iron paste. This material is designed to harden similar to the casting, and, when paint is applied, the repair is entirely unobtrusive. The proper method of casting salvage can only be decided when the individual casting is studied as to imperfection, type of material, and end use.

SURVEY QUESTIONS

11-1. What occurs at the foundry "shakeout"?

11-2. Is it possible to separate the cores from the molding sand at shakeout time?

11-3. Is there danger of marring or breaking castings at the time gates are removed?

11-4. In what type foundry would a sprue cutter be used?

11-5. What dual purpose is achieved on a gray iron casting that has been processed in a tumbling mill?

11-6. What is the composition of a charge in a tumbling mill?

11-7. On what class of work are tilted mills used?

11-8. Explain the basic idea of blast cleaning.

11-9. Mention at least three different types of abrasive that are being used in blast cleaning.

11-10. Would beach sand or olivine be the better material for use in air-blast cleaning?

11-11. Is there an advantage in water blast over air blast for casting cleaning?

11-12. How is the abrasive carried to the surface to be cleaned in an air-blast system?

11-13. Is all abrasive cleaning of the air-blast type?

11-14. How are fins removed from a gray iron casting?

11-15. Would the same thing hold true for a steel casting?

11-16. Mention some safety precautions necessary in the grinding room.

11-17. What two general uses will be found for an electric arc welder in the steel foundry cleaning room?

11-18. Are all chipping hammers air-operated?

11-19. Give a specific example where chipping is a necessity.

11-20. How are dry-sand cores removed from an automobile motor block casting?

REFERENCES FOR FOUNDRY TECHNOLOGY SECTION

Chaps. 5–11

"Casting of Steel," 1955, by Newell, Pergamon Press, London.

"Design of Gray Iron Castings," 1956, Gray Iron Founders Society, Cleveland.

"Die Casting for Engineers," 1953, New Jersey Zinc Company.

"Die Casting Process," 1956, by Barton, Odhams Press, London.

"Foundry Sand Testing Handbook," 5th ed., 1944, American Foundrymen's Society, Chicago.

"Fundamentals in the Production and Design of Castings," 1950, by Marek, John Wiley & Sons, Inc., New York.

"Gray Iron Castings Handbook," 1958, Gray Iron Founders Society, Cleveland.

"Introduction to Foundry Technology," 1958, by Ekey and Winter, McGraw-Hill Book Company, Inc., New York.

"Investment Casting Engineering and Design Manual," 1957, Investment Casting Institute, Chicago.

"Investment Casting for Engineers," 1952, by Wood and Von Ludwig, Reinhold Publishing Corporation, New York.

"Modern Pearlitic Malleable Castings Handbook," 1958, Malleable Research and Development Foundation, Albion, Mich.

"Patternmakers' Manual," 1947, by Wagner and McAfee, Patternmakers' League.

"Precision Investment Castings," 1948, by Cady, Reinhold Publishing Corporation, New York.

"Principles of Iron Founding," 1917, by Moldenke, McGraw-Hill Book Company, Inc., New York.

"Principles of Metal Casting," 1955, by Heine and Rosenthal, McGraw-Hill Book Company, Inc., New York.

"Steel Castings Handbook," 2d ed., 1950, Steel Founders' Society of America, Cleveland.

"Steel Foundry Practice," 1955, by Hall, Penton Publishing Company, Cleveland.

"The Cast Metals Handbook," 3d ed., 1944, American Foundrymen's Society, Chicago.

Chapter 12

COLD SHAPING

The preceding chapters have been devoted to the subject of shaping metal by casting. The final structure of a casting depends upon the combination of factors operative during the molding, melting, casting, and shakeout periods. Except for powder metal products, the forming of metal starts with a casting process. The cast-iron series is not subject to subsequent mechanical processing such as can be applied to other metals and alloys in both the ferrous and the nonferrous group.

Cold shaping is performed on metal that has previously been mechanically worked. By far the major part of cold shaping uses sheet metal as its raw material, although there are other cold-shaped products, such as wire and cold-drawn tubing, for example, that are not formed from sheet material. Viewed from an engineering standpoint, cold shaping has the merit of changing the mechanical properties of the metal that is so processed.

The real significance of the subject matter in this chapter arises from the processing occurring at room temperature. This means a genuine saving in manufacturing costs because no second operation of heating is required: when heating is omitted accompanying difficulties tend to disappear. It is for this reason that the student is urged especially to inform himself on the subject of cold shaping.

An extraordinarily wide range of components are produced by cold shaping. Some of the common ones are bolts, nuts, rivets, headed pins, wood screws, and nails of all types.

COLD WORKING

Cold working and cold forming are the two chief methods employed for cold-shaping metal. Cold working, as a general rule, is a process of finishing previously hot-formed material. The objectives of the process are improved surface and dimensional finish, increased yield and tensile strength, and, further, increased hardness, lowered ductility, increased endurance limit, and better machinability. By definition, cold working is "deforming a metal plastically at such a temperature and rate that strain hardening occurs. The upper limit of temperature for this process is the recrystallization temperature."[1] The two principal cold-working methods are rolling and drawing, the former applying to flat products and some bars and shapes, the latter to tubular products, wire, and bars. Other cold-working processes include swaging, cold heading, roll threading, knurling, coining, and, for some nonferrous alloys, cold forging, splining, extrusion, and pressing.

The effect of cold working on standard specification steels is shown in Table 12-1, where mechanical properties of some plain carbon steels are given.

TABLE 12-1. APPROXIMATE MECHANICAL PROPERTY VALUES FOR COLD-DRAWN AND HOT-ROLLED CARBON STEELS OF THE SAME ANALYSIS*

Mechanical properties	Grade of steel			
	AISI C1020 SAE 1020	AISI C1035 SAE 1035	AISI C1045 SAE 1045	AISI C1050 SAE 1050
Cold drawn				
Tensile strength, psi..	70,000–85,000	90,000–110,000	85,000–115,000	100,000–120,000
Yield strength, psi....	60,000–70,000	75,000–90,000	80,000–100,000	85,000–100,000
Elongation, per cent in 2 in............	15–25	10–20	10–15	10–15
Brinell hardness number.............	149–170	170–202	183–228	202–235
Hot rolled (Turned and polished on precision shafting)				
Tensile strength, psi..	50,000–70,000	70,000–90,000	80,000–100,000	90,000–110,000
Yield strength, psi...	25,000–45,000	30,000–50,000	35,000–55,000	45,000–65,000
Elongation, per cent in 2 in............	30–40	20–30	20–30	15–25
Brinell hardness number.............	110–140	143–182	156–202	179–223

* UDS "Steel Handbook No. 47," Republic Steel Corp., Union Drawn Steel Division.

Reference to the table shows the effect of cold working to be more pronounced on yield strength than on tensile strength; it also indicates that the improvement in these characteristics is more noticeable in the steels of lower carbon range. Steels are composed of definitely proportioned pearlite and ferrite grains, and the latter are susceptible to deformation or fragmentation under the influence of cold working. The

[1] "Metals Handbook," p. 4, American Society for Metals, Cleveland, 1948.

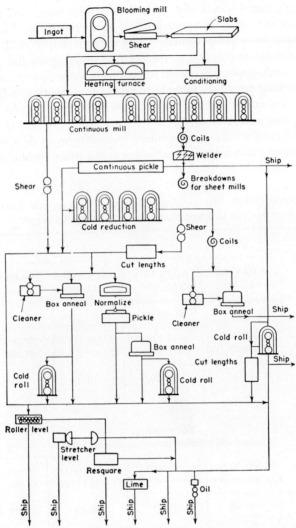

Fig. 12-1. Continuous mill flow chart. (Courtesy of American Iron and Steel Institute, New York.)

lower the carbon in the steel, the greater the ferrite constituent and consequently the greater the degree of grain deformation. Actually, a piece tested immediately after grain deformation occurs will have no elastic limit, but after a period of rest some elasticity will be regained owing to a reorientation of the deformed ferrite. The elastic limit, however, will be higher than that of the material prior to cold working.

Cold Rolling. Cold rolling is done on previously hot-rolled material that has been subjected to a surface cleaning treatment for the removal of adhering scale. Pickling in a hot sulfuric acid solution is the usual method for scale removal. The material thus cleaned is passed through roller dies during the cold-working operation. The amount of reduction per pass is slight; consequently, the number of passes used is a function of the surface finish desired as to both dimensional and smoothness characteristics. The continuous mill has been developed as a means of meeting the requirements for steel sheet. Figure 12-1 is a flow chart for a continuous mill (see also Fig. 2-6, page 20).

Cold-rolled Forming. The development in this area consists of using equipment to cold-form splines instead of cutting them. This can be accomplished at a very rapid rate to extremely accurate dimensions. It is

Fig. 12-2. Cold-forming helical splines with Roto-flow equipment. Note forming racks straddling the workpiece. (Courtesy of Michigan Tool Co., Detroit.)

also referred to as the rack-forming method by plastic deformation, which is known to produce high-quality work while, at the same time, substantially lowering manufacturing costs (Fig. 12-2). In this particular application it is well ahead of machining both from a cost as well as a quality viewpoint. Rear-axle shafts are regularly processed with cold-rolled splines. This equipment frequently operates in conjunction with hydroform equipment in a manner whereby the component is completely finished without forming the usual chips that result from machining and represent waste material.

Cold Drawing. Cold drawing employs a stationary die through which the metal is pulled. The amount of reduction, or draft, in the die is a variable, depending upon the analysis of the material being worked (Fig. 12-3). In the case of cold-drawn steel bars the die draft ranges from $\frac{1}{64}$ to as much as $\frac{1}{8}$ in. Wire is one of the volume products of cold drawing. Wire bars are cleaned of surface scale and pointed so that they will pass through the die a sufficient distance to be gripped for the drawing operation. The bar is drawn through a succession of dies in order to reduce it to final wire gage. Dies for wire drawing are chiefly made from tungsten carbide, although diamond dies remain popular for small diameters. The result of cold-work deformation may be so severe as to require annealing or other heat-treatments of the drawn wire. The

Fig. 12-3. Measuring cold-drawn bar on multiple-bar draw bench. (Courtesy of Union Drawn Steel Division, Republic Steel Corp., Cleveland.)

micrographs in Figs. 12-4 and 12-5 clearly show the effect of cold drawing. The distortion of grain in the direction of drawing is very pronounced at this degree of cold reduction.

Coining. The process of cold-working metal in a press-type die is termed coining. Common applications of coining are for making medals, badges, coins, and similar embossed parts. Heavy pressures are the rule in coining, since plastic flow must be induced in the metal so that die delineations can be faithfully reproduced. There are operations used on some castings whereby they are die-sized to produce pattern fidelity; however, that is not a coining operation in the usually understood sense of the term.

Cold Extrusion. This method of manufacture requires specially designed punches and dies working together to force steel to flow cold into required shapes. There are two fundamental movements or actions. In one, known as backward extrusion, the steel billet is placed in a closed die and forced to flow in the direction opposite to the travel of the punch. In forward extrusion, on the other hand, steel is forced to flow through an open die in the same direction as punch movement; on occasion these methods are used in combination. Furthermore, they may be used as supplemental operations to drawing, coining, flanging, and heading in order to produce shapes with varying wall thicknesses, flanges, internal webs, and similar requirements.

The advantages claimed for this method are less basic material requirement, excellent surface finish and tolerance, increased mechanical

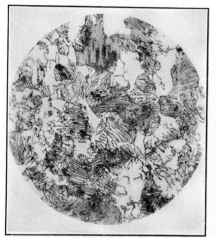

Fig. 12-4. AISI 4340 steel $\frac{7}{32}$-in.-diameter rod as annealed. Bhn 197. $\times$1,000. (Courtesy of Wyckoff Steel Co., Chicago.)

Fig. 12-5. AISI 4340 steel $\frac{7}{32}$-in.-diameter rod annealed and cold-drawn to $\frac{1}{8}$-in. diameter. 67 per cent reduction by cold work. $\times$1,000. (Courtesy of Wyckoff Steel Co., Chicago.)

properties, and frequently, because of one-piece extrusions, elimination of assembly. This is especially true of parts that are thin-walled cylinders with thick bases or flanges (Fig. 12-6). Components produced are as much as 6 in. OD and more than 20 in. in length. Shell components for ordnance are readily mass-produced in a variety of calibers. Cold extrusion offers a substantial saving and a method of metal forming that is of interest to every cost-conscious engineer.

Shot Peening. In the previous chapter the method of cleaning castings by air blasting was described. This technique has recently begun to be used as a method of cold working; however, when used for cold working it is referred to as shot peening. It consists of impinging fine-grain metal shot under high velocity against the metal surface to be peened.

The result of this shot impact is that the outer fibers of the metal flow plastically in tension. The effect is confined to a very narrow surface band, with the result that the layers immediately beneath the surface, which are not stretched, exert a force causing compression in the peened surface.

These residual compressive stresses are of profound significance in increasing fatigue resistance of the component so treated. Since fatigue failures generally result from tension stresses, it can be seen that a surface in compression will have a longer life. Shot peening of gear teeth has been developed into a standard manufacturing procedure because it has been found that gears thus treated exhibit longer operating life.

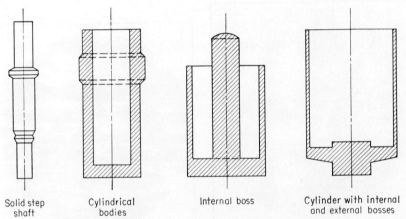

| Solid step shaft | Cylindrical bodies | Internal boss | Cylinder with internal and external bosses |

Fig. 12-6. Cold extruded components formed from steel by metal displacement rather than by metal removal. (Courtesy of Heinz Manufacturing Co., Philadelphia.)

Shot-peen Forming. The aircraft industry has adapted the practice of forming skin panels and wing panels by the newly developed shot-peening method. In this operation shot peening imparts a compressive layer to the outside of the panels which tends to increase fatigue life and retard stress corrosion. These gains are made in addition to having the new method for shaping panels. Investigations are still under way to determine the proper size shot to use for the attainment of desired properties. Equipment for shot-peen forming installations is not now available; obviously an extension of this method can be expected as it becomes better known.

COLD FORMING

Cold forming of metal is a fundamental method for manufacturing an increasingly wide array of products. Formerly, cold forming was associated exclusively with producing components for the engineering industries; however, the scope of application has broadened to include every phase of domestic product as well. This popularity has resulted from the development of metals and alloys which fit themselves into the cold-forming process both functionally and production-wise. The wide acceptance of cold-formed parts is demonstrated by the equipment of the modern home, where examples include everything from appliances, fixtures, and furniture to motorcars and components of the house itself. The automotive and aircraft industries depend largely on cold forming for the fabrication of component parts.

Cold forming is the process of shaping sheet metal or plate by mechanical means at room temperature. Fundamentally, two aspects are included in cold forming: either the metal is stressed beyond its elastic limit to the point of permanent deformation or it is worked beyond its ultimate strength to the point where fracture or severance occurs. In any event, cold forming is applicable only to those metals that are plastic at room temperature.

Plasticity is not a common term, since no unit value for measuring this property of a metal has been established. Plasticity is a function of temperature; further, it is dependent upon crystalline structure. Thus magnesium alloys, which have an hexagonal lattice, are difficult—in many instances even impossible—to shape by cold forming. Plastic behavior in metals is dependent upon deformation in the crystalline structure. In cold working, the deformation is considered to take place as a transcrystalline action in the sense that movement occurs along numerous slip planes within the crystals. Obviously, then, factors limiting deformation (plasticity) are crystal orientation and crystal structure in combination with the binding forces between atoms in the crystal. Detailed information on the phenomenon of plasticity is found in the section of the "Metals Handbook" entitled The Crystal Structure of Metals and Alloys, by Kent R. Van Horn.[2]

Cold forming results in a loss of ductility in the metal due to strain hardening—a condition mentioned earlier in this chapter in connection with cold working. In some cold forming it is necessary to introduce an annealing operation in the production sequence in order to restore plasticity for succeeding forming operations. An analogous situation is found in some cold-working processes; wire drawing offers an example.

Cold forming is applied principally to sheet metal, since such material lends itself well to high production rates. However, cold-forming equipment of greater capacities is being introduced in industry, widening the scope of components that can be produced. The type of equipment used for cold forming includes presses of all basic concepts, together with roll

[2] American Society for Metals, Cleveland, 1948.

formers, stretchers, spinning lathes, and drawbenches for longitudinal contours and moldings.

Drawbench. Moldings or contoured strip, when required in modest amounts, is readily produced on a drawbench. This equipment consists of a housing, in which the dies are held, mounted on a bench wherein a continuous chain is located. A clamping mechanism, which grips the stock to be formed, is arranged so that it can be connected to the chain, thus applying the power and movement necessary for drawing the strip through the die. The dies are made from hardwood, fiber, or steel, depending on the gage and kind of material to be formed. Although it is not generally realized, drawbenches offer an economical method for making moldings and, with slight modification of the die head, provide

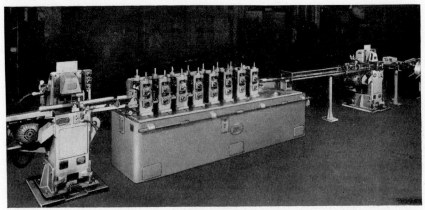

Fig. 12-7a. Yoder mill designed for roller die forming using metal strip, which is fed into the right end of this machine. (Courtesy of the Yoder Co., Cleveland.)

an excellent means of straightening extrusions and bars by straining along the major axis.

Roller Forming. Roller forming follows two general principles. Perhaps the best-known method is that of cold shaping previously formed sections into circles or areas. Another method of cold forming with roller dies is found in equipment that uses coiled strip as its raw material. Closed sections of innumerable cross-sectional designs are produced by cold forming in roller die machines. Designing roller dies requires ingenuity to hold the number of roll passes to a minimum. Too, the amount of forming per roller die pair needs to be correctly calculated in order to prevent rupture of the section being formed.

Contoured flat sections, where quantity requirements warrant, are produced in roller die equipment (Fig. 12-7a and 7b). Metal moldings of a wide variety of shapes are made on this equipment. This method competes with extrusion where shape imposes no limitations. Metal moldings can be produced economically on either drawbench or rolling equipment in those cases where wall or metal thickness is constant; when wall or metal thickness is a variable, extrusion is the indicated method of production.

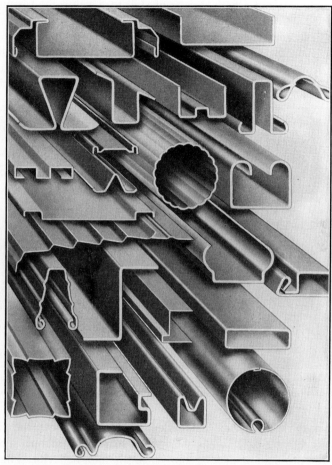

Fig. 12-7b. Typical sections produced on a cold rolling mill. Note that metal thickness remains constant in any section. (Courtesy of the Yoder Co., Cleveland.)

Sheet and plate are formed into cylindrical shapes or sections having compound curves on equipment of the pyramid roll type (Fig. 12-8). Rolled cylinders are removed by swinging down the end housing and stripping off the formed cylinder. Where heavy plates are to be rolled, it is the general practice to form the edge of the plate to the desired radius in a press, in order to prevent flat edges in the finished cylinder. There is a modified design of pyramid rolls known as pinch rolls wherein the roll location is changed from the true triangular to one in which two rolls are in vertical tandem with a third roll located to their rear. It is said that pinch rolls eliminate the flat edge that occurs on plate rolled with the pyramid type. Pyramid rolls are used for forming ships' plates for both bow and stern contours. In ship-plate work the roll operator must employ ingenuity and a high degree of skill to develop the forming that the hull lines require.

Brakes. Cold forming of sheet and plate for longitudinal bends is generally done on brakes. Two general categories cover the field—leaf brakes and press brakes. Leaf brakes are for the most part manually operated and are regarded as basic equipment in the sheet-metal shop. A

Fig. 12-8. Cold-forming plate into a firebox on pyramid rolls in the boiler shop of the Baldwin Locomotive Works, Eddystone Division. (Courtesy of Baldwin-Lima-Hamilton Corp., Philadelphia.)

skilled operator can produce a remarkably wide variety of products with a leaf brake. Spring-back of the work after forming confronts the operator with the problem of making allowance for such behavior. The degree of spring-back is a variable depending upon the character and gage of the metal being formed as well as the amount of deformation.

Press brakes are larger and of greater capacity than leaf brakes. For a comparison of these two types of machines, see Fig. 12-9 where a hydraulic press brake is shown in operation and a leaf brake can be seen at the rear of the shop. Press brakes are designed mainly for hydraulic operation.

Press brakes are built to accommodate dies for punching, blanking, wiring, beading, shearing, seaming, and forming. In consequence these machines are extremely versatile and perform a variety of work in the jobbing shop; so much so that they can be substituted for many types of presses. Press brakes offer an interesting study in construction since they are for the most part composed of heavy steel plates joined by welding. Press-brake design exemplifies the possibilities offered by the combination of flame cutting and arc welding.

Stretch Forming. When production requirements are insufficient to justify elaborate press tooling, cold-formed parts can be shaped rather inexpensively by stretch forming. This method is applied principally to the cold forming of aluminum alloys for aircraft components. The requisite shaping is obtained from a die positioned on the platen of the metal-stretching press. Such dies are made from wood or Kirksite.

Fig. 12-9. Press brake in operation on metal shelving. (Courtesy of Pacific Industrial Manufacturing Co., Oakland, Calif.)

In the latter instance the dies are cast in plaster molds and only hand finishing is necessary.

In operation the stretching press utilizes a set of jaws, located parallel to the major axis of the platen, which grip the edges of the sheet to be formed. The jaws are constructed in a manner that permits their moving away from the platen. When the press is operated, the jaws travel horizontally while the platen, carrying the die, moves vertically; this combined action forms or stretches the sheet to the die shape. It will be seen from Fig. 12-10 that the ends of the sheet are not confined; only the sides are gripped in the press.

Spinning. When a sheet-metal part is of such a shape that parallel planes through the part will be circular or oval, it can be formed by spinning. It is usually understood that spinning is the preferred cold-forming method where production is small. There are instances, though, where articles are spun in order to take advantage of the pleasing finish developed from the lines of the forming tool. Modifications of spinning such as bulging, trimming, necking, and wiring are important to cold forming.

Most types of sheet metal lend themselves to spinning. The chief precaution in selecting a material is to note its work-hardening properties, since materials that have this tendency to a marked degree will require annealing or continued heating during the spinning cycle. Magnesium

Fig. 12-10. Stretch forming a wing section. (Courtesy of the Boeing Airplane Co., Seattle, Wash.)

alloys cannot be spun at room temperatures excepting in those cases where very small amounts of forming are involved. More extensive shapes can readily be produced by playing a torch on the magnesium blank while it is being spun.

Spinning lathes (Fig. 12-11) are designed for a range of spindle speeds. The head stock spindle is threaded for mounting the chuck. The latter is made from cast iron, steel, or wood, the choice depending upon the job. Many shapes are not truly cylindrical, with the result that a solid chuck cannot be removed from the finished part; sectional chucks are used in such cases.

Tools and chucks should be polished to a high degree of surface finish as a means of avoiding scratches on the work. Chromium plating of tool

Fig. 12-11. Spinning a 163-in. diameter by ⅛-in. thickness steel dome. Note pit arrangement for accommodating large diameters. (Courtesy of Phoenix Products Co., Milwaukee.)

Fig. 12-12a. Hydrospin machine showing a tapered component being removed from spinning mandrel. (Courtesy of Cincinnati Milling and Grinding Machines, Inc., Cincinnati.)

and chuck equipment is recommended for increased life and improved surfaces on the spun part. Forming rolls and tools made from tool steel are given a high polish prior to being placed in service.

Tool mounting depends on the type of lathe and the shape of the part. In many cases tools are mounted on the compound rest of the lathe and guided by the controls on the apron. Other installations feature a work

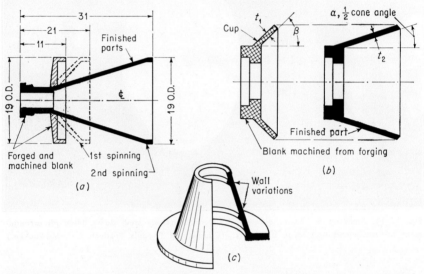

Fig. 12-12b. Components formed by hydrospinning. (Courtesy of Process Machinery Division, The Cincinnati Milling Machine Co., Cincinnati.)

Turbine shaft originally forged and then machined to 19 by 31 in. dimensions. Machining of thin tapered walls was difficult and resulted in much material waste. Forging and machining now reduced to 19 by 11 in. dimensions and power-spun in two passes to final dimensions using two mandrels. No heat-treating necessary between passes; strength of forging and quality of surface finish increased by spinning.

Machined blank made from shorter forging to reduce scrap loss. Blank is then power-spun to desired thickness and cone angle. Cup-shaped blank must be used for cone angles less than 30° to avoid exceeding a 75 per cent reduction in thickness.

Cutaway of cone with annular wall variations to allow more material for threading of fasteners. Variations are obtained by controlling path of rollers with tracer attachment.

rest equipped with fulcrum pins that act as points of leverage for tools held by the operator. Lubricants must be used on the metal blank in contact with the spinning tools.

Hydrospin. A new entry into the field of cold shaping is delivering spectacular achievements. This method, known as hydrospin, is used to cold-spin the toughest alloys, as evidenced by its ability to reduce wall thickness as much as 75 per cent in one pass.

On the hydrospin (Fig. 12-12a and 12b) the workpiece is forced to take the shape of a hardened, rotating mandrel. The basic piece of material is in the form of a disk that is held against the mandrel in somewhat the same manner as in spinning. As the disk and cone-shaped mandrel revolve, the desired shape is spirally generated by two hardened and polished rollers. The opposed rollers traverse the length of the mandrel, forcing the disk to take the mandrel shape. In so doing, the disk undergoes shear deformation, which results in considerable work hardening and in a significant increase in tensile strength. Additionally this method of forming produces a surface free of minute tears or ruptures, thereby giving the formed component high fatigue resistance. The roll force in hydrospinning is very high in that in some cases total pressure may reach 400,000 lb. The pressure is

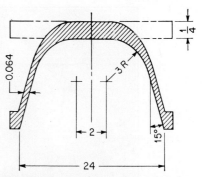

Fig. 12-13. Component hydrospun from ¼-in. boiler plate in 1.1 min. Shape combines bowed tapered base with straight conical wall.

sufficiently great to roll a ¾-in. thick flat disk of AISI 4340 steel down to a 60°-included-angle straight-wall cone in one pass.

Hydrospinning produces parts at a faster rate and with much less material waste than the comparable conventional production techniques including machining, welding, and deep drawing (Fig. 12-13). Production rates are competitive with deep drawing and in addition are lower in cost due to tooling.

The various components of the hydrospin machine are controlled hydraulically, meaning that an infinite number of speeds is available. On production runs an automatic spinning cycle is used to control the movements of the various machine components. This automatic cycle together with the universal slides and infinitely variable speeds makes the hydrospin suitable for high production as well as for spinning a variety of experimental parts.

Floturn. This development varies somewhat from the preceding one in that a single forming roller is used. The Floturn method is somewhat related to spinning; however, there are some important differences. In spinning the blank diameter is considerably larger than the product diameter. The metal blank is folded onto a chuck with moderate pressures; furthermore the metal is substantially of constant section. In the Floturning method the blank is exactly the same diameter as the finished product (Fig. 12-14). Metal is thinned by plastic deformation, with resulting increase in tensile strength and hardness. There is no metal removal in this operation. Interest in this method arises from its favorable cost position. It competes with some machining operations even though no metal is removed here; obviously the cost will be much more favorable. Tooling costs are very low and, in addition, tools are long lived.

Drop-hammer Forming. The aircraft industry has developed the method of cold forming sheet-metal parts under a drop hammer. The choice of

Fig. 12-14. Floturn operation showing tool action on workpiece. (Courtesy of The Lodge and Shipley Co., Cincinnati.)

this method is based on the relatively inexpensive dies, cast from Kirksite (Fig. 12-15). The force acting on the sheet to be formed is an impact one resulting from the kinetic energy developed by the falling of the upper die and holder. Aluminum alloys are most generally formed by the drop-hammer method, but stainless steel, magnesium, zinc, and other sheet stock have also been shaped in this manner.

Guerin Process. Hydraulic-press equipment was used by the Douglas Aircraft Company in 1935 in connection with an innovation in blanking

Fig. 12-15. Rope type drop hammer equipped with Kirksite die. Note formed part. (Courtesy of Boeing Airplane Co., Seattle, Wash.)

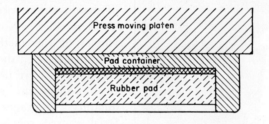

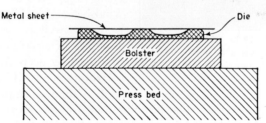

Fig. 12-16. Schematic drawing of Guerin Process.

as well as forming aluminum sheet. The success of this venture was so complete that the new method was patented as the Guerin Process. A live rubber pad acts as the medium for transmitting the force exerted by the press to the surface of the metal sheet that has been placed on the die block (Fig. 12-16).

The rubber pad is contained in a member that is fastened to the press moving platen. The sheet is placed on a die of such external dimensions that the pad holder will mate with it. The die is one-half of the orthodox die set, and it is made from a material such as wood, plastic, masonite, or plaster for forming. For blanking or cutting operations, the die is cut from tank or boiler plate in order that a cutting edge is available. Several different dies can be placed on the press bed simultaneously. A further speeding of production is obtained from the use of four tables that are loaded outside the press, thereby increasing the time the press is in actual operation.

Fig. 12-17. Blanks 19 in. OD by ⅜ in. steel thickness can be formed in this hydropress. (Courtesy of Hydroforming Co. of America, Chicago.)

Deep Drawing. Some of the deep-drawn parts that are now in production are spectacular achievements resulting from teamwork between metallurgy, engineering, and manufacturing. There are many instances where a deep-drawn part is produced through a sequence of operations because of design requirements or material characteristics. Noteworthy examples of this method are found in ordnance, e.g., shell cases. These components were universally made from copper-base alloys of high ductility. Shortages of that material caused specifications to be changed to ferrous materials. The windshields for large-caliber projectiles as well as rockets are other examples of ordnance components produced by deep drawing.

Hydroforming. This method is applied to deep-drawing a variety of engineering materials. The machine used for this work has a flexible diaphragm locked into the bottom of the dome-shaped hydraulic fluid container or cavity (Fig. 12-17). After the blank to be formed is placed over the draw ring on the bed of the press, the dome is lowered over the blank and locked into position and the initial pressure is applied. This movement is followed by a punch riding upward in the bed through the draw ring, pressing the blank against the flexible die member or diaphragm. This operation accomplishes the drawing operation. Following this the dome pressure is released and the dome is raised. The punch is next stripped from the finished part and the hydroforming cycle has been completed.

This method is extremely economical because the tooling is of the simplest, requiring only a punch cast or machined to the desired part shape and the draw ring to fit around the punch. This method has demonstrated in actual production that its costs are competitive with any other process designed to perform the same operations.

Heavy-gage Forming. The production achievements in this area are found in the automobile field preponderantly; automobile bumpers and bumper guards are typical heavy-gage cold-formed parts. Wheels, axle housings, frame members, cover plates, and jack components also belong in this category. Freight cars are built largely from heavy-gage cold-formed parts.

Can Making. The metal-container industry, especially the "tin can" phase, produces the largest number of cold-formed products in the entire field of cold shaping. This industry employs tin plate—a steel sheet coated on both sides with tin—as its principal raw material. The can lids are stamped out on standard-type presses. The can bodies are produced on bodymaking machines that are for the most part designed and manufactured by the can companies for their own manufacturing plants. These machines use a tin-plate sheet of precut size that is fed into the bodymaking machine automatically. The bodymaker produces a folded, soldered seam on the major axis of the can. In some types of can bodies there is a spot weld at each end of the seam as a replacement for the fold so that two rather than four thicknesses of metal may exist where the body is flanged to make the joint with the lid. These operations are all done automatically within one bodymaking machine at a production rate of approximately 400 can bodies/min. The exact production rate varies with body size and joint design and may total as high as 700/min.

Aluminum-alloy sheet is making its appearance in the closed container or can industry. The type equipment used varies considerably from that of the tin-plate industry. Impact extrusion in horizontal presses is producing cans as large as 2¾ in. diameter and 6 in. in length. The major development in aluminum cans has occurred in Europe; however, the idea is now firmly established in America since both production volume and competitive costs are a reality.

Impact Extrusion. Collapsible tubes are produced from aluminum or lead alloys by impact extrusion. This method is classified as cold shaping although there are some instances where the metal blank is heated for increased ductility. A male and a female die are employed, with clearance between the two equal to the thickness desired in the tube walls. A blank of the material to be extruded is placed in the female die; this is then struck by the descending punch, causing plastic flow. Since the only escape area for the metal is that surrounding the punch, it flows upward, encompassing the punch, from which it is stripped at the conclusion of the operation (Fig. 12-18).

Fig. 12-18. Impact extrusion of a collapsible tube from aluminum alloy. (Courtesy of Aluminum Co. of America, Pittsburgh.)

PRESS FORMING

The press forming of metal sheet of all compositions and gages in a prodigious array of designs characterizes the rapidly expanding pressed-metal industry. The range of possibilities open to the designer who contemplates using pressed-metal parts can be observed in the transportation, home appliance, and furniture industries. The equipment used by the transportation industries, as exemplified by aircraft, motorcars and trucks, trolley coaches, buses, and streamlined trains, demonstrates the utility and economy of cold-forming metal in presses. The development of press equipment continues to meet the demands for broader applications and lower cost of pressed-metal parts of stampings.

Fundamentally the two principles involved in the production of pressed-metal parts are: (1) cold-working the material below its ultimate strength and (2) working it beyond its ultimate strength to the point where severance occurs. The former group includes bending, drawing, deep drawing, flanging, bulging, necking, curling, and impact extrusion. All the processes in the latter group involve some form of severing the sheet or strip stock. Shearing sheet metal in press operations takes such forms as blanking, slitting, parting, piercing, and perforating.

Metal stampings, then, are essentially the products resulting from cold-forming sheet metal in tension, bending, compression, or shear, or of their several combinations.[3] In every case the degree to which a given metal will flow plastically at room temperature is the determining factor in selecting the tooling. Plastic flow varies with the differing compositions of one alloy as it does with alloys of different metals. Plasticity can be gaged by noting both the ductility and the malleability of the metal under consideration. It is well to remember that cold-rolled sheet has been strain-hardened during its manufacture, and the degree to which it

[3] For detailed information on calculating the magnitude of these forces see "Computations for Sheet Metal Working Operations," E. W. Bliss Company, New York.

has subsequently been annealed determines its ductility. Selection of the correct temper for a piece to be cold-formed frequently spells the difference between success or failure.

The grain of the sheet is an important consideration in tooling for stampings. Grain is considered as being in the direction of rolling (Fig. 12-5). Good design stipulates that no bends should be made in the direction of the grain, or that, if this condition cannot be met, dead-soft material should be specified. Material layouts for blanking overcome grain problems by using an angular pattern. This device may result in

Fig. 12-19. Roof stamping operation on form press in background. Press unloading is automatic. (Courtesy of Chrysler Corp., Detroit.)

large amounts of scrap remaining from the original sheet or strip, but it has the virtue of placing grain diagonally where its effect will be of least consequence. The use of generous radii on bends minimizes the adverse effect of grain. A case in point is the automobile body top stamping shown in Fig. 12-19.

Presses

The selection of the correct press for the production of a stamping offers a difficult problem, since there are a host of factors that require attention. It is a regrettable fact that in far too many instances press equipment is considered to belong in the ancient punch-press category rather than in the realm of modern machine tools. Pressed-metal parts are expected to fit as they come from the dies without any rework or restriking. These requirements can be and are being met by the proper combination of correct press equipment, press controls, die design and construction, and material selection.

Mechanical Presses. Presses are rated according to the pressure, in tons, that they are capable of exerting. The choice of a press becomes a matter of selecting one that has sufficient capacity to deliver the indicated pressure necessary for the contemplated operation. Consideration of

Fig. 12-20. Close-up of die stations for producing trim rings on a transfer press. (Courtesy of Verson All Steel Press Co., Chicago.)

equipment cost, plus the fact that mechanical presses operate on a faster cycle than hydraulic presses, largely explains this preference. Mechanical presses cover a wide range of design as to both physical form and mechanical details. In addition to transfer types, presses are available with single-stroke operation as well as fully automatic cycling.

Hydraulic Presses. Presses of the hydraulic type are usually built in capacities above 50 tons; the maximum size is being extended as requirements dictate.

Among the unique operating features of the hydraulic press are control over ram speed as well as pressures. These can be varied within the range of press capacity, as can the length of the stroke. The speed of the ram, whether high or low, is constant throughout the drawing stroke, an important consideration in deep drawing, since it permits the material being worked to respond to the operating pressure. Hydraulic-press design affords maximum protection against die breakage in cases of excessive stock thickness because ram pressures cannot exceed the maximum for the press. Inching the ram and the comparatively slow speed of entrance into the work are also characteristic of the hydraulic press.

Fig. 12-21. Automated forming line for wheel rims. (Courtesy of The McKay Co., Youngstown, Ohio.)

Transfer-type Presses. Fully automatic press operation combined with inter-die transfer in one machine is a current solution for automation. Such presses have one large, or master, slide on which the individual die station slides are mounted, with the result that all dies operate simultaneously. Each individual slide is arranged for separate adjustment, so that extreme flexibility in tooling is afforded (Fig. 12-20). In addition, this individual slide design permits the removal of any die or die set for sharpening or repair without interference with any of the other die stations.

These presses are equipped with automatic stock feed—roll feeds for coiled stock and stack feeds for prestamped blanks. The feed delivers the stock to the first die station, where the first operation of that sequence is performed. Following this, the partially formed part is mechanically transferred to station two for the second operation. This routine continues until the part has passed through all the required operations.

The number of stations is dependent upon the design of the stamping. If all stations are not required for a given piece, any in excess are left open so far as dies are concerned; however, the mechanical transfer continues to operate and move the pieces forward.

Automated Cold Forming. While the thinking on automation has been largely in the machine shop and machining operations, newer developments are finding this principle applied to cold shaping. There are many examples of automation, one of the most interesting being that of forming rims for all types of truck, automobile, and farm implement wheels. This is accomplished on the rim rolling line shown in Fig. 12-21. The equipment is noteworthy in that its design permits straight-line production for the first time in the industry. This is achieved by unique designs, including such features as lower roll shaft retraction. Indexing and transfer of rims is done by walking-beam transfer conveyors built into each unit and synchronized with the rolling cycle by cam-type limit switches.

While this equipment is quite complex, it is just another development in the area of automation which means that better products are being produced at lowered cost. This of course is the objective of every manufacturing program.

Dies

Dies are the tools of power presses. Essentially, a die is composed of an upper, or male, component known as the punch, which mates with the lower, or female, component called the die. This arrangement means that the punch moves and the die is stationary; in actual practice this order is sometimes reversed.

The die parts just described are mounted in a die set prior to installation in the press. Die sets can be secured from manufacturers of such equipment, or as is frequently done, the dies are constructed as a part of the die set. In either case a die set consists of a shank, a punch plate, and a punch holder, comprising the upper part, and a lower part made up of a die shoe equipped with clamping flanges and a die plate in which the die is mounted. To maintain alignment between the dies there are guideposts or leader pins fastened in the die shoe that have sliding contact through suitable bushings located in the punch holder. This is of importance, since it is essential to such operations as blanking and shearing in all its variations that the punch and die register correctly.

Blanking dies require a guide strip for the stock, stripper mechanisms, and stock stops to be built into the die set. The arrangement of these auxiliaries varies considerably. Blanking dies are made in many variations and combinations because, where design permits, the blanking operation is combined with such other features as piercing, edging, forming, and/or drawing.

A combination die is one in which more than one operation is performed. Careful evaluation is required in order to determine whether a combination die or a progressive die is indicated for a given job. In a progressive die one operation follows another at different stations in the die, whereas in a combination die the various operations follow each other while the part being worked remains in the same position in the die. A further solution is to use two individual dies in the same press, with each press stroke operating both dies.

Diemaking. Diemaking exemplifies craftsmanship of the highest caliber. There has been an evolution occurring in this craft through the introduction of high-precision machine tool equipment such as jig borers, duplicators, and novel grinding equipment. However, the skill of the diemaker has not become obsolete; his ability continues in demand and is accorded the universal respect it deserves.

The selection of die materials is not an easy matter, since both cost and production demands must be considered. Die steels are broadly considered as either water-hardening, oil-hardening, or, in a few cases, air-hardening. Other materials such as cemented carbides are gaining recognition because of their high production potential.

In order to reduce die costs, it is well to consider the possibility of composite dies. These are built up from standard tool-steel shapes to conform to the desired die contour. The tool-steel shapes are resistance-welded to low-carbon-steel backing plates which either replace or complement the die set. Machining is easier, since the soft steel offers no difficulty after the die has been heat-treated. Another similar device is that of contouring the die parts from mild steel and then surfacing them with hard facing or tool steel by means of electric arc welding.

Forming dies for large work are cast to shape from close-grained alloy cast iron; there remains only the necessity of putting a finish on the die. The forming dies for automobile body parts are primarily of this type. Despite the apparent saving of cast-iron dies, the tooling cost is such that a 200,000-model year is considered necessary to amortize die costs.

Diemakers are confronted with the problem of spring-back of the work-piece. Allowance for this behavior is built into the die, yet much trial-and-error experimentation is required in almost every die in order to arrive at the proper die compensation.

Lubrication of the die is commonly practiced with drawing operations. The lubricant used for this purpose varies with the material and the severity of the drawing operation. Mineral oil and lard oil (and its mixtures) have much to recommend them. Solutions of graphite in kerosene seem in greatest favor where heavy draws are made. In addition to these, soluble oils of the machine-shop coolant type are perhaps the widest used of all lubricants for drawing. The method of applying the lubricants varies from dipping the workpiece to automatic spraying.

Forming with Explosives

A new dimension has been added in the area of cold forming through the use of explosives or ballistics. This is especially true in connection with high-strength and heat-treated materials. The development is still in its infancy and its behavior is not completely understood. The pressure or force needed for the forming operation is supplied by an explosive charge usually consisting of prima cord or other TNT-type explosive. These charges must be of a correct size and properly placed with respect to the desired end-point configuration. Many arrangements have been developed in using this technique. Frequently, however, water is the medium for transmitting the shock and pressure waves. Present thinking is that the shock wave causes metal to reach a point of momentary plasticity when it will deform against the face of the retaining die. A serious problem here is the removal of air between the rapidly moving metal and the die face.

A modification of this method is known as explosive sizing, which is also receiving deserved attention. Here, parts are made undersize and with loose tolerances. These then can be sized accurately to very close tolerance by explosive pressure within a heavy die. Components that cannot be drawn, pressed, hydroformed, or fabricated in any other manner have been processed by this method. Among such materials are 17-7 PH stainless, 4330, and 4340 steels in various degrees of heat treatment. Difficult forming, such as a joggle around the circumference of a tank, is readily accomplished.

Metallurgical examination indicates that there is no detrimental effect on the material after forming. Its hardness remains essentially constant before and after the explosion. On the other hand, the weld seam on an external surface will be planished flat with the parent metal, thereby giving a supersmooth surface for supersonic speeds. The only change noted in the weld is a slight amount of recrystallization, which is most beneficial since it eliminates the directionality of the grains.

Further possibilities envisioned for future development would include coating steel with ceramics and punching burrless holes more cheaply and rapidly than can be done by drilling. Dissimilar metals could be joined by this method, and finished parts could actually be made from scrap metal or filings and shavings.

SURVEY QUESTIONS

12-1. What is the real significance of cold shaping?

12-2. Does cold working improve the mechanical properties of steel?

12-3. Cold-rolled steel exhibits an excellent surface; has this been preceded by hot rolling?

12-4. What is the function of pickling?

12-5. How are corrugated sheets produced?

12-6. Is steel shafting cold rolled, cold drawn, or both?

12-7. Is the size or gage or shape of a material developed by cold rolling?

12-8. Wherein do cold extruded parts offer a saving in manufacturing costs?

12-9. Why are gear teeth shot peened?

12-10. What industry uses shot peening as a metal forming method?

12-11. By what method are automobile body panels produced?

12-12. Give two examples of end products produced on drawbenches.

12-13. What type of components are made on a Yoder mill?

12-14. What advantage is claimed for "pinch rolls"?

12-15. Do press brakes and Yoder mills produce the same end products?

12-16. How are Kirksite dies made?

12-17. Why is stretch forming used for airframes and not for automobile body components?

12-18. Is metal spinning always performed at room temperature?

12-19. How can a spinning lathe be distinguished from an engine lathe?

12-20. Would the same products be produced by spinning as are produced on the hydrospin machine?

12-21. The nose cone on our first satellite was produced by Floturning. Could this have been made by metal spinning?

12-22. Give an economic advantage for the use of the Guerin Process of metal forming.

12-23. Mention an end product produced by hydroforming.

12-24. Could the above component have been produced by hydrospinning?

12-25. For what end products is tin plate used?

12-26. Can aluminum be substituted for tin plate without major revisions?

12-27. What is a major product of the impact extrusion?

12-28. Are ferrous metals shaped by impact extrusion?

12-29. For what class of work are mechanical presses used?

12-30. Mention at least three end products that should be made on a transfer press.

12-31. Are automobile wheels cold or hot formed?

12-32. Of what materials are blanking dies generally made?

12-33. List at least five household appliances that are wholly or partially made from cold-formed components.

12-34. Are strain-hardened A1 alloys capable of being cold shaped?

12-35. Suggest a material and a manufacturing method for producing a chip pan for an engine lathe.

Chapter 13

HOT SHAPING

Hot shaping is employed for forming all engineering metals with the exception of those that are produced as castings. Steel and wrought iron are best known for their capacity to be hot-worked; however, as was mentioned in Chap. 3, the nonferrous metals are gaining popularity because of their hot-forming properties. There is an interesting departure from the generally held concept of hot working in the case of the light alloys: their temperature range for hot shaping is such that they do not change color.

Hammering, either manual or mechanical, is one of the principal hot-shaping methods, although custom terms its end product a forging. When pressure instead of repeated blows is applied to a heated piece, the resulting product is termed a pressing or a press forging, depending upon the equipment used. The greatest tonnage of hot-shaped products, however, is produced in rolling mills, where the material is passed successively through roller dies. The nonferrous alloys can be hot-shaped into moldings, tubing, and shapes by forcing them through a die under heavy pressures in a method known as extrusion; the end products are termed extrusions. There is a modification of extrusion whereby steel is extruded in dies; this will be described in detail later in this chapter. Spinning, piercing, and fluing are other methods of hot-shaping metal. The change in structure of steel as a result of hot working is illustrated in Figs. 13-1 and 13-2.

HOT ROLLING

Production requirements for huge tonnages of bars, shapes, plates, and sheets are met by hot rolling. The limitations on hot rolling are section contour and cross-sectional area. Steel accounts for the bulk of the annual output of the rolling mill, although the light metals as well as the copper-base alloys are also produced in rolled form.

Ingots. Rolling starts with an ingot. Ingots are produced from furnace metal by teeming into metal molds. Large ingot molds are top-poured individually. When smaller ingots are desired, the molds are arranged for bottom pouring, several molds being connected by refractory runners to a master mold. The ladle, which is of the bottom-pour type, is brought over the master mold and the ladle stopper is then raised, permitting the steel to flow into the master mold, whence it enters the ingot molds.

Fig. 13-1. As-cast condition, 0.24C steel. ×100 etched with a combination of Picral and Nital. (Courtesy of Battelle Memorial Institute, Columbus, Ohio.)

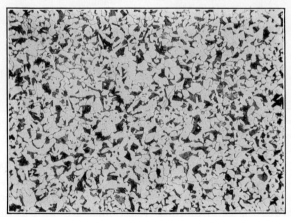

Fig. 13-2. Hot-worked condition, 0.24C steel. ×100 etched with a combination of Picral and Nital. (Courtesy of Battelle Memorial Institute, Columbus, Ohio.)

Ingots are of various shapes and sizes, depending upon the products for which they are intended. Square or rectangular ingot shapes predominate, but fluted or piecrust as well as flattened cross sections are also produced. The design of an ingot is critical, since the amount of shrinkage cavitation must be controlled for highest yield of sound steel. The shrinkage-affected portion is cropped from the upper part of the ingot prior to rolling in order to avoid seams and unsound areas in the rolled product.

Ingots are permitted to solidify in the molds. Solidification is accompanied by shrinkage and contraction, which tend to free the ingot from the mold. The ingot is not permitted to cool unduly; such practice would be wasteful in view of the fact that high rolling temperatures are necessary. The ingot is immediately placed in a soaking pit furnace, where it is stored at rolling temperature, approximately 2300°F, until needed. In cases where the ingots have been permitted to cool completely they are charged into reheating furnaces prior to rolling.

Fig. 13-3. Two-high reversing slabbing and blooming mill. Note heated ingot about to enter rolls. (Courtesy of Mesta Machine Co., Pittsburgh.)

Blooming Mill. A blooming mill is the first mill used in reducing an ingot in the production sequence leading to the finished product. Blooming mills receive the heated ingot and reduce it in size and shape by passing it through a stand of rolls. These mills are built in three designs —reversing, continuous, and three-high types. The first two are of two-high design, *i.e.*, there are two rolls, one above the other. Both rolls may be power-driven. The rolls are located in massive roll housings and the drive is arranged on the outside of one housing.

Continuous mills make one reduction in each roll stand. The reduction in any rolling operation is known as a pass. Since several passes are required, a continuous mill is composed of several roll stands arranged in tandem so that the ingot passes along a continuous path. Mills are equipped with manipulators—mechanical devices for turning the ingot —in order that the various faces will be in the rolls and a more uniform structure will be developed in the bloom.

Reversing mills operate so that the direction of rotation of the rolls can be reversed. In operation the ingot passes through the rolls, which are then closed; the amount of the next desired reduction, known as draft, and the direction of ingot travel as well as roll rotation is reversed. The ingot is thus subjected to repeated passes in a single roll stand. A reversing mill with the ingot entering the rolls is shown in Fig. 13-3. The rollers on the table in the immediate foreground are also reversible and govern the direction of travel of the ingot.

The three-high mill employs an additional roll located in line and above the two lower ones. This mill does not reverse; instead travel direction of the ingot is reversed. After going through the lower pass, the ingot lands on a lifting table which raises the ingot to the next pass between the intermediate roll and the top roll. Upon emerging from that pass, the ingot is taken by the lifting table on the opposite side of the roll stand and lowered to the level of the first pass.

Rolling Sequence. The function of the blooming mill is that of reducing an ingot to a bloom, which is the first intermediate product in the rolling sequence. Blooms are rolled to various shapes and sizes, depending upon their intended end use. The majority are square or rectangular in cross section,

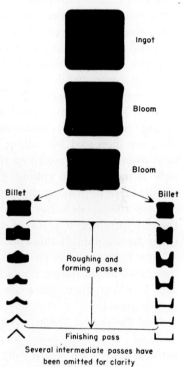

Fig. 13-4. Rolling sequence from ingot through structural shape. (Courtesy of American Iron and Steel Institute, New York.)

although some circular blooms are rolled for such items as projectiles, wheels, and circular shapes for tubing. Blooms are most frequently rolled into billets, which, in their turn, are semi-finished products that are further rolled into bars and small structural shapes. Large structurals are rolled directly from blooms. The flow sheet in Fig. 13-4 shows the various phases of the rolling sequence as applied to structurals.

Ingots destined for flat products such as plate, sheet, and strip are rolled into slabs. Slabs are much wider than they are thick. They are 16 sq in. or more in cross section and have a minimum thickness of 1½ in.

Rolls. The design and manufacture of rolls constitute a critical aspect of the production of rolled steel. Roll designers arrive at the finish pass for a given section by different steps and use differing amounts of draft in various passes. The objective sought is to employ as few passes as possible from billet to end product.

Rolls are machined from castings for the most part, although there are some roll forgings used for special categories. Castings require much less machining, since grooves can be cast, as can the wobbler sections. Rolls are plain cast iron, alloy cast iron, plain carbon steel, and alloy steel. The cast-iron rolls are chill-cast where hard surfaces are necessary, as on the finishing passes, while sand-cast rolls are more popular for the rougher and intermediate passes.

Plate Rolling. Two broad classifications of mills are used for plate rolling. In the sheared-plate mill, both the width and the length of the plate are increased by rolling, whereas in a universal mill, side rolls are used to control the width of the plate as it is rolled and therefore length only is increased by rolling. Cross rolling is used in sheared-plate mills as a means of improving the structure on the rolled plate.

Plate rolling demands rigidity in the rolls to avoid deflection and thereby produce a plate of constant gage across its entire width. In order to accomplish this end, four-high mills are used for rolling plate. A four-high mill has two smooth rolls for the actual work of rolling; these rolls are in rolling contact with a second roll, known as the backing roll. In effect, then, there are two rolls above and two below the plate as it is rolled.

Clad Plates and Sheets. As a means of combating surface corrosion, in some of the process industries a clad plate which has a corrosion-resistant surface is used for fabricating tanks and similar equipment. Clad plates are rolled by placing the clad material—for example, nickel, inconel, or stainless steel—on a carbon steel plate; then another plate is placed on the clad material, with parting compound between the latter two. This bundle is welded around its edges and heated to correct temperature prior to rolling to gage. After rolling, the plates are sheared around the edge to remove the welded portion and are separated; because of the parting compound, the clad material will have become welded only on one side.

Aluminum clad sheets are produced by a rolling-welding combination. The core alloy is stacked between two corrosion-resistant alloy slabs. The stack is furnace-heated to welding temperature and then rolled to gage. All three components are machined prior to stacking in order to ensure correct thicknesses in the end product.

Copper-base Alloys. In copper-base alloys, cakes—similar to ingots in their function—supply the basic metal in the rolling sequence. Most of the copper-base alloys have satisfactory hot-rolling characteristics; the exceptions are those with a pronounced lead content. Rods, bars, sheets, and shapes are produced by hot rolling. The mill equipment used for copper-base alloys is similar to that for steel. Rolls are used cold, as in rolling aluminum alloys, and in some instances oil is used to prevent scaling the product being rolled. Rolling temperatures for copper-base alloys fall in the range from 1300 to 1650°F.

Hot-rolling Light Alloys

Aluminum Alloys. Aluminum-alloy ingots are chill-cast by top pouring in water-cooled molds. The shell formed by rapid cooling is withdrawn from the mold at a uniform rate and further cooling is achieved by direct application of water. Ingots are sawed off to the desired length as the process proceeds continuously. Rapid cooling causes the ingot to contract in the mold so that it can be lowered. The objective of this system is to produce a sound ingot free from the piping effects.

Aluminum alloys are hot-rolled on equipment similar to that employed for steel. There are differences in rolling techniques; one is that the light metals require a lubricant. Soluble oil emulsion is used, which acts both as a lubricant and as a coolant on the rolls.

Magnesium Alloys. The slabs used for producing magnesium sheet and plate are extruded from cast ingots of circular contour. Heavy reduction is possible in hot rolling, with the result that sheet has but few cold finishing passes.

Frequently the rolls are maintained at a temperature range of 400 to 600°F during rolling. New technical developments have solved the problem of rolling magnesium alloys in light gages and commercial sizes.

Seamless Tubing

Seamless steel tubing is produced by a method akin to rolling in that two rolls are used at the start of the piercing process. These rolls are shaped like two truncated cones joined at their base. They are located directly above and at an angle to each other with a center spacing somewhat smaller than the billet diameter. The rolls revolve in the *same* direction. As a result the billet is alternately bulged and compressed; this causes cracking along its axis. Simultaneously with this action, the billet is forced over a pointed mandrel which serves both as a guide and as a means of producing a hole of nearly uniform diameter. The pierced billet then passes through further processing rolls where outside diameter is controlled and the center enlarged by an eccentrically operating bar.

FORGING

Forging methods are divided between hammer, press, and rolled types. The basic principle in forging is that of shaping metal by impact or pressure either on anvils, in open dies, or in closed dies. The choice of method is governed by size, design considerations, and production requirements. Forgings are produced at elevated temperatures. Forgings start from a previously rolled billet or bar in the majority of cases. Large forgings are made directly from the ingot. Production forging is based entirely on the use of rolled stock. Forgings show a fiberlike structure and flow lines that result in directional properties in the finished forging.

There are alloys in each group of the wrought engineering metals that can be forged. Not all the alloys in the nonferrous groups forge satisfactorily. Heating methods require consideration from the viewpoint of the scaling and, for some steels, of surface decarburization. Controlled furnace heating with reducing atmospheres is required when heating alloy steels for forging.

Hammered Forgings

When individual forgings are required, hammering is the indicated method of production. Such forgings are termed blacksmith, or hand, forgings when they are hammered out manually on an anvil. Hammered forgings are also termed flat die, open die, or miscellaneous forgings.

Blacksmith forgings are limited to small parts, principally repair work. Hammered forgings are most commonly produced with steam hammers similar to the one in Fig. 13-5. A typical forging crew consists of the blacksmith, hammer driver, and helper, or heater.

Steam Hammers. The two general types of steam hammers are known as the single-frame and the double-frame; they are also designed to operate on compressed air in some instances. Figure 13-5 shows a single-frame hammer that is steam-operated. Most single-frame hammers are built with the anvil separated from the frame; in a variation known as the self-contained hammer the anvil is integral with the frame. The latter type is preferred for contoured die forgings because of better die alignment.

Large hammered forgings are produced in double-frame hammers, which are of more massive construction than the single-frame type; the designs of the two, except for the frame, are similar. The double-frame hammer is of greatest importance in the production of heavy forgings. One special use for this hammer is that of reducing forging ingots into billets. This operation is termed cogging, and double-frame hammers are frequently designated as cogging hammers.

Impact Die Forgings. Impact die forgings are also known as drop forgings. Both titles are descriptive: the first one indicates that the forging

is made in a die by impact; the second refers to the fact that drop
hammers are used for supplying the impact. Forgings of this type are
produced in a tremendous variety of shapes and sizes from a diversified
assortment of metals. Steel drop forgings are in the majority and are well
known. Nonferrous die forgings are found in engineering construction.

Drop forgings are limited in both shape and size. Shape must permit
their removal from the dies without undue sticking. Steel drop forgings

Fig. 13-5. A typical steam-hammer forging operation. (Courtesy of Chambersburg Engineering Co., Chambersburg, Pa.

tend to stick in the die, since they contract on cooling. Another cause
for sticking is that the metal of the forging, being under plastic flow, will
intermingle with the die surface, which, even though it is polished,
remains sufficiently rough to offer anchor points for the forging metal.
Oil and mixtures of graphite are sparingly sprayed or swabbed into the
dies to overcome this difficulty.

The designer of die forgings must take into consideration the draft
necessary for removal from the die. Draft is used on both external and
internal surfaces. The latter is the larger because the internal surface
when shrinking tends to lock in the die, while external surfaces behave
in the opposite manner. Circular or oval cross sections are ideal, since

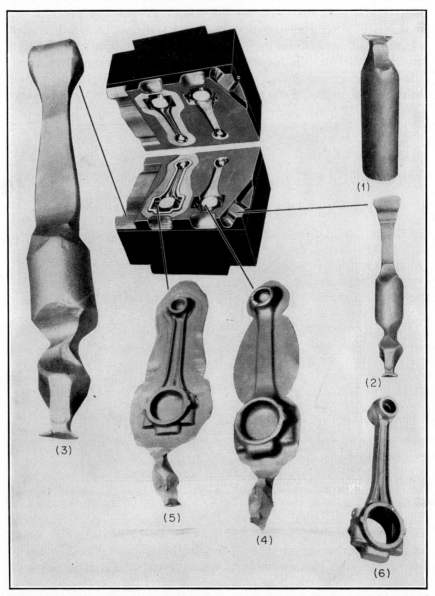

Fig. 13-6. Forging sequence and forging die for connecting rod: (1) Bar stock heated and tong drawn, (2) breakdown, (3) Fullering and edging, (4) blocking, (5) finishing for trim, (6) finished and trimmed connecting rod. (Courtesy of Drop Forge Assn., Cleveland.)

they are free of the draft requirement. Further design considerations include location of parting line, flash trim line, directional grain flow, corner radii, and die wear.

Forging Sequence. A typical sequence for a drop forging is exemplified by the connecting rod in Fig. 13-6 where the forging stock is a round bar. All the necessary forging operations are performed in one die, which is of a size permitting the necessary impressions for the various steps in the sequence. The flash is trimmed in a separate die mounted in a trimming press. The forging die for the connecting rod is also shown in Fig. 13-6, with both halves of the die on view.

Flash. Note that in 4 and 5 of Fig. 13-6 there is excess metal; this is termed flash from the fact that the extra metal not needed for the forging "flashes" out of the die cavity. Flash originates from the variance in the original stock and also from the shape of the stock being such that it will not fill the die at all points unless excess develops at the lower volume die cavities. The flash is removed from the forging in a trimming press in a separate operation.

Drop Hammers. Impact die forgings are generally produced in drop hammers equipped with closed impression dies. There are several types of drop hammers, including the board drop, the steam drop, and the gravity drop. The board drop hammer (Fig. 13-7) is designed for raising the upper die

Fig. 13-7. 2,000-lb motor-driven board drop hammer. (Courtesy of Erie Foundry Co., Erie, Pa.)

by means of boards attached to the die block. At the top of the frame, rollers are located on each side of the boards; the boards are raised by bringing the rollers, which are opposite in rotation, into contact with them. When the ram has reached its upper travel position, cams clamp the boards and hold them. The impact blow is delivered by releasing the holding cams; this permits the ram assembly to drop and strike the lower die, which is positioned on the anvil.

Press Forgings

The basic difference between press forging and hammer forging is that in the former, one stroke of the press is generally sufficient, whereas several blows are essential with hammer forgings. Press forging is employed for every type of forging operation, from open to closed die. Large forging ingots are worked in a forging press (Fig. 13-8). Manipulation of this 40T ingot is by an endless chain at each end which connects with an overhead crane; by these means the ingot can be rotated or translated as desired. The endless chain is driven by an air motor incorporated with the lifting hook sheave.

Fig. 13-8. A forging press engaged in forging a pie-crust-shaped ingot into a tail shaft for a ship. (Courtesy of Isaacson Iron Works, Seattle, Wash.)

Tail-shaft forgings for ships are produced in forging presses. In fact symmetrical forgings of circular or tapering cross section and of substantial length are typical forging press products. Forging presses for such work are of large capacity and operate on the hydraulic principle. There are also mechanical presses for the manufacture of press forgings.

Closed Die Press Forgings. Closed die forgings from nonferrous metals and alloys are generally made in a forging press. These materials exhibit the high degree of plastic flow which is necessary to filling die cavities in one stroke of the press. A major advantage of press forging is that much less draft is required in the dies—2 or 3°—in contrast to drop forgings, which need more than double that amount. This is important, since less machining will be necessary on vertical faces and, in some designs, no finish will be required because of the fact that the forged face is almost perpendicular to the trim line.

The answer to the question of the preferred method as between hammering and pressing die forgings can be reached through a study of material selection plus available equipment and forging volume. A successful press forging of a railroad car wheel is shown in Fig. 13-9. Despite this achievement in press forging, however, there is a competing method of roll forging such car wheels from circular blanks.

Aluminum No-draft Forgings. A development of significance in the production of forgings is in the area of draft elimination; as a result, forgings are produced with a reduced fillet and thinner webs. These

Fig. 13-9. Press-forging disk from ingot as first operation in forging steel car wheel. (Courtesy of Standard Steel Works, Burnham, Pa.)

forgings made their appearance in the airframe industry but have since moved into commercial application generally. Substantial savings in their use arises from the elimination of machine work, since faces are vertical and not tapered as in the standard-type forging. No-draft forgings are not necessarily precision forgings; on the contrary, the tolerances are the ones applied to forgings. Proper forging equipment and dies are necessary to produce no-draft forgings successfully.

Massive Forging Presses. A development program that will ultimately result in the production of forging presses of capacities reaching to 75,000 tons is now under way. The utility of extremely large presses was first demonstrated in the construction of German aircraft. Following World War II, several large presses were discovered in the manufacturing industries in Germany. The largest of these, a 33,000-ton forging press, built in 1943, ultimately went to Russia. Two 16,500-ton presses of German manufacture were captured by our forces and have been erected in this country. The heavy-press program has continued to develop, with two companies building extremely huge equipment as well as some of lesser sizes. The truly gigantic presses are of 50,000 tons

Fig. 13-10. Gigantic 50,000T press showing a forged spar in foreground. (Courtesy of Wyman-Gordon Co., Worcester, Mass.)

(Fig. 13-10). There are two of these, as well as one of 35,000 tons. The former press has produced forgings 12 ft in length for wing spars on supersonic jet fighters. These presses are so huge that the foundation excavations descend 100 ft to bedrock. It is believed that these are the deepest excavations ever made for machine tool installations in this country. The 50,000-ton press is the largest industrial machine man has ever made. It is equal in height to a ten-story building and is capable of exerting a pressure of 106 million lb; in turn, the machine itself weighs 10,750 tons.

The initial forgings from this press were aluminum landing gear support ribs, 105 in. long by 28 in. wide, more than 4 in. at the thickest point and only ¼ in. at the thinnest. The individual components of this press are among the largest steel parts ever produced. By way of example, each of the six columns is made up of forged steel sections more than 108 ft in length; each one weighs 330 tons. Moving parts of the press weigh 6,450 tons. It has a 6-ft stroke and the die-holding platens measure 32 ft in length by 12 ft in width. The platens will accommodate dies weighing as much as 50 tons the pair. Something of the economy to be gained by large forging can be realized when in one jet fighter there are four forged spars that replace 272 parts and 3,200 rivets.

The presses are hydraulically operated, which means that the power station is an impressive engineering project in itself. Seven triplex pumps, largest ever built, force water into eleven 38-ft steel bottles. Air is forced in from the opposite end to secure the pressure. During press operation, water speeds through the piping at 50 mph and at tremendous pressures.

Roll Forging

Circular-shaped products such as gear blanks, brake drums, and various wheel types can be roll forged in a mill between vertical dies. The forging blank is pierced at its geometrical center for mounting on the die arbor. The mating die closes against the blank with the pressure of a forging press. Following the closing operation, both dies revolve, causing upsetting and plastic flow sufficient to fill the die cavity.

Roll-forging equipment takes care of a variety of jobs that would otherwise be cumbersome or difficult. Interesting products of roll forging are tapered parts such as shafts, brake levers, and rifle barrels. The rolls are machined with an interrupted section which is used as the starting point for the stock to be rolled. Tapered grooves in the rolls are of different depths where the reduction is such as to require a series of passes.

The five forging operations for producing a connecting rod can be seen in Fig. 13-11. The necessary upsetting, gathering, and bending are roll-forged. The final two operations are performed in a forging press. Tooling the connecting rod production in this manner speeds output and lowers die and equipment costs. Roll forging frequently serves for the preliminary operations of both impact and press die forgings.

Upset Forging. Forging machines are designed to operate horizontally with dies opening vertically—the reverse of forging presses. The products of forging machines are known as upset forgings from the fact that bar stock is gripped in dies and then gathered, or upset, where an enlarged volume of metal is needed in the forging. The range of products that can be produced on forging machines is extremely wide. Relatively simple shapes such as ball races are produced in a two-stage die. More complicated shapes such as motorcar hubs and the like are also produced by the machine forging method.

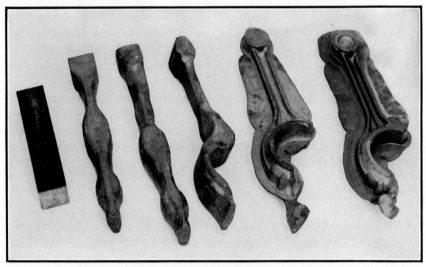

Fig. 13-11. Open-end connecting-rod forging. Operations: (1) first pass roll, (2) second pass roll, (3) bender, (4) blocker, (5) finish. (Courtesy of The National Machinery Co., Tiffin, Ohio.)

Forging machines are powered by electric motors through V-belt drives to inertia members that connect through air clutches to the crankshafts. The grip dies part vertically for insertion of the forging stock. Cams operate the punch, after the grip dies have closed. The die operation can be followed in Fig. 13-12, where a four-station die produces a clutch hub. The first operation is upsetting, wherein the bar stock is gathered for the requisite diameter. Subsequent stages continue the forging to finish size. The stock must be moved from each stage to the next upon completion of each operation. It is interesting to note that the hole is punched in a manner that forces the stock into the die cavity. As a result there is no loss of material from hole forming and there is no flash to be discarded. These are obvious advantages

Fig. 13-12. Dies and tools for forging a small clutch hub off the end of the bar. (Courtesy of The Ajax Manufacturing Co., Cleveland.)

that weigh heavily in favor of machine forging as compared to other forging methods.

Precision Forging

The development of jet engines has posed the problem of fabricating component parts of a high degree of accuracy. One of the methods that is contributing to progress in this direction is that of precision forging of turbine buckets (Fig. 13-13). The alloys used in this application are those resistant to high temperatures, *i.e.*, they possess major percentages of both chromium and nickel. The precision forging of a turbine bucket starts with an upsetting operation performed on a 35 kva resistance upsetter. A heading operation is necessary to establish grain flow in the root area in order to preclude any open-end grain fibers. Surface conditions are given close attention because the precision contours demand superior finish.

Extrusion Forging. Extrusion forging differs from conventional closed die forging; the dies are designed in a manner that permits the heated stock to flow only into the designed shape of the forging. The die set consists of a punch and die similar to those in Fig. 13-14. This die set more nearly resembles the design associated with cold forming metal sheet than it does impact forging dies. The stock used for an extrusion forging must be cut to close tolerances, since there is no flash on the finished forging nor is any metal allowed for a tong hold.

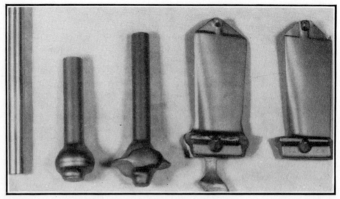

Fig. 13-13. Precision-forged turbine bucket for installation in a jet engine. Production sequence shown left to right: (1) Cut material, (2) upset, (3) headed, (4) blocked, (5) finished forged in board drop hammer. (Courtesy of The Steel Improvement and Forge Co., Cleveland.)

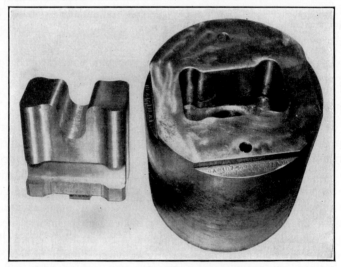

Fig. 13-14. Spindle extrusion die. (Courtesy of Ford Motor Co., Detroit.)

EXTRUSION

Nonferrous metals and alloys are fashioned into a multitude of shapes, bars, tubular products, and moldings by hot extrusion. Steel is now being extruded by a process developed in France in which glass fiber is used as a lubricant on the hot steel. This extrusion method is also being used in the United States. Examples of typical steel extrusions produced here are shown in Fig. 13-15. The end products of the hot extrusion process are generically termed extrusions. A familiar illustration of the extrusion process is the removal of tooth paste from its tube. In this example the tooth paste is the material to be extruded and the orifice of the tube acts as the extrusion die.

Extrusions are formed in horizontal extrusion presses of imposing operating capacities (Fig. 13-16). Presses are built in different capacities and on two operating principles. One design places the die ahead of the extrusion ingot; in the other design the die is carried in the piston, where

Fig. 13-15. Steel extrusions, showing stainless types in the two lower rows and alloy and carbon steels in the upper row.

it causes the extruded metal to flow through the hollow piston rod. The head-end die extrusion press is the more common type.

The major production of extrusions is in the field of aluminum alloys, but magnesium, lead, tin, and copper-base alloys are also frequently specified for extrusions. Items like pin tumbler lock parts are sometimes produced as copper-base extrusions, while some aircraft moldings are magnesium-alloy extrusions. Extrusions are produced in lengths that are limited only by customer requirements, although manufacturers' specification govern stock lengths, which in turn vary with the type of extrusion.

An aluminum-alloy extrusion starts with an ingot that has been cast to cylindrical shape in a metal mold. The ingot is permitted to cool prior to further processing. A continuous-type reheating furnace is auxiliary equipment in the extrusion shop. Heating the ingots is performed with care, since the final temperature is critical. Once the ingot has reached extrusion temperature—which, for these alloys, ranges between 800 and 900°F—it is placed in the extrusion press. Ingot diameter fits the extrusion cylinder bore.

The extrusion piston moves against the rear of the ingot, forcing the latter through the die located at the front, or opposite, end of the

Fig. 13-16. A billet (center) is shown being forced by hydraulic ram into extrusion press cylinder. Billet has been heated to facilitate normal flow through the die. Formed extrusion will emerge from hydraulic press at far left. (Courtesy of Aluminum Co. of America, Pittsburgh.)

cylinder. Extrusion is a single-operation process in that the ingot behind the die is converted into the finished extrusion by passage through the die. The extrusion issuing from the die is cut to desired length, and extrusion continues until the ingot has been reduced to a small stub, which is then scrapped.

Extrusion offers the designer a product that is unobtainable by any other metal-forming method. In extrusions there are no hampering restrictions about metal placement, nor is there any requirement about taper or undercutting—the designer can dispose the metal with a view to greatest resistance to imposed stresses in end use.

Extrusion dies should be provided with smooth surfaces in order to avoid serious scratching of the extrusion. A positive method of identifying an extrusion is to note the die marks running longitudinally on its surfaces. When small, plain shapes are to be extruded, the die may have multiple openings, thus making several extrusions simultaneously.

Tubular products and hollow extrusions are produced from either bridge or porthole dies. Dies for hollow extrusions are of two-part construction with parting line normal to the extrusion axis. The die part facing on the ingot holds the extrusion arbor, which in turn controls the internal shape of the extrusion. This die half is further equipped with rather large openings through which the extruding metal passes. The several streams of metal emerging from this die half are turned in toward the die arbor by the outer die half, whence they pass through the die opening. A hollow extrusion die for aluminum alloys actually combines in its design a pressure welding operation with a double extrusion process.

FORGING DIES

The manufacture of forging dies, in common with other die work, demands the highest type of craftsmanship to ensure the accuracy demanded in the end product. Forging dies requires special skill, since they must be made to compensate for both forging contraction and die wear in service. It is customary to purchase die blocks in the hardened condition in order to avoid distortion, cracking, or spoilage of a die by heat-treatment after the die is finished. The die sinker has in addition to his other problems the difficult task of machining hardened steel.

The choice for forging die steels ranges from plain carbon, for short-run dies, through the alloy grades, and includes some high-speed steels for extrusion forgings. Air-hardening steels find favor where dies are large and of heavy sections. In other instances dies are built up with extremely hard inserts; yet this procedure requires care, for any tendency to loosen during operation will ruin the die.

The final die impression is the first one made in a die block. Upon its completion, it is "proved" by pouring lead or wax into it to form a casting that reproduces the die cavity. This lead cast, or proof, is carefully checked for dimensional accuracy and is submitted to the customer for his approval. The other impressions are sunk into the die block only after the final forging impression has been accepted. A single-impression forging die that is used on the finishing operation for an aluminum-alloy housing is shown in Fig. 13-17. This housing is forged in five operations, requiring three forging hammers.

Die Typing and Broaching. Another procedure for making dies is that of producing an extremely accurate master die of high hardness. The typing blanks are heated and forced into the master die so that they assume the shape of its cavity. The die set shown in Fig. 13-14 was produced by this method. Die typing offers a quick and economical method for producing duplicate die parts. The procedure of forcing or pressing a hardened piece into a previously roughed-out die block, cold, for the purpose of forming a die half is known as broaching. Obviously

Fig. 13-17. Single-impression finishing die for an aluminum-alloy housing forging. (Courtesy of Drop Forging Assn., Cleveland.)

there are shape limitations to be considered, even though die broaching offers a rapid method for producing duplicate die parts.

HOT FORMING

Hot forming is primarily associated with the shaping of steel plate, although magnesium alloys, mentioned previously, also behave well in this process. Since steel furnishes the bulk of the material for hot forming, this discussion is confined to that material. Hot forming is usually performed at a temperature above the lower critical temperature of the steel and the piece is permitted to cool normally from the temperature at which the work is completed. Forming at elevated temperatures permits greater deformation of the workpiece, since it has greater ductility owing to the increased plastic flow potential. The final one of six operations in hot-pressing a boiler dome appears in Fig. 13-18. The member shown is formed from a steel circle 78 in. in diameter by 1⅛ in. in thickness weighing approximately 1,500 lb.

One chief disadvantage of hot forming can be observed in Fig. 13-18, which shows the heavy formation of scale on the workpiece. Scaling reduces gage to some extent and also produces a roughened surface

Fig. 13-18. Final pressing of a locomotive boiler dome on a 1,000-ton four-post press. (Courtesy of Lukens Steel Co., Coatesville, Pa.)

requiring considerable cleaning before a pleasing and satisfactory appearance is achieved.

Hot Pressing. Hot pressing is used for large plates of heavy section or where a high degree of deformation is required without rupture. Primarily it is a production process, since die and equipment costs are of a magnitude that can only be absorbed by the production of a considerable number of units. Because the plate is worked at elevated temperatures, a material-handling problem of some importance arises. Figure 13-19 shows the setup for hot-pressing the end plate for a gondola car. This operation is so contrived that the finished pressing is dis-

Fig. 13-19. Hot press forming gondola car end. The car end has been formed and is ready for ejection onto conveyor table for cooling. (Courtesy of American Car and Foundry Co., New York.)

Fig. 13-20. Forming an extremely large dished head by hot spinning. (Courtesy of Lukens Steel Co., Coatesville, Pa.)

charged at the side of the press, an arrangement that conserves floor space.

Hot Spinning. Dished heads of various designs that are used in pressure vessels are produced by either pressing or spinning. Hot spinning has one primary advantage over pressing, since there are no restrictions on the dimensions of the die. Spun heads can be fashioned to any desired configuration on contour and also to diameters limited only by the capacity of the spinning machine. A remarkable example of hot spinning is the one in Fig. 13-20 which is working a clad plate into a head 20 ft $4\frac{7}{32}$ in. OD. The spinning technique is shown clearly by the roller

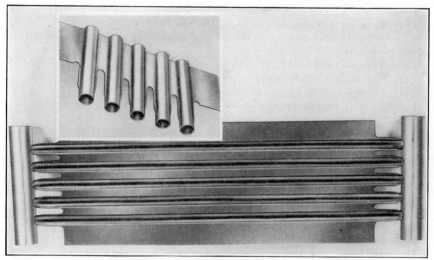

Fig. 13-21. Manifold designed from tube-in-strip; end preparation shown in insert. (Courtesy of Revere Copper and Brass, Inc., New York.)

at left, bearing against the revolving plate which started as a circle. Two plates were welded in order to obtain a steel circle of sufficient diameter. Hot spinning has been successful on plate thickness up to 6 in. There is some tendency to reduce gage at some areas in the spinning.

Tube-in-Strip. A unique development of considerable potential is that of metal strip equipped with integral longitudinal openings. These latter can be inflated to a wide variety of geometries. They are made by placing frangible inserts in the mold prior to pouring. Upon removal from the mold, the resultant ingot is rolled into sheet or strip. This product is being produced in copper, brass, and aluminum alloy. Tube-in-strip is an outstanding material for building heat exchangers, by way of example (Fig. 13-21).

SURVEY QUESTIONS

13-1. What is the physical state of metals that are being hot shaped—liquid, solid, or what?

13-2. Wrought iron can be hot-worked; is this also true of gray cast iron?

13-3. Would a magnesium alloy be red in color at the hot-forming temperature?

13-4. Wherein do forgings differ basically from castings?

13-5. What are the two main hot-forming methods for steel moldings?

13-6. Wherein do ingots differ from billets?

13-7. What is the end product of a blooming mill termed?

13-8. How is the term "draft" applied to steel rolling?

13-9. What do slabs and skelp have in common?

13-10. From what material are rolling mill rolls made?

13-11. What is meant by the term "roughing pass"?

13-12. Where can clad steel plates be used to advantage?

13-13. How are aluminum clad sheets made?

13-14. Wherein does the production of aluminum-alloy ingots differ from that of steel ingots?

13-15. Why are no flat die forgings used on automobile chassis?

13-16. Are steam hammers and drop hammers the same equipment?

13-17. Give an example of a copper-base impact die forging.

13-18. By what forging method are automotive connecting rods produced?

13-19. Are no-draft forgings of economic advantage?

13-20. What type forgings are produced on the massive forging presses?

13-21. Are similar end products produced by roll forging and hot rolling?

13-22. Describe one method for producing tapered rifle barrels.

13-23. Where are precision forgings used?

13-24. Are extrusions and extrusion forgings made on the same equipment?

13-25. What type of metal constitutes the greatest tonnage of extrusions?

13-26. Give an example of a steel extrusion.

13-27. Are forging dies made by casting?

13-28. Is die proving the same thing as die typing?

13-29. What light alloys are generally hot-formed?

13-30. Are components produced from steel sheet hot-formed?

13-31. Does hot forming improve mechanical properties of the material?

13-32. Is there any difference between a forging and a rolling ingot in external appearance?

13-33. Why are copper ingots, as well as other types, scalped?

13-34. What is a reversing mill?

13-35. Name a hot-pressed steel component.

13-36. Give some applications for hot spinning other than on boiler heads.

13-37. Is there any application for tube-in-sheet in current automobiles?

Chapter 14

HEAT-TREATING

The term heat-treatment includes a variety of processes applied to most of the engineering metals, both wrought and cast. Heat-treatment includes both heating and cooling operations—not heating alone. There are procedures that employ subnormal temperatures; solution heat-treated aluminum alloys are held at or near freezing in order to decelerate precipitation, and some steels are subjected to low temperatures during the stabilization treatment. From all this it is evident that treating metals thermally is a branch of metallurgy that has many ramifications and one that requires both knowledge and judgment.

The mechanical engineer, if he is to be held responsible for a design, should insist that his recommendations be followed exactly. There is no point in using a heat-treatable metal member unless that member is subjected to the particular heat-treatment which will develop the necessary properties. Neglect of this consideration arises all too frequently in manufacturing, with the result that costs are excessive or service life is impaired. When a metal has been chosen for a given component, the correct thermal treatment should be specified and a shop procedure established that will develop the required properties in that member.

The choice of an engineering material is frequently made from the narrow field of those known to the designer. He is generally opposed to specifying anything with which he is unfamiliar. As a result, high costs may attend the product, dooming it to obsolescence from its inception. The development of new alloys, coupled with an increasing knowledge of thermal treatment in all categories of metals and alloys, imposes the burden of continuing revision of designs and manufacturing methods on organizations or individuals dedicated to progress.

STEEL

Steel accounts for the greater part of work entering the heat-treat shop. Other metallic alloys that require thermal treatment will be discussed in a later section of this chapter. Steel is primarily an alloy of iron

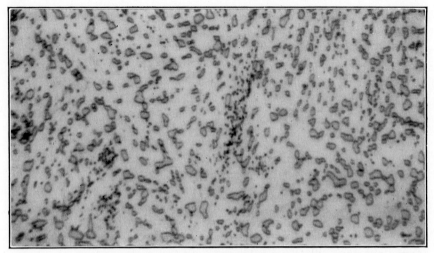

Fig. 14-1. 0.76 plain carbon steel. Spheroidized carbides, brine-quenched and tempered 12 hr at 1250°F. ×2,500. (Courtesy of United States Steel, Research Laboratory, Kearny, N.J.)

Fig. 14-2. 0.76 plain carbon steel. Coarse pearlite isothermally transformed, $3\frac{1}{2}$ hr at 1300°F. ×2,500. (Courtesy of United States Steel, Research Laboratory, Kearny, N.J.)

and carbon, with traces of other elements as residuals from the original raw materials or from processing materials. This base steel is termed carbon steel or plain carbon steel. The addition of other alloying elements to steel during its production cycle for the purpose of modifying its properties results in alloy steel. When an alloying element is added individually to steel, its behavior is different from that when it is added in combination with other alloys. As a result steel is a most versatile material; so much so that the mechanical engineer can find a steel suitable for practically any design requirement.

The fact that base steel is an alloy of iron and carbon indicates that the presence or absence of carbon is of predominant importance. The carbon content determines the properties of a given steel. However, the amount of carbon is not in itself so important as the *form* of the carbon and the way in which it is distributed in the steel. For example, Fig. 14-1 shows a spheroidized structure, in which the carbides are of globular form; this form of carbon and this distribution pattern impart toughness and machinability. This particular structure resulted from a heat-treatment designed to develop these specific properties in the steel. The structure was obtained by quenching the specimen in brine from its austenitizing temperature, followed by tempering of 1250°F for 12 hr.

The same steel transformed isothermally developed the structure pictured in Fig. 14-2. Examination of this micrograph shows a typically pearlitic structure which is characterized by alternate bands of cementite and ferrite, usually termed a lamellar structure. The heat-treatment consisted of an isothermal quench from austenitizing temperature at 1300°F for 3½ hr.

A study of the preceding structure, together with the procedures followed to obtain them, will clarify the fact that heat-treatment alone was responsible for the different structures and the changed properties of these specimens taken from the same steel.

Heat-treatment

Heat-treatment of steel concerns itself with altering the form and distribution of the carbon. In consequence the higher the carbon in a steel the greater will its effect be on the final properties of that steel. Heat-treatment can take many varied forms; the choice is based on the properties desired in the end product. Among the better-known heat-treating methods are: annealing, austempering, carbonitriding, carburizing, casehardening, hardening, homogenizing, isothermal transformation, martempering, nitriding, normalizing, patenting, and tempering.

Certain of these have a similar over-all objective; for example, carbonitriding, carburizing, casehardening, and nitriding function as surface hardening methods, whereas annealing, normalizing, and patenting act to modify the structure. This statement must be interpreted broadly since, if there were several identical methods for producing the same result, confusion would result.

Hardening. Heat-treatment is most frequently mentioned in connection with hardening. Hardening is desirable from the standpoint of strength development, since steel has its highest strength when it is in its

AISI-C 1080, Fine Grain
(Oil Quenched)

PROPERTIES CHART
(Average Values)

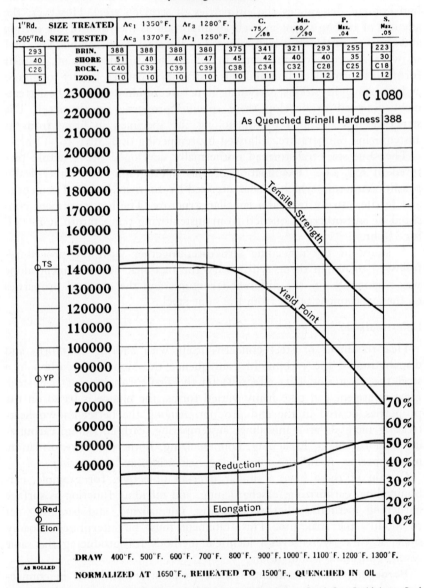

Fig. 14-3. Properties chart, C1080 steel. (Courtesy of Bethlehem Steel Co., Bethlehem, Pa.)

hardest condition. A study of Fig. 14-3 will reveal the strength properties of C1080 carbon steel treated to varying degrees of hardness. Similar property charts are available for all the better-known steels of the self-hardening types.

Hardness in steel is obtained by quenching from a temperature sufficiently high to ensure the structure's being wholly austenitic prior to the quench. The phenomenon involved here is that of a solid solution change within the steel. At room temperature and with a normal structure, carbon steel is composed of cementite (Fe_3C; iron carbide) and ferrite. When steel is heated through its critical temperature range a transformation occurs; the structure of the steel undergoes a complete change. The carbon has dissolved in gamma iron, resulting in the structure austenite. An austenitic structure has a face-centered cubic crystal in contrast with the body-centered type common to steel below its transformation range; furthermore, it is nonmagnetic.

Austenite forms at elevated temperatures and, in most steels, is stable only at those temperatures. If, then, the steel which has been heated to austenitizing temperature is permitted to cool at a normal rate, the austenite will revert to its original components of ferrite and cementite. However, when the steel is subjected to controlled conditions of cooling, the austenite can be transformed into various structures that impart distinct properties. Quenching is the term applied to controlled cooling from the austenitic range. Quenching is, therefore, a critical consideration in the steel-hardening routine.

The first step in hardening steel is to heat it to a temperature either in or above its transformation range in order that the iron may assume its gamma condition, in which it can dissolve the carbon and other elements present, thus forming the solid solution austenite. The dissolution of the carbides may be partial or total, depending upon their magnitude as well as the time at temperature. When either time or temperature is excessive, grain coarsening will result. Plain carbon hypereutectoid steels (carbon above 0.8 per cent) show a rapid increase in the upper transformation temperature; see Fig. 14-4, which charts the critical temperature curve for plain carbon steel. The alternative to avoidance of excessive temperatures is to permit a residue of undissolved carbides to remain. This practice is not uncommon, since recommended quenching temperatures for hypereutectoid steels are frequently below the A_{cm} line.

The treatment of the specimen following its austenitization is that of quenching. There are two distinct methods that can be followed: a drastic quench to be followed by a subsequent tempering (reheating), or an elevated temperature quench and a holding period of such duration that complete isothermal transformation occurs. Both of these methods are employed in the heat-treat shop, and both have much to recommend them; yet they are not at all similar. As has been said, austenite is unstable at temperatures below the transformation range, and any lowering of temperature will be accompanied by carbide separation. It follows from this that the more rapid the rate of cooling the less carbide separa-

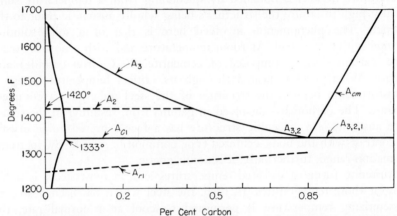

Fig. 14-4. Critical temperature diagram. (From W. T. Frier, "Elementary Metallurgy," McGraw-Hill Book Company, Inc., New York, 1942.)

Fig. 14-5. Martensite, brine-quenched not tempered. ×2,500. (Courtesy of United States Steel, Research Laboratory, Kearny, N.J.)

tion will occur; if this separation can be largely avoided, dissolved carbides will remain at room temperatures, resulting in a structure termed martensite, the chief constituent of fully hardened steel. Figure 14-5 shows martensite obtained in a specimen that was quenched in brine with no subsequent tempering operation. The structure is characterized by

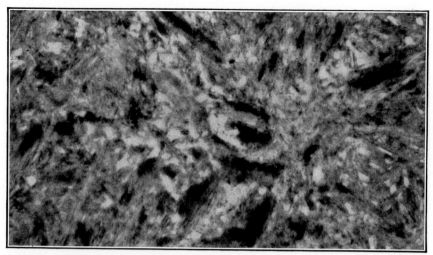

Fig. 14-6a. Martensite, brine-quenched and tempered 1 hr at 400°F. ✕2,500. (Courtesy of United States Steel, Research Laboratory, Kearny, N.J.)

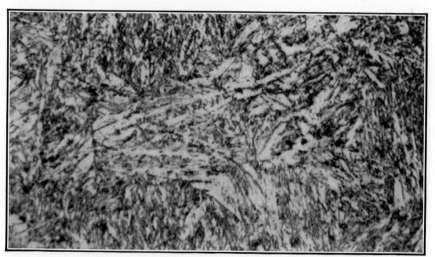

Fig. 14-6b. Martensite, brine-quenched and tempered 1 hr at 600°F. ✕2,500. (Courtesy of United States Steel, Research Laboratory, Kearny, N.J.)

needles and is referred to as an acicular one; the white areas are retained austenite.

Tempering. Fully hardened steel contains stresses resulting from the quenching operation which can be relieved by reheating following the quench. This reheating operation is termed tempering, drawing, or letting down; in addition to stress relief it effects the recovery of a degree of ductility and toughness in the steel under treatment. The higher the

Fig. 14-6c. Martensite, brine-quenched and tempered 1 hr at 800°F. ×2,500. (Courtesy of United States Steel, Research Laboratory, Kearny, N.J.)

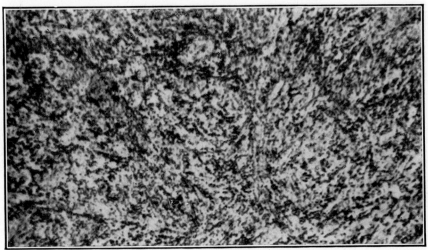

Fig. 14-6d. Martensite, brine-quenched and tempered at 1100°F. ×2,500. (Courtesy of United States Steel, Research Laboratory, Kearny, N.J.)

tempering temperature, the greater the increase in ductility (Fig. 14-3).

Tempering applied to a martensitic structure causes its decomposition. The resulting structures can be identified as individual ones although the gradation from one to the next is not abrupt. Examples of tempered structures are given in Figs. 14-6a, 6b, 6c, 6d. These structures were obtained by tempering martensite (Fig. 14-5). A study of the series of micrographs, which starts with a tempering temperature of 400°F (Fig.

14-6*a*) and concludes with a 12-hr 1250°F draw (Fig. 14-1), will reveal the effect of varying the tempering temperature. Any further increase in tempering temperature in this series would completely obliterate the quench effect and the steel would enter its transformation range.

The procedure just described is correctly known as tempering martensite. The processing routine consisted of heating the specimen in its transformation range for a time interval at temperature to assure austenization of the structure. The specimen was then given a brine quench to room temperature in order to fully harden the steel. The hardening operation was followed by a temper or draw at the several temperatures shown on the micrographs. Tempering is employed as a means of increasing the toughness of the member. It is advisable to employ the highest tempering temperature that will meet the strength specification, since this will ensure the greatest toughness/strength ratio. Tempering results in a reduction in hardness.

The relationship of hardness and strength is such that when steels exhibit the same hardness they will have about the same strength (Fig. 14-7). This is a point that needs emphasis, since it has a decided bearing on the choice of steel for a given application. Obtaining the *same hardness* in a number of steels of different composition requires control of the tempering operation, because higher temperatures or longer periods are needed for one steel than for another even though the two have the same carbon content. Thus 1045 steel tempered for 1 hr at 960°F and 6145 steel tempered for 1 hr at 1240°F will both show a 300 Brinell hardness number (Bhn).

Isothermal Transformation. The previously discussed method of heat-treatment is the one of greatest use in the heat-treat shop. The work of Davenport and Bain has been outstanding in developing a different concept for austenite transformation, one that is termed isothermal transformation. This is defined as "the process of transforming austenite in ferrous alloys to ferrite or a ferrite-carbide aggregate at any constant temperature within the *transformation range*."[1]

Heat-treating by this method starts with the specimen being heated to and held in its austenite transformation range until the desired austenitic structure is reached. Following the time at temperature interval, the specimen is quenched to and held at the temperature that will give the transformation product desired. It is important to recognize that the interval for the start of the austenitic transformation is different for each temperature, and further, that the transformation period also varies with the temperature. Experimental data have been obtained for many steels,

[1] The joint AFA-ASM-ASTM-SAE Committee on Definitions of Terms Relating to Heat Treatment, "Metals Handbook," American Society for Metals, Cleveland, 1948.

and from these data curves or charts of the isothermal transformation have been drawn.[2] The curves are termed isothermal transformation diagrams, transformation-temperature-time (TTT) curves, or S curves, the last being the most commonly used expression. Such a diagram for 4140 steel is shown in Fig. 14-8; it charts the behavior of 4140 steel from austenite to martensite. Temperatures are plotted as ordinates and time

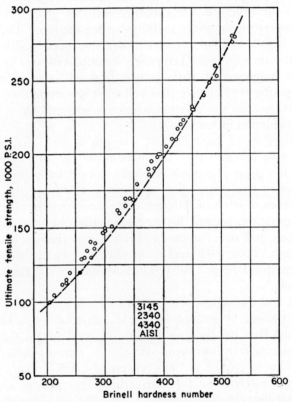

Fig. 14-7. The relation of ultimate tensile strength to Brinell hardness for three different steels of similar carbon content. (Courtesy of United States Steel Corp., New York.)

is plotted on a logarithmic scale that expands short and compresses long time intervals. The heavy curved line at the left marked "transformation begins" shows the time-temperature position for the start of austenite transformation. So long as the steel is in the area at the left of that line it retains its austenite structure; when the line is crossed, transformation of austenite begins. The heavy curved line at the right shows the end of transformation, and the structures in the area to the right are those of

[2] "Atlas of Isothermal Transformation Diagrams," Research Laboratories, United States Steel Corporation, Kearny, N.J., 1953.

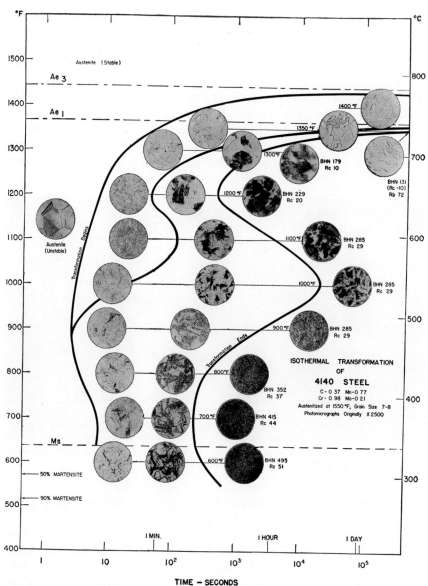

Fig. 14-8. Isothermal transformation diagram for 4140 steel. (Courtesy of United States Steel, Research Laboratory, Kearny, N.J.)

complete transformation. These structures will not transform further, regardless of subsequent cooling rates. The area between the boundary lines represents partial transformation.

The dotted horizontal line Ms shows the temperature for the start of the martensitic transformation. Martensite transforms only on a falling temperature and not at a constant temperature as do the other transformation products. The chart shows that at an approximate temperature of 575°F there is a 50 per cent martensite transformation, which has increased to 90 per cent with the temperature lowered to approximately 520°F. The important assumption here is that the rate of quenching has been sufficiently rapid to *prevent any austenite transformation until the Ms temperature has been reached.* Failure in this respect means that some transformation occurred before the temperature for the beginning of martensite formation was reached, and as a result maximum hardness was not attained in the specimen. The rate of quench is the key to obtaining

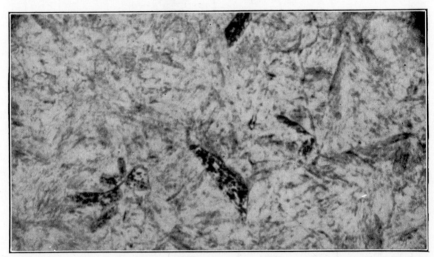

Fig. 14-9a. 4140 steel 5 per cent transformed, isothermally, at 800°F. ×2,500. (Courtesy of United States Steel, Research Laboratory, Kearny, N.J.)

a fully martensitic transformation; however, in the heat-treat shop problems of steel composition as well as mass must be dealt with.

Alloying additions in steel have the effect of slowing transformation; therefore there is a greater time interval available for the quench. Alloy steels show the "beginning of transformation" curve moved to the right in the isothermal transformation diagram. Transformation is more "sluggish" both on quenching and on tempering for the alloy steels.

In Fig. 14-8 micrographs are included for several structures, showing partial as well as complete transformations at given temperatures. In order to add clarity to this diagram, Figs. 14-9a, 9b, and 9c are presented. These are all taken from the transformation of 4140 steel at 800°F. The only difference between these structures is the element of *time;* temperature remained constant. This particular type of heat-treatment

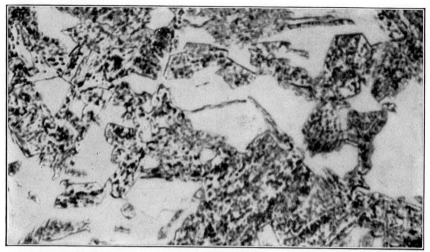

Fig. 14-9b. 4140 steel 50 per cent transformed, isothermally, at 800°F. ×2,500. (Courtesy of United States Steel, Research Laboratory, Kearny, N.J.)

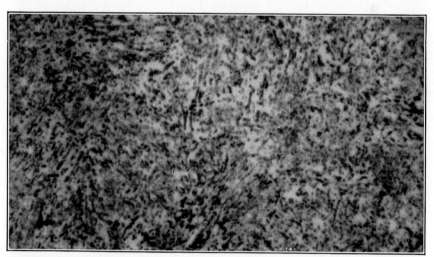

Fig. 14-9c. 4140 steel 100 per cent transformed, isothermally, at 800°F. ×2,500. (Courtesy of United States Steel, Research Laboratory, Kearny, N.J.)

is also known as austempering.[3] The structure developed in Fig. 14-9c is termed Bainite.

The two methods for heat-treating steel in order to develop the necessary strength coupled with toughness have been given in some detail. One method is based on the technique of tempering martensite, while the other represents transformation at a constant temperature (excepting

[3] Trade name of process patented by United States Steel Corporation.

martensite). To clarify further these two concepts of heat-treatment Figs. 14-10*a* and 10*b*, showing schematically the routine followed in each of the two methods, are included. The terminology applied to tempered structures in Fig. 14-10*a* is currently considered obsolete.

Which of these two methods should be applied to a given heat-treating problem is open to some difference of opinion. Primarily the decision is

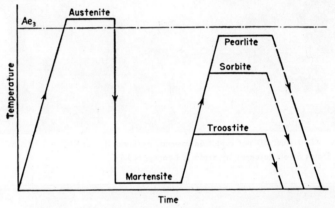

Fig. 14-10a. Schematic sketch of heat, quench, and temper.

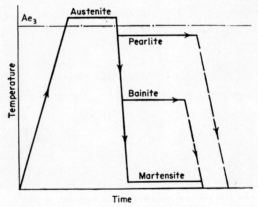

Fig. 14-10b. Schematic sketch of isothermal transformation.

based on the shape and size of the treated component. Isothermal transformations, when optimum results are expected, will function best on small-sectioned work. Quenching progresses inward from the surface; consequently a specimen of any appreciable volume will quench more slowly than will a thin section. The effect of mass on both quenching speed and depth of hardness should always be considered in connection with the establishment of a heat-treat procedure.

CASEHARDENING

The methods for hardening discussed thus far have dealt with the self-hardening steels—those that harden directly on quenching. There are instances where steels are selected that can be endowed with the combination of a hard surface backed by a strong, tough core. This desirable combination of properties can be obtained by casehardening. A wide choice of steels is available, from the alloys which will produce excellent core properties to the low plain-carbon grades that are economical to buy and that machine readily. Steels selected for casehardening are generally of low carbon content, rarely exceeding 0.25 per cent.

The necessity of obtaining satisfactory surface hardness in such steels is met by carburizing the part prior to any quench or reheat and quench. Steel is carburized for the purpose of increasing the carbon, and in some processes the nitrogen, or both, in the surface of the steel. Of several methods used in the heat-treat shop for accomplishing this, the oldest and best-known is pack carburizing.

Pack Carburizing. The parts to be carburized are packed in a heat-resistant alloy steel box where they are surrounded by carburizing compound. The latter is material high in carbon of a form that will readily develop CO and CO_2 when subjected to elevated temperatures. Energizers such as barium carbonate are used to speed the reaction and thus to shorten the carburizing time cycle. Carburizing temperatures are in the 1650 to 1700°F range for most steels. Temperatures at least 200° higher are proving of interest since they shorten carburizing time substantially.

Packing requires care inasmuch as the parts must be surrounded by an equal amount of carburizer for uniform results. The vitality of the carburizer is maintained by making additions to offset the loss incurred in the previous use. The prepared boxes, which are frequently cylindrical in shape, are sealed prior to being placed in the furnace. Upon completion of the carburizing cycle the boxes are withdrawn and contents emptied over a screen in order to separate the work from the carburizer.

Gas Carburizing. In this method a gaseous atmosphere is maintained in the furnace as the agency for imparting the necessary carbon to the steel surface. A diversity of practice governs the actual operation in that gases such as methane, ethane, and propane are used in the furnace atmosphere. There is the further practice of using oil vapors as a source of hydrocarbon, either separately or in combination with carbonaceous gases.

Gas carburizing has the advantages of cleanliness and reduced handling over the pack method. Flexibility is another desirable feature, since atmospheric composition is readily controlled by the combination of input and venting. Carburizing speed is claimed to be higher than it is when solid carburizers are used.

Liquid Carburizing. The development of liquid carburizing can be traced to the older cyaniding pot principle. Now, however, activated salts have replaced the potassium cyanide of former days. This is a most fortunate circumstance, for the elimination of potassium cyanide (KCN) has removed a deadly poison from the heat-treat shop. Sodium cyanide is the primary source of the carburizer, although calcium cyanide is of some importance in this connection. Liquid carburizers are used mainly for relatively shallow case depths on the order of 0.025 in.

Carbonitriding. This method is a combination of gas carburizing and nitriding. The process consists of bleeding ammonia gas into a carburizing atmosphere in the furnace in order to develop both carbon and nitrogen in the surface of the steel. The amount of ammonia gas required may be as low as 1 per cent where the work is given a quench upon removal from the furnace. When air quench is specified, ammonia is used in larger volumes as a means of obtaining the desired hardness.

Heat-treating Carburized Steel. The previous paragraphs have surveyed the more prominent methods used for changing the surface composition of the steel. Note that the objective in each instance is that of modifying the steel in preparation for further processing. It follows from this that *carburizing in itself does not harden steel.* There are designs in which local areas are not to be carburized. In such instances selective carburizing is used. The surfaces that are not to be treated are masked by copper plating, coating with proprietary compounds, or covering with sand. Following the carburizing process, the copper is ground off or removed by reverse plating.

A carburized part is a complex steel that has a high-carbon outer surface, with carbon content decreasing to the core, which has been unaffected insofar as chemical composition is concerned. The usual carburizing steels develop a range of from 1.0 to 1.3 per cent C on the surface, or for the case, while the core retains its approximate original analysis.

Quenching directly from the carburizing operation is not as common as formerly. Current practice specifies pot cooling, followed by reheating to the transformation range of the case to be followed in turn by a quench and a draw. This procedure, accompanied by the resulting data on properties, is given concisely in a properties chart (Fig. 14-11). Carburized parts are also subjected to double heat-treatments wherein both case and core are processed. Treatment to develop toughness in the core takes precedence over case considerations.

Nitriding. Surface hardening, in which the formation of iron nitrides predominates, is of interest to the designer. Best results for nitriding are obtained by employing nitralloy steels. These steels contain aluminum ranging from 0.85 to 1.20 per cent and as a result develop surface prop-

AISI– C 1015, Fine Grain

PROPERTIES

(Average Values)

1"RD. TREATED .505" RD. TESTED	Ac_1 1390 °F. Ac_3 1560 °F.	Ar_3 1510 °F. Ar_1 1390 °F.	C. .13/.18	Mn. .30/.60	P. Max. .04	S. Max. .05

	T.S. Lb./Sq.In.	Y.P. Lb./Sq. In.	Elon. % 2 In	Red'n. %	Brin. No.	Izod Ft. Lb.
AS ROLLED	61,000	45,500	39.0	61.0	126	81.5

CORE PROPERTIES

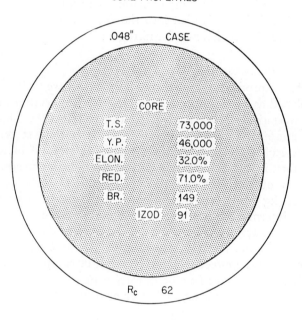

.048" CASE

CORE
T.S.	73,000
Y.P.	46,000
ELON.	32.0%
RED.	71.0%
BR.	149
IZOD	91

R_c 62

SINGLE QUENCH AND TEMPER

(1) Carburized at 1675 °F. for 8 hours

(2) Pot Cooled

(3) Reheated to 1425 °F.

(4) Water Quenched

(5) Tempered at 350 °F.

Fig. 14-11. Chart of properties for carburized and heat-treated C1015 steel. (Courtesy of Bethlehem Steel Co., Bethlehem, Pa.)

erties superior to any other nitrided steels. They contain appreciable percentages of chromium and molybdenum in addition to aluminum. The nitralloy steels are designated by types, viz., nitralloy 125 (Type H) and nitralloy 135 (Type G). The various types differ in both carbon content and alloy range.

Nitralloy steels are heat-treated to develop core properties prior to nitriding. It is customary to purchase such steel, if it is to be machined, in the heat-treated condition. When distortion is to be minimized, machined parts should be stress-relieved prior to nitriding. Forgings are produced from non-heat-treated stock, since subsequent heat-treatment is necessary as a finishing operation.

Nitriding is accomplished by subjecting the steel to an atmosphere rich in nitrogen; ammonia gas is most frequently used for this purpose, although organic nitrogen-bearing compounds as well as synthetic urea are possibilities. This gas is bled into the furnace at a volume that will yield the proper dissociation rate for nitrogen:

$$2NH_3 \rightleftarrows 2N + 3H_2$$

The dissociation products escape through a vent, where their composition can be analyzed as a guide to gas-flow control. Temperatures for nitriding are comparatively low, ranging from 930 to 1000°F. This desirable low-temperature treatment is offset by the long time at temperature, which may reach 90 hr. Case depths which average 0.015 in. are considerably less than in carburizing, despite the much longer treatment.

Advantages of nitriding are extreme hardness, 1000–1100 Vickers diamond (10 kg load), and retention of hardness to temperatures of 1200°F for intermittent heating. Corrosion resistance is excellent for nitrided surfaces. From a manufacturing standpoint the important thing about nitriding is the fact that no quenching is necessary. Claims have been advanced to the effect that the part can be finished ground to size prior to nitriding without fear of distortion or growth after treatment. Where growth occurs, it is on the order of 0.001 in. per inch of dimension.

Interest in nitriding arises primarily from the hard surface potential backed by a tough core. Nitrided parts, such as valve stems, show excellent wear resistance and justify their higher costs. Nitriding can be done selectively by masking with solder or tin plating. A gray mat surface is indicative of a superior nitrided case, while a lustrous appearance means an inferior one. Annealing of nitrided surfaces is best accomplished by dispersing the surface nitrides; however, a surface once annealed will never produce a nitrided surface comparable to the original one.

Floxe Process Nitriding—A two-stage process for nitriding has been developed under the Floxe title. Its advantages over the conventional method are the elimination of a nitride network and also a reduced consumption of ammonia gas. Furthermore, there is some shortening of the time cycle, which means a lower cost operation. In the first stage of the Floxe Process the concentration of nitride is produced at the surface, while the second stage diffuses these nitrides. As a result, the necessity of lapping is eliminated except for correcting dimensions.

Malcomizing—This method of surface treatment applies especially to the stainless steel series. It is one in which the action of nitrogen with the steel results in a superhard surface. It provides wear resistance of greater magnitudes when applied to the surfaces of stainless steels; at the same time it does not adversely affect their corrosion resistance. In applying this method it is necessary to pay strict attention to processing. Included in this is a necessity for pretreating the steels that are to be malcomized. There is some slight dimensional change occurring during this processing.

Glow Discharge Nitriding—A completely new method for surface hardening can be applied to a variety of low-alloy steels as well as to some stainless grades. In common with the conventional nitriding this method employs nascent nitrogen atmosphere; however, there is a profound difference between the methods. In this one no furnace is required. Instead, it makes use of the almost loss-free conversion of electrical energy into gas-ion energy and heat. The conversion is achieved by electrical glow discharge. The idea was developed in Europe and has received considerable application in Germany and Switzerland; it is also being used in America.

Liquid Nitriding—The metal chip antifriction qualities of specific types of cutting tools can be improved by this type of processing. Tools taking light cuts such as taps, chasers, broaches, form tools, etc., can benefit from such treatment since it assists in preventing chip pickup and failure from built-up cutting edges. Finished ground tools are immersed in an aged 50-50 KCN-NaCN bath operating at 1025°F for intervals of 15 to 45 min, depending on the tools. During this time a very shallow nitride case is obtained. Longer treating cycles must be carefully reviewed, since cutting edges may become too brittle because of overtreating.

Steam Treating. Another development for a similar improvement of tools is steam treating. It is generally applied in tempering furnaces by introducing live steam from a small generator or from the plant steam main. The action of the steam on the heated tool is such that a superficial light oxide forms which improves the antifriction qualities of the tool face in a manner described in the preceding paragraph. It is claimed that these methods have increased tool life from 10 to as much as 500 per cent. It seems obvious that such processing should be specified where long-run jobs are being processed.

Casehardening Reviewed. Casehardening means producing a hardened surface backed by the type of core necessary to meet design requirements. There are several methods of surface treatment. Some require subsequent heat-treating, some quench direct; in nitriding, no quench is needed. Casehardening is rarely applied to those steels whose compositions permit quenching from their transformation range, for the reason that such steels are inherently capable of direct heat-treatments to desired properties. Casehardening is specified for those applications where surface hardness and wear resistance are to be combined with toughness.

Applied Heat-treatment

Annealing. Annealing is accomplished by heating the work—which should be protected from any decarburization influences either by packing or by controlled furnace atmosphere, through its transformation range—and holding for a period that will ensure uniform temperature throughout, to be followed by slow cooling away from the air. The latter aspect of the annealing cycle requires special emphasis, since it is the cooling rate that governs final properties. For best results in annealing, the furnace heat is closed off and the work permitted to cool with the furnace. Such a procedure is costly from the viewpoint of furnace equipment use and can be successfully detoured by placing the heated pieces in lime, sand, or a similar insulating material that will ensure slow cooling.

Annealing is generally considered to mean softening. There are other interpretations of the term, some by custom and others by definition. Obviously, softening indicates a change in microstructure to pearlite (Fig. 14-2), which results in altered mechanical properties.

There are modifications applied to annealing, as is indicated by such terms as blue annealing, bright annealing, etc. In every instance, these terms refer to a specific annealing application designed to produce a unique end result.

Normalizing. Normalizing differs from annealing in both heating and cooling. Normalizing provides for heating well above the transformation range to temperatures higher than the annealing ones, since this process is widely used with alloy steels. After a short period at temperature, much shorter than in annealing, the piece is removed from the furnace and cooled in *still air*. In effect such cooling is a quench, a fact that explains the higher strength values as compared to annealing (Fig. 14-3).

Normalizing affects the part much in the manner of annealing, although it is sometimes specified in forgings for grain refining prior to annealing or to improve machinability. It is a faster method, owing to the increased cooling rate; however, because of the shorter heating time the structure and properties are not so uniform as in an annealed end product. The relative transformation temperature ranges for hardening, annealing, and normalizing are diagramed in Fig. 14-12.

Quenching. Quenching as a part of the heat-treating cycle is of fundamental importance. More frequently than not, failure to obtain expected hardness or the experience of outright cracking can be traced to improper quenching as to choice of both medium and technique. Quenching is a cooling operation. As the surface cools, convection of heat from the core starts cooling the center. The speed of quench varies with the composition and temperature of the bath as well as with its movement. Uniform results depend on maintaining the quenching bath at a constant temperature.

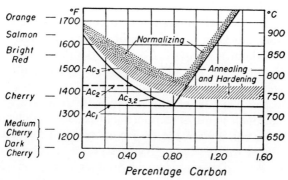

Fig. 14-12. Transformation temperature range for hardening, annealing, and normalizing. (From "Metals Handbook," American Society for Metals, Cleveland, 1948.)

When the heated piece strikes the quenching bath, a vapor film forms which acts as an insulator. This holds true whether an air or a liquid quench is used. Obviously this film must be dissipated in order to obtain the desired quenching action. Movement, of either the piece or the quenching medium, will aid materially in bringing about this desired condition. The skilled heat-treater always moves the heated piece in the quenching bath either in a circular motion or in a figure eight. Such motion should not be so rapid that cavitation of the medium directly behind the piece will occur, since differential cooling rates as indicated by soft areas will result. The importance of agitating the quenching medium is shown in Table 14-1.

Agitation may be taken to mean the movement of the quenching medium against the work. There is considerable interest in spraying liquid under pressure in order to attain high velocity of movement and thereby to increase quenching rates. There are also installations using a mist or fog blanket as a quenching medium.

TABLE 14-1. SEVERITY OF QUENCH (H VALUE)*

Agitation	Oil	Water	Brine
None............	0.25–0.30	0.9–1.0	2.0
Mild.............	0.3 –0.35	1.0–1.1	2.0–2.2
Moderate.........	0.35–0.40	1.2–1.3	
Good............	0.4 –0.50	1.4–1.5	
Strong...........	0.5 –0.80	1.6–2.0	
Violent...........	0.8 –1.10	4.0	5.0

* "Metals Handbook," American Society for Metals, Cleveland, 1948, p. 616.

The use of oil as a quench needs some clarification, since all types of oil—animal, vegetable, and mineral—are used, either singly or in combination. The important consideration about quenching oils is their vapor pressure because this is the determinant of their effectiveness.

Distortion and Cracking. The choice of a quenching method as well as a quenching medium is predicated both on the steel analysis and on the end use of the product. The objective in quenching is the avoidance of warping, cracking, or variable hardness. It is for this reason that the design of the part must be carefully studied with regard to its behavior during quench. Such items as section thickness, section changes, cavities, edges, and bores will govern the choice of steel and quench. Quenching is not always used for developing hardness; rather a substantial portion is given over to delivering a tough end product free of cracks, warpage, and distortion.

When such precision-machined members as gears are to be quenched, the above considerations require especial attention. Warpage in gears can be controlled by using a fixture in which the gear is placed prior to immersion in the quench. In fact the complete quenching cycle can be accommodated in a quenching press (Fig. 14-13). In such a press the gear is positioned in a fixture that holds it to shape during the quenching cycle.

Close examination of the gear in position in Fig. 14-13 will show that the area within the ring gear is taken up by a segmented expander. This device operates to take advantage of plastic flow in the gear steel to combat the normal contraction caused by the quench. The quenching oil is not used indiscriminately as an immersion bath; instead it is delivered against the gear through jets whose streams are baffled in order to provide differential cooling as the gear sections require. This quenching cycle is far from routine in that all features of the quench operation must be coordinated.

The size of the section as well as the temperature gradient within the piece will exert a pronounced influence on the amount of distortion or cracking that may occur. As the outer layers cool they will contract; however, they are limited in this because the center has not as yet cooled sufficiently to conform. As a result the surface layers are in tension and the center in compression at the beginning of the quench. When the surface layers reach a temperature in the Ms range, transformation of the austenite to martensite sets in, with the result that the outside undergoes slight expansion, which tends to relieve the tension stresses somewhat.

A specially designed electronic signaler has been developed to reduce quench cracking of steel during the heat-treating operation. Its design is such that the signaler does not come in actual contact with the part being quenched; rather it sends out electrical signals when the part has

Fig. 14-13. Close-up of ring gear in Gleason quenching press. (Courtesy of Western Gear Corp., Lynwood, Calif.)

hardened to a predetermined degree. Its design functions on the basis of change in magnetic permeability; such change occurs when austenite transforms to martensite. The part under treatment can be withdrawn from the quench when it reaches the predetermined degree of hardness. The residual temperature of the part then will be allowed to equalize through slow cooling, and, as a result, will avoid the build-up of severe internal stresses which are so frequently the cause of quench cracking.

Martempering. Evaluation of the transformation stresses has led to the idea of circumventing them by a type of interrupted quench termed martempering. In this method the piece is quenched rapidly from its austenitizing temperature to the Ms range, where it is removed from the bath and permitted to cool in air to room temperature. Since martensite forms at and below the Ms temperature, this microstructure will develop during the cooling to room temperature. The transformation stresses will be of a much lower magnitude, since the drastic temperature gradient within the piece is largely eliminated. As a result, there is much less danger of cracking with this method than with the full quench.

Heating

The modern heat-treat shop can choose heating equipment other than furnaces. These developments, including such items as electrical induction, oxyacetylene, and gas-flame heating, offer the heat-treater a *speed method* of heating. In addition, there are such items as salt, oil, and lead baths that can be described as secondary heating equipment, since the

Fig. 14-14. Temperature-control instrument panel installations. (Courtesy of Brown Instrument Division, Minneapolis-Honeywell Regulator Co., Minneapolis.)

materials that compose the heating bath are, in their turn, heated from an outside fuel source.

Temperature Control. Furnace temperatures are measured by means of some type of thermocouple connected with a pyrometer of either indicating or recording design. Further, thermocouples are used as a means of automatic regulation of the furnace. Some of this control equipment is extremely sensitive in that the tolerance in temperature range is specified at less than 5°F. Close control requires refinement in instrumentation and continued calibration of the thermocouples used. A typical temperature control instrument installation is shown in Fig. 14-14.

Temperature control equipment is of no value unless it is respected and cared for accordingly. Many failures in the heat-treat shop are traceable to neglect of this equipment. Instruments should be checked periodically, and thermocouples require frequent calibration.

Controlled Atmosphere. Separately controlled atmospheres within a heat-treating furnace have been in use for some time. Finished machined parts can be processed without loss of surface hardness during heating because decarburization can be eliminated, as can carbon pickup. Another attribute of controlled atmospheres is that scaling can be prevented; as a result, clean, accurate work is possible without resort to pickling and other forms of cleaning.

Controlled atmospheres are generated in equipment that is auxiliary to the furnaces. Atmospheres are produced from gases, liquids, and solids and also from combinations of these. This wide range of sources yields a large number of furnace atmospheres, each one designed to meet a specific condition.

Salt Baths. There are inherent advantages to the use of salt baths, among them being that the molten salt congeals on the newly immersed workpiece and insulates it from sudden heat-shock. A similar protection is afforded when the quenching cycle is reached. More important than these is the fact that the workpiece heats much more rapidly, with a time saving on the order of 4:1 to 6:1 over atmosphere heating. Heating will be uniform, since the molten salt completely surrounds the workpiece regardless of its shape. Scaling and decarburization are avoided when heating in salt baths because the workpiece is not in contact with the air. Composition of the salt bath requires close control in order to prevent any reactions with the metal being treated. Some salt-bath compositions and their applications appear in Table 14-2.

TABLE 14-2. TYPICAL SALT-BATH COMPOSITIONS*

Desig-nation	Weight percentage					Approx. melting point, °F	Recom-mended heating range, °F	Application
	NaCl	KCl	BaCl$_2$	NaNO$_2$	KNO$_3$			
I-1	45–55	45–55	. . . . .	. . . . .	. . . . .	1250	1350–1650	Neutral hardening
I$_2$-2	15–25	20–30	50–60	. . . . .	. . . . .	1100	1250–1700	Neutral hardening
I$_3$-3	20–30	. . . . .	70–80	. . . . .	. . . . .	1300	1400–1700	Neutral hardening
I-4	10–20	. . . . .	80–90	. . . . .	. . . . .	1400	1500–2000	Neutral hardening
L-1	. . . . .	. . . . .	. . . . .	40–50	50–60	290	325–1200	Austemper-ing

* Abstracted from "Metals Handbook," American Society for Metals, Cleveland, 1948.

Speed Heating

The following is descriptive of heat-treating methods wherein the heating is not performed in a furnace; instead some other heat source, as exemplified by electrical induction, oxyacetylene, or gas flame is used. The advantage is that heating time is reduced to a matter of seconds. Local heating can be applied, removing the necessity for masking; of equal importance, workpieces of great size can be treated by heating only the areas that require treatment. Large-diameter gears and machine tool ways are examples of components now locally hardened by speed heating. With a very rapid heating rate, the elevated temperature is confined to the surface layers; thus the tendency to distort or crack the workpiece is reduced.

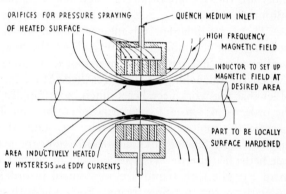

Fig. 14-15. Schematic diagram of induction heating. (Courtesy of The Ohio Crankshaft Co., Cleveland.)

Ultrasonics. The application of ultrasonic energy to steel during transformation from the austenite phase is capable of producing marked grain refinement. This new grain-refining development as applied to steel modifies the theory that properties of crystals can be altered solely by plastic deformation, alloying, or heat-treatment. The value of fine-grained steel is well known. Among its attributes are harder, tougher, and better wear-resisting properties; it is also less prone to warp during heat-treatment.

Induction Heating. Heating metals by high-frequency electrical currents is used in many phases of metal treating, forming, and joining. The induction heating circuit employs a high-frequency current whose source may be (a) motor-generator sets, (b) vacuum-tube oscillators, (c) mercury arc converters, or (d) spark-gap oscillators. Each of these varies somewhat as to available frequencies as well as capacities—a condition that limits equipment choice. Motor-generator sets, for example, are available for frequencies ranging from 1,000 to 30,000 cycles and have capacities reaching 1,500 kw.

The principle of the induction heating circuit is fundamentally that of a transformer, since the member carrying the current is the primary and the workpiece being placed in the inductor loop becomes the secondary. The flow of the current through the inductor sets up the familiar lines of force which cut through the workpiece that has previously been inserted in the circuit. The arrangement of an induction heating circuit for hardening can be seen in Fig. 14-15. Resulting heat develops from

Fig. 14-16. Ring gears in position for induction hardening of all teeth simultaneously. The gear is rotated and quenched in position. (Courtesy of The Ohio Crankshaft Co., Cleveland.)

both hysteresis and eddy current losses; the former are generally disregarded and the heat source is considered to be the eddy currents, which are resistance losses.

The application of induction heating to heat-treatment is accomplished by adapting the inductor coil to the workpiece. An example of an induction hardening installation used for gears is shown in Fig. 14-16. There are some extremely ingenious induction hardening installations such as the figure-eight coils used for treating two camshafts simultaneously. These coils heat the cam face, then move to the next one, until all, plus the camshaft bearings, have been hardened on both shafts.

Flame Hardening

The oxyacetylene flame is used for selective hardening in a manner similar to the previously described induction device. The flame is the same one used for welding. Torches bearing multiple flames have been developed for this application. The oxyacetylene flame, being capable of a temperature of 6300°F, gives an intense local heat; when several of these flames are used together, the workpiece can be heated rapidly. The flame-heating principle is the basis for design of heat-treating equipment as shown in Fig. 14-17. Multiple-flame torches play against a rapidly revolving workpiece, which results in an extremely short heating period. The piece, when heated, is quenched by being dropped into a quench tank that is located directly below the heating station. Splined ends of shafts lend themselves admirably to this system of hardening. Gear teeth

Fig. 14-17. Close-up of workpiece-holding device and flame head. Note how individual flame tips are positioned so as to concentrate the desired volume of heat on the two diameters of workpiece. (Courtesy of Cincinnati Milling Machine Co., Cincinnati.)

are flame-hardened by passing flames on opposite sides of the tooth, with a water quench following the progress of the flames.

NONFERROUS ALLOYS

The increased importance of the light metals and nonferrous alloys in engineering manufacture was discussed in Chap. 3. It seems desirable, therefore, to note that heat-treating is also applied to many of these materials. New methods, new techniques, and new concepts will be required of both supervisory and operating personnel, since the problems involved are largely of a nature that call for a clean break from the heat-treating of steel.

Aluminum Alloys

Alloying elements used in aluminum are termed hardeners. The metallic elements most commonly found in wrought alloys are Cu, Mg, Si, and Mn, while Zn, Cr, Ni, Pb, Sn, and Bi are also present in *some* alloys. They are capable of forming a considerable number of constituents. Heat-treatment of aluminum alloys concerns itself with the constituents and the form in which they are present.

There are three recognized heat-treatments applied to aluminum alloys: (*a*) annealing; (*b*) solution HT; (*c*) precipitation HT. Annealing has the same meaning as in ferrous alloys: further, annealing is applied to the strain-hardening, heat-treatable, and casting alloys. Temperatures for annealing lie somewhat below those for solution heat-treatment.

Solution Heat-treatment. The alloy B26 (Alcoa 195), essentially composed of 4.5 per cent Cu with the balance aluminum, is a prominent heat-treatable casting alloy that will serve here in the description of solution heat-treatment. When this alloy is molten, all the Cu is in solution; the Cu is completely dissolved in the liquid Al and the melt represents a molten solution of Cu in Al. With a lowering of the temperature, solid alloy will begin to form. The composition of these first crystals will be richer in Al than the indicated alloying properties. A continuation of the freezing process will find crystals, increasingly rich in Cu, forming in the melt until ultimately the final crystals forming are surrounded by melt containing 33 per cent Cu (eutectic). Upon solidification of this remaining liquid, it precipitates two constituents in a simultaneous action. One of these is a solid solution of approximately 5.5 per cent Cu, while the other is the intermetallic compound $CuAl_2$, which contains about 52 per cent Cu and is hard and brittle in character.

Obviously the solidified casting lacks homogeneity insofar as the distribution of the Cu component is concerned. Since, therefore, the solubility of Cu in Al increases with temperature, the solution heat-treatment is applied to obtain a better Cu distribution. The temperature is raised to 960°F for this alloy, where all the Cu is soluble in the solid Al. The specimen is held at this temperature; consequently a water quench quickly follows the heating period in order to retain the maximum amount of the solid solution. Quenching may be in boiling water as a means of controlling the warpage that can result from quenching strains.

The temperatures used for solution heat-treatment of Al alloys are chosen to be just below the melting point of the eutectic of that alloying system. The use of higher temperatures causes melting within the casting, which is rendered unfit for service application and must be regarded as scrap for remelt. Solution heat-treatment improves the properties of Al alloys.

Precipitation Heat-treatment. Quenching was employed, following solution heat-treatment, to retain the solid solution change developed. However, since solubility decreases with lowered temperatures, there is a tendency for the dissolved alloying component to precipitate to the ex-

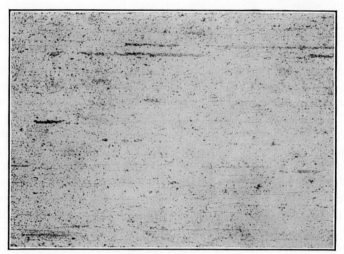

Fig. 14-18a. Aluminum alloy 2024-0 annealed condition, Bossert's etch. ×100.

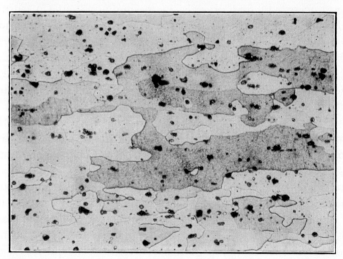

Fig. 14-18b. Aluminum alloy 2024-T6, solution plus precipitation heat-treated. Keller's etch. ×300.

tent of room temperature equilibrium conditions. This phenomenon is also termed aging. In the duralumin-type alloys, especially 2017, aging is extremely rapid at room temperatures and is essentially complete in four days. In consequence, these alloys are not subjected to a precipitation heat-treatment.

Reheating, following solution heat-treatment, for the purpose of precipitating the alloying components of an optimum critical size is termed precipitation heat-treatment. Its effects on the mechanical properties are increased yield and ultimate tensile strength as well as hardness; ductility may remain constant or tend toward lowered values, depending on the alloy. Figure 14-18a shows the microstructure of 2024 wrought alloy in the annealed condition and Fig. 14-18b the same alloy in the fully heat-treated condition—solution plus precipitation.

Natural aging following solution heat-treatment can be arrested by subjecting the material to subnormal temperatures. Rivets are stored at these temperatures in order that they may be headed readily prior to precipitation. Artificial aging is a term that is synonymous with precipitation heat-treatment. While all the Al alloys will precipitate following solution heat-treatment, the time element may be so great as to dictate artificial aging. The corrosion resistance of some of the Al alloys is closely interrelated with heat-treatment and deserves more than passing attention. Intergranular corrosion, or intergranular exfoliation, as it is sometimes termed, has been known to result from imperfect heat-treatment. This type of failure is critical, since the defect originates within the metal and is not readily observed, as is surface corrosion. Stress-carrying members should be given especially close inspection for evidence of intergranular deterioration.

Copper-base Alloys

The range of copper-base alloys is very broad as to composition and, further, is divided between wrought and cast products. In view of this diversity, any remarks on heat-treatment will need to be regarded as applying to specific alloys rather than to the entire field.

Homogenizing is a high-temperature treatment used on some copper-base alloys for the purpose of decreasing or even eliminating segregation within the specimen. Process annealing has a similar objective and finds its greatest usefulness in processing brass.

Heat-treatment is specified for copper-base alloys that are susceptible to solution and precipitation hardening of this group. Beryllium copper has the widest industrial application. ASTM specification B 194 governs beryllium copper strip and shows a range in tensile strength from 150 to 180,000 psi extending from the soft to the full hard temper.

Magnesium Alloys

Interest in heat-treatment of magnesium alloys is centered primarily in the cast products. In the wrought magnesium series alloy AZ80 is specified for heat-treatment in some applications.

There are three heat-treatments applicable to magnesium-alloy cast products: stabilizing, solution heat-treatment, and aging, or precipitation.

Stabilizing consists of heating the casting for 4 hr at a temperature of 500°F. The temperatures for solution heat-treatment are related to the specific alloy in question; however, a maximum of 800°F is general with time at temperature extending from 10 to 20 hr.

The objective of heat-treatment of magnesium alloys is similar to that of aluminum. Solution heat-treatment increases toughness and resistance to shock. The following precipitation or aging treatment promotes higher yield strength and greater hardness but sacrifices some ductility in so doing. Magnesium alloys carry a heat-treat designation as AZ92A-T4 or AZ92A-T6, depending on whether solution (T4) or solution plus precipitation (T6) is specified.

Nickel-base Alloys

There are several nickel-base alloys that respond to heat-treatment. These are best known to industry under their trade names, among which can be mentioned "K" monel, "Z" nickel, and Hastelloy. The heat-treatment consists of an aging process and is different from that associated with the light metals. The nickel alloys are heated in sealed containers or in controlled atmospheres with special attention given to the elimination of sulfur. Temperatures range from 1100 to 1600°F with time at temperature varying widely for the aging treatment. These alloys do not require a quench—rather, some are slow cooled to 900°F, while Hastelloy is cooled in air.

SURVEY QUESTIONS

14-1. Why, generally, are engineering components heat-treated?

14-2. Does heat-treating always refer to elevated-temperature processing?

14-3. To what engineering material is heat-treating most frequently applied?

14-4. Is steel of pearlitic structure hard or soft?

14-5. How is an austenitic structure produced in steel?

14-6. What steel structure is obtained by thoroughly quenching austenite?

14-7. What significance has the critical temperature of steel?

14-8. Why is steel tempered in the heat-treating sequence?

14-9. Mention two other expressions for tempering.

14-10. Does isothermal transformation processing generally use an oil quench?

14-11. What element in steel is most important from the standpoint of heat-treatment?

14-12. What effect do alloying elements have upon transformation time?

14-13. Wherein do austempering and tempering differ?

14-14. Would one or both apply to the heat-treatment of an edged tool?

14-15. Should a 1¼-in.-diameter axle shaft of C1040 be heat-treated by isothermal transformation?

14-16. Assume a ball bearing race is AISI-52100 steel. List the correct heat-treating routine in proper sequence.

14-17. Precisely what is meant by the term casehardening?

14-18. Is a carburized component casehardened as a result of the carburizing operation?

14-19. Some specifications call for pot cooling; what does this mean?

14-20. Wherein does gas carburizing differ from pot carburizing?

14-21. Can a component be carburized with the use of salts?

14-22. When a gear has been carburized, what is the next process in the heat-treating cycle?

14-23. Why are gears frequently given a double quench and temper?

14-24. What type of steels lend themselves best to nitriding?

14-25. Is nitriding a practical method for surface hardening?

14-26. Where is liquid nitriding used to best advantage?

14-27. Why are tools frequently steam-treated?

14-28. Are annealing and normalizing applied to the same component in the same series of processing?

14-29. How does normalizing differ from annealing?

14-30. When is quenching used?

14-31. List some end products that should be quenched in brine.

14-32. What quenching medium is usually used for auto transmission gears?

14-33. What is the benefit of martempering?

14-34. What is the simplest instrumentation for satisfactory temperature control in the heat-treat shop?

14-35. Are there any advantages of using controlled-atmosphere furnaces?

14-36. Is it possible to heat-treat gears by using induction heating?

14-37. What is the heat source when flame hardening is used?

14-38. Are nonferrous metals heat-treated similarly to steel?

14-39. What alloys used precipitation heat-treating to advantage?

14-40. What is meant by artificial aging?

14-41. Aluminum-alloy extrusions are usually 60 ft in length. Can they be heat-treated?

14-42. Which area of the magnesium alloys is primarily heat-treated?

14-43. When should alloy steel be specified over plain carbon steel?

14-44. Can a gear that warps in hardening be salvaged?

14-45. A hand reamer and a machine reamer made from the same steel have both been correctly heat-treated; would they both exhibit identical R_c values? Why?

REFERENCES FOR METAL FORMING AND TREATING SECTION

Chaps. 12–14

"Atlas of Isothermal Transformation Diagrams, Supplement," 1953, United States Steel Corporation, Pittsburgh.

"The Closed Die Forging Process," 1954, by Kyle, The Macmillan Company, New York.

"Die Design Handbook," 1955, American Society of Tool Engineers, McGraw-Hill Book Company, Inc., New York.

"Fundamentals of the Working of Metals," 1954, by Sachs, Pergamon Interscience Publishers, Inc., New York.

"The Making, Shaping and Treating of Steel," 7th ed., 1957, United States Steel Corp, Pittsburgh.

"Metallography and Heat Treatment of Iron and Steel," 4th ed., 1935, by Sauveur, Harvard University Press, Cambridge, Mass.

"Metals Handbook," and Supplements, 1948 and later, American Society for Metals, Cleveland.

"Physical Metallurgy," 1952, by Clark and Varney, D. Van Nostrand Company, Inc., Princeton, N.J.

"Press Working of Metals," 1950, by Hinman, McGraw-Hill Book Company, Inc., New York.

"Principles of Physical Metallurgy," 1953, by Doan, McGraw-Hill Book Company, Inc., New York.

"Steel and its Treatment," 4th ed., 1938, by Bullens, John Wiley & Sons, Inc., New York.

"Steel Plates and Their Fabrication," 1947, Lukens Steel Company, Coatesville, Pa.

"Structure of Metals," 1952, by Barrett, McGraw-Hill Book Co., Inc., New York.

"Techniques of Pressworking Steel," 1958, by Eary and Reed, Prentice-Hall, Inc., Englewood Cliffs, N.J.

Chapter 15

TURNING LATHES

In preceding chapters the shaping of metal by either casting or plastic flow at room or elevated temperature was surveyed. In some instances, these methods are sufficient unto themselves while in others supplemented machining operations are needed. Machining provides a means of producing desired surface finishes, dimensional characteristics, and, in some cases, actual forming. These objectives are achieved through the use of an extensive variety of machine tools.

In the machining section that follows, these machine tools and their capabilities are examined. Metal removal is common to all, yet specific types have been developed to meet definite production requirements at profitable cost levels. When a component is being machined, that procedure refers to the removal of metal through chips. This applies to cutting tools as well as to grinding wheels. The tools that are used for chip formation are of basic importance. Single-point tools continue to lead in the development of machining methods. Their importance to machine tool performance can be noted throughout this section devoted to machining, since they are duplicated in the design of milling cutter, broaches, and saws, to mention a few.

Shaping metal through chip removal was undoubtedly first done on a turning machine. Such machine tools are termed lathes in modern phraseology. Lathes had their beginning in antiquity and hence they can properly be credited with the honor of being the progenitor of the machine tool. With the advent of motive power the lathe became capable of a greater range of usefulness and it soon became known as the engine lathe. A further development saw the incorporation of a lead screw, which enables the lathe to increase its scope to include thread cutting. Improved design and constructional features have been continually added to this machine tool, which is currently known as the screw-cutting engine lathe.

The engine lathe is so basic in the machining process that it is treated here at some length. Undoubtedly, this machine tool represents better than any other one the employment of a single-point tool. This being

265

the case, tools can be ground to any conceivable shape and requirement. This possibility aids greatly in the flexibility of the engine lathe. This lathe has been used for just about every category of machining operation. In consequence, an understanding of the engine lathe is basic to the entire area of chip-removal processes.

THE ENGINE LATHE

Engine lathes are classified according to type as bench lathes, standard engine lathes, precision (toolroom) lathes, and special-duty lathes. Each of these types fits a specific class of work. The selection of an engine lathe will therefore be governed by the class of work and production requirements. There are other methods of classification in which design details are the dominant feature. The preponderance of current models

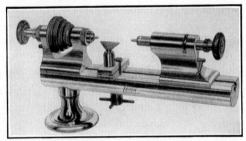

Fig. 15-1. Jeweler's lathe, 3.94-in. swing, 12-in. bed length. (Courtesy of Louis Levin & Son, Inc., Los Angeles.)

are geared-head drives, whereas formerly most were of cone-head design.

Bench Lathes. Bench lathes are built in two basic styles. The smaller is termed a jeweler's, or instrument maker's, lathe and is suited for turning small parts, usually from round stock of wire gage (Fig. 15-1). It has a single pedestal under the headstock end of the bed; thus the latter is open at its other end. These lathes are equipped with a cone pulley fitting a round belt; by this means different turning speeds are obtained.

The bench lathe common to the machine shop is similar in appearance to the standard engine lathe except for size and type of mounting. Obviously, from its name, a bench lathe is built to be mounted on a bench (Fig. 15-2). A bench lathe is a precision machine tool in every sense. This matter of precision is emphasized because a distinction exists between *bench* lathes and *bench-type* lathes.

Bench-type Lathes. Bench-type lathes abound in home workshops; their cost varies with the construction and the degree of accuracy to be expected. There are many of these lathes installed in industrial arts and apprentice training departments, where they serve admirably (Fig. 15-3). When jobs fitting their capacity are available, bench-type lathes are capable of delivering a low-cost product, and for that reason they are included in general machine-shop equipment.

Standard Engine Lathe. The standard, regular, or conventional engine lathe is the most widely used machine tool (Fig. 15-4). The distinguishing feature of a lathe countershaft bolted to the ceiling is rapidly passing from the shop in favor of the current trend toward individually

Fig. 15-2. 10-in. bench toolroom lathe. (Courtesy of Rivett Lathe & Grinder, Inc., Boston.)

driven equipment. This evidence of progress is inserted here merely to provide the occasion for remarking that in the days of the belt-driven, cone-head lathe the beginner was first taught the knack of shifting belts from one step on the cone to the next. The belted lathe had the virtue of being able to slip when the lathe was fouled by the novice!

There are many models of standard engine lathes, both as to specifications and as to manufacturers. The difference between the designs offered by the makers is analogous to that existing in the motorcar field; in other words, all engine lathes perform satisfactorily, but the controls, power applications, and construction vary. The purchaser should predicate his selection on those specifications most nearly meeting his requirements.

Fig. 15-3. Bench-type lathe, cabinet-mounted. (Courtesy of Sheldon Machine Co., Inc., Chicago.)

Fig. 15-4. Precision-type toolroom lathe. (Courtesy of Pratt & Whitney, West Hartford, Conn.)

Functional Design. The standard engine lathe is capable of performing the following operations:

Primary functions

1. Turning
   a. Cylindrical
   b. Taper
   c. Forming
2. Facing
   a. Straight
   b. Forming
   c. Trepanning
3. Boring
   a. Cylindrical
   b. Taper
4. Threading
   a. External
   b. Internal

Secondary functions

1. Drilling
2. Centering
3. Reaming
4. Knurling
5. Parting
6. Chamfering

This listing does not preclude other machining operations from being accomplished by the engine lathe. Lathe operations are performed by rotating the work against a stationary tool, be it lathe tool, boring bar, twist drill, reamer, or any other. When a special setup is used in the lathe, the usual practice is to reverse this procedure by mounting the work on the carriage, where it is held stationary, and placing the cutting tool in a spindle chuck, thereby causing it to rotate. By this method an end milling cutter can be used on a workpiece mounted on the carriage. Another example is that of boring an open-end cylinder by grasping one end of the boring bar in the lathe chuck and placing the opposite end on the tailstock center. These cases are cited as typical of the flexibility of the conventional engine lathe. The extent of this work classification is limited only by the ingenuity of the tool engineer and the degree to which improvisation is permitted or found desirable.

Work-holding Methods

The workpiece needs to be held firmly in order that its rotation contact with the tool will prevent its slipping. There are three general methods for holding the part: gripping it in a chuck which is fastened to the spindle; mounting it on a faceplate; and placing it on centers and driving through a dog contacting a small faceplate, or dog plate. The first method is termed chucking; the last is known as mounting on centers. In the instance of repetitive work where quantities justify the cost of such a procedure, specially built chucking fixtures or work-holding devices are used.

Chucks. It is impossible to make a definite statement about the class of work that is held in chucks. In general, such items as forgings, castings, and relatively short lengths of bar stock are usually considered suitable for this type of mounting. Jobs that require boring or other operations on an inside surface must be held in a chuck or chucking fixture. Lathe chucks are designed around three distinct operating principles. The chuck body is bolted to an adapter plate, or chuck nut, that fits the lathe spindle and is fastened thereto by threaded, cam-lock, or taper and keyed connections. On the opposite side of the body there is a series of jaws three, four, or more in number. These jaws are fitted to move in T slots by means of a screw that has a hollow head fitting the chuck wrench.

Fig. 15-5. Conventional independent four-jaw lathe chuck. (Courtesy of The Skinner Chuck Co., New Britain, Conn.)

The independent type of chuck, which usually has four jaws, is constructed to permit the movement of each jaw separately (Fig. 15-5). Chucks of this type have the advantage of being able to grasp unsymmetrical work. There is a series of concentric grooved circles on the face of the chuck body that greatly aid the operator when chucking symmetrical work, since he can note the position of each jaw with respect to a given circle and then adjust the jaws accordingly.

The universal chuck usually has three jaws, but four are found in some designs. The jaws operate by a scroll that causes them to move in unison. When the workpiece is of a true diameter, it can be chucked centrally by turning only one chuck jaw screw. The difficulty with these chucks arises when careless operators place unsymmetrical work therein and then proceed to tighten the jaws, causing them to spring and lose their alignment. The combination lathe chuck is built to operate either as an independent or a universal chuck. A locking device on the back of the chuck body controls its operation. Lathe chucks are accessory equipment not supplied by the lathe builder.

These lathe chucks all open and close manually. There are other styles of chucks which are rarely found on engine lathes but which are common on automatic and productive equipment. In this category are air-operated chucks, magnetic types which are found on grinding equipment, and also electric chucks. These are used in every case to increase

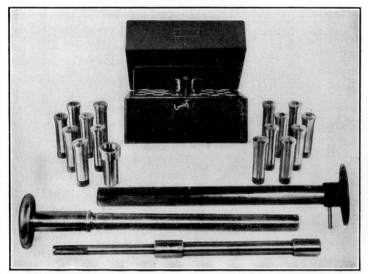

Fig. 15-6. Draw-in collet-chuck equipment, including a range of spring collets. (Courtesy of The Hendey Machine Co., Torrington, Conn.)

the productive potential of the machine through the elimination of manual chucking effort.

Collet Chucks. When small, accurate bar stock is to be machined, a lathe can best be equipped with a collet chuck. There are several designs; all have the same objective of centering and holding the stock accurately. Collet equipment is shown in Fig. 15-6. It consists of spring collets in a range of sizes to fit the bar stock, a draw-in sleeve, a closer, and a knockout rod. The collets themselves are slotted so that they can be compressed around the work, thereby gripping it firmly. Spring collet chucks should be used only to grip finished or machined surfaces. Furthermore, in order to avoid damage to the collet, these chucks should not be used to grip work that is more than 0.002 to 0.003 in. over or 0.005 to 0.008 in. under the nominal size of the collet.

Another development in collet chucks is the Rubber-flex collet. This chuck is mounted directly on the spindle nose. It contains many thin strips of hardened steel bonded together by synthetic rubber. This type of collet has greater flexibility than the spring type. A further advantage is that fewer collets are necessary to cover a range of sizes.

Mounting on Centers. Any workpiece that is of considerable length or otherwise of a shape requiring outboard support should be mounted on centers. Note that the length of the lathe is a limiting factor, since a piece longer than the distance between centers of a lathe cannot be mounted in this manner.

Where exceptionally long pieces are to be machined, the tailstock can be removed and a steady rest set up to support the outboard end (Fig. 15-7). Steady rest mounting is also used where end facing or internal machining is desired. Further, the steady rest is sometimes placed between centers as a means of preventing springing of the workpiece.

Fig. 15-7. Conventional-type steady rest. (Courtesy of The Hendey Machine Co., Torrington, Conn.)

A follower rest which clamps to the carriage and moves with it is also employed as a means of preventing deflection of the workpiece. The follower rest is equipped with two supporting points while the cutting tool acts as a third one.

Prior to mounting, the workpiece must be drilled with a center drill at each end. The center drill produces a 60° angle hole, which fits the angle of the centers. The center in the headstock spindle is termed the live center, since it rotates with the work. The tailstock center is the dead center because it is fixed and the work rotates thereon. Because of this bearing condition, the *tail center must be lubricated* and must be made of hardened tool steel. Where extremely high speeds or heavy cuts are used, the dead center is tipped with a cemented carbide or the tailstock spindle is designed to contain a rotating center. As the workpiece heats up, it expands, which means that the operator must be alert to retract the center in order to prevent burning. The center should at all times be set loosely enough to permit the workpiece to rotate freely but not so loosely as to allow chattering.

The work on centers is driven by a lathe dog whose tail engages a

Fig. 15-8. Turning workpiece held on centers. Drive effected through dog and small face-plate. (Courtesy of Springfield Machine Tool Co., Springfield, Ohio.)

Fig. 15-9. Turning a cast iron component that is mounted on a tapered mandrel.

slot in the faceplate, or dog plate (Fig. 15-8). The dog is fastened by means of a setscrew. Care must be exercised to prevent this screw from marring a finished surface. A piece of soft metal such as copper or aluminum wrapped on the piece under the screw point will prevent disfiguration.

Mandrels. A workpiece that has been bored can be worked on centers by pressing it on a mandrel. The mandrel is hardened and has centers in its ends. There is a slight taper on the mandrel which acts to tighten in the bore as the mandrel is pressed home. Work on a mandrel presents all faces to the tool—an impossibility with a chuck. A conventional mandrel-held operation is pictured in Fig. 15-9. There are a number of different styles of mandrels, such as the cone, expanding, gang, and nut types.

Primary Functions

Straight Turning. Turning is the operation used for reducing an outside diameter. When the workpiece being turned is held by a chuck, fixture, or faceplate, there should be little difficulty about producing a true cylinder. When a taper develops on the workpiece, the difficulty can be traced to one of three sources: (1) tool wear; (2) tool mounted insecurely; (3) the ways of the lathe being worn, permitting uneven travel of the carriage, misalignment of the headstock, or deflection. The first two of these difficulties can be remedied, but a worn lathe bed is beyond repair short of a complete reworking and overhauling.

There is a greater likelihood of obtaining unwanted taper when turning on centers. If the tailstock center is misaligned in a horizontal plane, a taper will result on the workpiece. In consequence it is desirable to check center alignment prior to turning. Prior to placing the live center, the lathe spindle seat should be wiped clean with the finger tips to ensure complete freedom from any foreign particles lodging there. Be sure that the spindle is at rest; otherwise serious personal injury can result. The center itself should be similarly cleaned at the time it is inserted in the lathe spindle. The live center must run true. Its truth can be checked by a dial indicator placed in the tool post. Where extreme accuracy is desired, a very light cut should be taken off the live center to assure its concentricity.

The dead center is placed in the tailstock spindle by applying the precautions used for the live center. With both centers in place, the workpiece is mounted thereon and the tailstock spindle is locked. The cutting tool is set correctly and brought against the workpiece near the live center. The procedure from here on is as follows: Take a cut deep enough to develop a fully turned area on the workpiece. Engage the feed in a direction toward the headstock and machine an area $\frac{1}{2}$ in. in length. Note carefully the reading on the cross-feed dial. Then withdraw the tool and move it to the dead center end and clear of the workpiece. Reset the tool to the precise previous dial reading and, with the power feed engaged, machine a similar area. Check these two turned areas with a micrometer caliper. The amount of setover for the tail-stock will equal one-half the difference of these readings. It is usually necessary to repeat this operation before an accurate setover is obtained.

Taper Turning. A primary asset of the engine lathe is its ability to turn controlled tapers. The conventional lathe offers two distinct methods for accomplishing this end, viz., the setover tailstock for long tapers and the compound rest for short tapers. In addition to these, a taper attachment, which is listed as auxiliary equipment by most lathe manufacturers, makes a third taper turning method possible. The two latter methods can be applied for *internal* as well as *external* tapers, while the setover tailstock one is only possible for external tapers.

The setover tailstock method is difficult, since an accurate setover requires extreme care. The measurement can be made by bringing the tool against the work (assuming correct center alignment), noting the cross-feed dial reading, and then moving the tool the amount of the calculated setover by again reading the dial. The amount of setover is calculated from the specified taper dimensions. A simplified method for calculating the amount of setover is based on reducing taper dimensions to taper per inch. When that value is established, setover is calculated:

$$\text{Setover} = \frac{\text{taper per inch} \times \text{length of workpiece}}{2}$$

Since the small diameter is located at the end of the shaft, the tail center would be set over *toward* the operator. This method of taper turning imposes severe operating stresses on the dead center, since the center in the shaft and the dead center are not concentric.

The compound rest is the preferred method for turning steep tapers (Fig. 15-10). A scale, graduated in degrees, is located at the base of the compound rest. The base is of swivel construction and contains two locking screws. In setting a taper, the witness mark is brought to the desired angle graduation and locked into position. The angle setting is the complement of the angle shown on the drawing when that angle is measured from the center line of the work corresponding to the lathe axis. The procedure varies here somewhat, depending upon the pattern of graduations, which is not the same on all makes of lathes.

The compound rest has a dovetailed slide which is actuated by a screw whose end carries a hand wheel for manual operation. The compound is always manually operated, there being no power feed. A necessary precaution is that of noting the position of the compound at the start of the cut, since sufficient travel is needed to cover the entire length of the taper cut in one setting. Stopping the feed rod and lead screw will guard against accidental engagement of any power feeds on the carriage. It is

Fig. 15-10. Compound rest holding tool post with toolholder. (Courtesy of Reed-Prentice Corp., Worcester, Mass.)

Fig. 15-11. Taper attachment. (Courtesy of Monarch Machine Tool Co., Sidney, Ohio.)

sound practice to check the compound taper setting by means of a vernier bevel protractor.

The taper attachment (Fig. 15-11) is employed on both long and short tapers for center-mounted work. It has the advantage of permitting the workpiece to remain on center alignment, thereby eliminating the overload condition on the dead center and increasing accuracy. The taper attachment carries graduations in terms of taper per foot as well as degrees of taper.

For repetitive work requiring great accuracy, the taper attachment is the answer to taper turning. It is the best method for cutting tapered threads; the threading tool should be set normal to the axis of the work and not perpendicular to the tapered surface.

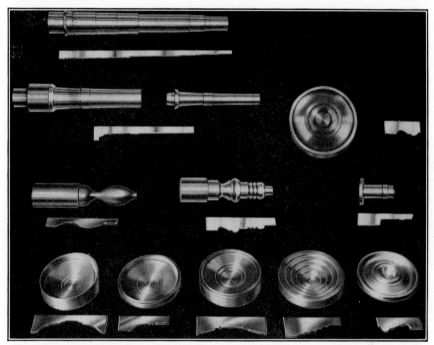

Fig. 15-12. Shaft and profile facing jobs. (Courtesy of The R. K. LeBlond Machine Tool Co., Cincinnati.)

Form Turning and Facing. Accessory equipment is available from some lathe manufacturers for form turning and profile facing (Fig. 15-12). This development permits the use of an engine lathe for accurate form turning—a decided improvement over the tedious manual method of manipulating both cross and longitudinal feeds simultaneously.

Facing. Facing refers to taking a machining cut in a direction normal to the lathe axis. The cutting tool travels *across* the work, in contradistinction to turning, where the tool travels *along* the work. A straight facing cut produces a flat surface. The cutting tool can be manually operated, or, for uniform results, the power cross-feed is engaged. Tool travel can be either from the periphery toward the center or the reverse.

Such considerations as method of mounting, bores, type of materials, and periphery shape are governing factors in deciding tool travel direction.

Precautions are necessary to ensure straight facing cuts. The carriage should be locked to the bed, using the locking screw provided for that purpose. Casting scale may be of sufficient hardness to cause undue tool wear, which will result in a taper on the facing cut. A typical facing operation is pictured in Fig. 15-13. Form facing and profiling are performed on an engine lathe equipped with a form-turning attachment.

Trepanning. Trepanning is a type of facing operation in which a modified parting tool is used for machining a concentric groove from the face side. A cutting-off operation will then part the trepanned piece from its base material (Fig. 15-14).

Fig. 15-13. Typical facing cut on aluminum-alloy casting.

An impressive saving in machining time and material is possible with high-speed trepanning. Gun tubes as well as heavy-walled tubing are of special interest in this new trepanning concept. The solid forging or round bar is trepanned instead of being bored in the conventional manner. The material removed from the bore is in the form of a solid core instead of the chips that result from conventional boring.

Trepanning is gaining in recognition to the extent that there are lathes built primarily for this particular machining operation. On such equipment it is possible to have the tool as well as a workpiece rotate. They turn in opposite directions at similar speeds during the operating cycle. In all trepanning a copious supply of coolant under heavy pressure is needed to flush the chips and maintain a cool bore and tool. On holes above 2 in. in diameter, trepanning has reduced operating time substantially in comparison with former machining techniques.

Boring. Boring is an internal machining operation whose objective is to increase the size of an existing hole or to bring it to concentricity and dimension. For the most part, boring is confined to components gripped in a chuck or chucking fixture or mounted on a faceplate. Boring may take the form of a straight, a taper, or a formed contour.

In all these, the same general principles are used that were discussed in the section on turning. The difference between boring and turning is found in the tooling. Boring requires the use of a boring bar. This tool is available in a variety of designs, both as to mounting and as to method of clamping the cutting tool. The position of the cutting tool edge must

Fig. 15-14. Trepanning operation. Cutting out center of solid bar stock with an L-shaped tool preparatory to parting off collars; note solid bar remaining after trepanning operation is completed. (Courtesy of Lodge & Shipley Co., Cincinnati.)

project beyond the end of the boring bar so that the bore can be made to full depth.

The possibility of deflection in the boring bar is always present during the boring operation. The deflection may be of sufficient magnitude to cause chattering, or, what is worse, to produce a bellmouthed bore. Another defect arising from boring bar deflection is that a taper will result, with the large diameter being on the entering end. This difficulty can be eliminated by taking two cuts in the same direction; however, the boring bar setting must not be altered. A typical boring operation is shown in Fig. 15-15.

The position of the cutting edge of the tool with respect to the horizontal center line of the bore requires attention. It is common practice to set this edge exactly on the center line.

In the majority of boring operations, the tool is moved inward, which means that the boring bar is in compression. This does not always give desired results, because of tool behavior and the diversity of materials being machined. In order to resolve this difficulty, pull boring has been developed. The primary difference between pull boring and the more usual method is that the boring bar is in tension; in consequence, there is a lessened tendency in pull boring for the bar to deflect or bend than when it is used in compression as in "push" boring, the usual type of operation.

Taper bores are made by employing the same techniques that are applied to taper turning. The compound rest and taper attachment methods are applicable. It is a relatively difficult matter to measure a tapered bore. When possible, the male taper should be used as a gage, since such

Fig. 15-15. Boring an aluminum-alloy casting in a typical boring operation. Casting is mounted on a specially designed fixture.

a procedure will save considerable time in bringing the bore taper to a proper fit.

Threading. Threads of all forms can be cut on a screw-cutting engine lathe. They can also be produced in either right- or left-hand lead, as well as in multiple threads. The only limitations are those imposed by the available change gear combinations. The thread pitches that a given lathe is capable of cutting can be read from the index plate on the change gearbox. Thread cutting, both external and internal, is presented in Chap. 18.

Secondary Functions

Lathe operations discussed thus far have been those employing a single-point tool mounted directly or indirectly in the tool post on the carriage. The tailstock has been considered only in respect to holding the dead center. There are several functions that can be performed by replacing the dead center with a cutting tool.

Drilling. Placing a taper-shank twist drill directly in the tailstock makes it possible to drill holes in a workpiece that is rotated by the chuck against the stationary drill. When a straight-shank drill is to be used, it is held in a drill chuck whose shank fits into the tailstock spindle tapered seat. It is desirable to place a lathe dog or other clamping device on the drill in order to prevent its rotation in the tailstock spindle.

Centering. A center drill, held in a drill chuck, is used to drill a small 60° hole in the end of the workpiece. The hole depth is governed by the function it is to perform. If it is to act as a starter for a following drilling operation, the center may be drilled to an appreciable depth. If, on the other hand, the center hole is intended for mounting the workpiece on centers, the center hole should not be large. The center drill pilot, being small, is prone to break off under conditions of too low rotation speed, heavy crowding, or roughened stock ends. Carelessness here will result in a broken pilot embedded in the workpiece where it will be difficult to remove or the workpiece will need to be scrapped.

A twist drill placed in the tailstock spindle will tend to follow the previously drilled center hole. Should the twist drill develop a tendency to wander, it can be guided by bringing pressure against it with the tool-holder in the tool post. When drilling a deep hole, the drill should be backed off occasionally to free the chips.

Reaming. Machine reamers are made with taper shanks that permit their placement in the tailstock spindle after the manner of a twist drill. A reaming operation is always a delicate one requiring judgment on the part of the lathe operator. A reamer should never be turned in a reverse direction. The correct amount of stock should be left for removal by the reamer—too much stock should never be allowed. Improper attention to correct reaming procedure will lead to chatter marks or a broken reamer. Excellent results are possible with lathe reaming; this is especially true when the reamer is used to follow the boring bar.

The sequence of operations for producing an accurate hole in solid stock starts with the center, or starting, drill. A drilling operation follows, wherein more drills of increasingly larger diameters are used. A boring operation may or may not be used then, depending on stock structure, to bring the drilled hole to concentricity and also to size it for the reaming operation. There should be about 0.005 to 0.015 in. stock remaining for the machine reamer to clean up to exact size. In these operations all the tools used are positioned in the tailstock spindle excepting only the boring bar, which is held in the tool post.

Parting. A parting cut is a cutting-off operation in which a narrow-bladed tool whose cross section resembles a trapezium is used. Since the tool is narrow and its end is unsupported, it has a tendency to deflect and chatter unless its cutting point is accurately positioned at the horizontal axis of the stock being cut. The cutting edge should be slightly tapered in order that there be a leading point which will cut through cleanly.

Chamfering. It is generally undesirable to permit sharp corners to remain on finished work. Breaking the corners, such as rim edges and entrances to bores, is known as chamfering. The operation consists of bringing the edge of the turning tool against the offending corner and relieving it so that a beveled surface results. Should a chamfer of any appreciable amount be required, the compound rest is used in order to machine the designed angle.

Knurling. This produces a surface that has a raised pattern for nonslip gripping. The knurling tool consists of a pair of narrow hardened steel rollers carrying a crosshatch pattern on their periphery. Rollers are rigidly held in a head or shank so they can rotate about their centers. One style of knurling tool holds three pairs of knurling rollers in which each succeeding pair has a finer configuration pattern. The head floats in a holder to permit the chosen pair of rollers to engage the workpiece uniformly. The rollers are forced against the workpiece under considerable pressure and are caused to turn by the former's rotation. The longitudinal movement of the knurling tool can be activated either by power or by manual feed.

Construction of the Engine Lathe

The design of engine lathes varies with the different manufacturers and also between the models within one line. As a result engine lathes have considerably different appearances even though they are all designed to perform similar functions.

The principal components of an engine lathe are the bed with its supporting mountings and the headstock with its accompanying drive, carriage, and tailstock. In addition to these main members, there is a change gear train, gearbox, feed rod, and lead screw. These are delineated in Fig. 15-16 together with additional functional features.

Lathe Bed. The bed is a gray iron casting because of this material's ability to dampen vibrations and provide excellent wearing surfaces. There are several cross ribs integrally cast into the bed for rigidity and stiffness. The length of the bed is commonly given as the dimension for specifying the size of an engine lathe; for example, a 13–6 lathe is one that can swing a 13-in.-diameter workpiece (or its equivalent) and that has a bed 6 ft long over-all.

The top of the bed has machined ways which guide the longitudinal movement of both the carriage and the tailstock and also position the headstock for alignment. The ways, which are usually of an inverted V

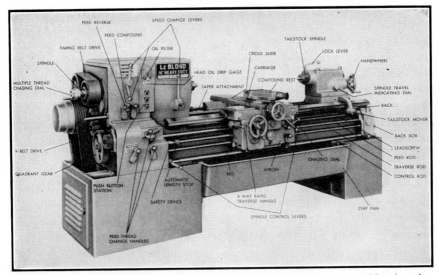

Fig. 15-16a. Nomenclature of the components of a conventional-type geared-head engine lathe. (Courtesy of the R. K. LeBlond Machine Tool Co., Cincinnati.)

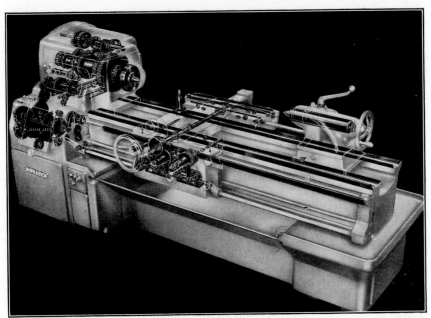

Fig. 15-16b. Phantom illustration of a geared head lathe showing power transmission and operating gearing. (Courtesy of the Monarch Machine Tool Co., Sidney, Ohio.)

shape, are generally integral with the bed casting. On some designs the ways are flame-hardened and ground to alignment. The accuracy of the ways determines in great part the performance that can be expected from the lathe; worn ways cannot produce precision machine work. On the front side of the bed, below the ways, there is a geared rack bolted into position. The rack serves for moving the carriage, either manually or by power, through a gear train in the apron.

The lathe bed is mounted on legs at its ends. The trend is toward cabinet legs under the headstock, since this design permits housing the driving motor there in an inconspicuous out-of-the-way place. There may or may not be a chip pan located under the bed.

Lathe Headstock. The headstock is, in effect, a transmission. It receives its power from an individual motor in most designs and transmits the power to the workpiece. The headstock also delivers power to the change gear train for driving the carriage or cross-feed (Fig. 15-16a). For the most part, lathe headstocks are equipped with gear trains for imparting various rotational speeds and power increments to the workpiece.

A lathe spindle is a hollow shaft carrying an internal taper at its nose end. The taper is of a standard that will accommodate lathe centers and collet chuck components. The diameter of the hole through the spindle is important, since it limits the maximum size of bar stock that can be projected through the spindle. The nose of the spindle is designed to hold the chuck, faceplate, or other work-carrying fixture. Formerly the nose carried a straight thread ending at a shoulder; there was no standardization in this construction. Present designs conform to American Standard B5.9—1954,[1] which features two types of spindle nose, designated as D-1 and type L, respectively (Fig. 15-17). All dimensions and pertinent information regarding these are found in the above-mentioned standard. The use of constant surface cutting speed is of definite interest in production turning operations. It involves the determination of the correct cutting speed for a given material, then the maintenance of that speed on all diameters throughout the machining cycle. Although d-c drives are common on machine tools, that in itself does not constitute constant speed. Rather a lathe equipped with constant cutting speed control means that the motor speed must be synchronized with tool movement and rate of feed. Lathes equipped with d-c drives and constant surface speed control are especially valuable for machining large-diameter parts and for facing operations where surface finish is a principal factor.

The spindle influences the quality of production, since deflection or any other shortcoming of the spindle immediately becomes apparent in the workpiece. The condition of the spindle bearings, regardless of

[1] "Standard for Spindle Noses," American Standards Association, New York.

bearing type, is critical. The height of the spindle governs the swing of a lathe, because a workpiece cannot be held in a lathe whose maximum diameter measures more than two times the distance from the center of the spindle to the ways of the lathe bed. The gap bed affords a means of increasing the swing of a lathe for workpieces held in a chuck or on a faceplate. Gap bed design permits either the removal of a block section of the bed entirely or sliding a divided bed section longitudinally.

Fig. 15-17. Type D-1, camlock spindle nose. (Courtesy of Monarch Machine Tool Co., Sidney, Ohio.)

Change Gear Train. The general location of the first gear of the change gear train is at the spindle end opposite the nose. This gear train functions to transmit both power and speed of rotation to the change gearbox. In some designs there are tumbler gears for the purpose of changing the direction of rotation of the feed rod and lead screw.

The gearbox, located on the side of the bed and below the headstock (Fig. 15-18), carries a series of gears so arranged that different speeds of rotation can be given to the feed rod and lead screw. An index plate on the front of the gearbox indicates the feed and screw thread pitch for each setting. The range covered by a gearbox is noted on its index plate.

The feed rod is a plain shaft with a spline running its entire length. Mounted in the apron is a floating sleeve equipped with bevel gears at its ends that is keyed to the feed rod. It is by this construction that power and motion are transmitted to the carriage.

The lead screw, on the other hand, is threaded most of its length. A split nut inside the apron can be made to clamp on this screw as a means of driving the carriage for thread-cutting operations. Note the difference in function: *The lead screw is used only for cutting threads and never for any other purpose.* On some lathes the lead screw and feed rod are combined into one; in such instances there is a spline in the lead screw.

Lathe Carriage. The carriage is composed of saddle, apron, cross slide, and compound rest. The saddle is an H-shaped casting that rides on the

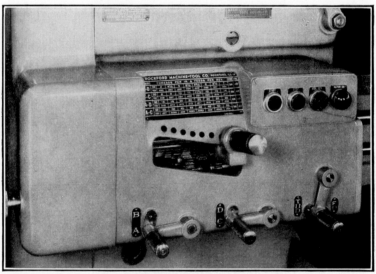

Fig. 15-18. Change gearbox, quick-change type. (Courtesy of Rockford Machine Tool Co., Rockford, Ill.)

lathe ways. It carries the cross slide and compound rest mechanisms and the taper attachment when one is present. The apron is fastened to the saddle in a position normal to it. All the operating mechanisms for power longitudinal and cross-feeds as well as thread cutting are housed in the apron (Figs. 15-19 and 15-20).

The chief variations in lathe design center around the construction and operation of the apron. There are some designs that have an apron reverse whose purpose it is to change feed travel direction. The matter of clutch design within the apron is also variable. Controls and safety features are found in varying degrees in all apron mechanisms. The apron also carries the handwheel that moves the carriage longitudinally. This is the larger of the two handwheels on the front of the carriage.

The smaller handwheel, which is equipped with a graduated dial for setting the depth of cut, operates the cross-feed.

Lathe Tailstock. The tailstock, or footstock, as it is also termed, consists of two castings. The lower one is machined to fit the bed ways and

Fig. 15-19. Lathe apron, top view. Operating levers on front of apron, left to right: split nut, apron reverse, cross-feed clutch, longitudinal-feed clutch, and longitudinal-feed handwheel. (Courtesy of Rockford Machine Tool Co., Rockford, Ill.)

Fig. 15-20. Lathe apron, rear view. Split nut at left in open position. Bevel gears at bottom provide apron reverse. This design employs separate lead screw and feed rod. (Courtesy of Rockford Machine Tool Co., Rockford, Ill.)

slide thereon. The upper casting, which is tongued to the lower one, is equipped with a spindle. The latter can be extended or withdrawn by means of a handwheel. The tailstock has two clamping screws that engage a clamp fitting the underside of the bed ways. The clamping feature is used to hold the tailstock in position on the ways. There is a locking lever for maintaining spindle position. The tailstock is moved along the bed manually; however, on large lathes there is a geared mechanism for this purpose. The tailstock can be removed from the lathe by loosening the clamp and sliding it off the end of the bed. There are horizontal screws on each side of the tailstock that are used for moving the upper section in order to shift the center horizontally for taper turning. It is always well to check this setting before using a lathe for cylindrical turning in order to be sure that the tail center is in correct alignment.

Attachments for Engine Lathes

The taper turning attachment is a leading example of supplementary equipment capable of simplifying a lathe operation. A thread chasing dial is indispensable for thread cutting; that this is recognized is indicated by the fact that many builders include the dial as standard equipment.

Less commonly known is the micrometer carriage stop, which offers an accurate means of measuring longitudinal travel of the carriage. The stop clamps to the top of the lathe bed and is equipped with a spindle whose extension is controlled by a micrometer dial. A machined boss on the edge of the carriage is brought into contact with the spindle end. This device is not to be confused with automatic carriage stops, which are used for spacing the position of shoulders or grooves on a workpiece.

In the second category of attachments are those that extend the scope of lathe functions. Included are such items as bed turrets, which replace the tailstock and transform the engine lathe into a turret lathe. Milling attachments of various kinds are available, as is grinding equipment. Others are gear cutting, cutter relieving, and rapid traverse attachments. Taken together, such supplemental equipment is of interest where the cost of a machine tool is not justified for a special job.

A somewhat different aspect of accessory equipment is to be found in the field of contour turning, especially production turning. In the former instance, there are several systems available whose mechanisms may be controlled by mechanical, hydraulic, pneumatic, or electrical devices as well as electronic (NC) Chap. 18). A well-established electrical control is known as the Walker (Fig. 15-21), while the Bailey pneumatic-hydraulic system has also found many adherents.

Repetitive turning on a production basis is possible on a standard engine lathe that requires only a control attachment conversion unit. This type of equipment is proving popular because of its ability to reduce turning costs substantially. The basis of the duplicating method is that of generating work shapes from a template, or master, by means of a hydraulically controlled cutting tool. This design permits the tool to make an uninterrupted cut over the workpiece, regardless of contours such as shoulders, tapers, and the like. Motor shafts, spindles, valve stems,

Fig. 15-21. Engine lathe equipped with a Walker hydraulic duplicator. (Courtesy of Boye and Emmes Machine Tool Co., Cincinnati.)

and piston rods are examples of components readily adapted to this type of production turning.

Specialized Lathes

There are lathe designs fitted to special work. They are, in effect, engine lathes suited to one particular type of work. Some depart widely from engine lathes in appearance as well as design. A center-drive axle lathe is an example, since the drive is located on the center of the lathe bed and there is a footstock at each end, the headstock, as such, being omitted (Fig. 15-22).

Other lathes fitting into the category of specialized equipment are oil-country lathes which feature an excessively large opening through the headstock, roll-turning lathes used for machining rolling-mill rolls, and crankshaft turning lathes that find their field of usefulness in automotive-engine and similar shops. The best method of describing this lathe classification is to state that when a turning problem of a specialized nature offers sufficient production possibilities, the lathe builders are capable of producing a piece of equipment that will effect a solution.

Examples include such designs as the one shown in Fig. 15-23. This lathe is a conventional type except that it has an unusually long bed,

Fig. 15-22. Betts-Bridgeford center-drive axle turning lathe equipped with two carriages. (Courtesy of Consolidated Machine Tool Corp., Rochester, N.Y.)

Fig. 15-23. Extended bed lathe, 252-in. capacity between centers. This lathe is equipped with three front-turning carriages and three heavy-duty steady rests. Equipment shown was used for turning 105-mm high-velocity gun tubes. (Courtesy of Seneca Falls Machine Co., Seneca Falls, N.Y.)

which makes possible its use on long shafts and pipe work. Lathes having an exceptionally large swing also belong in this classification.

SURVEY QUESTIONS

15-1. Is the metal removal operation similar on all types of machine tools?
15-2. Explain the term "engine lathe."
15-3. What is a single-point tool?

15-4. What type lathe would be installed in a tool and die shop?

15-5. What are the basic functions that can be performed on an engine lathe?

15-6. What is the meaning of the term "independent chuck"?

15-7. Why is there a series of concentric circles on the face of an independent chuck?

15-8. On what class of work are universal chucks used?

15-9. Should collet chucks be used for castings or forgings?

15-10. Are the centers of the lathe interchangeable as to function?

15-11. Is it desirable to back off the tail center during turning?

15-12. What is a dog plate?

15-13. Is it possible to prevent a piece being turned on centers from deflecting?

15-14. What is a lathe mandrel?

15-15. Will a piece being turned on centers always be truly cylindrical?

15-16. On an engine lathe, where is the taper attachment located?

15-17. A rear axle shaft for an automobile is being machined as a repair job. What would be the best way to set it up for turning the taper at the wheel end?

15-18. Does the lathe carriage travel during a facing operation?

15-19. Is trepanning more economical on material than boring?

15-20. Are boring and drilling the same operation?

15-21. Is there any limitation on the thread type, style, or pitch that can be cut on a screw-cutting engine lathe?

15-22. How is it possible to determine the various screw pitches that a given lathe will cut?

15-23. Is it possible to cut metric threads on a standard screw-cutting engine lathe?

15-24. When would a parting tool be used?

15-25. Is it possible to tell from a drawing whether chamfer is to be used?

15-26. Give an example of a component in which knurling is necessary.

15-27. How is the size of an engine lathe stated?

15-28. What two characteristics of a lathe spindle should be carefully evaluated when purchasing a lathe?

15-29. Where is the change gear train located on a lathe?

15-30. Which part of the lathe carriage holds the compound rest?

15-31. By what mechanism is the carriage translated along the lathe bed?

15-32. Does the half nut engage the feed rod for driving the carriage during turning or boring?

15-33. Is it possible to measure accurately the longitudinal travel of the carriage?

15-34. Mention one specialized lathe and give its function.

15-35. A section of a tailshaft for a ship is 40 ft in length and 11 in. OD with connected flanges at each end 18 in. OD and is finished all over. On what machine tool could such a shaft be machined?

Chapter 16

TURRET LATHES

The turret lathe came into being as the result of new requirements in the metal shaping industry. The evolution of the idea of interchangeability of parts manufacture gave rise to new concepts of machining. A demand was developed for the repetition of accuracy over a substantial number of identical components. These new conditions were met by a revision of engine lathe construction through replacing the tailstock with a tool-carrying member termed a turret. The turret, whose original shape was cylindrical, was provided with a series of equally spaced mounting holes. Each of these holes, or stations, carried a tool arranged in a succession corresponding with the sequence of the machining operations to be performed on the workpiece. This tooling arrangement provided for both speedy and accurate machining.

The trend of current turret lathe design is toward both greater production and increased precision. These objectives are achieved by the combination of expert tooling and dependable equipment. Tooling a turret lathe for optimum performance is a task that demands of the tool engineer knowledge and vision of a high order.

Classification of Turret Lathes. Fundamentally turret lathes can be classified as either horizontal or vertical, depending upon the direction of the main axis. Horizontal types are in the majority, primarily because they can be adapted to a greater range of work.

HORIZONTAL TURRET LATHES

Horizontal turret lathes fit two general patterns so far as the class of work they will take care of is concerned. On this basis they are divided into the bar type and the chucking type. This terminology refers primarily to the raw material classification fitted to each. The bar-type turret lathe (Fig. 16-1) is specified for use with bar stock of every shape known to engineering production, be it round, square, hexagonal, or other. Since bar stock is of uniform cross section throughout its length, the stock is held by means of collets in the headstock. Jawed chucks

292

can also be used on bar-type machines when the workpiece is a forging or a casting.

The chucking type of turret lathe (Fig. 16-2) is designed primarily for machining forgings and castings. Workpieces of this type are held in a chuck mounted on the spindle nosepiece. There is a wide range of chucks available, ranging from two-jaw types through the conventional ones to specialized chucking fixtures. The need for such diversity arises from the multiplicity of shapes that forgings and castings attain. The

Fig. 16-1. Bar-type turret lathe in operation. Note bar stock under coolant stream. (Courtesy of Bardons and Oliver, Inc., Cleveland.)

chucking type of turret lathe can also generally be equipped with collets for bar work.

Another method of classification of turret lathes is based on the turret mounting. The main ones are the saddle and the ram types. The former has heavier construction throughout the entire lathe than does the ram type. The point of difference between them is traceable to the construction of the turret setting.

Saddle Type. The saddle type of turret is built with the turret mounted on a saddle that can be moved along the bed ways. The saddle is complemented by an apron that in appearance resembles engine lathe construction. The apron houses mechanisms for longitudinal saddle travel by both power and manual operation. There is also provision for power rapid traverse, a desirable feature for returning the saddle because of its comparatively long travel during the machining cycle.

Fixed-center turret construction is one in which the center of the operating turret station coincides with the lathe axis; there is no movement of the turret tool other than the longitudinal. If, then, a facing or similar machining operation is desired, that feature must be built into the tooling independently of the turret. The turret mounting is such that it must be indexed manually and then clamped into position by an extending side lever.

The cross-sliding turret is built to permit sidewise movement of the entire turret. This construction is of decided convenience where facing

Fig. 16-2. Large chucking-type turret lathe tooled for machining an aluminum air cylinder body. (Courtesy of Gisholt Machine Co., Madison, Wis.)

cuts need to be taken. A stop roll unit, located beneath the saddle, controls the longitudinal movement of the turret for a given cut. The cross-sliding turret is adaptable to machining contours, counterbores, threading, and internal tapers. It adds considerable scope to the potentialities of the turret lathe especially for short-run production and jobbing work.

The side-hung carriage is usually associated with the saddle turret. Its advantages—traceable to its cantilever construction, which provides no contact with the rear bed way—are found in permitting greater swing capacity. The carriage houses the operating mechanisms and work stops. The latter feature provides the means for producing duplicate parts without the necessity of measuring each one independently. Stops can be relied upon to produce repetitive work to limits of ±0.001 in. on the longitudinal dimensions.

Ram Type. On a ram-type turret there is a decided difference in turret mounting. The ram type does have a saddle; however, the latter fastens to the bed and the turret slides in a longitudinal direction thereon as the means of feeding the turret tool into the workpiece. Ram-type construction is found on bar as well as on chucking turret lathes. The ram type is readily distinguished by a prominently spoked turnstile handle with its end knobs (Fig. 16-3). This device functions to move the turret in longitudinal travel. In addition, by bringing the turret to the end of its travel,

Fig. 16-3. Ram-type universal turret lathe tooled for chuck work. (Courtesy of Jones & Lamson Machine Co., Springfield, Vt.)

on the reverse stroke it automatically indexes the turret. The stop screws controlling longitudinal turret travel are located at the rear of the turret slide.

The ram type of turret is usually equipped with a reach-over type of carriage because this lathe is used largely on bar work. The reach-over type rides on both bed ways and, in some designs, is supported by a lower rail. Because of its construction it is possible to add tooling at the rear or opposite to the square turret. The cross-slide unit, on any design, can be operated simultaneously with the turret; in this way, combined cuts can be taken on the workpiece.

Turret lathes can be provided with additional equipment. Taper turning attachments are of decided convenience where there is any appreciable amount of taper turning to be done. This attachment is placed on the front rather than the rear of the carriage. It is also possible to equip a turret lathe for thread chasing by the installation of additional components consisting of a lead screw with its accompanying split nut.

Headstocks. Headstock design for turret lathes does not follow a single pattern. The most elementary headstock design has a cone pulley drive. The construction is used only on small turret lathes, occasionally termed hand turret lathes. It is limited in the two essentials of power and speed range.

Spindle speed of wide range is available with the electric spindle turret lathe. A variable-speed electric motor is connected directly to the spindle

Fig. 16-4. Automatic turret lathe equipped with hydraulic controls. (Courtesy of Gisholt Machine Co., Madison, Wis.)

inside the headstock housing. Speeds as high as 3,600 rpm are obtainable with this type of drive. There is a single lever controlling forward and reverse in addition to the full speed range. Light work such as nonferrous alloys, plastics, and small ferrous parts are best suited to turret lathes embodying this headstock construction.

It is in the heavy equipment, however, that headstock development has shown marked progress. All turret lathe builders offer a type of geared construction. Some of these are built with a series of control levers for spindle speed changes since there are a substantial number of the latter available. A simplified headstock control employs but a single lever which functions in connection with a small handwheel located at the side. This arrangement is termed a preselector because of the fact that the operator can select a succeeding speed while the lathe is in operation by merely turning the handwheel until the desired spindle speed is set.

Power is generally delivered to a geared headstock through a single pulley-type drive. Power application is made through clutches that are located on the main drive pulley shaft. Both forward and reverse spindle rotation are available by means of separate clutches which are frequently of the multiple-disk type.

Automatic Turret Lathes. The substitution of various types of automatic control for manual operation is proving to be a revelation. Figure

Fig. 16-5. Electro-cycle turret lathe equipped with toggle switch panel for quick setup of control circuits. (Courtesy of the Warner & Swasey Co., Cleveland.)

16-4 portrays the use of a hydraulic control system. Conventional turret mounting and hand controls have been eliminated in favor of a hydraulic system. The entire appearance of the lathe has undergone revision. The multiplicity of levers has been replaced by a simple, easily operated hydraulic system. All this has been accomplished without sacrificing anything in the way of metal-cutting possibilities.

In harmony with automatic turning lathe design, turret lathes are employing various control systems. An example of an electrical control to provide automatic operation for the turret lathe is pictured in Fig. 16-5. Among the features of this design is one for providing an electrical brake on the spindle that causes it to stop at exactly the same position each time. The particular model shown is especially recommended for machining brass, although it is also adapted to the other nonferrous alloys and plastic materials.

Automatic turret lathes are built for heavy-duty operation. Production potentials are high with a design like that shown in Fig. 16-6, since it has two spindles and dual tooling on the turret faces. The automatic features of this machine are such that changes of speed and feed can be accomplished while the machine is under cutting load. Automatic spindle stop is provided, permitting tools to return to neutral position without unnecessarily scoring the work.

Fig. 16-6. Two-spindle automatic turret lathe. (Courtesy of Potter & Johnson Co., Pawtucket, R.I.)

Automatic horizontal turret lathes have all the advantages of the conventional ones plus the gains resulting from an automatic cycle that relieves the operator of many manual duties. The nature of an automatic cycle is such that it tends to pace the operator, thereby establishing a dependable rate of production. There are some disadvantages to be considered, such as higher initial investment and increased tooling time; yet these are not significant where production runs are of a magnitude that will justify the installation of automatic equipment.

VERTICAL TURRET LATHES

Turret lathes are specified machine tool equipment primarily for turning, boring, and facing operations, including their modifications such as counterboring, chamfering, grooving, radii, and the like. Castings and forgings requiring several turned surfaces are especially well adapted to turret lathes. However, as these elements increase in size they become more difficult to place in a horizontal turret lathe. This problem is solved by the vertical turret lathe. One equipped with a five-sided turret located on the horizontal crossrail is shown in Fig. 16-7. Its location is such that

Fig. 16-7. Vertical turret lathe, showing ram head (left), vertical turret and sidehead (right). (Courtesy of The Bullard Co., Bridgeport, Conn.)

it can be traveled vertically in two directions as well as horizontally, forward and reverse. These movements can be conducted either under power or manually. In addition, a rapid traverse is available as a power drive. The turret is indexed by means of a crank located on its front face.

A side turret head entirely independent of the main turret is mounted at the side. It moves vertically as well as horizontally and permits machining a second operation concurrently with the main turret; such procedure is termed *combined cutting*. All operations are possible with the sidehead, although boring is done principally with the vertical turret.

When two or more cuts are taken from the same station at the same time, the procedure is known as *multiple cutting*.

Vertical Turret Lathe Table. Vertical turret lathes are equipped with a circular table that is, in effect, a chuck, or has a chuck built into it. In addition, there are T slots in the table face for strapping on fixtures or clamping the workpiece directly. There is an accurately machined straight hole in the center of the table where plugs can be inserted as a means of locating fixtures for concentric rotation. The table is the basic locating and gaging surface for the vertical turret lathe and should be given the consideration that such a critical member deserves. A vertical turret lathe is specified as to size by the diameter of the table; thus a 36-in. vertical turret means that the table has a 36-in. diameter.

Automatic Vertical Turret Lathes. Repetitive work is best machined on an automatic vertical turret lathe. The vertical automatic turret is constructed so that it can be operated either manually or automatically.

TURRET LATHE TOOLING

Genuine production gains resulting in low machining cost can be had from correctly engineered turret lathe tooling. The tooling equipment is reflected in the ingenuity of the tool engineer. Total production time for any turret lathe job is comprised of three elements: setup, handling, and cutting time. It is the responsibility of the tool engineer to keep each of these three elements in their proper perspective regardless of production lot size.

Two broad basic principles to be observed are present in the bar type and chucking type respectively. Insofar as the bar type is concerned, the cutting tool can generally be arranged so that the bar stock is supported, in the manner of a steady rest, opposite to the cutting edge by rollers adjustable to stock size. This type of tooling is termed box tooling. A universal set of representative tools should be the basis of any tooling program; these tools can be adapted to a range of bar stock sizes. A group of universal bar-type tools is shown in Fig. 16-8. This group should be augmented by such additional items as a drill chuck, a self-opening die head, and flanged toolholders. Since bar turner cutters are usually held in a semivertical position, the cutting angles are ground on the top end rather than the side. Care must be exercised in getting the cutting edge and the rollers in proper position.

The tooling for chucking-type turret lathes varies considerably from bar equipment, since it tends in the direction of boring and turning. A further difference arises because castings and forgings do not follow the uniform cross section of bar work. A variety of tool heads and holders are necessary for chucking work. Heavy work demanding rigidity in the setup employs overhead pilot bars (Figs. 16-3 and 16-4). There is no such thing as a standard tooling setup for a turret, inasmuch as each job is in effect an individual problem. It seems wiser to adopt tooling to fit the necessities of a given workpiece than it is to attempt to use some

A

B

Fig. 16-8. Turret lathe tools. (A) Single cutter turner, (B) multiple cutter turner. (Courtesy of Bardons and Oliver, Inc., Cleveland.)

so-called standard tooling setup just because it may be on hand. By way of illustration, Figs. 16-9 and 16-10 show the tooling for a gear blank casting. Note that the square turret carries a substantial amount of tooling while the hexagon turret has two skip-index stations.

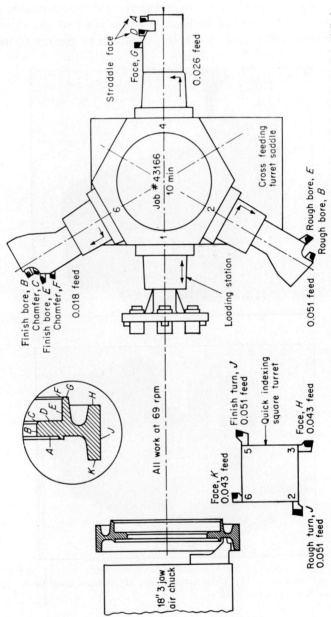

Straddle face

Face, G

D A

0.026 feed

Job #43166
10 min

4

Cross feeding
turret saddle

6

1

2

Rough bore, E
Rough bore, B

0.051 feed

Loading station

Finish bore, B
Chamfer, C
Finish bore, E
Chamfer, F

0.018 feed

All work at 69 rpm

B C D E F G H

A

J

K

Finish turn, J
0.051 feed

Quick indexing
square turret

Face, H
0.043 feed

5

3

6

2

Face, K
0.043 feed

Rough turn, J
0.051 feed

18" 3 jaw
air chuck

Fig. 16-9. Outline drawing of tooling for machining a gear blank casting. (Courtesy of Gisholt Machine Co., Madison, Wis.)

Vertical turret tooling has but five stations to work with on the main turret. The square side turret provides additional tooling space, which is utilized to the extent that the workpiece will permit. Figure 16-11 is included to show the tooling layout for a typical casting. The sequence of operations is designed to give the best possible cutting time for the job.

Fundamental Tooling Considerations. In the operation of a turret lathe the over-all time required for machining a given workpiece equals the sum of the individual times for cutting, setup, and handling. Of these three elements, cutting time is the function of feed and speed which, in turn, is governed by the capabilities of the turret lathe and the tool material and design of the cutters.

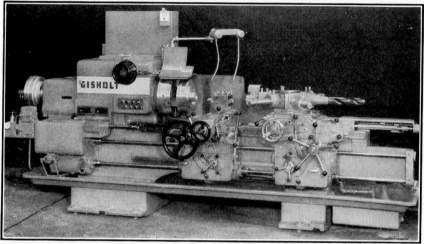

Fig. 16-10. Turret lathe tooled with gear blank tooling shown in preceding figure. (Courtesy of Gisholt Machine Co., Madison, Wis.)

Setup time is related to the tooling, since the simplicity of the tooling layout controls this factor. Any complications arising from special connections, and the like, will make themselves known by increasing the time required to set up the job.

Handling time should be broken down into its elements: loading and unloading time as one set of factors, and machine handling or operating time as the second component. Machine operating or handling time is governed by the design of the turret lathe and the ability of the operator. On automatic turret lathes the automatic cycle governs both the cutting time and the indexing and tool approach time. These are then known as the cycle time, over which the operator has no control once the machine has been set up.

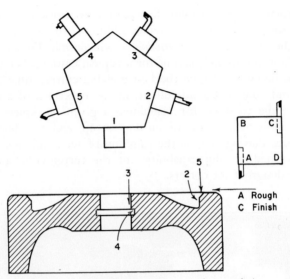

Fig. 16-11. Tooling layout for vertical turret lathe.

1. Skip index
A. Rough face
2. Rough and finish form snap diameter
3. Rough and finish bore
4. Form oil groove
C. Finish face
5. Chamfer

Fig. 16-12. Drum-type turret head lathe. (Courtesy of Gildemeister, Bielefeld, West Germany.)

Drum-type Turret Head. Another innovation in turret lathe design is the one which uses a drum-type head located in a vertical plane, rotating on an axis parallel to a lathe bed. This type design is of special interest where precision work is to be machined. An advantage of this design is that the head not only moves in a longitudinal direction but it can also be rotated about its own axis. This combination makes possible some very simple tooling for facing and kindred operations. Depending upon the design of the workpiece, it is possible to utilize three different tools working simultaneously. For example, a boring bar or tool can be used together with a turning tool located to the right and to the left. An example of such a turret lathe is shown in Fig. 16-12. The turret head is shown at the center while some of the operating mechanisms are located at either end. It is not uncommon for such equipment to have hydraulic as well as pneumatic clamping and feeding devices.

SURVEY QUESTIONS

16-1. What is the origin of the term "turret lathe"?

16-2. How can a turret lathe be distinguished from an engine lathe?

16-3. What is the basic consideration for acquiring a turret lathe?

16-4. How can a saddle-type turret be distinguished from a ram-type?

16-5. Are turret lathes used for machining individual castings or forgings?

16-6. Mention a component of an automobile chassis that should be machined on a turret lathe wholly or in part.

16-7. Is turret lathe tooling confined to the turret itself?

16-8. Are there turret lathe designs in which there is more than one turret per machine?

16-9. Assume that a turret lathe is tooled for the production of gudgeon pins. What type of turret lathe would be best?

16-10. Are turret lathes always single-spindle machines?

16-11. How is the size of a vertical turret lathe specified?

16-12. A 24-in. OD steel gear blank casting is to be machined, including the hub. What type of machine tool should be chosen for machining such a casting?

16-13. What is a box tool?

16-14. Are there any advantages in using a multiple cutter?

16-15. Is unloading time a critical consideration in developing turret lathe tooling?

16-16. Wherein does a drum-type turret head differ from a conventional one?

16-17. What factors would enter into a decision as between machining components on an engine lathe or on a horizontal turret lathe?

16-18. Can a vertical turret lathe be considered as flexible as a horizontal type?

16-19. Are turret lathes included in toolroom equipment? Why?

16-20. Explain whether screw threads can be cut on a turret lathe.

Chapter 17

AUTOMATIC LATHES, CHUCKING MACHINES, AND SCREW MACHINES

AUTOMATIC LATHES

The automatic lathe embodies all the capacities of a single-spindle turning lathe with the addition of multiple tooling on a simultaneous cut. The automatic lathe is capable of carrying multiple tooling in a versatile arrangement that permits machining operations of similar or different characteristics to be performed at the same time. A second unique feature is its operating cycle. The sequence of machining a given workpiece, once decided upon, is set on the lathe's mechanism so that operation becomes entirely automatic.

It is possible to adapt the automatic lathe to short-run production, especially where a variety of workpieces have some dimensional requirements—face widths, for example—in common. Adjustments of this type are considerably less time-consuming than is a complete change-over from one style of workpiece to another. It is frequently possible to make such adjustments to fit small-lot production and still run the job at a saving over conventional lathe operation.

The automatic lathe can be applied to bar stock, forgings, and castings. Its greatest field of usefulness is in machining work held on centers. Thus, for example, the automatic lathe shown in Fig. 17-1 is available in a series of models ranging up to 17½-in. swing with center distances as great as 87 in. and 75-hp input. The automatic lathe is generally of shorter bed length, for the same swing, than is an engine lathe of similar capacity. Multiple tooling requires high power input. The construction of automatic lathes features ruggedness without sacrifice in the precision of the machined product.

Construction Features. An automatic lathe is composed of a head-stock, cycling mechanisms, a bed, tool-carrying components, and a tailstock. The general appearance of automatics varies substantially between the different makes and also between different models of a single manufacturer. Control and operational features are of different designs with the idea of rapid, effortless, and positive movement predominating. All the control systems previously described for specialized turning lathes have been engineered into the automatics. An example of a hydraulically controlled automatic lathe is given in Fig. 17-2.

Fig. 17-1. 8-in. Fay automatic lathe, showing control camming and tool blocks. (Courtesy of Jones and Lamson Machine Co., Springfield, Vt.)

Two distinguishing features are the cycling mechanism and the tool blocks, or arms. The cycling is provided for the tool blocks in a manner enabling them to operate independently of each other. The front tools are provided with longitudinal as well as transverse travel, acting either singly or in combination. These movements can be modified with additional equipment in the form of cam bars, in order to provide taper and form turning where such operations are required.

The rear tool block is designed primarily for transverse movement used in facing, shoulder cutting, relieving, and chamfering operations. It does not, in general practice, move longitudinally; rather, cuts of any considerable width are made by employing wide tool faces either singly or in multiple. The cycle for the rear tool block is primarily that of feeding in toward the center: a slight sidewise movement away from the cut as a matter of tool relief to prevent scoring the workpiece, followed by a quick return to position. Cycling includes such features as infeed, travel, dwell, tool relief, and return to position. Rapid traverse is used wherever possible in the cycle. This applies specifically to tool approach and return when not engaged in actual cutting.

Fig. 17-2. Automatic production lathe shown without accessories or tooling. (Courtesy of Gisholt Machine Co., Madison, Wis.)

There is some difference in terminology relative to the tool-carrying components of an automatic lathe. The term tool block is used here, but such other expressions as tool slide and back arm have their adherents. Mention has been made of two tool blocks, front and rear; while this is the conventional construction, there are also designs in which a third block, placed above the workpiece and termed the overhead slide, is used. The advantage of the overhead, or additional, slide is that it offers increased tool-carrying capacity, thus making possible the use of smaller tools and reducing the likelihood of stalling the lathe.

Workpiece Drivers. Substantial power requirements require positive workpiece driving mechanisms. The workpiece must be mounted and released rapidly and located accurately. The majority of the workpieces are mounted on self-mounting centers or on arbors. The footstock spindle must be traveled twice for each workpiece. This is taken care of in some designs by the use of either rapid hydraulic or pneumatic spindle movement. Similar systems for clamping the footstock spindle are employed as an additional positive and time-saving device.

Chucking work is prominent on the list of automatic lathe operations. Some very ingenious devices have been built to accommodate workpieces. The tendency is toward chucks that operate with a hydraulic or pneumatic system. There are also chucks embodying quick-opening mechanisms designed to save both time and effort. Other equipment includes such items as magnetic chucks, power-operated collet chucks, and internal chucking devices.

Tooling Setups. Every setup needs to be engineered with the objective of reducing the number of operations to a minimum. This imposes a demand for a single operation to perform the entire machining sequence; surprisingly enough, this objective is frequently attained.

The starting point of the tooling program concerns itself with the power input potential of the lathe. In order to meet this condition, the tendency on the part of the builders is to equip the automatic with ample reserve power that can be drawn on when necessary. This increased power requirement is directly traceable to multiple tools, in contrast to the single tool on an engine lathe.

Actually the final tooling setup is reached as a result of experience on similar work. A given length of cut is frequently made with several tools set to the same depth, so that the longitudinal travel is much less than it would be with a single tool. The question of making concurrent cuts with the front and back tool blocks can best be answered by a study of the amount of stock removal, finish, and accuracy required. Some operations must be made at a lower rate than others because of these factors.

Tooling is an individual problem with every different workpiece. Surfaces requiring machining constitute the major problem, although the specification of the workpiece material is also important. The truck transmission cluster gear forging whose four operations are shown in Fig. 17-3 will serve as a typical example of both tooling and production; specific information on operations as well as production times are given with each drawing. In addition, Fig. 17-4 is included to show the actual setup for operation D. Note that the individual tools differ in that some have inserted tips while others are clamped tips. These variations are traceable to the fact that economy in tooling governs final selections.

Tool blocks used on the automatic lathe are either universal, special, or solid types. The choice is generally predicated on the production run.

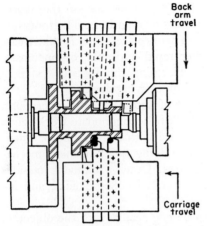

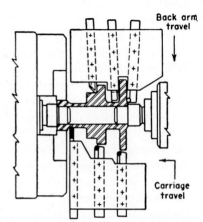

A, *First operation:* Turning speed 450 fpm—feed 0.015. Facing speed 580 fpm—feed 0.020. Power required—approx. 68 hp. Machining time—24 sec. Hold on stub centers and drive with two-jaw compensating air chuck. Depth of cut averages ¼ in. on a side. Rough turn, face, and form.

B, *Second operation:* Turning speed 520 fpm—feed 0.017. Facing speed 520 fpm—feed 0.025. Power required—approx. 35 hp. Machining time—28 sec. Hold on stub centers and drive with two-jaw compensating air chuck, turn, face, and form.

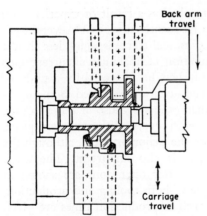

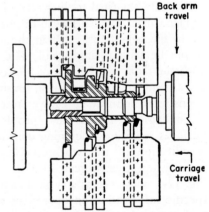

C, *Third operation:* Speed 470 fpm—feed 0.0075. Power required—approx. 28 hp. Machining time—18 sec. Hold on stub centers and drive with two-jaw compensating air chuck. Form, groove, face, and chamfer.

D, *Fourth operation:* Turning speed 660 fpm—feed 0.13. Facing speed 660 fpm—feed 0.025. Power required—approx. 20 hp. Machining time—23 sec. Hold on air-operated expanding fixture. Finish turn, face, and form. All diameters that must be concentric with one another and run true with the locating surfaces are machined in this operation.

Fig. 17-3. Machining truck transmission cluster gear forging on automatic lathe. (Courtesy of Jones and Lamson Machine Co., Springfield, Vt.)

Universal blocks are readily adaptable to a wide range of requirements in that individual tools of various shapes and sizes can be accommodated. The shortcomings of this equipment arise from the possibility that too much flexibility in toolsetting proves time consuming. In connection with machine operating time, it is well to consider the use of a solid tool block wherein the individual tools are preset to master gages in the toolroom; this effects a saving in setup time at the machine. The individual tools must always be set in the block in such a position that their cutting

Fig. 17-4. Tooling and setup used in operation D in preceding figure. (Courtesy of Jones and Lamson Machine Co., Springfield, Vt.)

edges meet the oncoming metal. The tools in the rear tool block are inverted with respect to those in the front tool block. Where production is of a character as to cause retooling after a relatively short run, it is wise to maintain master samples as an aid in toolsetting. When a change-over is necessary, it is a relatively simple matter to mount the master sample in the lathe and set the tooling to fit.

Specialized Automatic Lathes

Despite the impressive production potential of the automatic lathe, it is not a "one part" machine tool. Further development of the automatic lathe is the design for machining one part on a continuing basis (Fig. 17-5). This crankshaft lathe is capable of turning two forgings simul-

Fig. 17-5. Automated crankshaft line, cycle time per crank—54 sec, conveyor system includes automatic gaging after line bearings are turned. (Courtesy of R. K. LeBlond Machine Tool Co., Cincinnati.)

taneously. The example mentioned is not an isolated one; there are many other similar single-purpose automatic lathes.

AUTOMATIC VERTICAL AND HORIZONTAL CHUCKING MACHINES

There are several unique features incorporated in the design of the automatic vertical and horizontal chucking machines. The table carries a number of spindle chucks so arranged that they match a corresponding number of work stations. Capacities vary in that six-, eight-, twelve-, and sixteen-spindle types are available. The term chucks is used here in a generic sense, since both conventional chucks as well as chucking fixtures are used. The work stations carry the tooling, which is arranged in a variety of combinations engineered in a sequence so that, as the main table indexes, succeeding machining operations are performed. The type and amount of tooling at each station must fit into a pattern that will machine the workpiece in one complete index cycle. There may, of course, be duplicate tooling arranged to machine two workpieces per cycle.

It is frequently necessary to send the workpiece through a second machining cycle, since only surfaces accessible to the tooling can be machined. A repeat cycle, or second chucking, inverts the workpiece in order to expose the hidden surfaces of the first chucking operation. Second operations need not necessarily be done on this machine tool. A typical example is found in machining an automobile motor flywheel, a casting that requires machining over its entire surface.

The automatic multiple-spindle vertical chucking machine (Fig. 17-6) is well adapted for machining castings and forgings although short lengths of bar stock are also considered suitable. The keynote of these machines is their high production potential on repetitive work. They are prominent equipment in those shops where production schedules are both tight and extensive. These machines save considerable floor space as compared to their horizontal counterparts. Tooling and setup are major

Fig. 17-6. Rotary-type vertical chucking machine, six-spindle, 20-in. capacity. Equipped with Woodworth expanding arbor fixtures. (Courtesy of The Bullard Co., Bridgeport, Conn.)

and costly considerations that can be justified only by long-run production.

The presentation on chucking machines here has been devoted to vertical types. There is at least one instance in which a builder refers to an automatic horizontal single-spindle turret lathe as a chucking machine. There are also multiple-spindle horizontal chucking machines. They are designed on two basic principles: in one the tool rotates, while in the other the workpiece rotates. In the former there are either four or seven spindles designed to give variable swing capacities. Work rotating designs are built in five-, six-, or eight-spindle models. There are also designs using eight horizontal spindles in an arrangement that employs double indexing in conjunction with duplicate tooling. By this device, two workpieces are completed with each cycle. The operating

Fig. 17-7. A 12-in. six-spindle automatic horizontal chucking machine. (Courtesy of The National Acme Co., Cleveland.)

cycle is such that the two spindles at the center position are stopped in order that loading and unloading can be accommodated (Fig. 17-7).

AUTOMATIC SCREW MACHINES

Automatic screw machines produce finished parts from bar stock. This is an accurate description so far as single-spindle machines are concerned; but it is not entirely true for multiple-spindle designs, since there are some chucking types built in that classification. The operating cycle of the screw machine is an automatic one whose various phases of operation are controlled mechanically by cam action. An operator is needed only for loading the bar stock and giving requisite supervisory attention. Even the manual loading function can be eliminated on those classes of work where magazine feed is possible. Screw machine products are generally small parts (Fig. 17-8). Larger production parts than those shown are possible, the limiting factor being that of machine capacity. Because of the multiplicity of tool-carrying possibilities, every type of turning, facing, drilling, boring, reaming, threading, cutoff, and chamfering operation is possible. In addition, milling and broaching, which are never considered as being lathe operations, are also included in screw machine production.

Single-spindle Automatic Screw Machines. The common characteristic of this type is that there is but one spindle. There are simultaneous machining operations by tools located in the turret and on the front and rear of the cross slide. Several designs of the single-spindle type

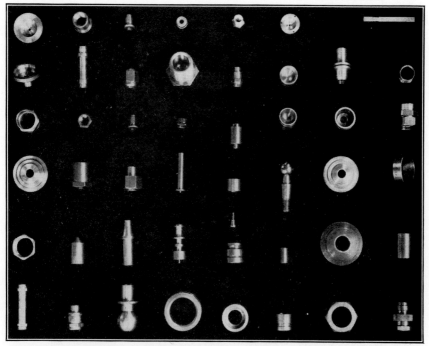

Fig. 17-8. View of various parts produced on Greenlee automatic screw machines (half-size). (Courtesy of Greenlee Bros. & Co., Rockford, Ill.)

are available, but two types predominate. These have two distinguishing features: turret position and type of cam construction, the latter being divided between disk- and drum-type cams.

Disk Cam-operated Screw Machine. In Fig. 17-9 the operating cycle, which includes bar feeding and clamping, is controlled by two cams carried on an operating shaft at the front of the machine, while an additional cam, located at the rear, governs the turret feed. The turret lies in a vertical plane and indexes in a direction parallel with the work. Turret mounting is on a slide that permits its movement into the work. All turret indexing and longitudinal travel are controlled by cams. For the most part the turret is of the six-station type, whose tooling, while of smaller proportions, bears close resemblance to that of the conventional turret lathe.

There are two cross slides which are designed to operate independently of each other and in a direction normal to the workpiece. Cross-slide movement to and from the work is controlled by cams that give desired feed to each tool. It is sound tooling practice to place all possible tooling on the cross slides as a means of relieving the turret.

Fig. 17-9. Single-spindle automatic screw machine. (Courtesy of Brown & Sharpe Manufacturing Co., Providence, R.I.)

When this principle is followed, over-all machining time is reduced, since both side tools and turret tools can operate simultaneously.

Stock is positioned by being fed against an overhead swing stop, or, on occasion, a turret stop may be more convenient. The bar stock is fed forward automatically to its correct machining position immediately following the completion of the preceding workpiece. The stock-feeding interval is referred to as an "idle movement," as are turret indexing and spindle reverse.

There is a considerable degree of flexibility in spindle speed, and this is useful as a means of accommodating the varying requirements of the different machining operations. These machines use a spindle speed as great as the workpiece and tooling will permit. Spindle speed changes are effected through the combination of change gears and clutches. Another important feature is that spindle rotation can be reversed—a desirable feature for backing off thread tools and in some turning operations.

Tooling. Automatic screw machines favor circular tools for both cross slides. A circular cutoff tool is always placed on the back slide, which means that it must be in an inverse position. The cutoff tool is shaped to suit each individual job, since the width of the cut will be varied according to workpiece design and material.

Circular forming tools are placed on the front slide. These tools are simple or elaborate as the workpiece demands. The outstanding advantages of circular tools are that they can be turned to shape easily and that once the shape has been established it will remain true for the life of the tool. These tools can be sharpened by merely grinding the face of the offset. A disadvantage is that they must be positioned accurately with respect to the workpiece axis in order to machine the desired contour accurately. Turret tooling follows conventional turret lathe practice, but the tools are smaller and solid dies are common, since spindle reverse is available.

Drum Cam-operated Screw Machines. Single-spindle screw machines in which cycling operation is controlled by drum-type cams are sometimes termed ram-type automatics. Although their construction is considerably different from the disk-cam-operated type, in the final analysis production potentials and work types are similar for equal machine capacities. The outward appearance of these two types of automatic screw machines is strikingly different, as are design details (Fig. 17-10). There are, in fact, two fundamental designs of the drum cam automatics: one, termed the turret type, is built in capacity ranges from $\frac{9}{16}$ to 10 in., while its companion style, the slide type, is available in capacities from $1\frac{1}{16}$ to $5\frac{3}{4}$ in. inclusive.

The distinguishing characteristics of these machines is their cam design. Drums, on which steel strips or contoured plates are bolted, act as cams that control the various automatic cycles. Because of this cam construction, these machines are extremely flexible; the strips or plates can be repositioned by merely relocating them on the drum surface.

There are three cams included in the operating mechanism. One cam, located on the spindle ram, controls the movement of the turret as to both indexing and longitudinal movement. A second cam functions as a cross-slide control, while the third cam directs the bar feed and chucking operations.

The turret is located on the front end of the ram, forward of the main operating cam. It rotates in a vertical plane normal to the workpiece axis. In this position the tools project away from the turret face and directly toward the workpiece. Tool mounting is variable, depending on types and individual operation requirements of turning, forming, threading, and the like.

Swiss-type Screw Machines. The development of automatic screw machines capable of high precision on small dimensions has come from Switzerland. Similar designs are produced in America with modifications in the direction of increased capacities (Fig. 17-11). The position of the

Fig. 17-10. Rear view of single-spindle 2½-in. capacity automatic with cam drums at center. (Courtesy of The Cleveland Automatic Machine Co., Cleveland.)

ment is controlled by a disk-type cam, as is the movement of the bar stock. Cam layout requires a high degree of accuracy as well as inge- tools is such that the stock is fed into them while rotating. Tool move- nuity. In fact the capabilities of this type of screw machine depend in large measure on the ability of the cam designer.

The headstock which carries the bar is reciprocated by cam action that must be synchronized with the tool rocker and cam and the frame cam controlling tool movement. Tooling is distinctive in that the tools are predominantly of the single-point type. Tools operate directly in front of the headstock bushing, thereby relieving the workpiece of any load-carrying requirement.

Swiss-type screw machines are employed primarily on small-diameter precision parts such as instruments, meters, watches, and clocks. The diameters and accuracy obtainable from these machines are unique. Tolerances on diameters are held as close as 0.0002 in. total, while shoulder lengths are produced to total tolerance of 0.0005 in. These tolerances are not the exception; rather, they have been held over long

Fig. 17-11. Swiss-type automatic screw machine. (Courtesy of George Gorton Machine Co., Racine, Wis.)

production runs. Surface finish is of a quality comparable to superior ground finishes.

MULTIPLE-SPINDLE AUTOMATIC MACHINES

Multiple-spindle automatic machines are fundamentally production types, and their acquisition should only be considered where production runs of some consequence are projected. Their initial and tooling costs are substantially greater and setup time is considerably longer than in the case of the single-spindle designs. The capacities of these machine tools have been expanded from the point where they were merely competing with single-spindle screw machines to the point where they operate in the field of turret lathe production. Their rugged construction and ample power input formed a combination capable of tooling applications unique among lathe accomplishments.

Regardless of the number of spindles on a given machine, its operation is such that all the tool slides are engaged on a workpiece simultaneously. The unit production time is equal to the greatest single-operation time. This is in contrast to the single-spindle machine, in which unit production time is equal to the sum of all the operation times, combined cuts being considered as a single operation time. A workpiece is completed each time the cycle indexes one position.

Spindles. Multiple-spindle machines are built in a variety of spindle combinations. The most usual arrangement is that with the spindle axes

Fig. 17-12. Six-spindle 2-in. automatic bar machine equipped with a precipitron above tool area for removing fumes. (Courtesy of Greenlee Bros. & Co., Rockford, Ill.)

spaced equidistant in a radial pattern on the circumference of a circle. In this arrangement there are four, five, six, or eight spindles in the conventional designs. The choice of the number of spindles is predicated on such considerations as production requirements and product design. Another possibility with a large number of spindles arises from the fact that duplicate tooling can be utilized so that more than one part can be finished per cycle. Progress in the direction of product quality is enhanced by greater numbers of spindles, since tooling can be arranged for both roughing and finishing cuts. Six-spindle machines represent the greatest number of installations (Fig. 17-12). All spindle arrangements

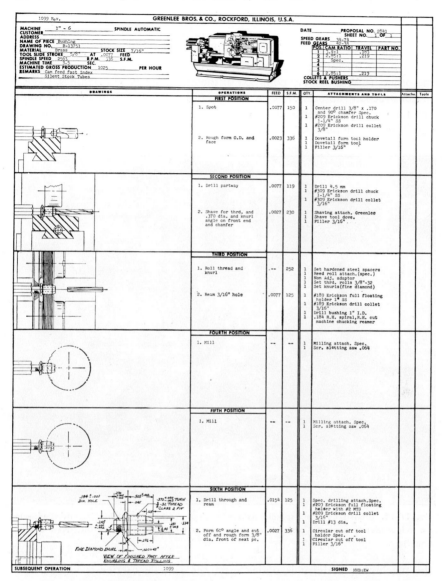

Fig. 17-13. Layout and tooling sheet for a brass bushing on a six-spindle automatic. (Courtesy of Greenlee Bros. & Co., Rockford, Ill.)

do not follow the radial pattern; one design employs a vertical in-line principle wherein the spindles are banked one directly above another.

Operating Principles. The conventional design in multiple-spindle machines embodies the principle of the work rotating and the tooling remaining stationary. There are other designs in which the tool rotates.

Tool-rotating types are not, in the strict sense, bar machines; rather, they are common for machining castings, forgings, and second operations on bar workpieces previously cut off. Indexing is generally arranged for one position per operating cycle on the bar-type machines. Skip indexing, on the other hand, is largely confined to the chucking-type machines.

Construction Features. The two basic components of these machine tools are the spindle carrier and the main tool slide. The spindle carrier, located on the inboard side of the headstock, indexes the headstock. When

Fig. 17-14. Tooling on a six-spindle automatic screw machine 1⅝ by 6 in. equipped with six independently operated cross slides. (Courtesy of New Britain-Gridley Div., New Britain, Conn.)

the machining activity is under way, the spindle carrier is locked into position rigidly. Thus the spindle carrier controls and aids in the operating cycle.

The main tool slide is in a location that brings the individual tooling into alignment with the end of the bar stock. Longitudinal feed is controlled by camming action in order that fluctuating tooling demands can be accommodated. Tooling here, for the most part, is of the end-working type of which roller and knee turners, drilling, boring, reaming, tapping, and threading are representative.

Cross slides are mounted directly on the headstock and are positioned to operate radially on the center line of the work. The movement of the cross slides is controlled by camming, and they operate independently of the main tool slide. There are instances, however, in which cross-slide and main tool side motions are synchronized. Additional slides are added from overarms in an arrangement termed swinging arm slides.

The tooling and production possibilities of a representative six-spindle automatic can be visualized with the aid of Figs. 17-13 and 17-14. The first of these shows the operations, a working drawing, and tooling for each station; the second is a view of the automatic which accommodates this type tooling. The production on this job is stated to be 1,025 parts/hr.

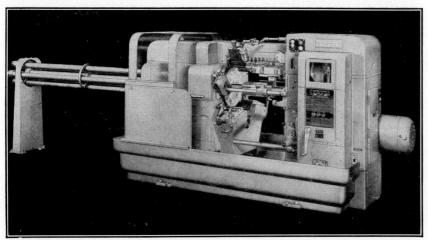

Fig. 17-15. Five-spindle automatic bar machine equipped with quadrant feed control. (Courtesy of The Warner & Swasey Co., Cleveland.)

Camless Automatics. While cams are used in conventional designs, there is a development in which quadrants equipped with stops act to replace cam action. This construction permits the adjustment of the feed stroke by setting the quadrants in place of removing cams. Because of this approach, no cam replacement is necessary and setup time is materially reduced. Short-run work can be placed on these machines to good advantage. A typical automatic built with quadrant feed adjustment is shown in Fig. 17-15.

SURVEY QUESTIONS

17-1. How can an automatic lathe be readily distinguished from an engine lathe?

17-2. What is meant by multiple tooling as this term applies to an automatic lathe?

17-3. What type work is best adapted to an automatic lathe?

17-4. Is mass production necessary to justify machining a component on an automatic lathe?

17-5. What are tool blocks?

17-6. What features are included in cycling?

17-7. Why is power input greater on an automatic than on an engine lathe doing a similar job?

17-8. Are chucks used on automatics?

17-9. When is a stub center used?

17-10. Are the cutting tools set up the same in the rear as they are in the front tool block? Explain.

17-11. What is a single-purpose automatic lathe?

17-12. Wherein do chucking machines differ from automatic lathes?

17-13. Is bar stock adaptable to vertical chucking machines?

17-14. Would railway car wheels be suited to machining on a vertical chucking machine?

17-15. On what type material are horizontal chucking machines operated to best advantage?

17-16. Is an automatic screw machine as large as a turret lathe?

17-17. What class of work is adapted to automatic screw machines?

17-18. What are cam drums?

17-19. If automatic screw machines are equipped with turrets, are the latter found in the same location as on a turret lathe?

17-20. In what class of work are Swiss-type screw machines used?

17-21. Are automatic screw machines multiple-spindle types?

17-22. Mention some part of a chain saw that would be made on an automatic screw machine.

17-23. Are there any advantages to camless automatic screw machines?

17-24. On what type equipment would 6 by 32 by $\frac{3}{8}$ in. roundhead machine screws be made?

Chapter 18

NUMERICAL CONTROL FOR MACHINE TOOLS

Machine tool development since the latter part of the eighteenth century, when Eli Whitney invented the milling machine, has been phenomenal. While machine tools have, for the most part, been manufactured by relatively small producers, they have, nonetheless, individually and collectively set the pace for the American metal-cutting industry. The colossal manufacturing capacity of our metal industry is a direct result

Fig. 18-1. Spar and skin milling machine equipped with both horizontal and vertical heads for dual type profiling operating under numerical control. (Courtesy of Giddings & Lewis, Fond du Lac, Wis.)

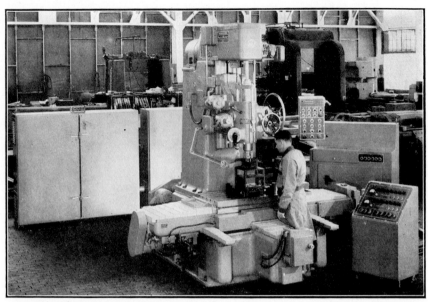

Fig. 18-2A. Jig borer equipped with numerical control. (Courtesy of Pratt & Whitney Co., West Hartford, Conn.)

Fig. 18-2B. Numerically controlled four-spindle boring machine for programming vertical spindle movement and rotary table positioning. (Courtesy of Barnes Drill Co., Rockford, Ill.)

of machine tool adaptability to a unique mass market. It has become possible to produce greater amounts of goods with a lesser quantity of direct labor. The result is that the human equation has a diminished influence on the end product. In this unfolding program of more production within a given time unit, control devices of every conceivable type have been incorporated into the machine tool.

In a continuing program of further extension of automatic operation and production, the introduction of electronic devices teamed with servomechanisms used in conjunction with electronic calculators or computers has developed a completely new horizon. It can well be said that the pursuit of this new concept signalizes the greatest single progression in the entire area of machine tool development since the introduction of power (Fig. 18-1). Several different approaches have been explored in solving this new machine tool operating conception. Some of these are in development, while others are in successful operation.

The aircraft industry must be given deserved credit for its vision in accepting and adopting these new developments. Specifically, the Aircraft Industries Association, through its airframe manufacturing equipment committee, contributed significantly to this development.[1] However, design progress is not limited to the large and specialized machining equipment of airframe manufacture; rather, it has entered the area of all-purpose machine tools such as knee-type milling machines, horizontal boring machines, jig borers (Fig. 18-2A), turret lathes, and many others (Fig. 18-2B).

NUMERICAL CONTROL

The AIA-AMEC Committee[2] has offered some standard definitions in this new field. They define numerical control as "the operation of general purpose machines from instructions stored on a roll of tape or other portable means, for use or for re-use and it includes a closely integrated numerical data processing system." Numerical control methods make it possible to machine one or a few parts with simplified work holders at nearly the same speed per part as if that part were one of hundreds made in a single production run on an automatic machine. In further clarification of the above definition, the same committee has stated that "numerical data processing for numerical control means the translation of part dimensions and tolerances, cutter shape and size, cutting paths and sequences, and much other data, into numbers or codes representing num-

---

[1] Air Materiel Command of the U.S. Air Force contributed significantly to this pioneering effort.

[2] Subcommittee Report, Airframe Manufacturing Equipment Committee, April, 1957.

bers. Then, computation and interpolation is performed to convert the data into a form suitable to actuate the machine tool."

The basic element in this control system is the storage media, either a magnetic or punched tape or punched cards. The information stored on the media includes the controlling of all motions of the machine tool as well as on-and-off and speed commands. Because of the potential stowing of information on the media, machine set-up time is sharply reduced as is the investment in machining fixtures, jigs, templates, holding devices, and similar rigging.

The functioning of numerically controlled machine tools demonstrates that in addition to their ability to speed production, they also contain

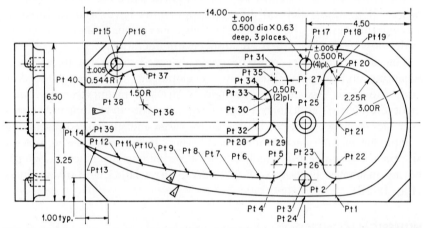

Fig. 18-3. Numerical data for AIA test part. NOTE: Points computed for 1.000-in. diameter cutter. No depth or feed rate information computed since these are manually controlled on early model unit.

the potential for greater accuracy of product than any of the control systems currently known.

Comparative Tests. The survey made by the AIA committee on a test component which was designed by them (Fig. 18-3) developed some startling information. The first test run was by accepted machining methods; following that a second test was set up using the numerical control method. These tests developed the following results:

A. Present Method

	Tracer control	Hours	Cumulative
1. Manual office paperwork		3	3
2. Templates		97.5	100.5
3. Machining—tracer		3.6	104.1
4. Machining, boring		0.5	104.6

B. Numerical Control Method

Tape control	Hours	Cumulative
1. Manual office paperwork	1	1
2. Data processing by computer	1.5	2.5
3. Machining—magnetic tape	0.9	3.4
4. Machining, boring—magnetic tape	0.1	3.5

C. Comparisons between *A* and *B* above Show:

	Reduction, per cent
1. Manual office paperwork	66.6
2. Data processing	98.5
3. Machining	75.0
4. Boring	80.0

The numerical control test was conducted on a standard general purpose machine, converted to but not specifically designed for numerical control.[3] Furthermore, the above data are for the first test piece, which was machined on the same day the shop first saw the drawing. Upon completion the test component was subjected to an extremely searching inspection lasting 12 hr, yet no cause to reject the machined part was found.

Computers. The principle of the computer has been established as an instrument able to accept information, *i.e.*, problems and data, and perform logical and mathematical operations thereon to the point of developing answers. Computer development has followed two basic concepts known as analog and digital. The main difference between digital and analog computers is that the former calculates by counting while the latter operates by measuring. The analog computer is capable, in effect, of being wired up with electronic circuitry to behave mathematically like the physical system under study. By performing measurements on the electronic circuitry it is possible to determine the behavior of the equivalent physical system.

The basic characteristic of the digital computer is that it performs the arithmetical processes of addition, subtraction, multiplication, and division. This computer functions by receiving information, performing calculations or arithmetical operations thereon, and producing the resultant information in readable form. The installation consists of five basic components: input, storage, or memory, arithmetic, output, and control. Information fed to a digital computer must be in a form that can be "read" by the machine, which means that its physical form must be punched tape or cards or the like.

[3] Cincinnati Milling Machine Co., Cincinnati, Ohio.

By way of illustration, it can be said that the signal from an automobile speedometer is analog, whereas the signal from the switch is digital in nature. Data given in numbers are digital, whereas when they are described in a graph, the data become analog. Digital computers are used predominantly in the field of numerical control, because information describing geometric shapes is digital (numerical) and is, therefore, compatible with the required input; secondly, the digital computer is accurate to at least seven significant figures.

The application of computers to numerically controlled machine tools is relatively new. Essentially, the computer is used here in order to reduce the control tape preparation time. It can readily be understood that to calculate manually sufficient points to give an accurate approximation of a curve and to calculate feed rates, tool center paths, point intersections, and similar necessary information would require a prodigious amount of time. The computer is capable of reducing such computations to a matter of minutes.

The successful growth of numerical control is keyed to the electronic digital computer. The ability to "program" a computer to understand a simple logical language description of a workpiece in the form of numbers and words (symbolic language) is essential to economical communication of man and machine. The extent of this program is evident in the AMC-sponsored APT 2 and APT 3 (Automatic Programming Technique) at MIT and the AIA coordinated effort to develop a universal computer program for three-dimensional part programming.

Large general-purpose digital computers of the IBM 704 type are desirable because of the large storage capacity, but the smaller computers will be capable of using these programs at a sacrifice of time. (Each computer coded program must be in the form acceptable to the specific type of computer input and output.)

Programming the computer for this type of mathematical computation is an enormous task, involving numerous man-hours of subroutine development, coding, and proof testing. The benefit of this effort will be a universal and powerful programming tool to add speed, accuracy, and convenience to the users of numerical control. This program is only in its infancy for it is only logical to place more of the burden of decision in the computer.

In connection with installation of numerical control, several different systems are available from competing producers. Each of these systems is marked by differing instrumentation, operation, and capabilities.

Application Potential. It is well to understand that the numerical control concept is not limited to machine tools; rather, it is adaptable to process control generally. Operating items of speed, feed, length, flow, temperature, and pressure, for example, are amenable to control. These elements can be translated by electrical or electronic signals or mechanical devices to control the basic operation. Procedure routine assigns a numerical value to each item within the process.

Processing data for numerical control, while largely stored on magnetic or punched tape, need not adhere to that particular media, since punched cards of many categories as well as optical systems, telephone dialing, or even push buttons have been and are being used. After all, the particular media that is chosen for storing and feeding information is a matter suited to the individual system.

Control Concepts. The most widely recognized application of numerical control is the continuous path system. Actually, in the RETMA[4] classification, three different categories are recognized. Class 1, the simplest form, is used primarily for hole location or table positioning and sequencing. Class 2 provides point-to-point positioning while exerting definite control over the linear path traveled. Obviously, this results in motion in a straight line. Class 2 control has been applied to standard, all-purpose machine tools.

Continuous path control, or Class 3, has been developed to a considerable degree. In the development of such a system, the element of time needs to be incorporated as an indispensable factor. This is necessary in order to distribute signals to each of the motions or coordinates simultaneously. This principle is basic if numerical control is to be applied to contouring equipment such as milling machines.

Another feature of Class 1 is its ability of discrete positioning. This potential alludes to the possibility whereby any point can be located on a surface by merely moving the individual coordinates until the intersection of two or three points establishes the desired point. The discrete or point-locating system requires less equipment than does continuous path control. In consequence, it is a simple system to install and is less costly. Programming is very simple in comparison to Class 3.

Feedback. Feedback system, as a component of the numerical control system, is, in effect, a form of continuous automatic inspection. It functions so that the commanded motion position is under continuous observation. This means a comparison between the actual position and the instructed one. When a difference in these two positions occurs, it generates an error signal, which the numerical control unit accepts as a correction factor. It will be noted, therefore, that the feedback part of the installation is really basic and indispensable.

PREPARATION FOR SYSTEM USE

There are five major functions involved in the complete use of automatically controlled production. In order to develop proper procedures and orientation of personnel, the functions can be outlined as follows:

[4] RETMA = Radio, Electronics, and Television Manufacturers Association.

1. Standardizing design elements and criteria for parts to be produced by numerically controlled machine tools.

2. Defining mathematically the part to be produced.

3. Numerical processing. Movements of the cutter are programmed in correct sequence to cut metal along the line defining the part to be produced. The program is coded on a storage media and fed into the machine control unit. From this point, manual operations have been virtually eliminated.

4. Operating the machine. Manual machine operations are reduced to initial orientation of cutter and to starting and stopping, coupled with necessary loading and unloading.

5. Maintaining the machine. It is essential that numerically controlled systems be maintained at top condition and efficiency to obtain maximum utilization.

System Details. It is impossible to generalize on actual procedures, inasmuch as the different systems for numerical control require different methods of approach. Two systems are briefly described here. The Bendix tape control system is diagramed in Fig. 18-4. Note that in all systems the complete processing is divided into two parts, namely, tape preparation and actual machining. The data required serve as input to the digital computer and are of two kinds: dimensional data defining the path geometry, and information concerned with the metal-cutting aspects of the job—cutter size, feed rates, sequence of cuts, etc. In common with other systems, a process sheet or manuscript is used as the means for organizing this information for input to the computer. The process sheet itself is a printed form which serves as a work sheet for the process planner. However, the act of filling out the sheet automatically compiles and arranges in proper sequence the information needed by the computer.

The next step in the process is that of producing a tape from the process sheet which can be read by the computer. This tape, referred to as a process tape, contains exactly the same information as the process sheet. It is produced on a Flexowriter, which, in essence, is an electric typewriter with a tape reader and tape punch attached. The punching of the process tape is done as the original hand-written process sheet is copied on the typewriter. When the original tape is finished, it is inserted into the motorized tape reader connected to the Flexowriter. The same process sheet is manually typed again to produce a second tape, while the first tape is read in synchronism.

The process tape now contains, in condensed and coded form, all necessary data; it is fed into the computer by way of a tape reader. The computer interprets the data provided by the process tape, carries out all the necessary computations, arranges the results in the required format,

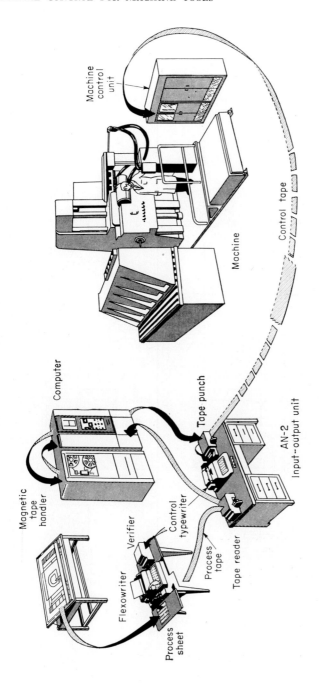

TAPE PREPARATION   MACHINING

Fig. 18-4. Pictorial diagram of the Bendix numerical control system.

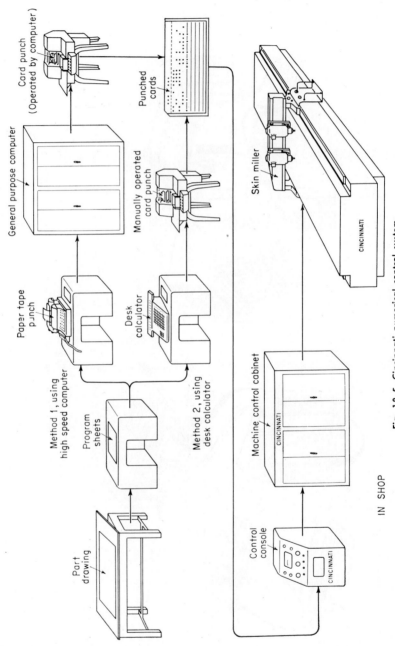

Fig. 18-5. Cincinnati numerical control system.

and punches a control tape exactly as required by the machine control unit in the factory.

Another recognized development is termed the Cincinnati numerical control system. This one is outlined in Fig. 18-5, where it will be noted again that the complete operation is divided between the office, where the punched cards are produced, and the shop, where the actual machine work is done.

Fig. 18-6. Programmed numerical data.

Part Drawing

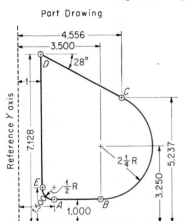

SAMPLE PROGRAMMING SHEET

Section	End point of section			Informational tolerance	Feed rate, in./min	Radius, in.	Cutter radius, in.
	X	Y	Z				
Start	01.500	01.000	05.000	0.001	. . .	. . . . .	0.500
A B	03.500	01.000	05.000	0.001	50	. . . . .	0.500
B C	04.556	05.237	05.000	0.001	50	2.250	0.500
C D	01.000	07.128	05.000	0.001	50	. . . . .	0.500
D E	01.000	01.500	05.000	0.001	50	. . . . .	0.500
E A	01.500	01.000	05.000	0.001	50	0.500	0.500

The initial preparation of numerical data starts with a parts drawing, from which the program sheet is prepared. While standard drawings may be used, programming and computing can be simplified by preparing these drawings with numerical control in mind. The necessary "blend" and "in-between" points that are needed in addition to basic information normally found on a drawing can be calculated by using a high-speed electronic computer or a desk calculator and associated math tables; this latter technique is worth consideration, particularly on less complex jobs. Following programming and its computations, with cards punched accordingly, the next step is to feed this information to the control unit. This unit takes the digital information from the cards and converts it

Fig. 18-7. Computed numerical data.

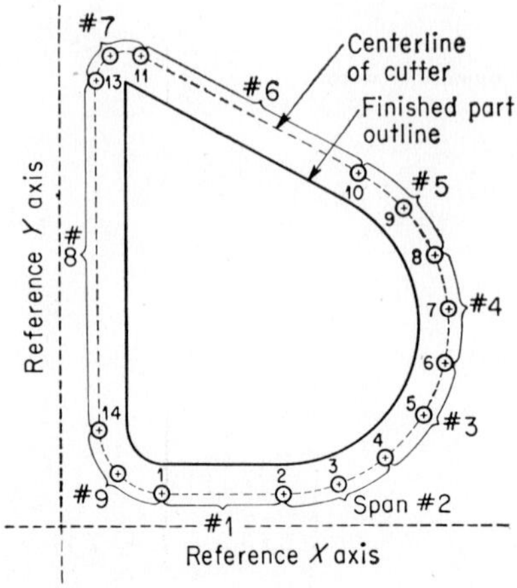

Card (span) no.	Pt. no.	Point coordinates								Interpolator speed, rpm
		Midpoint			Pt. no.	End point			
		X_m, in.	Y_m, in.	Z_m, in.		X_e, in.	Y_e, in.	Z_e, in.	
0	1	1.500	0.500	5.000	1	1.500	0.500	5.000	0 (Starting pt.)
1	*	.....	.....	.....	2	3.500	0.500	5.000	12.5
2	3	4.395	0.650	5.000	4	5.193	1.083	5.000	27.4
3	5	5.806	1.752	5.000	6	6.168	2.585	5.000	27.4
4	7	6.240	3.490	5.000	8	6.012	4.369	5.000	27.4
5	9	5.511	5.125	5.000	10	4.791	5.678	5.000	27.4
6	*	.....	.....	.....	11	1.235	7.569	5.000	7.0
7	12	0.748	7.557	5.000	13	0.500	7.128	5.000	24.3
8	*	.....	.....	.....	14	0.500	1.500	5.000	4.4
9	15	0.793	0.793	5.000	1	1.500	0.500	5.000	16.0

NOTE: * indicates straight-line interpolated span. No midpoint required.

into precise voltage analogs representative of absolute positions of the various units of the machine tool. The system is an absolute voltage ratio system. Since a common source supplies both the information analog and the feedback position analog, line voltage variations have no effect. The use of punched cards is particularly suitable for jobs where frequent changes are made. Special colored cards can be used for transmitting instructions to the operator.

Programming. Numerical control is so named because numerical values are given to the various dimensions of the parts, to feeds, speeds, and other auxiliary operations. The initial preparation for this numerical data is referred to as programming. A simple drawing and a sample programming sheet with basic information are shown in Fig. 18-6.

Generally, the information on the programming sheet is insufficient for actual operation. It is usually necessary to take these basic data and perform additional computations in order to provide sufficient information to operate the machine. This computation will result in information as shown in Fig. 18-7, which fully describes the part for manufacture under this system.

There is much more detail in all the systems and there are other systems beyond those described here; however, a detailed study is beyond the scope of this presentation. With revisions coming rapidly, it is suggested that the manufacturers be contacted for further detailed information and progress.

NUMERICALLY CONTROLLED TRANSFER LINE

Further acceleration of the adoption of the numerical control idea has proved itself in the successful application to transfer line operation. The potential significance of this development is impossible to assess. The ability of the numerically controlled line to shorten the time between engineering release and production of parts, coupled with the ability of making engineering changes without sacrifice of production rates, opens a new concept in manufacturing. A basic philosophy of economical manufacturing has been that of tooling for mass production. It seems probable that this concept is in line for revision, if not total discard, in favor of the new accomplishments as demonstrated by the numerically controlled transfer line. A part of such a line, installed by the Hughes Aircraft Company, is shown in Fig. 18-8.

This installation, which operates a completely automated line of machine tools controlled by transistorized digital computers, makes impressive cuts in the "lead time" between delivery of blueprints and production of components. To appreciate fully the versatility of this development, Fig. 18-9 is of interest. Here is shown a series of tapes, together with the components whose machining each tape controls. This means simultaneous production of all the parts shown, an indication that small job lots can be machined with expediency and low cost. This new line is sufficiently flexible to produce several different machine parts during a single run, in any quantity. The tape, which retains the "knowledge," can be stored for future production. As currently constituted, the line includes a horizontal milling machine, a drilling machine, and a boring machine.

The tape-controlled system brings different cutters to operate in sequence on the piece to be machined. Some cutters are in the magazine of a single machine; others are associated with different machines. The milling machine is arranged so that the head can move in three axes, and

Fig. 18-8. Numerically controlled transfer line built by Kearney & Trecker for Hughes Aircraft Company, Los Angeles.

work, which is secured to a pallet, may be rotated 360°. Feed and speed are controlled electronically in all axes.

The boring machine has a boring bar that is set to operate automatically by the signals read from the tape. It has two spindles, either to cover different ranges of bored holes or to provide for having a milling cutter in one spindle to make the machine tool more versatile.

The drilling machine has a magazine in which various size drills and taps can be stored. Each drill has its own drill bushing, which is extended when the drill is extended. This eliminates the need for separate drill boxes or plates for different parts. It ensures accurate chordal dimensions because the drill cannot walk or bend. It is held rigidly by a bushing at the point where the drill enters the work. Each tap has its own lead screw to ensure accurate thread cutting. When a drill or tap breaks, a safety is actuated, causing the drill or tap to be retracted automatically. The drilling machine is further equipped with a unique, fast-operating tool change mechanism, accommodating 20 mixed drills, reamers, taps,

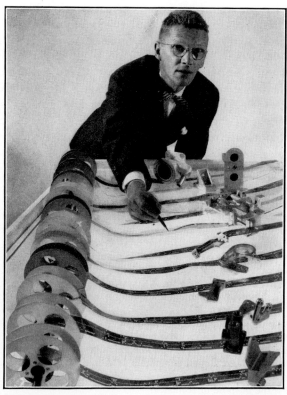

Fig. 18-9. Machined components together with their respective control tapes. (Courtesy of Hughes Aircraft Co., Los Angeles.)

boring tools, etc. Optimum speeds and feeds are automatically selected as part of the programmed information on the machine control tapes.

Flexibility, built into this electronically controlled automated line of machine tools, permits simultaneous operation and "intermix" of work-pieces. For example, it is possible, by inserting four different tapes in the three-machine line, to machine four entirely unrelated parts. This is the most practical application of the line, insofar as tooling cost is concerned. Only one work-holding fixture is required for each different part. Fully automatic transfer mechanisms practically eliminate materials handling; parts are merely loaded and unloaded.

SUMMARY

The content of this chapter refers to the future of industrial manufacturing potential. It is obvious that prior concepts must be drastically revised and new potentialities accepted. Our concept of mass manufacturing, which has lived throughout this century, is now under severe scrutiny that is so revealing as to suggest that the time has come for new thinking. In this connection, it is entirely conceivable that the machine tool of the future will be designed for numerical rather than human control. This projects the possibility of a complete revision in machine tool design, appearance, and operation. By way of illustration, one milling machine has a turret drum attachment which holds 30 different tools. This unit is capable of automatic changing and random selection of tools into and out of the spindle by coded signals from the tape. Handwheels are eliminated from numerical control machine tools since such gear is unnecessary to the operation of the machine.

SURVEY QUESTIONS

18-1. Are machine tools manufactured in the sense that electric motors are?

18-2. How have machine tools affected the human equation in manufacturing?

18-3. How will numerical control govern production in the future?

18-4. In what industry has NC seen its real beginning?

18-5. Is numerical control confined to new type or individualized machine tools?

18-6. What is the basic element in the NC system?

18-7. Why is a lesser investment in machining fixtures and templates possible with numerical control?

18-8. What is a decided advantage in favor of numerical control insofar as a repeat performance of a machining operation is concerned?

18-9. What are the two basic types of computers in the NC program?

18-10. Why are the large digital computers preferred in numerical control installations?

18-11. What is the purpose of feedback?

18-12. Is the storage media the same for the Bendix as for the Cincinnati NC system?

18-13. Whence does numerical control derive its name?

18-14. Explain a new concept of unit cost as between mass production and lesser production.

18-15. Is NC adaptable to other phases of manufacturing besides machining?

Chapter 19

SCREW THREADS

The American Society of Mechanical Engineers accepted the responsibility for the development of screw thread standards by authorizing committee study of the problem as early as 1905. In this worthwhile endeavor it was joined by the Society of Automotive Engineers in 1911. There were three thread systems recognized until well after World War I: the United States Standard covered coarse pitch, the SAE fine pitch, and the ASME extra-fine pitch screw threads. Coordination of these systems resulted in the establishment of the American National Screw Thread System, in which the coarse, fine, and extra-fine series were recognized. Congress established a National Screw Thread Commission in 1918 which provided the authoritative center for correlating the development work on screw thread standards. For the first time in our history we were confronted in World War I with the necessity of screw thread fits in components originating in different factories in widely separated geographic areas.

An agreement was signed in Washington on November 18, 1948, by representatives of Great Britain, Canada, and the United States that created the Unified Screw Thread Standard for screws, bolts, nuts, and other threaded parts. This standard brings affected screw threads of these three countries into complete accord.

UNIFIED AND AMERICAN SCREW THREADS

The Unified standard is issued as American Standard B1.1—1950 in complete detail.[1] Thread forms for both the internal and external designs are sketched in Fig. 19-1. It will be noted that the thread form shows something of the Whitworth influence on the external thread; however, the 60° thread angle of previous American standards is retained. These conditions mean that the newly developed Unified standard can be readily adapted to American practice.

[1] American Society of Mechanical Engineers, 3d ed., New York, 1950.

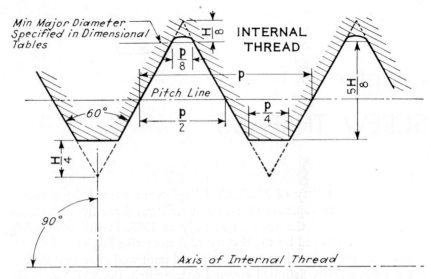

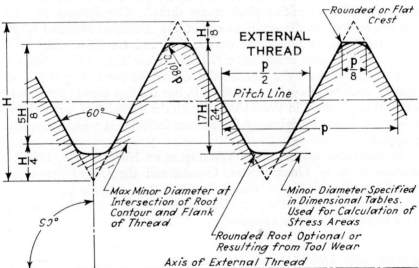

Fig. 19-1. Unified and American internal and external screw thread design forms, American Standard B1.1—1949, 3d ed., 1950. (Courtesy of The American Society of Mechanical Engineers, New York.)

Thread Series

The previously quoted American Standard B1.1—1950 covers both Unified and American standard threads. This fact is mentioned because the Unified screw threads are limited to the coarse and fine series of classes 1A, 1B, 2A, 2B, 3A, 3B, 2, and 3. When requirements go beyond these, other thread series should be investigated before the expedient of using special threads is resorted to.

Fine-thread Series—UNF and NF. In this series the former SAE standard is supplemented by ASME machine screw sizes below ¼ in. They are in general use in automotive and aircraft work, where fine threads are desirable because of prevailing requirements.

Extra-fine Thread Series—NEF. This is the same as the present SAE extra-fine series. It is used primarily in aircraft for thin-walled equipment where thread depth must be held to a minimum or where a maximum practicable number of threads is required within a given thread length.

8-Thread Series—8N. These threads are used on bolts for high-pressure flanges, cylinder head studs, and like applications against pressure. They are set up to an initial tension resulting from elastic deformation so that the joint will not open under the application of steam or other pressure.

12-Thread Series—12UN or 12N. Note that this series is found in both the Unified and the American thread series. It is used in boiler work in sizes from ½ through 1¾ in. Machine construction uses this series for thin nuts on shafts and sleeves.

16-Thread Series—16UN or 16N. This is another constant thread series that is used for adjusting collars, bearing retaining nuts, and other applications requiring a very fine thread.

Special Threads. These comprise a group of nonstandard, or special, combinations of diameter, pitch, and length of engagement, whose basic thread form conforms to the Unified and the American National standard.

Thread Classes. Screw threads are classified or distinguished by the amounts of tolerance and allowance specified. This information is of direct concern to the production department, since it devolves upon them to produce thread fits in accordance with design specifications. Design specifications, in turn, are predicated on product end use as well as production cost.

There are several classes recognized in American Standard B1.1—1950; this is a revision of previously issued standards and therefore some additions are present. Classes 1A and 1B are designed for ordnance and similar special applications. Class 2A, on external threads, and 2B, on internal threads, are considered the standard ones for the usual production of bolts, nuts, and screws. A recent addition to this standard includes classes 3A and 3B, while classes 2 and 3 have been carried over from earlier standards.

The dimensions applying to each of these classes can be found in tabular form in the published standard. In order to use the information on screw threads correctly, the designer should use the designations incorporated in the standard. An example for an external thread follows:

$$\frac{1}{4}'' \quad - \quad 2O \text{ UNC} \quad - \quad 2A$$

          └ Class of screw thread

        └ Thread series

      └ Number of threads per inch

  └ Nominal size

This designation applies to right-hand threads; when left-hand threads are wanted, the symbol LH follows the class designation.

Additional Standard Screw Threads

There are additional standard screw threads for purposes of a specialized nature such as pipe threads. Other standard screw threads perform

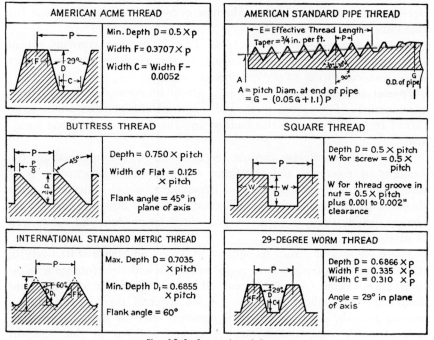

Fig. 19-2. Screw thread forms.

such functions as power transmission, as in the case of lead screws or closures exemplified by breach blocks. The list of standard thread forms is quite extensive; since several are of limited application, only the better-known ones will be considered here. A concise presentation of these is given in Fig. 19-2, where thread form and general dimensions are shown.

Special Thread Forms. The list of standard threads is being continually augmented by special ones. In each new development some specific condition is basic; for example, threads in which ball bearings form the contacting element are one such development. Special thread forms must not be confused with nonstandard threads of individual pitch. The policy of using nonstandard threads on an individual product has largely been abandoned in America. We should recognize the profound influence that thread standards exert in engineering manufacture—we have better products at lower costs as a result of standardization.

LATHE-CUT THREADS

Mention was made in Chap. 15 of the fact that threads can be cut on engine lathes equipped with lead screws. This is a versatile thread-cutting method, since any desired thread form, external or internal, can be produced through the device of grinding the single-point tool to the contour of the wanted thread. The diameter of an external thread is limited by the swing of the lathe and the length is restricted to the distance between centers, except in those cases where expedients in setup are used. Internal threads are limited to the bore that the workpiece can accommodate, as it is by swing in the lathe. Since internal lathe-produced threads are generally cut with a holder of the boring bar type, mounted on a tool post, their length is limited by the boring bar overhang and rigidity. External and internal threads can be lathe-cut both as straight and as taper.

Another feature of engine lathe thread cutting is the wide range of thread pitches that are available. The index plate on the change gearbox shown in Fig. 15-18 indicates the thread pitches that this lathe can cut: not all makes of lathes are identical in this respect. It is sound practice to check available thread pitch prior to purchasing a lathe. At the same time it is well to note whether an $11\frac{1}{2}$ pitch can be had, since this pitch is common to several pipe sizes.

The engine lathe has the further virtue of being able to cut either right- or left-hand threads; the change-over is made by reversing the direction of rotation of the lead screw. Right-hand threads are cut by starting the tool at the right-hand end of the thread and feeding to the left (toward the headstock) (Fig. 19-3). A left-hand thread is cut by starting at the left and feeding to the right (toward the tailstock).

Multiple-start threads can also be cut on the lathe. This is not a simple task with the conventional lathe, since extreme care must be observed in index from one turned thread to the next. Assuming a double thread is to be cut, one thread of the desired pitch is cut, then, with the lathe stopped, the workpiece is indexed precisely 180° by one of several methods and the second thread is cut. Should a triple thread be desired, the index is 120°, while a quadruple thread indexes to 90°.

Nonlinear-pitch Threads. A simple lathe attachment has been developed that will cut screw threads with a nonlinear pitch. This device can be attached to a standard lathe without altering it in any way. It is desirable, however, to remove the apron prior to locking the attachment

Fig. 19-3. Thread cutting in a conventional engine lathe with workpiece mounted on centers and driven with bent-tail lathe dog.

rigidly to the bed. Basically, the device consists of a vertically moving cam plate that bears against the tool holder saddle and causes it to move horizontally. Nonlinear-pitch threads are sometimes required in electromechanical equipment.

THREAD CHASING

In order to avoid confusion about the nomenclature of threading as between cutting and chasing, it should be stated here that the term *chasing* is used in this chapter to mean threading by multiple cutting edges. It might be desirable to point out further that the term thread chasing is usually associated with mass production of screw threads by machine tools equipped with some type of die head. Die heads are assembled units with removable cutting elements, termed chasers. This construction is in contrast with the solid die, which is a single unit.

Self-opening Die Heads

A self-opening die head has four or more chasers mounted in a carrier that is designed to open at the end of the thread-cut so that the die head

A

B

Fig. 19-4. (A) Rotating-type die head equipped with insert chasers, (B) rotating-type die head equipped with hobbed cutters. (Courtesy of The Eastern Screw Machine Corp., New Haven, Conn.)

can be speedily withdrawn from the workpiece. Die heads are used on many different machine tools, including drill presses, turret lathes, chucking machines, automatic screw machines, and threading machines. Designs of self-opening die heads vary as to both condition of operation and mechanical construction. Selection of the die head is governed by such factors as size and type of screw material, thread size, machine installation, and production runs. Broadly classified, die heads are either rotating or stationary.

Rotating Die Heads. As the name indicates, the rotating die head is one that is used where the material to be threaded is stationary and the die head rotates. Two designs are shown in Fig. 19-4. These heads are used on multiple-spindle screw machines, chucking machines, threading machines, and drill presses. They are constructed to open and close by means of a yoke. They can also be used in a stationary position in those instances where the workpiece rotates.

Fig. 19-5. Phantom view of stationary-type die head. (Courtesy of The Geometric Tool Co., New Haven, Conn.)

Stationary Die Heads. These heads are used where the workpiece rotates. There are several designs in respect to the opening and the closing mechanism. Die heads of the design shown in Fig. 19-5 find wide application as turret lathe tooling. The die head is self-opening at the end of the thread; however it is closed manually by means of the closing handle incorporated in the carrier. These heads are always constructed with a view to rapid and easy chaser removal.

Stationary die heads designed for automatic screw machines (Fig. 19-6) are much smaller and of different construction from the turret lathe types. In these installations the operation of the die head is synchronized with the operating cycle of the screw machine. In consequence the tripping and closing mechanisms are frequently built for external operation by suitable cam or stop devices on the machine.

Die Head Chasers. Chasers are of three distinct types as to design and appearance. Radial and tangential chasers are most common, but there are heads equipped with circular chasers. Radial chasers are produced in three types: insert chasers, milled chasers, and hobbed chasers. These classifications refer to the method of manufacture, which imparts distinctive characteristics to each. The hobbed, or tapped, chaser represents a theoretically correct thread shape in that it fits around the screw much in the manner of a nut. The helix angle in the chaser is correct at all points. Another characteristic of the hobbed chaser is that it can be reground at both the chamfer and the cutting face repeatedly.

Insert chasers are free-cutting and are capable of exceptionally long runs between grinds. They are easily removed from the carrier and can be readily reground. A die head designed for insert chasers will

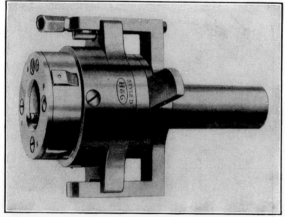

Fig. 19-6. Die heads for B & S and similar screw machines. (Courtesy of The Eastern Screw Machine Corp., New Haven, Conn.)

accommodate several sizes to the full operating capacity of the carrier. Left-hand chasers require the use of left-hand carriers.

The design of tangential chasers imparts a free-cutting action and a natural clearance like those of a lathe tool. It is claimed, therefore, that these chasers are easily sharpened and that they produce a smoothly finished, accurate thread. The reduced area of contact results in low friction, and consequently maximum threading speeds are possible. A die head equipped with tangential chasers can be seen in Fig. 19-7. This particular head is designed for cutting taper threads. The taper attachment causes the head to expand on the diameter as the work enters the die head. Cutting action is limited to the throat section of the chaser; this lessens cutting strains. The desired taper is regulated by cam action.

Circular chasers are made with ground annular grooves spaced at desired thread pitch. The circular form is interrupted in a manner that permits grinding a cutting edge on the chaser (Fig. 19-8). The correct thread lead is gained by grinding the face of the chaser-holding block to the required helix angle. Because of this design the same chasers, ground the opposite way, will produce left-hand threads. These chasers

Fig. 19-7. Die head for cutting taper threads equipped with tangential chasers. (Courtesy of Landis Machine Co., Waynesboro, Pa.)

Fig. 19-8. Self-opening die head equipped with circular chasers. (Courtesy of the National Acme Co., Cleveland.)

can be reground repeatedly or until 270° of the chaser circumference has been consumed.

Solid Dies. There are solid dies available which are used for every threading operation. Some of these are employed for restriking threads after a plating operation or for precision sizing. Manual threading is usually done with solid dies or with a die head containing two adjustable chasers which are positioned by screws. These chasers are removable for regrinding, a feature that the solid die lacks.

Thread Tapping

Internal threads are produced by taps whenever requirements permit. A table of tap drill sizes should be consulted prior to drilling a hole that is to be tapped. The tap drill size governs the minor diameter of the thread; a too large hole will result in a weakened thread. Solid taps are used where possible, since they are simple, rugged, and accurate. The threaded portion of the tap is produced either by machining or by grinding.

Fig. 19-9. Collapsing tap for turret lathe installation. (Courtesy of The Geometric Tool Co., New Haven, Conn.)

There are taps of many descriptions; each of these forms has been developed for a specialized application. Among those encountered in the general run of work are nut taps, pulley taps, pipe taps, boiler taps, stay-bolt taps, and spiral taps. Hand taps for American standard screw threads can be had in a series of three, respectively termed taper, plug, and bottoming. The difference between them is the amount of chamfer of the tap thread; thus a taper tap is used as a starting tap; while a bottoming tap is used on a blind hole where threads must reach to full depth.

Collapsible Taps. The counterpart of self-opening die heads is found in the collapsible tap (Fig. 19-9). This is used in both the rotating and the stationary type. When it is used as a stationary tap, collapsing is usually done by trip ring and resetting by a handle. If, however, the tap is of the rotating type, collapsing and resetting are accomplished by an outside yoke or by a trip plate and yolk. The collapsing feature pulls the blade-type chasers toward the center of the tap in order to clear the threaded hole as the tap is withdrawn.

Taps, regardless of design, are used in tapping machines in addition to the machine tools used for producing threaded components. Tapping machines represent specialized equipment designed for production run work. They can be had in every type of operating cycle, including fully automatic operation.

Threading Machines

When threading is a major part of machining a component, the operation is performed in a threading machine. Such machine tools are built

Fig. 19-10. Single-spindle threading machine. (Courtesy of The Hill Acme Co., Cleveland.)

in a variety of designs. The conventional threading machine has a single spindle equipped with a geared headstock that has several speeds (Fig. 19-10). The die head, which is of substantial construction, is arranged for automatic trip operation. Die heads are available for machine threads, pipe threads, and large-size API threads for oil-well casings.

The carriage is generally arranged for manual thread start by means of a handwheel; there are designs equipped for lead-screw operation. Change gears are provided for the lead screw to meet screw pitch requirements. Threading machines can be used for tapping by attaching a tap chuck to the die head. Lead-screw-equipped threading machines are especially desirable for tapping work because of the power-fed carriage feature.

Threading machines are used for threading bolts, rods, and similar components in addition to pipe. In the latter application, the machine can be equipped so that threading, reaming, and chamfering are performed in a single operation. Pipe nipples are threaded on this equipment to good advantage.

Automatic Threading Machines. A further development is that of the hydraulically operated threading machine equipped for either automatic or semiautomatic cycling. In addition, the machine is built on the double-end principle; the heads can be used singly or in unison, depending on the type of workpiece. Double-end threading is applied to

Fig. 19-11. Threading machine for small-parts production. (Courtesy of The Eastern Screw Machine Corp., New Haven, Conn.)

electrical conduit, tie rods, pipe, brace rods, and other workpieces requiring threads at both ends. Operation is simplified, since such functions as carriage movement, feeding, gripping, and releasing are all fitted into the hydraulic cycle which is controlled by a single lever.

Small Parts Threading. The automatic screw machine is always considered first where threading of small parts on a production basis is required. There are instances where such equipment is used for second operation work in connection with threading. Another solution to the problem of threading small parts is found in a threading machine built for this particular purpose (Fig. 19-11). The machine is equipped with a variable-speed motor drive that makes the most efficient threading speed possible. Production rates as great as 1,000 parts/hr have been achieved; obviously, though, production is dependent on many variables, not the least of which is the thread length.

Thread Rolling

The production of screw threads by rolling is distinctive in that there is no metal removed from the workpiece. In effect, thread rolling is a cold-swaging operation in which the workpiece surface is caused to flow into the rolling die cavities. It is obvious, therefore, that the external diameter of the workpiece will govern the final major diameter of the thread. The workpiece section must be prepared to a predetermined diameter, which is generally about equal to the pitch diameter of the thread. Since the final major thread diameter is usually of a standard size, it is necessary to prepare the workpiece diameter to a nonstandard size or undersize. This means that where a thread covers only a portion of the length of the workpiece, a shoulder must be formed prior to rolling.

Thread rolling is applied only to external threads. There are no limitations as to thread form, since every type of standard thread including wood and lag screws and other similar threads are produced by rolling. Rolled threads can be produced in right- or left-hand, multiple-start, and conical types. They can be applied on short surfaces or full rod length. Rolled threads are accurate and uniform, since the roller dies are never resharpened and as a result are not subject to the vagaries of adjustment. The dies continue in service until their entire face has virtually failed. The rolls perform in a manner similar to burnishing, with a resulting smooth finish on the thread surface.

Thread-rolling Methods. There are two principal methods for rolling threads. In one system, flat dies having ribbed surfaces at the proper helical angle pass over each other in a reciprocating motion. At the start of the cycle the workpiece is placed against the forward edge of the stationary die; the movable die then comes forward, thereby causing the component to roll and feed inward across the die face. The completion of the stroke cycle delivers the threaded piece from the dies.

The second basic method employs cylindrical dies, either two or three per die head. The cylindrical roller dies are power driven; hence the workpiece feeds forward through the central space at their junction. A thread-rolling machine employing thread die rollers is shown in Fig. 19-12; the workpiece is guided by the knobbed lever shown in the center foreground. Thread-rolling machines are built in every cycling category, from manual to magazine-feed, hydraulically controlled operation. Thread-rolling heads are occasionally installed on turret lathes.

Fig. 19-12. Thread-rolling machine employing three roller dies. (Courtesy of The National Acme Co., Cleveland.)

Thread Grinding

One means of producing precision threads, both internal and external, is by grinding. Thread grinding is accomplished by rotating the workpiece against a grinding wheel whose periphery has been shaped to the desired thread form. There is a relative axial traverse between the workpiece and the grinding wheel of one thread lead per workpiece revolution. Another thread-grinding method employs a multi-rib wheel in which several adjacent grinding ribs are present on the wheel surface. This type of wheel is generally employed on short threads whose total length is but one pitch longer than the wheel face width. In this instance the work rotates only one revolution while generating the complete thread length. Wheel face contours are preserved by diamond dressing and also by crush forming.

Thread grinding is especially suited to producing accurate threads in hardened steel where no other thread-producing method can be applied. Ground threads are characterized by their precision and excellent finish. Since grinding eliminates the possibility of cuts or tears, ground threads are specified where fatigue and bending stresses are of consequence.

Lead screws are commonly specified as ground threads, as are other components where precision is important.

Thread-grinding Machines. Even though grinding threads on a production basis is a relatively recent development, thread-grinding machines in many types and styles are available. External grinding machines are in the majority, but there are also several styles of internal ones. Universal thread grinders (Fig. 19-13) are designed for every type of operation from manual through hydraulically controlled automatic cycles. Threads are also ground on centerless grinding equipment. Plunge grinding is used for producing headless set screws of ¼ by 20 by ¼ in. at a rate of 7,000/hr. This is an example of what centerless grinding

Fig. 19-13. Universal precision thread grinder equipped with hydraulic controls. (Courtesy of Ex-Cell-O Corp., Detroit.)

equipment is contributing to the area of thread production. The grinding wheel is redressed or grooved by a steel dresser less than twice per shift.

Thread Milling

Threads can be cut by milling; in this process either a single form cutter or a multiple one is employed. There is a considerable difference between these two methods. The single form cutter is used for long threads of relatively coarse pitch such as lead and feed screws, multiple worms, and other heavy types; both the workpiece and the cutter rotate. Correct thread lead is obtained by moving the cutter carriage longitudinally by means of a lead screw.

A multiple cutter has annular rows of teeth that are perpendicular to the cutter axis; however, these cutters are devoid of lead. In consequence the cutter length must exceed the required thread length by several thread forms to allow for overrun. In operation, the cutter is "plunged" to thread depth and the workpiece need be rotated but $1\frac{1}{10}$ revolutions in order to complete the thread to length. This type of thread milling offers competition to self-opening die work on large production runs. Accuracy of milled threads is one of the chief assets of this method of thread production, since close tolerances and excellent finishes are characteristic. A further advantage of thread milling is the possibility of cutting large thread forms on small-diameter stock.

Thread-milling Machines. The machine tools employed for thread milling (Fig. 19-14) are different in design and appearance from conven-

Fig. 19-14. Thread milling operation, showing a finished threaded component at right. (Courtesy of The Lees-Brandner Co., Cleveland.)

tional milling machines. Their operating cycles vary in accordance with production requirements. There are also differences in operating mechanisms. Since thread milling is applicable to both external and internal threads, thread millers are built to accommodate either system. Universal thread millers which can be used for generating both external and internal threads are also available.

SURVEY QUESTIONS

19-1. Why are SAE threads used in engineering industries?

19-2. What countries collaborated in the development of a Unified Screw Thread standard?

19-3. Wherein does the Whitworth thread vary from the U.S. standard?

19-4. Will a U.S. standard nut fit a Unified standard screw of coarse pitch?

19-5. Give one specific application for a left-hand thread.

19-6. Would a class 1A thread be used on the same component as a class 2A thread?

19-7. On an engine lathe, where would an Acme thread be used?

19-8. Can internal threads be cut on a lathe?

19-9. Is it possible to cut a left-hand, multiple-start taper thread on a lathe?

19-10. Give a common example of the application of a multiple-start thread.

19-11. Would a single- or double-point tool be used for cutting a double thread?

19-12. What is a nonlinear-pitch thread?

19-13. Wherein does thread chasing differ from thread cutting?

19-14. Are die heads standard equipment on an engine lathe?

19-15. What is a thread chaser?

19-16. How does a self-opening die head operate?

19-17. What is the difference between circular and tangential chasers?

19-18. What application is there for a solid die?

19-19. Why are collapsible taps used?

19-20. If a die head is used on a turret lathe, where is it placed?

19-21. API threads are used for oil-well casings. What standard is this?

19-22. Are self-opening die heads used on automatic screw machines?

19-23. If screw threads are produced without metal removal, state the process involved.

19-24. Would such a process be used on both internal and external threads?

19-25. Which is the stronger thread, a rolled one or a cut one of the same dimensions?

19-26. How are the most accurate threads produced?

19-27. What types of grinding equipment are used for producing threads?

19-28. What type of equipment is used for thread milling?

Chapter 20

BORING

The term *boring* when used in connection with machining metal refers to enlarging an existing hole. It does not mean the production of a hole in a solid piece; this is known as *drilling*. In its restricted sense, then, a boring mill would be used to machine a previously made hole regardless of whether that hole resulted from drilling, from coring done in the casting, or from punching, as in a forging. However, boring mills have been broadened in scope to the point where they are capable of performing a variety of machining operations. Some boring mills are so versatile that their functions overlap those of other conventional machine tools.

The boring mill has the distinction of being the largest or most massive of the machine tools. Although there may be a few exceptions to this generalization, for example, the large metal planer, it is certainly true

Fig. 20-1. Boring mill equipped with 40-ft table erected in a pit. Right rail head protracted, left rail head plumb. (Courtesy of The Niles Tool Works Division, Lima-Hamilton Corp., Hamilton, Ohio.)

359

that no other machine tool combines size and flexibility to the degree found in the modern boring mill. An idea of the size attained by boring mills can be gained from Fig. 20-1.

VERTICAL BORING AND TURNING MILLS

The machine tools accurately fitting into this category are in effect vertical turning lathes, insofar as their functioning is concerned. They have a rotating table whose diameter is used to specify their size. Thus a 36-in. boring and turning mill is equipped with a table having a 36-in. diameter. These machine tools are built with a crossrail that mounts a saddle for holding the cutting tool.

Construction Details. The design details of vertical boring and turning mills are such that as sizes increase, more tool mounting is provided. The crossrail may carry two or more saddles, which can be arranged to follow in the same cut or can be used for combined cutting. Sideheads mounted on the housing can be added in some designs as a means of providing additional tooling capacity.

Operation. Vertical boring and turning mills make boring, facing, or turning cuts either singly or in combination. Because of this flexibility these machine tools are frequently used for facing and turning operations. Gear blanks are favorite workpieces. The outside diameter can be turned, one side or the rim and hub faced, and the bore made in one setting. The gear blank is then turned over and the second side finished; thus the machining is completed to the point of cutting the teeth.

Vertical boring and turning machines are capable of producing accurate work in every phase of their operation. In consequence they are frequently chosen in preference to other machine tools for facing workpieces of all shapes; the only requirement is that the piece be of a size that can be swung on the mill. As a means of offering greater flexibility, some designs are arranged for sliding housings so that the table can be clear.

Automatic Vertical Boring and Turning Mills. A specialized design for machining rolled steel car wheels has been developed in which the operating cycle is automatic (Fig. 20-2). One head cares for boring and facing the wheel hub while a second one faces the rim. Two sideheads turn the wheel tread in an operation where all four of these heads operate simultaneously. They are equipped with rapid traverse and operating feed all built into the automatic cycle; at the completion of the cycle, heads return to their starting position.

Specialized Boring Machines. Individual-type boring machines are sometimes built to meet specific situations. A heavy-duty inverted boring machine has been developed for the express purpose of boring

Fig. 20-2. Automatic vertical boring mill tooled for machining car wheels. (Courtesy of Giddings & Lewis Machine Tool Co., Fond du Lac, Wis.)

and finishing military tank hulls and turrets. This machine is built in a pattern that is just the reverse of the normal one.

HORIZONTAL BORING, DRILLING, AND MILLING MACHINES

The machine tool known as a combined boring, drilling, and milling machine is capable of performing many of the machining operations associated with individual machine tools in these three classifications. Fundamentally it is a boring machine designed for operation with a rotating tool on a stationary (nonrotating) workpiece. Frequently, however, the cutting tool rotates and traverses in a simultaneous movement; this is different from the operation of the milling machine, where the tool rotates on a stationary axis.

The basic operations performed by these machines are boring, drilling, and milling, including modifications of each one. In common with many machine tools, horizontal boring, drilling, and milling machines can be adapted to other than their fundamental operations. They perform such further operations as facing, turning, and threading, as well as tapping, reaming, shaping, forming, and duplicating. A wide choice is available, including rotary tables, which are most convenient for positioning the workpiece for subsequent operations; both horizontal and vertical tables are used in this manner.

There are several types of these machines, classification being based primarily on table arrangement. The three best-known ones are the table type, the floor type, and the planer type. A fourth is known as the

Fig. 20-3. Table-type horizontal milling, drilling, and boring machine equipped with electric pendant control. (Courtesy of Lucas Machine Division, The New Britain Machine Co., Cleveland.)

portable type because of the fact that it is taken to the job for such applications as work on board ship.

Table-type Machines. The table type was the forerunner of subsequent model developments in horizontal boring, drilling, and milling machines (Fig. 20-3). The essential components of this machine are base, saddle, table, main column, headstock with one or more spindles, end column, and end support. Of these components only the bed and main column are fixed; all the other members are capable of movement.

The basic feature of these machines is that cuts can be made longitudinally, laterally, and vertically. The workpiece can be moved horizontally by sliding the saddle on the bed and transversely by table movement on the saddle. The headstock in turn can be moved vertically on the main column; this allows for the raising or lowering of the tooling as desired.

Table-type machines are the most versatile of all the designs because of their ability to maneuver in three planes. They are constructed for accuracy, a characteristic which is furthered by such refinements as depth gages and direct-reading dials for speeds and feeds and micrometer adjustments to all units. Speed and feed selectors, independent reverse to all units, and remote control are other features characterizing table-type machines.

Table types are the smallest of these machines, although some imposing models are built. They are especially convenient for machining gear cases, machine-tool components, diesel- and gas-engine members, machinery parts, castings, weldments, and forgings where there are several pads, holes, or bores. It is possible to perform many machining operations with one setup.

Floor-type Machines. Floor-type machines mount the workpiece on floor plates instead of a table. It is for this reason that these machines take care of heavier work than the table ones. The basic difference between the two, however, is the fact that in the floor type the spindle traverses past the workpiece while in the table type the workpiece is traversed past the spindle.

The columns are mounted on runways which, because of sectional construction, can be extended to any reasonable length, as can the floor plates. In consequence the floor-type machines can be built to great size for machining extremely large workpieces. Some designs do not make use of an end column for support; rather, a very rugged main column is relied upon to give the necessary rigidity and support to the tooling. The choice of support is predicated on the workpiece shape and machining requirements. Floor-type machines are chosen for machining reduction gear cases, turbine housing, electrical generator frames, and other components of large size.

Planer-type Machines. This design has a reciprocating table—a modification of the table type, since the saddle-table unit is replaced. Instead of the table and saddle unit being adjustable to and from the face of the headstock, the column and end column are each separately provided with adjustment to and from the bed and table (Fig. 20-4). The planer-type or milling planer is selected for those jobs that require exceptional rigidity on heavy and long work.

Multiple-head Types. This machine departs from the basic design to the point where its scope and appearance are notably changed. A second column is used in such a position that the table is straddled. In addition there is a crossrail which accommodates one or more vertical headstocks.

Each column carries one or more heads designed to swivel when angular work such as large V-type motor blocks are to be machined. In appearance, multiple-head machines are similar to large milling machines although construction details are unlike (Fig. 20-5).

Multiple-head machines are used on semi-production work where simultaneous operations are needed. The heads can be operated singly

Fig. 20-4. Planer-type horizontal boring, drilling, and milling machine equipped with 8-in. bar driven with a 75-hp motor. The workpiece shown weighs 50 tons. (Courtesy of The G. A. Gray Co., Cincinnati.)

or in combination. Because of this design, vertical operations can be in progress while sideheads are being used. The swivel-head features eliminate the necessity for angle plates and other auxiliary tooling or multiple setups. The jobs for which these machines are ideal are castings that require machining on three sides, since these can be accomplished at the same time and with a single setup.

Tooling. Tooling combinations are extremely widespread; however, since such tools are fundamentally designed for boring machines, boring bars are of chief interest. Boring bars are of two main types, known as stub bars and line bars, respectively. The spindle has a Morse taper socket which fits the end of the boring bar and is equipped with a locking device. Boring bars are not integral parts of the machine in any sense.

Stub bars are supported solely by the spindle connection, which means that their alignment depends on this fastening. Stub bars are limited in their application to workpieces that can be brought close to the headstock; any excessive overhang will develop vibration during machining. It is desirable to employ stub bars whenever machining requirements will permit, since they are easy to install and require no additional alignment.

Fig. 20-5. Multiple-head horizontal boring, drilling, and milling machine. (Courtesy of Giddings & Lewis Machine Tool Co., Fond du Lac, Wis.)

The line bar is of a length that will give its outboard end a bearing in the end column support, requiring careful alignment between the two columns. When the bar is of any extended length, intermediate bearing supports are desirable. These can be arranged by using boring fixtures designed to hold suitable bearings. It is possible to use the workpiece itself as a means of providing intermediate bearing supports for the line bar where bushings can be inserted in previously machined holes.

Boring bars are frequently made of soft steel to permit ease of slotting and modification. They may develop wear at the bearing surfaces and have only a short service life. This condition can be remedied by attaching hardened steel wear strips, which are then ground to the required bearing diameter. Hardened steel bars are another answer to the problem of bearing wear.

Boring bars are equipped with single cutters or fly cutters which correspond to single-point tools. This is by far the most common type of boring tool. It is possible to use a double-end boring tool under some conditions; either a single tool bit or two independent tool bits are used for double-end boring. Boring bars can be provided with attached heads capable of carrying several tools for making concurrent cuts.

Precision Production Boring

The continued demand for precision boring, on a production basis, is being met by the development of machine tool equipment utilizing the

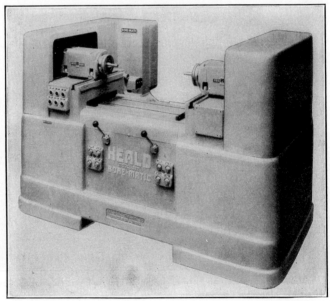

Fig. 20-6. Precision boring machine for use with single-point tool. (Courtesy of Heald Machine Co., Worcester, Mass.)

principle of extremely hard single-point tools operating at high speed. An early term for the basic method was diamond boring; this has been replaced by the coined word "borizing." The machine tool equipment built for this process is extensive in that single- and multiple-spindle designs as well as a variety of operating combinations, including fully automatic cycling, are available.

Machine tools of this classification are not confined to boring alone, since such additional operations as turning, chamfering, grooving, and facing are also performed on a precision production basis. Mechanical details of these machines vary as to work placement, spindle location, number of heads, and operating mechanisms.

The cutting tool used is an extremely hard one such as a diamond or cemented carbide. The tool rotates, while the workpiece is stationary; however, both can be moved for longitudinal or cross feeds (Fig. 20-6).

Any engineering materials not exceeding 400 Bhn can be machined to a high degree of accuracy. Efficient production can be expected when tolerances for dimensional accuracy, roundness, and straightness are on the order of 0.0001 to 0.0002 in. The degree of finish depends on the material, machine equipment, and mounting; finishes equaling 1 micro-inch root-mean-square have been achieved on a production basis.

JIG BORERS

In the area of precision locating and boring of holes the jig borer is preeminent. This equipment is undoubtedly the most accurately and soundly built of all machine tools. It produces precision work to the degree where measurements in ten-thousandths of an inch are considered routine, and operates with this precision over its entire lifetime. Every device and every precaution that can contribute to precision are called into play in the building of a jig borer.

The term jig borer does not do justice to the capabilities of this fine machine tool (Fig. 20-7). The primary function of jig borers is to produce accurate jigs, fixtures, dies, and similar work. With the increased demand for precision in small-lot manufacturing the jig borer should come into its own, as it can be fitted into such production programs in an altogether satisfactory manner. Its ability to produce precision work without the necessity of using jigs has given rise to the application of the expression *jig eliminator* to the jig borer.

Construction Features. The degree of precision is the same for all jig borers in the same classification. Construction details vary although close attention is given to lifetime accuracy. This ideal is achieved by designing, machining, finishing, and erecting the components with expert care. Consideration is given to such details as temperature changes and the anticipated behavior of the constructional material over a period of time. Thus hardened steel parts as well as castings are stabilized to prevent any change in dimensional accuracy over their lifetime.

The precision of which a jig borer is capable results from the methods used for controlling the table movement transversely and longitudinally. Vertical movement is cared for primarily by gaging tool depth although the spindle head can slide on the machined ways of the column. The table is restricted to movement in one plane—longitudinally and transversely.

A unique means of controlling table movement consists of measuring the travel entirely independently of its operating mechanisms. Built-in electrolimit measuring devices control the movement in a horizontal plane. The electrolimit measuring system currently used is built on the same principle as the gages of the same name. To locate the table longitudinally, master bar *A*—permanently mounted beneath the work table

Fig. 20-7. Electrolimit jig borer equipped with positive table-locating system. (Courtesy of Pratt & Whitney Co., West Hartford, Conn.)

—has ½-in. sections cut out, leaving ½-in. blocks. The distance between the magnetic centers of adjacent blocks is exactly 1 in. (The total accumulated error of the entire bar is only 0.00002 in.) The electromagnetic head is equipped with two balanced coils that enable it to detect the exact magnetic center of each block.

To obtain basic 1-in. spacings, the table is moved until one of the blocks on the master bar is exactly centered over the electromagnetic head and the indicating meter registers zero. Since there is no physical contact made with the master bar at any time, there is no wear, and the original high accuracy is retained indefinitely. In order to obtain settings in fractions of an inch, the electromagnetic head is moved left or right from zero position by means of the precision micrometer screw.

A hardened, ground, and draw polished spindle quill is mounted on preloaded ball roll mountings. A full range of infinitely variable milling feeds from 1 to 15 in./min, plus a rapid power traverse of 60 in./min, is provided for table and carriage. All positioning and operating controls are readily accessible from a single control zone. Taken together, this jig borer is capable of locating boring, and checking to 0.0002 in. accuracy with unequaled ease and dependability.

Accurately made lead screws have much to recommend them. They constitute the most rapid means for positioning, since the same device that moves the table also measures that movement. The manufacture of a precision lead screw, which is held to approximately 18 in. in length, involves many problems such as lead error and temperature change; however, the task is not insurmountable, as is evidenced by its use in jig borers (Fig. 20-8).

The Sipp jig borer, manufactured in Switzerland, uses a long lead screw equipped with cam lead error correction. The Hauser type of jig boring machine, also produced in Switzerland, operates on the coordinate system. Movement of table, boring head, and traverse slide are in accordance with the axis of coordinates, by means of high-precision micrometer screws fitted with correcting devices (Fig. 20-9).

Fig. 20-8. Jig borer built with precision lead screw for table movement. (Courtesy of Moore Special Tool Co., Inc., Bridgeport, Conn.)

Jig Borer Tools. Work is held rigidly while the cutting tool rotates in jig borer operation. A single-point tool is favored, since it generates a theoretically true hole, owing to its rotation about the exact center of the hole. There are a considerable number of boring heads, drill chucks, spotting tools, boring bars, boring tools, and precision end mill reamers in a variety of styles and sizes available for tooling a jig borer. Tooling, when mounted directly in the borer spindle, is equipped with taper shanks; the spindle nose usually has a threaded end nut, or keeper, but this detail varies with different models. Solid boring tools are graded in sets according to capacity; they are made from high-speed steel or, in some cases are carbide-tipped.

Accessory equipment extends the scope of jig borers. The extent to which such added expense is justified can only be determined by the job itself. Such items as tilting rotary tables, plain rotary tables, both manual and motor-driven types, and power traverse units are most common. There is much small equipment—for example, gages, precision angle

Fig. 20-9. Swiss-built precision jig boring machine. (Courtesy of Henri Hauser, Ltd., Bienne, Switzerland.)

plates, parallel bars, indicators, and proving bars—that completes the tooling requirements.

Deep-hole Boring

When holes whose length is greater than 20 diameters are to be bored, a nonrotating boring bar equipped with a pilot is generally used in an operation termed deep-hole boring. In some instances this method is employed on holes as shallow as 10 diameters. Regardless of the choice, deep-hole boring is of special interest on long production runs where the operation is integrated with the production program.

The deep-hole boring machines are designed for horizontal (Fig. 20-10) or for vertical operation. The tooling is designed to permit the

Fig. 20-10. Deep-hole boring machine. (Courtesy of W. F. and John Barnes Co., Rockford, Ill.)

flow of coolant to wash the chips through the hollow tool shank. The tool is fed by means of a whip support in which the tool is clamped. The cutting is done by any one of a number of designs, including such items as single or two-lipped deep-hole drills, pack bits, multi-lipped hollow core drills, and multi-fluted reamers.

SURVEY QUESTIONS

20-1. Wherein do the terms "boring" and "drilling" differ in metal machining?

20-2. How is the size of a boring mill designated?

20-3. Are vertical boring mills and vertical turret lathes identical equipment?

20-4. Why are sliding housings used on some types of boring mills?

20-5. Is an automatic vertical boring mill a general-purpose machine tool?

20-6. Is it possible to perform all three operations simultaneously on a horizontal boring, drilling, and milling machine?

20-7. On what type machine tool would a lathe headstock be machined to best advantage?

20-8. Give an example of the use of a stub boring bar.

20-9. Why are boring bars frequently made of C-1020 steel?

20-10. What is the function of hardened wear strips?

20-11. When is diamond boring used?

20-12. Does a jig borer resemble a boring mill?

20-13. Where in the manufacturing plant would a jig borer be installed?

20-14. State two different classes of work that would be done on a jig borer.

20-15. What type of cutting tools are used for deep-hole boring?

20-16. Name some accessories used with jig borers.

20-17. Why are fly cutters used?

20-18. Suggest at least two different components that would be machined on a 40-ft vertical boring mill.

Chapter 21

DRILLING

Drilling a hole is an operation in which an end cutting tool, termed a drill, is rotated about its major axis as it is fed into the workpiece (Fig. 21-1). An exception to this general statement is the case of impact, or star drills, as they are generally termed. The latter are not used on metal;

Fig. 21-1. Drilling operation using a twist drill. Note that drill flutes provide for chip escape and also serve as coolant carriers. (Courtesy of The American Tool Works Co., Cincinnati.)

their field of application includes concrete, stone, brick, and similar materials. A combination of the two procedures alluded to above is applied to flat drills and star drills in jackhammers, where the drill is given some rotation while it is under impact. An innovation in drilling is that of holding the drill stationary and causing the workpiece to rotate, as in some screw-machine and turret-lathe tooling.

Drills are for the most part of the twist type, although flat drills are of importance in certain classes of drilling. There are some specialized types of drills which have been developed to take care of individual requirements. Classification of drills is based on details such as method of manufacture, material, shape, length, design (helix or flute), shank type, point characteristics, and, above all, size (diameter).

TWIST DRILLS

Twist drills are composed of point, body, neck, and shank, all included in a solid tool. The most widely used type of drills, viz., straight- and taper-shank twist drills, are covered by American Standard B5.12—1949, entitled "Twist Drills—Straight Shank and Taper Shank."[1] The terminology used in that standard is followed in this chapter (Fig. 21-2).

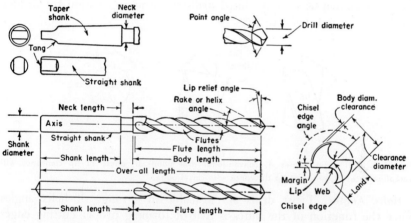

Fig. 21-2. Standard twist drill terms. Proposed revision ASA B5.12—1949. (Published by The American Society of Mechanical Engineers, New York.)

This nomenclature pertains to conventional twist drills primarily; there are many types of specialized drills, and there are innovations present on most of them. By way of example, the flute helix can be either right- or left-hand, thereby establishing the direction of rotation for the drill. A left-hand twist drill must be rotated clockwise—the direction of rotation is determined by viewing the drill from its point while its axis is along the line of sight.

The history of drilling tools indicates that early drills were flat or rectangular in cross section. The edges of the flat were generally convex by an amount fitting to the hole diameter. The cutting end of the drill was pointed, like that of currently used twist drills. The other end of the drill was forged or turned down to a round shank that fitted into the drilling machine spindle or chuck where it was fastened.

[1] American Society of Mechanical Engineers, New York.

Flat drills were further improved by twisting them about their major axis. This construction resulted in improved drilling, since it aided in guiding the drill in the hole and provided a means for chip escape and rake angle. The manufacture of twist drills by this method has largely been abandoned in favor of forming the flutes by machining them from solid stock. This operation is performed by a method that in its general principles is similar to the cutting of a helical gear. In two-fluted twist drills, the fluting is usually a single operation, the two flutes being cut concurrently. Machine tools are specially designed for this purpose, with basic features differing in that some are vertical and others are of the horizontal type of operation. Twist drills are made from high-speed steel as well as carbon steel. Production drilling is largely done with high-speed or carbide-tipped drills. There are twist drills with 0° helix angles; these are known as straight fluted drills and find application for drilling copper alloys and sheet stock.

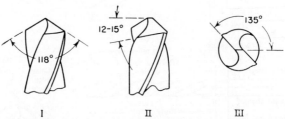

Fig. 21-3. Drill point angles. I, conventional drill point; II, angle of lip clearance with workpiece face; III, angle of lip clearance with chisel edge.

Helix Angles. Twist drills are available in a range of helix angles. Since the function of the flutes is that of forming proper cutting edges, chip curling, chip removal, and coolant carrier, it is obvious that the nature of the metal being drilled will be the determinant of the helix angle. Conventional twist drills have helix angles of approximately 24°. When drilling materials where chip formation is voluminous owing to high penetration rates, helix angles should be increased. Drilling the softer types of aluminum alloys is best accomplished with twist drills having 48° helix angles. The classification known as high-helix drills includes those twist drills whose helix angles range upward from 30°. There is also a series termed low-helix drills using helix angles ranging downward from the conventional 24° angle. Drills in this category are mainly those used for drilling plastics and others used for copper-base alloys. In addition to variations in helix angles, these drills have further modifications such as changes in web thickness, polished flutes, and other innovations designed to aid their performance.

Drill Points. The performance of a twist drill is dependent on the treatment accorded to its point. This takes precedence over all other consid-

erations. Helix angles were given prior mention only because they are
built into the drill; they are not subject to change, whereas drill-point
angles can be ground to suit the use for which they are intended. There
are three different angles that require consideration in connection with
a properly ground, or "pointed," drill, viz., point angle, lip relief, and
chisel edge (Fig. 21-3). Recommended values for these angles are not
fixed; however, Table 21-1 indicates accepted practice in this regard.
Twist drills when received from the manufacturer generally conform to
the specifications given in the first line of the table.

TABLE 21-1*

Types of drilling	Reference—Fig. 21-3		
	I	II	III
General shop usage.............	118	12–15	125–135
Gray cast iron..................	90–118	12–15	125–135
White cast iron.................	118–135	5–7	115–125
Mild steel—wrought or cast........	118	12–15	125–135
Alloy steel.....................	125–135	6–10	115–125
Aluminum alloys................	118–130	12	125–135
Magnesium alloys...............	118 max.	12–15	120–145
Copper alloys..................	115–130	10–15	115–125
Plastics—molded...............	70–95	12–15	125–135

* Compiled from manufacturers' and material suppliers' data.

Improperly pointed drills will not produce acceptable work. A dull
drill will cause trouble by burning the drill point, with the result that
either the drill will be ruined or an inordinate amount of grinding will be
necessary to resharpen it. A high degree of skill is required to sharpen
a drill properly by offhand grinding. It is a far better procedure to employ a suitable drill-grinding machine (Fig. 21-4) for this purpose, since
this equipment will produce a correct drill point. In the drill-grinding
machine shown, the grinding wheel rotates, reciprocates, and oscillates
in a unique path while in contact with the drill point, which rotates
about its own axis. An example of a drill point ground in this machine
is shown in Fig. 21-5. There are other designs of drill-grinding machines;
one of these operates on the principle of manually swinging the drill in
its holder across the grinding wheel.

Essentials of Drill Sharpening. As noted in position 3 of Fig. 21-3, the
drill point is shaped like a chisel. This type point has been standard for
a very long time. Recent research on the geometry of the drill point has
been most revealing.[2] The shortcoming of the chisel-type drill point is

[2] Ernst, Hans, and W. A. Haggarty: "The Spiral Point Drill—A New Development in Drilling," Cincinnati Milling Machine Co., Cincinnati, 1958.

that one end of the edge is generally slightly higher than the other because of grinding imperfection. Under this condition, there is a tendency
for the drill to wander to one side or the other of its intended center. A
method of overcoming this difficulty is to grind the drill point with a
true center, so that it will have self-centering action.

The spiral-point edge is formed as a three-dimensional spiral surface
that extends from the axis of the drill to its periphery. This configuration is obtained by a drill sharpener that has been developed especially
for this purpose. On the spiral drill point, the normal rake angle is much
less negative, the shear angle is greater, and the chip space ahead of the

Fig. 21-4. Drill grinding operation. Note sparks from drill point and position of the drill.
(Courtesy of Machine Tool Laboratory, University of Washington, Seattle, Wash.)

tool is larger. The result is much more effective cutting action at the
center, and, because of the greater chip space, a considerably lower
thrust force when drilling. Extensive research and application indicate
that the spiral-point drill contributes significantly to greater accuracy
of holes and higher production possibilities.

While it is true that correctly sharpened drills are obtained from drill-
grinding machines, it seems desirable to detail the essentials necessary to
a properly functioning drill. The three characteristics shown in Fig. 21-3
must be understood in their respective relation to drilling results.

Lip Clearance—If there is no lip clearance, the drill will not cut
because it cannot penetrate. It is not merely ground on the circumference of the drill; it covers the entire surface back from the point. The
heel of the drill, which is the surface back of the cutting lip, should be
ground away at an angle, as indicated in column II of Table 21-1. This

angle is in all cases the one measured at the circumference of the drill. The angle of the lip clearance should be gradually increased, however, as the center of the drill is approached until the line across the chisel edge of the drill gives the values shown in column III.

Faulty lip clearance angles are the cause of much drilling difficulty. If the angle of lip clearance is too great, the edges of the cutting lips will fail because of a lack of support when they enter the workpiece. A too shallow angle will prevent proper cutting action.

Length of Lip—It is necessary that the lips of a drill be of identical length. Should one be longer than the other, they will not remove equal amounts of metal. Such a condition frequently leads to drill breakage. Another fault resulting from unequal lip lengths is that an oversize hole

Fig. 21-5. Correctly ground drill points. Note especially the upper point (ground in the operation shown in the preceding figure), with its thinned web.

will be drilled. Too much emphasis cannot be placed on the subject of properly ground drill points.

The web of a twist drill increases in thickness in a direction away from the drill point. In order to secure the desired drill-point angles after repeated resharpening, it is necessary to thin the web by grinding. Twist drills increase in diameter from the point to the shank in a variable amount of from 0.0005 to 0.00075 in. per inch of length. This affords relief from the drill binding in the hole.

Rates for Drilling. The "speed" of a drill refers to its peripheral speed and is measured in feet per minute. The term speed should not be confused with rotational speed, which is measured in revolutions per minute. More faulty work results from driving drills too slow than from driving them too fast; this applies especially to small drill sizes.

It is sound procedure to inaugurate a drilling operation by combining high speed and low feed. Feed rates are governed by drill size and are stated in thousandths per revolution. A very general rule to follow in this regard is a feed of 0.001 to 0.002 in. for drills under ⅛ in.;

0.002 to 0.004 in. for ⅛ to ¼ in.; 0.004 to 0.007 in. for ¼ to ½ in.; 0.007 to 0.015 in. for ½ to 1 in.; and 0.015 to 0.025 in. for drill sizes greater than 1 in. The drill should be started with a light feed and care must be exercised in lightening the feed at the time the drill breaks through, especially when drilling sheet stock or working on curved surfaces.

Drill Types and Designations

Reference has been made to the fact that drills are available in a broad range of types and styles. Among these, the two-fluted, or two-lipped, twist drills are regarded as conventional. So far as sizes are concerned, classification is designated as follows:

Numerical—no. 80 to no. 1 (0.0135 to 0.228 in.)
Alphabetical—Letters A to Z (0.234 to 0.413 in.)
Fractional—¹⁄₆₄ to 4 in. and over by 64ths

This listing refers to standard stock sizes; these include metric sizes, which are considered standard. There are other sizes to be had by special order.

Shank Styles. A drill is held in the drill chuck or spindle by means of its shank, which provides the driving effort. Shanks are either straight

Fig. 21-6. Shank styles common to twist drills.

or tapered, the former applying to small- and the latter to larger-diameter drills as a general rule. There are also squared taper shanks such as those found on wood bits; a modification of this design is termed the ratchet shank (Fig. 21-6).

Taper shanks are of different sizes, following the Morse taper system. These drills fit directly into the drilling machine spindle which is equipped with a Morse taper hole. The range is from no. 1 for ⅛-in. taper-shank drills to no. 6 for drills of 3½-in. diameter. Placing a drill in the machine spindle offers no problem so long as the shank size is equal to or smaller than the spindle hole. In the event that the taper shank is smaller than the spindle, it can be brought to size by using drill sleeves. Sleeves are graduated by taper sizes so that they nest in a perfect fit. They are separated by inserting a key, or drift, that acts as a pry against the tang. The advantages of taper-shank drills are their freedom from slippage when in use and the fact that they rotate in truth unless injured by abuse. Straight-shank drills require the use of a drill chuck for a driver. Drill chucks are equipped with a taper shank for spindle fit. Chucks are self-centering on the drill and are operated either manually or with a key. A drill should always be firmly held in the chuck; if slippage occurs, the shank will be fouled and will run out of truth.

Special Drill Types. In addition to the conventional drill types there is a host of special ones designed to fit local applications. In this category such items as three- and four-fluted core drills, oil-groove drills, oil-hole drills, multi-cut drills, step drills, hard-steel drills, threaded-shank aircraft drills, and crankshaft drills are included. Drills are also classified as short length, taper length, jobbers' length, automotive series, and long length.

Related Tools

Reamers. A reamer is a rotating cutting tool, generally of cylindrical or conical shape, that is used for enlarging or finishing an existing hole. A reamer is designated by its nominal size or diameter; its length is measured parallel to its axis. There is a vast number of reamer types both in conventional and in special categories.

A finishing reamer is expected to remove a very small amount of metal. Reaming is, in effect, a sizing, or scraping, operation. Hand reamers should not be expected to remove more than 0.002 to 0.003 in. of stock on the diameter. Machine reamers, on the other hand, can take care of greater amounts. In no case should stock removal exceed 0.012 in.; removal of from 0.003 to 0.005 in. is preferable.

Counterbores. A counterbore is a tool designed to enlarge a previously formed hole for a part of its depth and at the same time to produce a shoulder at the bottom of the enlarged portion (Fig. 21-7). The counterbore tool is frequently equipped with a pilot that fits the base hole diameter, where it acts to ensure concentricity with the original hole; however, there are counterbores that do not have this aligning feature. There are step counterbores that produce more than one diameter in a single operation.

Countersinks. Tools in this classification fall somewhere between drills and counterbores. Countersinks are employed to produce a taper in an existing hole (Fig. 21-7). A hole is countersunk to accommodate a fastener head such as a screw, rivet, or the like. Countersinks used for wood screws have an included angle of 82°, while machine screws are 60, 82, or 90°. Another series that is used for ships plates, boilers, and tanks has 37, 45, 53, or 78° included angles.

Spot Facers. A further operation related to drilling is termed spot facing. Spot-facing tools are modified counterbores. The difference between them is that spot facing is applied to the face or top of a machine boss that generally has a hole normal to its surface. Spot facing produces a finished surface that acts as a seat for bolt- or screwheads or

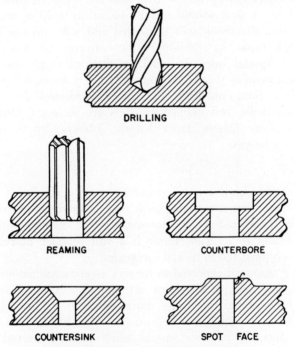

Fig. 21-7. Drilling and related operations.

for mountings. The spot-facing tool, commonly termed a spot facer, takes several forms, but in every case it is an end cutting tool.

UPRIGHT DRILLING MACHINES

The familiar term "drill press" has, technically, passed from drilling-machine terminology. The more accurate expression "drilling machine" has been inaugurated to describe the category which includes the single-spindle general-purpose machine tool. The more important ones are the sensitive type, the bench type, and the floor type. Each of these has some design modifications made by the different manufacturers of drilling machines.

Sensitive Drilling Machine. Drilling machines of this type are small, high-speed ones intended for driving letter-size and other small drills. These drilling machines are virtually indispensable to such operations as those of the tool and die shop, the template shop, and the instrument shop and laboratory.

Bench-type Drilling Machine. The drilling machines in this classification are for the most part small editions of the column floor types. Their name is descriptive, since they are intended for mounting on a bench or table. They are usually equipped with a V-belt drive employing a stepped pulley for spindle speed variation. Hand feed is common since these machines are generally limited to driving drills up to ½ in. in diameter. Bench-type drilling machines are popular in all branches of manufacturing, in addition to being prominent in hobby and home workshops.

Floor-type Drilling Machines. In this group is found the familiar column drilling machine. The two principal types in this classification are the round-column and the box-type upright. These designs differ in both column as well as table treatment. They are both specified as to size by the distance from the center of the spindle to the face of the column.

Round-column Type—This drilling machine has great adaptability. The driving head is mounted at the top of the column. The drilling

Fig. 21-8. 21-in. all geared upright round-column drilling machine. (Courtesy of The Cincinnati Bickford Tool Co., Cincinnati.)

round table is clamped to the column in a manner that permits its vertical movement as well as its being swung about the column (Fig. 21-8). This table can also be rotated about its center for convenience in bringing mounted workpieces under the drill.

The round table can be swung clear in order that large workpieces can be placed on the floor plate. This feature contributes in a major way to the adaptability of the round-column upright drilling machine. The spindle carries a Morse taper for direct insertion of taper-shank drills or for drill chucks. There are several spindle speeds obtainable from the change gearbox that receives its power from a directly connected motor. Both hand and power feeds can be employed.

Box-column Upright—These drilling machines are built with a box-type column that enables them to handle heavier drilling operations. The front of the column has machined ways for adjusting the drilling head vertically. A second set of ways serves as table guides.

Upright Gang Drilling Machines. There are operations adapted to a single table served by several individual spindles. Machines that handle

Fig. 21-9. Six-spindle upright gang drill equipped with multi-strand V-belt drive. (Courtesy of The Avey Drilling Machine Co., Cincinnati.)

such operations are in effect a series of box-column drillers connected to a single table (Fig. 21-9). A variety of arrangements are possible, although four or six spindle types predominate. The individual spindles can be set up for different speeds in order to accommodate varying requirements of a workpiece that can be passed from one drilling operation to another.

Radial Drilling Machines

There is a distinctive classification of upright drilling machines known as radial drills. They derive their name from the design whereby an arm, carrying the drilling head, is constructed to permit it to be swung in a complete circle about its upright column. Radial drilling machines have a working capacity that is capable of more substantial operations than those associated with the conventional type of upright drilling machine. They are designed and built to accommodate drilling, boring, reaming, tapping, spot facing, and related operations.

The radial drilling machine is simple in construction, since it consists of a base, a vertical column, and an arm carrying the drilling head. The head traverses on the radial arm either by power rapid traverse or by manual movement. The head carries the drill spindle; the lower end of

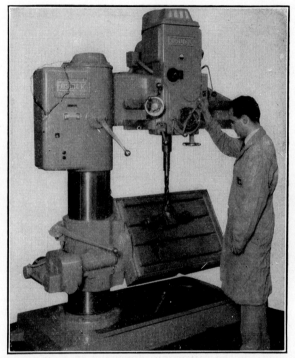

Fig. 21-10. Radial drilling machine equipped wth column-mounted swivel table. (Courtesy of The Fosdick Machine Tool Co., Cincinnati.)

the spindle is equipped with a Morse female taper whose size, depending on the machine capacity, usually ranges between no. 4 and no. 6. There is a range of spindle speeds provided that can be readily engaged by means of conveniently located controls. Feeds are likewise obtainable in a wide choice by suitable controls; however, manual feed is also available when desired. The machine spindle moves in a vertical plane on most designs; these are termed plain-type radials. In universal and semi-universal radials, the spindle can be rotated to angular positions with the radial arm.

The workpiece is fastened to the base of the radial drilling machine where the piece to be drilled is too large for table mounting. However, a separate table, in a variety of designs, can also be had where smaller workpieces are being machined (Fig. 21-10). Such tables are generally built of swiveling construction and carry graduations for exact positioning. Not all manufacturers use the same design; in some machines this table mounts on the bed rather than on the column.

Traveling Radial Drilling Machines. The utility of a radial drill can be expanded by altering its design so that the column, with its accompanying radial arm and head, can be traversed along a longitudinal bed table

Fig. 21-11. Traversing-type radial drilling machine tooled for machining diesel-engine blocks mounted in a swinging fixture. (Courtesy of The American Tool Works Co., Cincinnati.)

(Fig. 21-11). This feature is sometimes modified to the point where power is applied for the traversing movement in a design known as the truck type. In this type a truck or tractor carrying the column and radial arm travels on rails, whereas in the conventional traversing type the movement is along the machine bed. The job setup shown is indicative of the machining possibilities possessed by this design when accompanied by versatile fixtures.

PRODUCTION-TYPE DRILLING MACHINES

Undoubtedly the most diversified line of machine tools is found among production-type drilling machines. This term has been used to cover an extremely wide field; in consequence, some doubt can be expressed as to its appropriateness. Irrespective of the choice of terms, the development of machines for performing drilling and related operations is continuing at a rate that indicates further startling innovations can be expected.

Multiple-spindle Drilling Machines

Multiple-spindle drilling machines afford a means of drilling a number of holes simultaneously (Fig. 21-12). The number of spindles is fixed in

Fig. 21-12. Vertical hydraulic multiple-spindle drilling machine equipped with 30 spindles and tooled for drilling and reaming diesel cylinder head. (Courtesy of Baush Machine Tool Co., Springfield, Mass.)

some designs; in others, spindles can be added to the capacity of the machine. Construction and operating details are different among the various manufacturers of these machine tools. Multiple-spindle designs are most common in vertical styles; however, the same principle has been adapted to horizontal drilling machines.

Specialized Heavy-duty Drilling Machines

Machine tools fitting into this classification are of highly specialized designs. They are a distinct departure from the all-purpose drilling machine, since they are built for maximum production on a given workpiece. Instead of an abbreviated survey of a field that is replete with spectacular accomplishments, summaries of representative cases chosen at random are offered here.

Fig. 21-13. Two-way horizontal machine for drilling and reaming operations on a crankshaft. (Courtesy of Baker Bros., Inc., Toledo, Ohio.)

Case I. The series of operations performed on a crankshaft in the two-way horizontal machine with auxiliary units and trunnion-type fixture (Fig. 21-13) are the following:

	Left-hand side	Right-hand side
Station 1	Load and	Unload
Station 2	$2^{9}\!\!/_{64}$-in. drill-1 hole	$1\frac{1}{8}$-in. end cut-1 hole, $\frac{7}{8}$-in. drill-1 hole
Station 3	Spot-face and chamfer	$\frac{3}{8}$-in. drill and chamfer (6), $1\frac{1}{8}$-in. core drill (1)
Station 4	$\frac{1}{2}$-in. C' bore (1)	0.875 drill (1)
Station 5	$\frac{7}{8}$ drill web hole	$1^{7}\!\!/_{32}$-in. C' bore, 0.484 bore and chamfer
Station 6	Chamfer $\frac{1}{32} \times 45°$ OD	1.6094-in. semifinished C' bore
Station 7	Mill $\frac{3}{16}$-in. keyway, rear	$1\frac{1}{16}$-in.-diameter undercut and chamfer
Station 8	Blank	0.3906 ream (6) holes
Station 9	Blank	0.4995 ream (1) hole
Station 10	$\frac{1}{2}$-20 tap 1 hole	$\frac{7}{16}$-20 tap (6) holes

Production for the above operations is estimated at 32 pieces/hr net.

Auxiliary equipment includes a milling attachment mounted on a drive bracket. The fixture is a trunnion type having automatic power index with ten stations. A study of the operations shows that drilling is but one of the types of machining, since related operations are also included. This versatility adds much interest to an evaluation of the suitability of this type of equipment for a specific installation.

Case II. The trend toward automation is reaching into every activity of machining. An example is portrayed in Fig. 21-14, where a continuous drum-type milling machine has been coupled with a vertical multiple-spindle reaming machine. The particular part being machined is a support valve rocker arm shaft which is loaded, automatically positioned, clamped, and discharged. The production is prodigious in that 3,000

Fig. 21-14. Automated unit with reaming operation at the right and milling at the left. Workpieces shown above. (Courtesy of Davis & Thompson Co., Milwaukee.)

gross/hr or 432,000 pieces/hr are completed. The entire automated unit and equipment weigh 12½ tons. This machining setup represents a small-scale transfermatic unit, although it has greater flexibility.

Portable Horizontal Drilling and Tapping Machines. A development of interest is that of a portable drilling machine designed to be taken to the work. This design features a central column carrying a crossarm containing the machine head, which can be rotated 360° and swiveled 180° (Fig. 21-15). The top of the column has a built-in bail for ease of lifting by a crane. To give the machine stability, stabilizing spreader arms are hinged to the machine runway.

This particular design is extremely flexible in that the head can be arranged for drilling vertically upward or downward as well as horizontally or at any angle. In addition, the entire rail and head stock are provided with vertical traverse on the column, thereby allowing for consid-

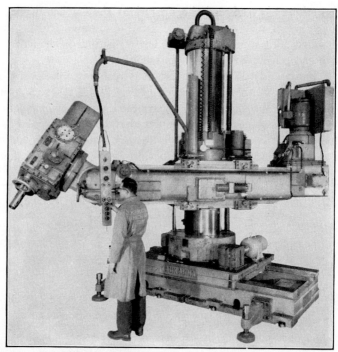

Fig. 21-15. Portable universal radial drilling machine. (Courtesy of the Kaukauna Machine and Foundry Division, Kaukauna, Wis.)

erable spindle height. The entire column assembly has horizontal traverse on the runway, so that positioning in that direction as well is afforded.

SPARK DRILLING

With the increasing interest in gas turbines and similar type equipment, drilling small holes accurately in heat-resisting steel and other metals, especially those which work-harden rapidly, proves a serious problem. This has been resolved through the development of the spark erosion method of drilling. The mechanics of this method is entirely different from the usual type drilling that has been described in this chapter, since no twist drill as such is used; instead, an electrode is substituted. This electrode is generally made from some type of brass or soft tubing that has a very small bore, on the order of 0.010 in.

The actual hole penetration is brought about by the creation of an electric spark between the electrode and the workpiece that causes fusion resulting in microscopic globules of metal. In order to carry on this operation, it is important that a dielectric fluid, usually paraffin, be pumped under considerable pressure through the bore in the electrode.

(a)

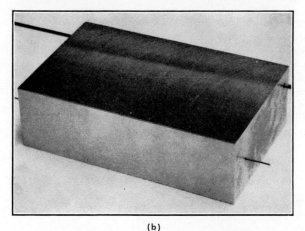

(b)

Fig. 21-16. Spark drilling equipment above, with drilled block at bottom. (Courtesy of Wickham, Ltd., Coventry, England.)

The function of this fluid is to wash out the displaced material as the hole progresses. The electrode is caused to rotate in order to maintain the proper hole shape and size. In one series of tests, holes with diameters of 0.076 and 0.035 in. were drilled through a nickel-base alloy component; these holes were 4½ in. in length. It required 31 min to drill the larger hole and 3 hr 50 min to drill the smaller one (Fig. 21-16). Nonetheless, this method offers a means of drilling material that previously was impossible to machine. Modifications of this spark method have been employed on die sinking and other machining operations.

SURVEY QUESTIONS

21-1. What part of the drill does the actual cutting?

21-2. What is a flat drill?

21-3. Are twist drills made by twisting or otherwise?

21-4. Are these twist drills of more than two flutes?

21-5. Why is the helix angle important to a twist drill?

21-6. Give one reason for a drill "wandering."

21-7. What is the importance of lip clearance on a drill point?

21-8. What is the meaning of numerical size drills?

21-9. What drill shank is most common in industry?

21-10. Are reamers primarily metal-removal tools?

21-11. Why are counterbores used?

21-12. Why are the flutes on a hand reamer of unequal depth on each half of the circumference?

21-13. Is spot facing similar to countersinking?

21-14. Give an example of the application of a sensitive drill.

21-15. Are drilling machines and drill presses the same thing?

21-16. Give an example of a job that should be done on a gang drill.

21-17. Do radial drills and drilling machines generally use the same type of cutting tool?

21-18. Does the radial drill carry more than one tool for simultaneous machining?

21-19. Are multiple spindle and gage drills the same type equipment?

21-20. On what type of machine tool would automotive type cylinder heads be drilled?

21-21. Are there production machines that combine operations other than drilling?

21-22. Are radial drills fixed for portable machine tools?

21-23. How are small holes drilled accurately?

21-24. Can spark drilling or machining be regarded as a production process?

Chapter 22

PLANING, SHAPING, AND SLOTTING

Basically, the machine tools used in planing, shaping, and slotting function to produce a flat surface or a modification thereof. The workpiece moves in a horizontal plane in a reciprocating motion under the tool in a planer; this movement is reversed in the case of the shaper and the slotter. A simple analogy is that of a carpenter using a hand plane on a piece of wood to bring it to dimension or to smoothness or both.

METAL PLANERS

The metal planer consists of a bed, a table, a housing, and crossrail components; these are found in several arrangements, and it is the arrangement that gives each type its name. The double-housing planer is the best known and most widely used type (Fig. 22-1). All planers, regardless of type or operating mechanism, feature a table reciprocating on the bedways. The workpiece is mounted rigidly on the bed in order to prevent any movement from tool cutting action. The planer tool is carried in a head mounted on the crossrail that permits lateral or vertical travel. The arrangement of heads is varied, several heads being installed both on crossrail and columns on large-size planers, as shown in Fig. 22-1.

Capacity. The double-housing planer can only machine workpieces within certain limits of width, height, and length. The restriction on width is governed by the clearance between the two housings; the maximum height is held to the vertical distance between the table and the crossrail when the latter is elevated to its upper limit; the length that can be planed is governed by maximum table travel. The limiting, or capacity, dimensions are stated in inches for width and height and feet for length and are always given in that order. A planer specified as a 48 by 36 by 12 size will accommodate a workpiece 48 in. wide, 36 in. in height, and 12 ft in length.

Openside Planers. Planers having a single vertical column are termed openside planers. Since but one housing is used, the workpiece can extend beyond the table width. Extension may be so great as to require an auxiliary support in the form of a track to carry the overhung workpiece. Openside planers offer greater versatility because of the increased range of work that can be machined.

Crossrail construction on openside planers requires special attention inasmuch as there is no support offered to the outboard end. There is a design known as the convertible openside planer in which a second housing can be placed if desired. This design offers the advantages of a double-housing and an openside planer in a single machine tool.

Fig. 22-1. A 48 by 48 in. by 14-ft heavy-duty double-housing planer equipped with four heads. (Courtesy of G. A. Gray Co., Cincinnati.)

The direct motor drive employs a reversing electric motor. The table is driven by means of a gear rack fastened to its underside, resulting in dependable, trouble-free operation. The rack is driven by a gear train connecting with the motor. Spur-gear and helical types are found in current designs as well as a worm-drive type.

Hydraulic drives on planers follow in general the principle used on other machine tools (Fig. 22-2). A constant-speed motor drives a pump that circulates oil through the hydraulic system. The table is connected to a piston rod, which in turn connects to the piston located in the main drive cylinder. Advantages claimed for this equipment include such items as great flexibility in cutting speed and simplicity resulting from the elimination of gear trains. The hydraulic pump unit is connected directly to the electric motor in a combined unit that is self-contained and located independently of the planer.

Heads located on the crossrail are sometimes of right- and left-hand pattern in order that they may work close to each other. The tool-carrying clapper blocks mounted on the heads are equipped with hydraulic devices that lift the tool clear of the workpiece on the return stroke. Heads are mounted on saddles similar to those on boring mills where swivel action is provided for angular cuts.

Fig. 22-2. Hydraulically driven and controlled openside planer. (Courtesy of Rockford Machine Tool Co., Rockford, Ill.)

Workpiece Mounting. It is a wise precaution to give close attention to mounting the workpiece, or pieces, on the planer bed. Above all, the workpiece should be clamped only where solid support is afforded; straining the workpiece by clamp bolts should be avoided. One method of checking the clamping effectiveness is to place tissue paper or cellophane between workpiece and table; if at any point the paper can be pulled free, there is no support for the workpiece at that point.

Uneven surfaces are supported by inserting wedges or shims between them and the table. Clamping should then be done directly over the shims or immediately adjacent to them. Frequently one face of the workpiece is rough-planed and then turned over for the planing of the opposite side. When opposite faces are rough-planed before finishing cuts are taken, the danger of warpage on finish planing is largely overcome.

Planer Applications. Planers are chosen for machining flat surfaces on a wide range of work. A listing of typical planer work would include such components as machinery bases, rolling-mill frames and housings,

Fig. 22-3. Planing four propeller blades simultaneously from a single master. Blades are 4340; 1⅛-in. stock is reamed in three cuts. (Courtesy of Rockford Machine Tool Co., Rockford, Ill.)

printing-press machinery, steam- and drop-hammer parts, textile machinery, and machine tool members such as beds, slides, carriage, and tables. A planer is rarely regarded as a mass-production tool; rather it fits into industries of the toolroom and job-shop type. It does offer the possibility of machining many duplicate parts with a single setup by stringing them on the table. It is suited to such jobs as T slots, V ways, angular surfaces, and horizontal slotting. Planer tables are ideal for mounting work-holding fixtures and chucks for small or odd-shaped workpieces.

Accessory Equipment. There is a wealth of accessory equipment available for adapting planers to specialized work. These include such appurtenances as radius planing and duplicating devices. An example of a tracer installation for planing contours is shown in Fig. 22-3. It can be seen that complicated shapes rarely associated with the general concept of planer work are possible when suitable accessory tooling is engineered for a given job requirement.

Planer Tools. The planer employs the single-point tool principle of metal removal. A planer tool can have many modifications in shape, size, construction, arrangement, and material; the selection for a given application is based upon requirements for that job. Planer tools are either forged in their entirety from high-speed steel or they are built up using

Fig. 22-4. A 60/114 by 60 in. by 36 ft adjustable convertible openside universal planer with four heads equipped for double cutting. (Courtesy of The G. A. Gray Co., Cincinnati.)

a medium carbon steel shank welded to a short piece of high-speed steel. Another method, and one of considerable prominence, is that of tipping a medium carbon steel shank with high-speed steel, cemented carbide, or cast alloys. Toolholders equipped with bits are common.

Double-cutting Planers. It is now possible to make use of the return stroke when planing—there is no more "cutting air." The idea is not new, since many attempts have been made to solve this problem effectively. The planer design must be revised fundamentally since return-stroke cutting causes tool presses against dovetailed crossrails and tool slides that lead to looseness and chatter. On the current design (Fig. 22-4), the column, crossrail, and heads are built to resist the return-stroke pressures by using oversize bearings and square lock gibs.

The toolheads provide double cutting by pivoting the tool post. The post is mounted at a slight angle to the vertical in the case of a railhead. It is pivoted only a few degrees by air pressure at the beginning and end of each stroke. The resultant slight motion is sufficient to lift the forward cutting tool clear of the workpiece and, at the same time, to set the second tool for the reverse stroke. The planer speed is constant since the tool positions itself instantly at the end of each stroke. One installation reports a job planed in 10 hr on this equipment in contrast to about 30 hr previously required on a standard planer.

SHAPERS

A shaper is a machine tool that provides a reciprocating movement of the cutting tool over the workpiece. At the same time the workpiece is moved across the tool path to give the requisite feed. In shaper operation the tool travels in the same horizontal path for each stroke. In consequence the contour of the resulting machined surface is governed by the path of that surface. The tool is mounted so that it can be fed vertically or be given angularity by manual means.

By far the greater part of shaper work is confined to machining flat surfaces or modifications thereof. The tool cuts on the pushing or outward stroke as it travels across the work; there is one design in which this action is reversed. Shapers are designated by their maximum stroke; thus a 24-in. shaper refers to one capable of machining a surface 24 in. in the direction of tool travel. Shapers range in size from the bench models with 6-in. stroke to the large industrial types with a 36-in. stroke. The stroke length can be adjusted from the minimum up to the capacity of the shaper.

Horizontal Shapers

Among shaper installations horizontal types are in the majority. They are capable of a great range of machining operations on both external and internal surfaces. A shaper is constructed with a housing containing the operating mechanisms and a ram that travels in ways at the top of the housing (Fig. 22-5), together with a driving motor and a crossrail carrying the table on the front to the housing.

The operating end of the ram carries the toolhead, which is equipped with swivel mounting carrying graduations permitting the tool slide to be set for angular cuts. A clapper box is fitted to the lower end of the slide and it, in turn, carries the tool post.

The clapper box pivots at its upper end to permit tool freedom on the reverse stroke. For the most part the tool drags lightly on the workpiece during this part of the stroke, although there are some designs in which the tool is raised and held free of the surface on return by mechanical or hydraulic means. The tooling is similar to that of planer types, but smaller, and tool bits in holders are much more common than are solid forged tools.

The ram is reciprocated with a quick return motion that imparts a noticeably greater speed to the return stroke than it does to the cutting stroke. This is achieved, on the mechanical types, by the basic principle of a crank and pin arrangement that, for the most part, is derived from the Whitworth quick-return motion. Hydraulic drives are built on a different principle but achieve the same result.

Fig. 22-5. 36-in. heavy-duty universal table shaper. (Courtesy of Nebel Machine Tool Co., Cincinnati.)

The table can be traversed by a manual crank for setup or hand feed of an individual nature. However, when performing conventional operations, the table traverse, which actually feeds the workpiece, is driven mechanically. The drive is arranged so that the table can be traversed in either direction by a control lever. In addition, many designs are equipped with a rapid traverse.

It is the type of table mounting and support that identifies the shaper as either plain or universal. Those of the latter type are usually equipped with tables having two working surfaces, one of which is solid for planing flat and angular work, while the other has a tilting surface useful for combination and compound angle work. In addition, the worktable can be rotated about its axis with graduations provided for accurate settings.

Operating Drives. Mechanical details differ to the extent that some makers employ helical gearing whereas others provide spur-gear trains. Some modification of a sliding-gear transmission is employed, either singly or in combination, with a double main gear, to develop the ram speed range, which may offer as many as sixteen speeds. The speed range varies with different makes and models; by way of example, one design offers 12 to 200 strokes/min.

A hydraulic shaper is designed on the principle of the hydraulic system of power transmission (Fig. 22-6). The main ram drive and also the

Fig. 22-6. Plain horizontal-type hydraulic shaper. (Courtesy of Rockford Machine Tool Co., Rockford, Ill.)

table traverse are operated hydraulically and mechanically. The latter, as in mechanical types, has rapid traverse both horizontally and vertically. Hydraulic ram operation results in a constant cutting speed throughout the stroke, and the range of strokes per minute is infinite within the limits of the machine. The hydraulic cylinder is located below and parallel to the ram to which it is directly connected resulting in a design whereby the power stroke is approximately on a straight line with the tool cutting point.

Shaper Accessories. Workpiece mounting governs the extent to which the conventional shaper can be employed for contouring and other specialized operations. There is a trend toward placing accessory equipment on the shaper itself for contouring by tracer attachments (Fig.

Fig. 22-7. Horizontal shaper equipped with hydraulic duplicating attachment, shaping a bit for making wood molding. (Courtesy of The Cincinnati Shaper Co., Cincinnati.)

Fig. 22-8. Heavy-duty draw-cut die-block shaper. (Courtesy of Morton Manufacturing Co., Muskegon Heights, Mich.)

22-7). A work-holding fixture is used to give the workpiece proper positioning under the cutting tool. There is an infinite number of fixtures and accessories for shapers. Automatic power down-feed, auxiliary front cross-feeds, indexing centers, profilers, circular feeding heads, table front hand feeds, and an array of vises are available for shaper application.

Draw-cut Shapers. All the shaper designs presented in this section have been of the push-cut type, wherein the tool cuts on its forward or outward stroke. That principle is basic and is the method favored by the great majority of shaper manufacturers. The draw-cut principle of shaping metal reverses the above procedure in the sense that cutting is performed on the inward or return stroke (Fig. 22-8). The advantages of this design are its capacity for taking extremely heavy cuts without fear of deflection and chatter. The ram is equipped with an overarm support, throughout its travel, which, coupled with adequate table support, offers the necessary rigidity for heavy cutting.

Vertical Shapers

This classification may be open to question, since in many instances vertical shapers are also termed slotters—and with good reason, because the latter expression is descriptive of their general application. Vertical shapers have a horizontal table; in some designs this is rotated by power

Fig. 22-9. Hydraulic vertical shaper machining internal ratchet teeth in a crane ladle control gear. (Courtesy of Rockford Machine Tool Co., Rockford, Ill.)

while in others the table is stationary. The ram moves in a vertical plane with the familiar reciprocating motion. The operating details of ram drive and table movements (Fig. 22-9) are basically those of the horizontal shaper. Some designs permit adjustable forward inclination of the ram as a means of machining angular surfaces. The stroke is adjustable, the usual range being 6 to 36 in.; longer strokes can be had in large machines. Operating design details of vertical shapers are divided between mechanical (Fig. 22-9) and hydraulic types.

Applications of the Vertical Shaper. Vertical shapers are large, substantially built machine tools whose primary application is that of planing surfaces such as splines, ratchets, slots, keyways, and pads. They are also useful for machining the sides and ends of large castings and weldments.

SLOTTERS

The terminology applied to vertical shapers and slotters is a controversial matter insofar as some design and makes are concerned; however, the type in Fig. 22-10 is termed a slotter by its builder. Construction

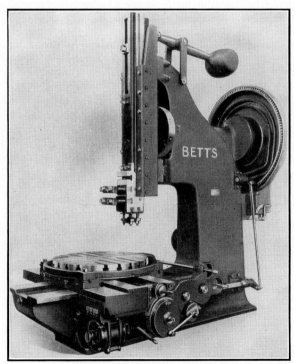

Fig. 22-10. Betts 18-in. crank-type slotter equipped with Whitworth quick-return ram movement. (Courtesy of Consolidated Machine Tool Corp., Rochester, N.Y.)

details are individual; this design is in effect crank-operated, with a counterweighted ram. Table movement and control are similar to those of the mechanically operated vertical shaper. There is also a model of this machine in which the ram drive is accomplished by means of a worm and rack.

SURVEY QUESTIONS

22-1. Could a metal planer be fitted into a mass-production tooling layout?

22-2. How is the size of a planer designated?

22-3. How can an openside planer be distinguished from any other type?

22-4. What is the meaning of "hydraulic" when used in connection with the description of a planer?

22-5. How is a workpiece fastened to a planer table?

22-6. Why are sideheads used on a planer?

22-7. Where is the clapper block located?

22-8. Can multiple work setups be done on a planer?

22-9. Does a planer use a single-point tool?

22-10. Describe the physical form of a planer cutting tool.

22-11. Why is a double-cutting planer a more efficient type?

22-12. What feature distinguishes a metal shaper?

22-13. A cylinder head is to be cut down for a racing auto. On what machine tool would this job be done?

22-14. What is meant by a duplicating shaper?

22-15. What type work would be machined on a draw-cut shaper?

22-16. Does a vertical shaper operate on the same principle as the horizontal type?

22-17. How can a slotter be distinguished from a vertical shaper?

22-18. Is a vertical shaper used for production of flat surfaces primarily?

Chapter 23

MILLING

Milling is performed with a rotating cutting tool termed a milling cutter; normally this has multiple teeth, but occasionally a single-tooth cutter is found. The milling process is accomplished by relative motion between the workpiece and the rotating cutter in a combined action that generates the milled surface. In general milling, the cutter merely rotates and the workpiece is fed past the cutter, whose position is fixed with respect to its axis. Another method holds the workpiece stationary and traverses the rotating cutter. The third method has both the workpiece and the cutter moving relative to each other and to the machine.

The milling machine is a flexible machine tool, since its potentialities extend over an imposing array of machining operations. It is employed mainly for straight-milling flat and irregularly shaped surfaces. However, the milling machine is regularly used also for cutting gears of many types as well as threads in a variety of forms. In addition, drilling, boring, reaming, slotting, keyseating, and profiling are within its scope. Milling machines are considered standard equipment for toolroom, die shop, experimental laboratory, instrument shop, and manufacturing shop and in any machining line where production requirements predominate. Another advantage is the high degree of accuracy that can be expected from the milling machine.

TYPES OF MILLING OPERATIONS

There are many different possibilities for removing metal by milling. Fundamentally, however, there are two distinct types or classifications which cover all milling operations. The order of listing here is arbitrary.

1. **Peripheral Milling.** In this type of milling, which includes slab and form milling, the milled surface is parallel or parallel and perpendicular to the cutter axis, depending upon the particular application (Fig. 23-1). Chip formation and surface condition are governed by the direction of cutter rotation with respect to the workpiece movement.

2. **Face Milling.** Another concept of milling is that in which the finished

Fig. 23-1. Peripheral milling using slab and forming cutters as a gang setup. (Courtesy of Barber-Colman Co., Rockford, Ill.)

Fig. 23-2. Face milling armature plates with a 12-in. carbide-tipped cutter on a 24-in. circular milling fixture designed to hold two different sizes of these plates. (Courtesy of Cincinnati Milling and Grinding Machines, Inc., Cincinnati.)

surface is generated perpendicular to the cutter axis, *i.e.*, parallel to the face of the cutter (Fig. 23-2). Milling to a shoulder where the latter is parallel to the cutter axis is a modification of face milling.

In these two methods surface generation is different, owing to the type of contact rotation between the cutter and the workpiece and, predominantly, the manner of chip formation. Surface appearance is distinctive, since cutter behavior is not the same for both methods; however, in both methods the major portion of the chip load is carried by the circumferential teeth.

SURFACE GENERATION

There are two distinct possibilities in peripheral milling insofar as cutter action on the workpiece is concerned. The action that is most

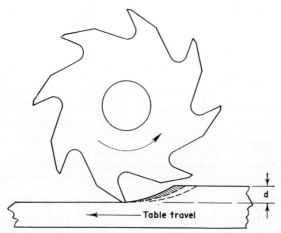

Fig. 23-3. Up milling—path generated by a plain milling cutter tooth. Note shape of chip.

used is variously designated as conventional, out-cut, up milling, and feeding against the cutter. The other method, which is the reverse of this one, is termed climb, in-cut, down milling, and feeding with the cutter.

Up Milling. This represents the practice of feeding the workpiece against the cutter in such a manner that the chip varies in thickness from a minimum at the point of contact to a maximum at tooth exit (Fig. 23-3). The tendency is to push the work along the table in a direction away from the cutter. Surface finish, in up milling, is a function of cutter speed and keenness coupled with choice of feed as well as cutter material and coolant; it is not primarily dependent on milling principle. However, the forces exerted by the cutter against the workpiece and the table tend to keep the lost motion in the feed screw and nut in a direction away from the cutter, a condition that promotes a smooth cut.

Down Milling. When down milling—the reverse of up milling—is used, the action of the cutter is that of starting the chip with maximum thickness and finishing with a minimum one. The rotation of the cutter is in the direction of workpiece travel (Fig. 23-4). One result of down milling is that the finished surface will bear evidence of tool revolution; similarly, coarse feeds in up milling will also cause tool revolution marks. The frequency and spacing of these marks are a function of cutter rotative speed and workpiece feed. It is contended that the degree of surface finish obtainable with this principle rivals that obtainable by up milling.

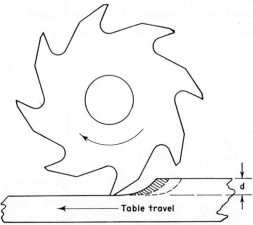

Fig. 23-4. Down milling—path generated by a plain milling cutter tooth. Note shape of chip.

Down milling should never be attempted with a milling machine that has not been expressly built for this technique. The action of the cutter against the workpiece and table tends to pull them under the cutter, because of lost motion in the feed screw. Failure to take this precaution will certainly result in broken cutters, scrapped workpieces, or sprung arbors—or all three. A proper machine for down milling must be equipped with a compensating nut that will eliminate lost motion in the table screw where mechanical feed is used; some designs employ a hydraulic table feed. Down milling is used to advantage where thin workpieces are to be milled, since the cutting action tends to keep such parts firmly seated in the work-holding device. Research indicates that down milling requires less energy for a given cut in practically all applications.

Face Milling. A face-milled surface is generated by the peripheral cutting edges of the face milling cutter teeth. The distinction between peripheral and face milling cutters is shown in Fig. 23-5*A* and *5B*. A

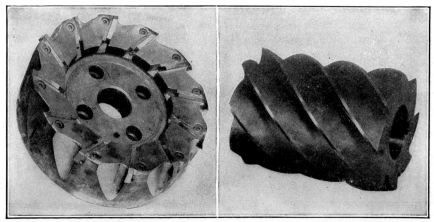

Fig. 23-5A. Face milling cutter of inserted-tooth type. Insert blades are tipped with carbide. (Courtesy of Kearney & Trecker Corp., Milwaukee.)

Fig. 23-5B. Plain milling cutter with helical teeth used for flat peripheral milling cuts.

face-milled surface has a pleasing appearance characterized by an arclike pattern.

MILLING CUTTERS

Milling cutters are available in both standard and special types in a range that will produce every kind of contoured surface, from plain to complicated. Standard types are defined and classified in American Standard B5.3—1950.[1] For the sake of consistency, the terminology used in this section will follow this standard, which also includes dimensions covering the listed milling cutters. These dimensions are followed by the cutter manufacturers, so that a milling cutter of a given type and size can be obtained from any one of the several sources.

Classifications of Milling Cutters. There are two principal classifications, each of which has subdivisions; the two main divisions are based on relief of teeth and on method of mounting, respectively.

1. Classification based on relief of teeth
   a. Profile cutters
      All forms of cutters which are sharpened by grinding on the periphery of the teeth; the clearance, or relief, is obtained by grinding a narrow land back of the cutting edge. Shaped profile cutters are characterized by curved or irregularly shaped cutting edges.

[1] American Standards Association, New York.

b. Formed cutters

In cutters of this classification, the eccentric relief back of the cutting edge is of the same contour as the cutting edge itself. These cutters are sharpened by grinding the face of the teeth.

2. Classification based on method of mounting

a. Arbor cutters are those with a center hole for mounting on an arbor.

b. Shank cutters have either a tapered or a straight shank integral with the cutter.

c. Facing cutters attach directly to the milling machine spindle end or to a stub arbor.

Among all the types of milling cutters, only face mills and end mills can be classified as to direction of rotation. The "hand" of a cutter is determined by the direction of rotation necessary to make it cut. A cutter is *right-hand* if it rotates counterclockwise and *left-hand* if it rotates clockwise, when viewed from the front end as mounted on the spindle. Cutters other than face and end mills are changed from one hand to the other by reversing their mounting on the arbor.

Arbor-mounting Type

Plain Milling Cutter. This cutter is a cylinder carrying teeth only on its circumferential surface. The tooth pattern is generally helical, with helix angles of 25 to 45°; when the helix angle is greater than 45° the cutter is known as a helical mill. The helical form enables each tooth to take a gradual cut, so that shock is reduced and chattering tendencies are eliminated. Plain milling cutters with straight teeth are also available.

Side Milling Cutter. In simplest terms, this is a plain milling cutter with the addition of teeth on both sides. The side teeth extend only a portion of the distance from the circumference to the center. When teeth are present on but one side, this type is termed a half-side cutter.

Straddle mills consist of two or more side cutters spaced on an arbor for the purpose of making parallel cuts, as in the case of boltheads and the like.

Interlocking cutters are similar in design to side milling ones except that they are made in a unit of two interlocking sections for the purpose of milling slots to exact width. They are maintained at a constant width by shims inserted between their inner hub faces.

Staggered-tooth Milling Cutters. Cutters of this type are of a narrow cylindrical shape and have teeth on the circumferential surface; these teeth, alternately of opposite helix angles, do the cutting. The side teeth, which extend a short distance from the circumference to the center, are for chip clearance only; they are not ground for cutting purposes.

These cutters are free-cutting and are capable of greater speeds and feeds than conventional plain types. Because of the alternate right- and left-hand helix angle of the teeth and the large undercut, these cutters operate almost without chatter. They are especially adapted to milling slots, in which depth exceeds width. The tops of the teeth are only two-thirds of the full cutter width.

Metal-slitting Saw Cutters. Another modification of plain milling cutters is the slitting saw. These saws are plain milling cutters with the sides relieved, or "dished," to afford side clearance. They are generally made in ⅜-in. maximum thickness and have more teeth for a given diameter than does a plain milling cutter. Metal-slitting saws are procurable in both side and staggered tooth patterns. Applications such as cutting off work or milling narrow slots are suited to cutters of this type.

Angle Milling Cutters. Cutters in this category are both single-angle and double-angle, with teeth on the conical surfaces. Single-angle cutters are made both with and without teeth on one flat side or both. These cutters are used for milling grooves of various kinds and also for milling the edge of a workpiece to a given angle.

Inserted-tooth Cutters. Cutters of this type are made for heavy-duty application. The body of the cutter is made of non-cutting material which can be either machined or cast. The body is slotted at its circumference for the insertion of the cutting blades. These are made from high-speed steel, cast nonferrous alloys of the stellite type, or cemented carbides. Provision for securely anchoring and adjusting the blades is made adjacent to their slots. There are examples of inserted-tooth cutters in which the cutter body is cast around the cutter blades; such blades cannot be replaced.

The advantage of inserted-tooth cutters is that they are less expensive, since low-cost material is used for the body of the cutter (Fig. 23-5A). An additional favorable factor is the removable blade, which permits renewal or the insertion of a different contour. A single cutter body can serve indefinitely, with blade renewals as the only expense.

Fly Cutters. This is a single-point tool rotated by an arbor. It is not a production tool but finds its greatest application in experimental work, since the single cutter can readily be ground to any desired shape. The potentialities of fly cutters are often overlooked. The single-blade cutter can be ground to a contour or shape and used instead of a form cutter where the latter is unavailable. Too, its single-point cutting principle can be employed for obtaining an excellently finished and precision surface.

Formed Cutters. There is a wide range of cutters in this classification, including such diverse types as gear cutters, sprocket cutters, convex cutters, concave cutters, corner-rounding cutters, thread-milling cutters, and hobbing cutters. In manufacturing intricate duplicate parts as those for typewriters, sewing machines, ordnance, and instruments, formed cutters are prominently used. Formed cutters are generally of curved irregular outline. The contour of the tooth will remain unchanged so long as the face of a tooth is maintained in its original plane with respect to the axis of rotation. These cutters are used for duplicate interchangeable work and can be resharpened until the teeth become so slender as to be unable to withstand the forces of cutting.

Fig. 23-6. Arbor-mounting-type milling cutters.

The cutters described thus far are all of the arbor-mounting type. They are shown in Fig. 23-6, where their distinguishing features can be noted.

Shank-mounting Type

End Mills. These cutters are distinctive in appearance; in addition to teeth on their circumferential surface, they also have teeth on one end. The teeth may be parallel to the axis of rotation or of a helical pattern in either right- or left-hand styles. Those of moderate angle are frequently termed spiral end mills. End mills are made in five general types, known respectively as solid, shell, hollow, helical, and two-lipped, or slotting.

Solid end mills are made with toothed portion and shank (which is either tapered or straight) as an integral unit. They find application in profiling, facing narrow surfaces, spotting bosses, milling slots and keyways, and light milling operations.

Shell end mills are distinctive in that the tooth end is recessed to receive a nut- or screwhead for fastening the cutter on an arbor. The cutter is usually driven from the key slot across its back face. In tooth design these mills follow solid end mills. The chief asset of shell end mills is that their replacement cost is less because the arbor need not be renewed each time the cutting element breaks or wears out.

Hollow end mills are of tubular cross section, with teeth on one end and an internal clearance. Hollow end mills are used for milling bosses, removing cylindrical projections from solid metal, and sizing cylinder stock. Their shank, which is straight, is a continuation of the cutter body. These cutters are predominantly used for tooling automatic screw machines.

T-slot Cutters. Such cutters are of the integral shank type. The cutting element has teeth on its periphery as well as both sides. Such

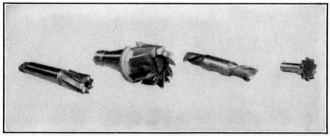

Fig. 23-7. Shank-type milling cutters.

cutters are used for machining the wide groove of a T-slot. The vertical groove must be milled first in order to provide clearance for the shank of the T-slot cutter.

Woodruff Keyseat Cutters. This type of cutter has but one application—the milling of semicylindrical keyseats in shafts for seating Woodruff keys. These cutters are made in shank as well as arbor types. The former have teeth only on the circumferential surface and are made in the smaller sizes. Arbor types are a minimum of 2 in. in diameter, with staggered front teeth for cutting and side teeth for clearance.

The cutters in this last group are of the shank type for mounting directly into the spindle nose. There is a great diversity of styles and sizes in this classification; several are shown in Fig. 23-7.

Carbide Milling. Carbide-tipped cutters, or carbide cutters, as they are more commonly termed, won popularity in connection with wartime production requirements. There are many grades of carbides and several sources of supply, with the result that carbide cutters are being engineered to meet specific production problems.

Their chief application has been in face milling cutters, although other aspects have shown promise. The problem of shock has limited their acceptance for use on certain cutter types. Another deterrent is that many milling machines now installed are incapable of delivering the high speed and power that carbide milling demands. Milling machine designers are cognizant of carbide milling possibilities and are responding with improved models featuring rigidity in the machine, cutter mounting, and work-holding tables.

MILLING MACHINES

The design of milling machines has advanced to the point where some models appear to have only one element, the rotating cutter, in common with the basic types. Such a diversified concept is convincing testimony of the soundness of milling as a machining method. While many modifications exist, four fundamental classifications are generally recognized: (1) column-and-knee type; (2) manufacturing, or bed type; (3) special type; (4) controlled cutter path types, such as profile, tracer, and numerically controlled types.

Column-and-knee Types

There is some variation in terminology in this classification, knee-and-column, knee-type, column-type, and column-and-knee type all referring to the same basic design. There are two distinct styles, horizontal and vertical (referring to spindle position). Operating details and construction are similar except for the spindle position.

Horizontal Type. Milling machines of this general classification have as their main components a column base, knee, saddle, table, overarm, drive, and feed mechanisms, together with necessary controls. The foundation of these milling machines is the main casting, which serves as the column bed. The bed is machined on its underside in order to give the entire machine a level setting. The column part of this foundation casting houses the driving mechanisms and the spindle. At its top, provision for the overarm is made and its front face is machined for attaching the knee and permitting vertical travel of the knee.

The knee is a casting that mounts normal to the column; it carries the vertical operating mechanisms, and its upper surface is machined for the saddle movement. The knee is supported and traveled by means of a telescoping, elevating screw located on its underside, away from the column.

The saddle, in its turn, is designed for cross movement normal to the column; its action is similar to that of the cross slide on a lathe. The saddle usually houses the power feed for the table.

One important feature to be noted is the distinction between plain and universal milling machines. Universal types have a swivel block mounted directly on the knee; the universal saddle mounts on the swivel block to permit angular movement of the table in a horizontal plane. The universal feature is desirable for such operations as milling helical flutes in cutting tools, cutting helical gears, and other similar work. Plain milling machines do not have the swivel table feature; otherwise they are the same as the universal ones.

The milling machine table is mounted on the saddle in a design that permits longitudinal travel. Together with this longitudinal travel, the cross travel of the saddle on the knee and the vertical travel of the knee on the column give the three-dimensional movement characteristic of the column-and-knee-type milling machine. Table movement can be either manual or with power. There is a range of power feeds, including rapid table traverse. Table drive is usually accomplished by a screw.

Spindle. The milling cutter is given its rotation by the spindle, which is in effect the main drive shaft for the milling cutter. The spindle is a critical component, since to a large degree its accuracy determines the precision that can be expected from the milling machine. Spindles are mounted in antifriction bearings and are capable of a range of speeds. Speed range is obtained through suitable gearing that is housed in the milling machine column. Spindles must be accurately aligned with the table top.

The spindle nose is made to accommodate the arbors, cutter shanks, and chucks and to provide positive drive for them. The nose has an inside taper. Prior to 1927, taper was not standard with all manufacturers; that year, taper was standardized at 3.50 in./ft. Further uniformity has been achieved through invoking American Standard B5.18—1943.[2] This should be consulted for complete information on milling machine spindle noses and keys. There are four sizes of spindle-nose openings; however, sizes no. 40 and 50 are used most on column-and-knee milling machines. Arbors are held in the spindle with a draw-in rod that is threaded into them.

Overarm. The overarm is mounted and guided at or near the top of the column. This may be either a single or a double element. Its purpose is that of providing alignment and support for the arbor and other attachments. It can be adjusted in its longitudinal movement and is held in position by a clamping mechanism at the top of the column. Braces can be placed on the outboard end of the overarm to give it rigid support from the knee, where the lower end of the braces attach (Fig. 23-8*A*).

Controls. All three of the slides, the table, saddle, and the knee are equipped with manual as well as power feeds. The travel movement is

[2] American Standards Association, New York.

subject to accurate control, since each slide is equipped with a micrometer dial. Power feed is used when the milling machine is in operation; hand feed is employed for setting up the job and for positioning the travel stops. It is important to see that stops are fastened into position prior to operation, especially when rapid traverse is to be used. Rapid traverse functions to bring the workpiece to the cutter or to return the table at the finish of an operation. Available feeds cover a broad range, especially now that carbide milling is important. Spindle speeds likewise

Fig. 23-8A. Double overarm with braces on horizontal column-and knee-type milling machine. This model has a built-in automatic table cycling design. (Courtesy of Kearney & Trecker Corp., Milwaukee.)

offer a considerable choice. All feeds and spindle speeds can be changed through levers and dials located conveniently for the operator.

Automatic Cycle. Automatic cycling is used on milling machines as a means for increased production at less cost per workpiece by adjusting to an automatic repetitive cycle (Fig. 23-8A). This control is incorporated into a standard milling machine to permit individual, small lot, or production runs to be made. It also permits calculating predetermined cycle time, thereby assuring uniform hourly production rates. Automatic controls govern cycle operation, which can be applied both to horizontal and to vertical column-and-knee milling machines.

Typical cycling arrangements are known as plain, intermittent, and continuous cycles (Fig. 23-8B). The automatic operation of the table

How Job Is Done

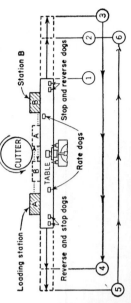

1. Operator loads (A) and engages mono-lever. Table advances in rapid traverse to point of cut on workpiece (A) at (2).
2. Feed dog changes rapid traverse to selected table feed for cut on (A). Operator loads at station (B).
3. Upon completion of cut, stop and reverse dogs reverse table and rapid traverse to point of cut on workpiece (B). Operator unloads and reloads at station (A).
4. Feed dog changes rapid traverse to selected table feed on (B). Operator unloads and reloads at station (A).
5. Stop and reverse dogs reverse table in rapid traverse to point of cut on workpiece (A).
6. Cycle repeats from (2).

How It Works

Typical Cycles You Can Use

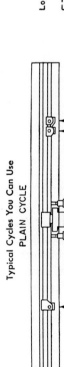

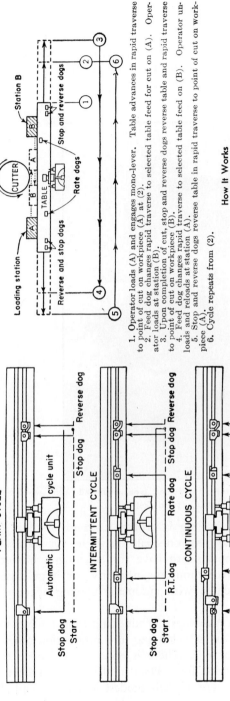

Fig. 23-8B Typical cycle settings used for automatic cycle milling (with automatic table cycle and mono-lever control). (Courtesy of Kearney & Trecker Corp., Milwaukee.)

movement is governed by dogs located on the table edge. These dogs are positioned to suit the desired operation sequence. The established cycle includes loading and unloading time as well as feed reverse and rapid traverse. Frequently it is possible to have two identical fixtures or stations located at opposite ends of the table in an arrangement whereby one station is unloading and loading while the other station is under the cutter.

Fig. 23-9. Vertical milling machine, column-and-knee type, equipped with swivel head. (Courtesy of Brown & Sharpe Manufacturing Co., Providence, R.I.)

It is claimed that automatic cycling is profitable on production lots as small as ten. Savings in milling time on small lots set up for automatic cycling are substantial. It is possible to have the advantages of automatic equipment and operation without the necessity for large investments: a standard milling machine with automatic cycling accessories covers all requirements.

Other Column-and-knee-type Machines. While hand-type milling machines are not usually thought of as belonging in a production scheme, they are nevertheless of importance. There is abundant evidence that these millers do fit into production lines. Hand milling machines are of importance to the job shop because of their modest initial cost and also because of the range of work they can handle. Any milling machine installation program would do well to include them.

Vertical Milling Machines. The column-and-knee design is applied to vertical milling machines. Vertical milling machines derive their name from the spindle position, which is vertical to the table and parallel to the column. Some designs are equipped with a swivel head (Fig. 23-9). The swivel-head feature permits the spindle to be positioned at any point in a 180° arc that lies 90° each way from the vertical.

Ram-type Milling Machine. Another modification of the column-and-knee principle is embodied in the ram-type milling machine (Fig. 23-10). While this design is built in both plain and universal table types, it has two distinguishing features. First, in effect this miller combines the horizontal and vertical milling machine principles into one design, since its milling head can be positioned for horizontal, vertical, or angular milling by simple adjustment, without the addition or removal of any attachments or accessories.

The second feature is that the ram, which carries the milling head, can be moved outward or inward with respect to the table, thus bringing the milling cutter to the workpiece for greatest rigidity in setup. The table is equipped with cross and longi-

Fig. 23-10. Ram-type milling machine, plain table model. (Courtesy of Van Norman Co., Springfield, Mass.)

tudinal power feeds, and the saddle assembly has vertical travel; these means afford tri-directional table movement.

Attachments and Accessories. Arbors and some similar items are classed as extra equipment. In addition, there is a range of attachments and accessories available to the column-and-knee type of milling machine. Taken in their broadest sense, attachments can be grouped as (1) cutter-driving and related attachments; (2) work-holding attachments and fixtures.

Universal Milling Head. This head attaches to the front of the column so that the milling machine spindle of the horizontal type acts as the driving unit for the head. This head can be swiveled through a complete circle in a vertical plane. A horizontal miller can by this means be converted to function as a vertical one and perform angular milling as well.

Additional heads or accessories include slotting attachments that give the cutter a reciprocating motion as in a slotter. Others include rack milling, circular milling, cam milling, helical milling, and thread milling attachments of various designs. Some of these—the rack milling attachment, for example—are accompanied by other equipment such as indexing attachments.

Fig. 23-11. Dividing-head setup for indexing spur gear. (Courtesy of Machine Tool Laboratory, University of Washington, Seattle, Wash.)

Dividing Head. The universal dividing head is an extremely accurate and at the same time a versatile indexing attachment. It holds mandrel-mounted workpieces between its center and a footstock center, or a chuck can be attached for holding workpieces by chucking in a horizontal, vertical, or angular plane. It has an indexing feature and can be attached to gearing for helical milling operations. The usual setup is that in which the dividing head is mounted directly on the milling table, with the index plate facing outward for both mandrel and chuck work (Fig. 23-11).

The dividing head is equipped with an index plate. This plate carries a number of hole circles in a concentric pattern. Each successive circle carries a larger number of spacing holes in a pattern where, by interchanging index plates, a large index range is available. Index plates usually carry hole space circles on both sides in a supplementary arrangement.

The crank on the dividing head is turned as a means of imparting an indexed motion to the head spindle. The ratio of the dividing head depends upon its type. Formerly the ratio of 40:1 was considered standard. With that ratio, 1 complete turn of the crank indexed the work $\frac{1}{40}$ revolution. Thus if a 40-tooth gear was wanted, the crank on the dividing head would be given 1 complete turn; for an 80-tooth gear the crank would be given $\frac{40}{80}$, or $\frac{1}{2}$ turn, whereas a 20-tooth gear would be indexed $\frac{40}{20}$, or 2 turns. Other indexing can be readily calculated and the increment obtained by setting off the calculated number of hole *spaces* on the index plate.

Other developments include the 5:1 ratio hypoid dividing head. On this design, 5 complete turns of the crank equal 1 complete revolution of the spindle. Index plates carrying hole circles similar to those previously described are included with the dividing head. The indexing crank is equipped with a plunger pin that serves to anchor the crank in its exact location on the index plate. Through an extension of the indexing principle on the 5:1 dividing head, it is possible to obtain 1,296,000 equal divisions in one circle.

Milling Machine Arbors. In order to get the benefit of the full possibilities of a milling machine it is necessary to equip it with a complete set of arbors. Arbors are available in several types and sizes. Three styles are regarded as basic (Fig. 23-12); they are classified as style A, B, and C, respectively, and are made in accordance with American Standard B5.9—1948.[3] A standard numbering system is applied to arbors, and the following specifications are listed in sequence: taper size, diameter, style, length from shoulder to nut, and size of bearing. Thus, for example, arbor no. 41¼A 16-3 specifies an arbor of no. 40 taper, 1¼-in. diameter, style A, length from shoulder to nut 16 in., equipped with a no. 3 bearing. Arbor styles A and B are designed for use with cutters having center hole mounting. These cutters have a keyway by means of which they are keyed to the arbor. Cutter spacing or positioning is by means of spacing collars. The collar-cutter assembly is held snugly by tightening the nut on the end of the arbor. A supply of collars of different widths should be maintained in order to fill out arbor spacing correctly.

The arbor-cutter assembly is held in position in the milling machine spindle by means of a draw-in rod that reaches through the spindle and

[3] American Standards Association, New York.

screws into the tapered end of the arbor. The arbor is supported on its outboard end by a bearing in the overarm support. Style C arbors, being of the stub type, have no provision for, nor do they require, this outboard bearing support.

A small pilot end distinguishes the style A arbor, which is used for light work generally. The style B arbor, on the other hand, is of uniform diameter throughout its length and is used where less clearance is necessary and heavy milling, such as carbide milling, is performed. The stub arbor, style C, is designed for holding shell end mills and face milling cutters that are too small to be bolted directly to the spindle nose.

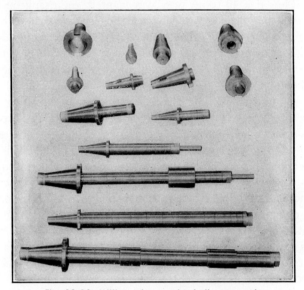

Fig. 23-12. Milling arbors and spindle accessories.

The cutters fit the end of the arbor and are held in position by means of a screw whose head fits the cutter recess. All arbors are equipped with a keyway which makes up with a key in the spindle nose for driving the arbor-cutter assembly.

Arbors for milling machines are precision equipment. The accuracy of a milled surface depends in large measure on the truth of the arbor. Abuse and careless handling will result in poor performance. Arbors should be wiped, as should the spindle taper, prior to insertion; the *wiping must be performed when the spindle is at rest* as a safety precaution.

Bed-type Milling Machines

Milling machines of the bed type are designed primarily for production and, for this reason, are also termed manufacturing or production millers. The versatility of the column-and-knee type is largely sacrificed in an all-out effort to gain greater milling production. This statement should not be interpreted to mean that bed-type millers are a one-part or specialized design; on the contrary they are capable of a wide range of application.

The term bed type is derived from the fact that the bed casting is large and rugged and supports all the machine components (Fig. 23-13). In this particular design there are two columns in a parallel setting so arranged that the spindle head can be adjusted vertically between them.

The table movement is confined to longitudinal travel, which is obtained by either hydraulic or mechanical means, depending on the

Fig. 23-13. Bed-type milling machine, showing single-column design. (Courtesy of The Ohio Machine Tool Co., Kenton, Ohio.)

design. Rapid traverse as well as feed in both longitudinal directions is available. There is no three-directional table movement on bed-type millers; rather, a job is set up with the objective of repetitive operation.

Frequently a production job is tooled in a duplicate arrangement with an identical fixture in accurate alignment located at each end of the table. This arrangement provides for up-milling one workpiece and down-milling the other in a continuing operation cycle. A substantial saving in time is realized, since loading and unloading can be done while milling is proceeding at the opposite station.

Duplex Milling Machines. There are several modifications of the basic bed-type design. One of these is termed a duplex miller because it has two heads, facing each other yet served by a common table (Fig.

Fig. 23-14. Duplex milling machine face milling two sides of a cylinder head casting. (Courtesy of Cincinnati Milling and Grinding Machines Co., Cincinnati.)

23-14). This construction permits two separate or identical milling operations to proceed concurrently, although each one is driven independently.

Duplex milling machines are particularly adaptable to milling parallel surfaces on the opposite sides of workpieces, as illustrated by the cylinder head casting in Fig. 23-14. On this and similar work where carbide face milling cutters are utilized, high production rates can be expected.

Special Milling Machines

Planer-type Milling Machines. There is some question about including planer-type mills under the classification of special milling machines. This doubt stems from the fact that planer types have established themselves rather clearly as an individual classification. They are built in two-column styles and openside models as well as in a number of variations of these concepts. The similarity to the planer, insofar as appearance is concerned, is clear from Fig. 23-15. The planer-type miller shown is equipped with two sideheads in addition to a railhead, each of which is individually motor-driven. The cutter-head assemblies can be positioned to suit the requirements of the workpiece. Further, the cutter head on the rail can be given either vertical or cross-feed travel.

Feed, rapid traverse, and return are obtained from variable-speed hydraulic motors connected to feed screws. The milling cutter spindles are

Fig. 23-15. Double-housing planer-type heavy-duty milling machine equipped with four milling heads. Workpiece capacity, 84 by 84 in. by 18 ft. (Courtesy of Consolidated Machine Tool Corp., Rochester, N.Y.)

Fig. 23-16. Roto-matic shuttle-type milling and centering machine. (Courtesy of the Davis and Thompson Co., Milwaukee.)

equipped with endwise micrometer adjustment. When electric limit switches are incorporated into the control of the movement of the different units, a semiautomatic cycle for production milling of a wide variety of work can be established. Planer-type millers, termed rail-type by some makers, are built to accommodate modern high-speed carbide milling cutters and, when thus tooled, deliver outstanding production records.

Milling machines of this type are especially well adapted to a wide variety of milling operations on large iron and steel castings, weldments, and machinery components. Work-holding fixtures can play an important part in increasing both the flexibility and the production possibilities of the planer type of milling machine.

Shuttle Milling and Centering Machine. In keeping with the trend for greater production per unit of time, an increasing number of milling machines of varying types are being tooled to specific requirements. A representative example of such equipment is shown in Fig. 23-16. This particular machine was adapted to milling slots 0.641 in. in width in steering couplings. The machine features both magazine loading and automatic discharge. Production rates are quite impressive, reaching 500 gross (72,000 pieces)/hr on this milling machine, which weighs about 11 tons. It should be understood that this machine can be adapted to other similar operations, a circumstance that is decidedly favorable.

Controlled Cutter Path Types

Tracer Milling Machines. There are several different models of tracer milling machines, in respect both to operating characteristics and to de-

Fig. 23-17. Pratt & Whitney-Keller three-spindle duplicator, milling an aluminum-alloy core box, using the center spindle. (Courtesy of Machine Tool Laboratory, University of Washington, Seattle, Wash.)

sign principles. Irrespective of these variations, basically tracer milling technique is that of controlling and guiding the cutting tool across the work by means of a tracer or feeler. The tracer element moves in contact with the surface or contour of a master as it controls the cutter in its movement (Fig. 23-17). The master may be a model, a pattern, or a template. However, it is common practice to mold the master of plaster because of the facility with which this can be achieved. Where considerable production is desired, a metal master is employed on account •

Fig. 23-18. Vertical single-spindle profiling machine. (Courtesy of Machine Tool Laboratory, University of Washington, Seattle, Wash.)

of its greater durability. Plastics are also used for masters where conditions dictate their use.

Tracer milling is general for contour machining and the machining of complicated parts. Formerly this technique was confined primarily to die making and kindred work; it remains important in that field, especially on auto body and other dies. However, aircraft and missile manufacture offers many opportunities for tracer milling. There are numerous aircraft components that can best be machined on this equipment. In order to meet production requirements, tracer milling machines are built in multispindle types. The miller in Fig. 23-17 is capable of milling three identical workpieces simultaneously from one master.

The tracer millers described thus far have horizontal spindles and in consequence are termed horizontal types. There are also examples of vertical spindle designs in both single- and multispindle models. Manually operated vertical tracer milling, or, as they are sometimes called, profiling machines, are considerably less complicated in construction (Fig. 23-18).

The profiler shown has a single vertical spindle driven by V belts. A template is followed by means of a tracer that is mounted adjacent

Fig. 23-19. Vertical rotary-head milling machine profiling a vertical surface. (Courtesy of Kearney & Trecker Corp., Milwaukee.)

to the spindle. The workpiece is mounted on the horizontal table, which is in turn moved longitudinally. The spindle head is traversed on the crossrail by means of a separate handwheel. All movement is made manually on this profiler—there are no automatic controls or power feeds. Machining is performed by end-mill-type cutters; a single cutter is used in the single-spindle machine. Two-spindle machines of the identical type are also available.

Rotary-head Milling Machines. These millers are derived from the vertical column-and-knee type of milling machine. They can mill intricate shapes without the use of models or templates (Fig. 23-19). The construction is such that the spindle can be offset from the center of the head. This device, coupled with the use of a rotating table, enables the machine to mill any geometrical shape. These machines are provided with power feed and are capable of production milling.

Milling Machine Development. Inasmuch as this chapter is intended as a survey of milling machines and techniques, it is not a complete or a comprehensive treatise. Developments and new designs arise continually

Fig. 23-20. Straddle-type Invomil. (Courtesy of Onsrud Machine Works, Chicago.)

in this interesting field of machining. The most novel of these have been mentioned in Chap. 18. Other developments continue to appear as requirements for new production methods occur. There seemingly is no end to milling machine versatility. All manufacturers in this area continually offer further ingenious designs to meet the continuing demand for greater production for less cost. One especially interesting application is in the field of skin milling for aircraft. Milling equipment of substantial size and versatility (Fig. 23-20) is an example of what has been accomplished in this area to meet some entirely novel and remarkable requirements. These milling machines have developed so that now they are becoming automatic, as mentioned in Chap. 18.

CHEMICAL MILLING

The work in this field is not basically new; however, it is a development of etching which has been applied for a great period of time. Chemical milling is variously known as acid-etch milling and chem-milling. This method has progressed most in the aircraft industry. Among the possibilities claimed for this development is its unlimited application; complex shapes, broad or narrow cuts, and comparatively sharp corners are possible in a single operation, although depth of cut is limited.

Chemical milling is a process for metal removal used on all alloys. Aluminum, magnesium, stainless steel, and titanium are some of the metals that have been successfully machined. The limitations of chemical milling are that the radius of the cut is approximately equal to the depth,

Fig. 23-21. Titanium panel for aircraft machined by chem-milling.

and that the etching depth is uniform with time of exposure. The physical and mechanical properties of the material under treatment are not impaired by chemical milling. The only possibility is that a rough surface may possibly affect fatigue properties. Masking materials are used in this process in order to develop the desired pattern areas (Fig. 23-21).

The cost of chemical milling varies with the complexity of the part and the depth of cut. There are examples of parts that have been etch-milled at one-fourth the cost of equivalent stock removal by conventional milling. The process for this method has another benefit in showing up inclusions or other subsurface flaws which would not be evident to usual inspection. An outstanding advantage is its ability to remove excess metal from out-of-the-way spots without endangering part strength. The application is limited only by the ingenuity of the designer; for example, spiral grooves on rocket engine parts have been formed by the chem-milling process.

SURVEY QUESTIONS

23-1. Does a milling cutter resemble a tool for any other machining operation?

23-2 Is a milling cutter a single-point tool?

23-3. Which is a more flexible machine tool, a milling machine or an engine lathe?

23-4. List five applications for milling machines.

23-5. What type surface does peripheral milling produce?

23-6. Is there any distinction between face milling and facing on an engine lathe?

23-7. Does up milling apply to face milling?

23-8. Is there any advantage to the use of down milling?

23-9. Are there any disadvantages to an inserted tooth cutter?

23-10. Why do peripheral cutters frequently have helical teeth?

23-11. Where are staggered-tooth milling cutters used?

23-12. How are arbor-mounted cutters driven?

23-13. Wherein do shell end mills differ from shell reamers?

23-14. Can a Woodruff keyseat cutter be used for peripheral milling?

23-15. What is meant by carbide milling?

23-16. Which type of milling machine is usually included in toolroom equipment?

23-17. If there is any difference in overarm design as between manufacturers, describe two.

23-18. What importance attaches to the spindle nose?

23-19. Wherein does a universal column-and-knee mill differ from a plain type?

23-20. Mention a job that could be done on a universal that cannot be done on a plain mill.

23-21. Are there vertical milling machines of the column-and-knee design?

23-22. Which is the most versatile type of the column-and-knee designed millers?

23-23. What is the function of a dividing head?

23-24. Give the ratio of one type of dividing head.

23-25. Is it possible to cut a spur gear of 47 teeth on a standard index head?

23-26. What is a milling arbor?

23-27. How are arbors driven?

23-28. In what class of operation would a duplex mill be most adaptable?

23-29. On what type mill could an engine lathe bed be machined?

23-30. On what equipment are wing spars for airframes machined?

23-31. If a tracer milling machine is used in manufacturing, is it confined to tooling?

23-32. What is meant by skin milling?

23-33. In what industry is chem-milling of primary interest?

23-34. On what specific equipment are auto fender dies, which are frequently cast, finish-machined?

23-35. Describe "straddle milling."

Chapter 24

BROACHING

Broaching, as a machining method, has several characteristic features that distinguish it as to both fundamental operation and equipment. It is unique in that roughing, finishing, and, in some applications, burnishing are performed by a single broaching tool in one operation. In broaching more than in any other machining method the tool rather than the machine controls production rate and quality. This statement should not be interpreted to mean that broaching machines serve only incidentally; rather, it is intended to focus attention on the fact that any consideration given to a possible broaching application must start with the broaching tool.

The term broach is applied both to the broaching tool and to the broaching machine. In this chapter the term broach will be used consistently to identify the broaching tool, whereas "broaching machine" will refer to the machine in which the broach is operated.

Metal removal is accomplished by a broach designed with a series of multiple teeth, or cutting edges, positioned in tandem, in an arrangement whereby each successive tooth is slightly higher than its predecessor and, therefore, each tooth takes a cut. The amount of metal removal is a function of the tooth depth and the number of teeth in the broach. It can be understood from this that broaching is in effect a generating process. The shape of the broached surface, the feed, and the cutting speed are dependent on broach design. The broaching machine may impose limitations such as power availability and length of stroke; however, these are secondary considerations and can be disregarded where production runs are concerned. Correct machine selection is always critical under such circumstances.

Broaching was originally conceived of as a method for machining internal surfaces, and in this field it retains its preeminence. Further extension of the broaching method has led to the inclusion of surface broaching, for which the largest broaches are used. Broaching has, by custom, been divided into internal and surface types, each one having modifications suitable for given requirements.

Broaching is primarily a production process in the sense that a broach is made for a given job and is not, except in rare cases, adaptable to a range of applications. This situation is different from milling, where general cutters such as plain mills, for example, can be used on a variety of workpieces requiring flat surface machining. There can be no denying the fact that broaching offers serious competition to milling in those areas where it can be applied.

BROACHES

A broach is a precision metal-cutting tool. It can perform a complete machining job, from roughing to finish, because it is a combination of

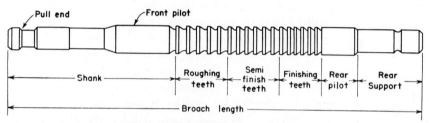

PULL TYPE INTERNAL BROACH

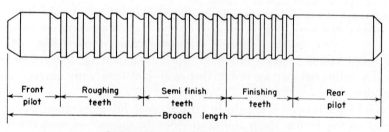

PUSH TYPE INTERNAL BROACH

Fig. 24-1. Pull-type internal broach. Push-type internal broach. (From "Metal Cutting Tool Handbook," Metal Cutting Tool Institute, New York, 1949.)

the several types of tools usually needed for such a machining sequence. There are literally a multitude of broach designs, since their adoption is increasing with the wider knowledge of the broaching method. Two representative broach designs, one of the pull and the other of the push type, are shown and the various sections of the broach are detailed in Fig. 24-1. The front pilot serves to align and steer the broach squarely as a means of guaranteeing correct positioning in the workpiece. The roughing teeth perform the function of major metal removal. Since they take rather deep cuts, it is common practice to nick these teeth in order to achieve a discontinuous chip. The nicking follows a staggered pattern to prevent any uncut surface remaining.

Semifinishing teeth take a shallower cut than do the roughing ones, while the finishing teeth serve to bring the broached surface to dimension. The rear pilot acts to keep the broach square with the hole as it passes out of the workpiece. On some broaches, burnishing buttons serve the dual function of burnishing and guiding.

A broach has a chip-removal problem that is unique among metal-cutting tools. There is no opportunity for the removal of chips when they are formed, as there is in the case of single-point tools and milling cutters. Each broach tooth must accommodate its own chip and carry that chip through to the completion of the cut. It is only after the tooth leaves the workpiece that the chip can clear the broach tooth. This imposes limitations on broach design, since sufficient space must be provided for a chip pocket. The pitch of the broach teeth, their depth, shape, and length of land, all must conform to a pattern that will result in allowing sufficient chip space and proper cutting action. The chip spiral is also affected by the thickness of the material cut.

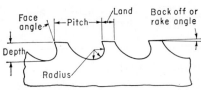

Fig. 24-2. Typical broach tooth form. (From "Broaches and Broaching," The Broaching Tool Institute, New York, 1944.)

The terminology applied to an individual broach tooth includes many expressions common to other metal-cutting tools (Fig. 24-2). The tooth radius requires attention when resharpening, lest compound and discontinuous curves result that will interfere with correct chip formation.

Pitch of the broach is extremely critical, since broach strength depends largely on this factor. Pitch also determines the number of teeth that will be cutting metal at a given instant. The nature of the material being broached governs the pitch, as do length of cut and chip thickness. Since cast-iron chips crumble and do not spiral as do steel ones, cast iron requires less chip space; therefore, finer pitch can be used on the broach. The usual recommendation calls for a minimum of two teeth being in engagement in the cut; a greater number is preferable for both broach alignment and elimination of chatter. It is sometimes desirable to use differential spacing in a pattern as a means of eliminating vibration during cutting; in this practice the same pitch is used for a group of teeth, followed by a different pitch for the succeeding group.

The teeth on a broach are not always normal to the broach axis; this is especially true of surface broaching, where the principle of shear cutting is used. Shear cuts give a better surface finish and eliminate vibration, since several teeth are engaged simultaneously. Shear angles are generally in the range of 5 to 20°. Disposal of chips on shear cuts poses the problem of the chips crowding to one edge, thereby causing roughening at that surface.

The depth of cut per tooth depends on several factors. When the cut is too great, broach strain or even failure is likely to result; a cut that is too shallow is also undesirable, since rubbing rather than cutting action will result. The cut per tooth in free-cutting steel ranges around 0.0015 in.; for splines the diameter is around 0.006 in.; depth of cut on round broaches is about 0.003 in.

These values are greatly exceeded in the jump-broach design. This development is aimed toward cutting beneath the scale of a cored or forged hole. Broach teeth of the same diameter occur in pairs. The first tooth is splined and therefore takes out half of the metal of the circumference. The following tooth, which is of the same diameter but solid, cuts the remainder of the circle. Such broaches have a normal step, or increase, in tooth diameter from one pair to the next of 0.030 in. The steps are lessened materially at the sizing section. These broaches are much shorter than those of standard length because of the substantial cuts made by the double jump teeth.

Speed of broaching varies with different materials and different jobs. A general rule is to broach workpieces at a rate between 12 and 24 fpm, while small jobs are cut at 30 fpm or more. The capacity of the broaching machine is a determinant, since it limits the possible speed.

On some class of materials, a difficulty arising in broaching is that of work hardening, which can become quite a serious problem. In some cases this has been overcome by a change in basic broach design in a pattern whereby work-hardened surfaces are removed before they can contact and damage finishing teeth. Other design improvements consist of controlled back-off angles and narrow lands for the finishing teeth. This combination contributes to better broach performance. With this design, tolerance on a broached hole was held to 0.0005 in. during a production run.

Broach Construction. Internal broaches are usually of one-piece construction regardless of their contour or length. They are made of high-speed steel almost without exception, although carbide tipping is used on some applications, especially for finishing teeth. Making a broach is a costly procedure, since its accuracy must be consistently maintained. There is always the possibility of difficulty in machining or in heat-treating, a difficulty that increases with broach length and contour. This

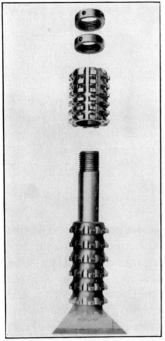

Fig. 24-3. Example of a shell broach with one section assembled.

problem is solved in some instances by using shell construction, similar in principle to that of shell end mills (Fig. 24-3).

Surface broaches are either solid or built-up, depending primarily on their size and type. Large surface broaches are invariably of the built-up type, with the teeth made in sections and mounted in a holder. When several cuts are to be made simultaneously with the same broach, it is not uncommon to mount teeth in sub-holders, which in turn are mounted in a main holder. The advantage of sectional broaches is obvious, since any tooth breakage can be repaired by removing the affected section without scrapping the entire broach. Examples of built-up surface broaches and broach sections are given in Fig. 24-4. Section broaches are an extremely convenient design where contour changes are wanted because the transition can be built into sections that are more conveniently machined than are long, cumbersome solid broaches.

Broach Sharpening. A sharp broach, like any metal-cutting tool, will deliver the sort of production that is expected of it. A dull broach will not produce to dimension and will require excessive power for its opera-

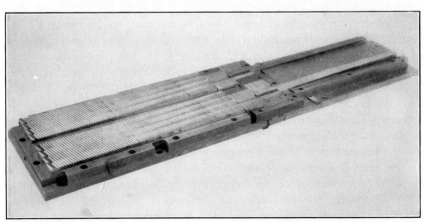

Fig. 24-4. Surface broach assembled from insert sections. (Courtesy of Colonial Broach Co., Detroit.)

tion. Only enough metal should be ground from a tooth to bring that tooth to the required degree of sharpness. Each tooth should be considered as an individual grinding job.

Broach Shanks. When a broach is used, it is pulled or pushed through the workpiece in the case of internal broaching. Surface, or external, broaching is performed in a similar manner; however, there are some examples where the broach is held stationary and the workpiece is moved past the broach while it is in contact with the surface to be machined.

Pull broaches operate either as a pull-up or a pull-down type. In the former, the broach is pulled upward, through or past the workpiece, which is held below the broaching machine platen. The pull-up, pull-down distinction does not apply to horizontal broaching for obvious reasons.

BROACHING MACHINES

Basically a broaching machine is of simple construction and operation, since its only function is that of exerting sufficient force to move the

Fig. 24-5. A horizontal broaching machine tooled and fixtured for broaching titanium jet engine blades. (Courtesy of The Lapointe Machine Tool Co., Hudson, Mass.)

broach. As broaching increases in importance in the machining field, refinements and automatic cycling, indexing, rapid traverse, and other functions are being incorporated in the design of the machine to the point where it is difficult to recognize the basic machine as a simple one.

Broaching machines are built in two principal types, termed horizontal and vertical, respectively. Each of these has many modifications; the principal one is that of having more than one ram. Rams are driven either hydraulically or mechanically; those machines known as screw-type broaching machines employ the latter method.

Horizontal-type Broaching Machines. Broaching machines of the horizontal type are built with the broach operating in a horizontal plane (Fig. 24-5). They are regarded as the most universal of all types because of the diversity of work they can handle. On internal broaching, the operator generally needs to pass the pilot end of the broach through the work-piece and make connection with the pull-head. Horizontal machines are also adapted to surface broaching. There are applications such as automotive cylinder heads where the broach is connected permanently to the ram for surface broaching. While this application is that of producing a flat surface, external broaching in horizontal machines is also applied

Fig. 24-6A. Automotive gears before and after broaching. Gear of 3¾ in. O.D. by 1¾ in. face has 42 involute helical splines broached in one pass. Production exceeds 125 gears/hr. (Courtesy of Sundstrand Machine Tool Co., Rockford, Ill.)

on contours. Horizontal broaching machines are built in a wide range of sizes and with a wide range of operating characteristics that include automatic cycling, indexing, and helical broaching (Fig. 24-6A). Where broaches are of some length, intermediate supports such as crossheads are provided to preserve alignment.

Vertical-type Broaching Machines. As the name indicates, the broaches are operated in a vertical plane in these machines, which means less floor space than horizontal installations. On production work, vertical broaching machines invariably carry two broaches which can be operated in several sequences, such as pull-up and pull-down or parallel operation in one cycle (Fig. 24-6B). In addition, automatic broach handling is featured, which relieves the operator of the task of manually threading the broach through the workpiece. A further advantage of the vertical design is the ease with which fixtures can be placed on the table.

Vertical broaching machines are built in three general styles, known respectively as pull-up, pull-down, and push-down types. The pull-up concept was first used in broaching. It is especially effective for internal broaching where no relationship needs to be maintained with an external surface. The workpiece is held beneath the table and the broach is pulled upward through it.

Pull-down styles were a development following the pull-up type. The workpiece is placed above the table and the broach is pulled down through it. Automatic broach and ram connections coupled with rapid

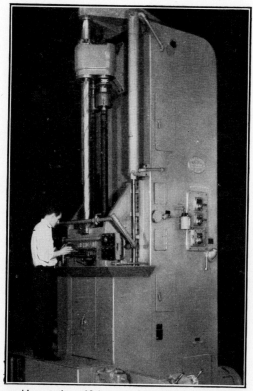

Fig. 24-6B. Dual broaching station. 60-in. stroke by 30T vertical broaching machine tooled for broaching internal gears. (Courtesy of Sundstrand Machine Tool Co., Rockford, Ill.)

ram reverse stroke combine to give these machines high production capabilities.

Push-type broaching machines are designed in several styles. One type is built for pushing internal broaches; in another instance the ram is designed for surface broaching. There is a distinction in appearance between these types, since in the latter the ram operates against the machine column in suitable guides for proper alignment and requisite stiffness to prevent broach buckling. There are vertical broaching machines that offer a universal pattern of push as well as pull types.

Mill Broach. The machine tool under this classification is designed for special applications. It functions to combine both milling and broaching as well as drilling in a single machine tool. It is capable of substantial production in that several operations occur simultaneously. The result is

Fig. 24-7. Vertical broaching machine tooled with tip-down style fixtures. (Courtesy of Lapointe Machine Tool Co., Hudson, Mass.)

that the machining cycle time for a component is extremely small. Such machines are available in a variety of designs which are adapted to specific production requirements.

Broaching Fixtures. Broaching fixtures are designed to hold the workpiece during the machining operation. The usual considerations regarding loading and unloading the workpiece need to be studied. Fixtures must be able to align work with the broach for correct cut. Such a requirement poses a difficult problem in cases where rough castings or forgings must be held in alignment. One method of solving this problem is by designing a compensating fixture capable of equalizing the holding position.

After alignment problems have been solved, attention should be given to fixture design from the viewpoint of operating ease. Loading and unloading times are critical in broaching as in other machining operations. An example of a tip-down fixture on a double-ram machine is shown in Fig. 24-7. A design of this nature greatly facilitates loading and unloading operations. Clamping devices, while largely of toggle design, include mechanical as well as pneumatic and hydraulic principles. Whatever system is followed, it is always necessary to secure a solid mounting of the workpiece in order to avoid slippage or shifting.

Indexing broaching fixtures play a prominent part in tooling for production. An especially fine example of this design is its application to stacking (Fig. 24-8). The workpieces shown are metal stampings of automotive window-operating mechanisms. Production possibilities are high and machining cost is low, since these parts are geared segments that would be difficult to machine by conventional methods.

Broaching fixtures are not con-

Fig. 24-8. Indexing fixture for window gear mechanism. Note provision for coolant supply. (Courtesy of The Lapointe Machine Tool Co., Hudson, Mass.)

fined to workpiece holding; there are situations in which they also act as broach guides or supports. The spline broach is rectangular in cross section and as a result requires support in the bore of the workpiece. A horn is inserted in the workpiece both to guide and to support the broach. The horn should extend beyond the workpiece in both directions to ensure correct broach cutting action and alignment.

The demands on broaching fixtures for horizontal broaching are similar to those for vertical broaching. If a distinction is to be made in broaching fixtures it should be between internal and external types. This is readily understandable, since in internal broaching the bore serves as a guide and positioning member.

Horizontal external broaching is for the most part associated with heavy work involving a combination of large broaches and substantial machine equipment (Fig. 24-9). A survey of automotive-parts machining procedures gives evidence of considerable interest in this type of broaching application. The methods vary with different shops; yet motor block

Fig. 24-9. Horizontal broach serrating a steering bracket. Note broached part shown resting on broaching fixture. (Courtesy of National Broach and Machine Co., Detroit.)

castings have been broached both top and bottom, as have their attachment pads and other finished surfaces.

CASE STUDIES OF BROACHING

Broaching accomplishments are so widespread that they touch on virtually all machining requirements short of cylindrical turning. However, this chapter should not be concluded without calling attention to the broaching applications wherein two or more complementary broaching operations perform the necessary machining. In the example shown in Fig. 24-10 the necessary production is obtained from four broaching machines that replace the total of twenty-one machine tools of various

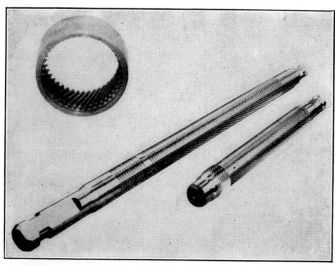

Fig. 24-10. Roughing and finishing broaches for machining internal helical gear teeth. (Courtesy of National Broach and Machine Co., Detroit.)

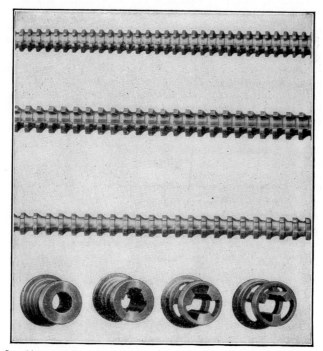

Fig. 24-11. Roughing and finishing internal spline broaches. Workpiece is shown before and after each operation. (Courtesy of National Broach and Machine Co., Detroit.)

types formerly needed. The teeth of the helical overdrive ring gear are completely machined in two broach passes to a tolerance of 0.0002 in. on all tooth characteristics.

Another application of multiple broaching is shown in Fig. 24-11. The part is produced in an automatic screw machine, yet the added requirement of splines must be met. This is accomplished by three broaching operations, as shown. Formerly there were holes drilled and the remaining metal was removed by two broaching operations. Substitution of a third broaching operation for the drilling has resulted in an over-all production increase of more than 80 per cent, due primarily to the elimination of index drilling.

Another example of broaching potential is that of cutting the teeth in a 4-in.-diameter cast-iron helical gear. The broach in this case slips over the outside of the gear blank, which is rotated mechanically as the broach descends. This development indicates that gear cutting is about to undergo some profound changes.

SURVEY QUESTIONS

24-1. Is broaching a chip-removal machining method?

24-2. What different aspects of machining can be performed in a single broaching operation?

24-3. Does the term "broach" apply to a tool as well as a machine tool?

24-4. Is it possible to perform broaching without having a specialized broaching machine?

24-5. What determines the production rate in broaching, the tool or the machine?

24-6. Is broaching confined to machining internal surfaces?

24-7. Why does a broach have a pilot in some cases?

24-8. How is a push broach distinguished from a pull type?

24-9. What is a shell broach?

24-10. Give an example of a flat surface broaching.

24-11. Are broaches used in multiple?

24-12. How does a tip-down fixture function?

24-13. Give an example of a job for an indexing fixture on a broach.

24-14. Where would a burnishing broach be used?

24-15. Is gear cutting related to broaching?

24-16. Can stacked parts be broached?

24-17. Give an application for a spline broach.

24-18. How are chips removed from a broached internal surface?

24-19. Where would a jump broach be used?

24-20. Is vertical broaching confined to a single method?

Chapter 25
GEARING

The production of satisfactory gears involves more than gear cutting equipment and its proper operation; of equal importance is the selection of a correct gear material. The gear material chosen must bear close scrutiny in respect to functionality, machinability, heat-treating behavior as to both hardness and distortion, forgeability, weldability (for fabricated gears), and, above all, manufacturing costs.

GEAR CLASSIFICATIONS

Gears are employed as a positive means of transmitting motion or power; some gear types are shown in Fig. 25-1. There are modifications of this principle in the sense that changes in direction as well as changes in speed can be effected by gearing. Bevel gears are designed to change direction of the transmitted motion, while worm gears combine this feature with a change in speed, as between the worm and the worm gear.

Fig. 25-1. A variety of cut teeth gears of modern design. (Courtesy of Foote Bros. Gear and Machine Corp., Chicago.)

There are shape modifications, especially in spur gears, whose objective is that of transmitting motion at a nonuniform rate.

Spur Gears. These are the most widely used gears. The face of the spur gear is parallel to the axis, which limits application to transmitting motion between parallel shafts. Spur gears can be regarded as the least complicated ones to cut, since they have uniform straight teeth.

Helical Gears. The teeth of these gears are in the form of a helix with respect to their axis. This tooth design results in more than a single tooth being in contact, which ensures silent operation and provides greater gear strength.

Herringbone Gears. These are a modification of the helical type in the sense that they are in effect a double helical. They are employed for

Fig. 25-2. Bevel gears with herringbone teeth. (Courtesy of Douglas Fraser & Sons, Ltd., Arbroath, Scotland.)

transmitting motion between parallel shafts. There is a novel design in which bevel gear teeth use a herringbone pattern (Fig. 25-2A). These gears eliminate the tendency toward side thrust that is characteristic of helical gears. From the manufacturing viewpoint, there are two types of herringbone gears. The conventional one has a circular recess extending around the circumference of the gear at the junction of the teeth; the second type omits this clearance groove and has continuous teeth that meet at the center of the gear face.

The latter type of herringbone gears is produced on the Farrel-Sykes gear generating machine (Fig. 25-2B). This equipment is a gear shaping machine having two cutters, which are mounted with their cutting faces opposed. In cutting continuous-tooth herringbone gears, each cutter alternately ends its stroke when its cutting edges are at the center of the gear blank being cut. The cutters rotate during their reciprocation in

Fig. 25-2.A. Farrel-Sykes continuous-tooth herringbone gear generator. Cutting action occurs on opposite face where operator is observing. (Courtesy of Farrell-Birmingham Co., Ansonia, Conn.)

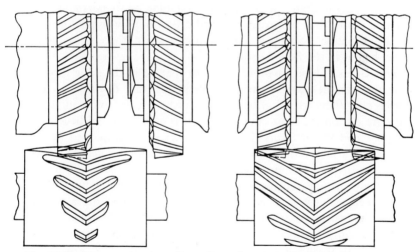

Fig. 25-2B. Diagram of reciprocating cutters when generating herringbone gears.

order to generate the helices; furthermore, they revolve slowly in unison with the wheel blank, thus generating the tooth contours. In consequence, the apices of the teeth are finished perfectly. There is no burr left at the center because of the alternate action of the cutters. As each cutting tool recedes from engagement with the tooth space it is generating, the chip tapers off to an infinitesimal thickness, leaving a perfectly clean junction of the two helices. A line drawing of the action of the cutters is shown in Fig. 25-2B.

Herringbone gears have a broad range of application and are manufactured in a considerable variety of designs. Among these are angle gears, herringbone rack and pinions, as well as herringbone pump rotors. Continuous-tooth herringbone gears are consistently used for transmitting heavy loads inasmuch as the entire face of the gear is engaged.

Bevel Gears. Gears of this type are employed for transmitting motion between shafts located at an angle to each other. Bevel gears include several modifications both as to tooth and as to design concept. Those having straight teeth are best known. Spiral bevels, which were formerly the standard method for motorcar rear-end drives because of their quieter operating characteristics, are also well known in machinery design and construction. Spiral bevel gears are one example of the curved-tooth type of bevel gear; other examples are the hypoid and the zerol.

Hypoid Gears. These gears are similar to spiral bevels, with the difference that the pinion axis of the hypoid is offset either above or below the gear axis. They resemble spiral bevels in that the teeth are curved and oblique in a pattern that permits gradual engagement and overlapping tooth contact. The offset of the pinion permits the crossing of the gear and pinion shaft, permitting several pinions to be mounted on a common shaft. Most motorcar rear-end drives employ hypoid gears, since the offset pinion permits a lowered drive shaft, thereby reducing the tunnel height in the floor boards.

Zerol Gears. These have curved teeth that lie in the same direction as those on straight bevel gears. The most accurate description of these gears is that they are spiral bevel gears in which the spiral angle is zero. They are cut on the same equipment that is used for spiral bevels.

Worms and Worm Gears. Gears of this type are employed in applications where a substantial reduction in relative motion is desired, especially where the drive shafts are at right angles to each other. The usual concept of a worm-gear drive is that of a screw driving a nut. There are two elements, the worm and the worm wheel, comprising a worm-gear drive. The worm has a constant thread form and uniform axial lead, while the worm wheel is constructed to partially envelop the worm. Single-thread worms are conventional because of their lower cost of manufacture; however, there are multiple-thread designs as well.

Cone-drive Worm Gearing. This is a modification of the conventional worm-gear drive. The difference between the two is that in the cone drive there is a double enveloping of one gear by the other. This design employs a concave-faced worm in place of a straight-faced one.

Spiroid Gears. These gears represent a revolutionary advance in reduction-gear technology. They offer an improved relationship between power transmission, gear size, and shock strength in practically every application. Some of the advantages claimed for this system are these: positive control of backlash, extreme accuracy, low noise level, and very high ratio. These gears fit into the area which was formerly occupied exclusively by worm gearing. They are right-angle gears for ratios of 10:1 and larger. The spiroid pinions are tapered pinions of constant lead and pressure angle over their entire length.

Geared Rack. This is a spur gear whose pitch diameter is infinity. A rack of a given pitch will mesh with any gear of the same pitch and tooth form. A well-known application of a rack is its use on an engine lathe

Fig. 25-3. Square spur gears demonstrate the rack and pinion principle of operation.

as a means of traveling the carriage longitudinally. A combination of quadrant spur gears and four racks results in a "square" gear (Fig. 25-3).

GEAR CUTTING METHODS AND MACHINES

Every metal-shaping process has its examples of gear making. Cast gears, or gears with cast teeth, are produced in ferrous as well as non-ferrous metals. They are precision-cast, die-cast, or cast in green-sand, shell, and dry-sand molds. Generally such gears are assembled into the end product with no machine work on their teeth beyond de-burring. Die casting and investment casting are both capable of producing gear teeth whose accuracy approaches those produced by machine cutting.

Press-forged gears of nonferrous metals are well known; since they are forged in a die, they compare in accuracy and finish with machine-cut gears. Gear blanks are produced in large volume by impact die forging.

Metal stampings are common for gears that are intended for slow speeds and low power input. These stampings are sometimes stacked and then riveted into what amounts to a laminated whole. This procedure is followed in order to develop the necessary face width for the gear.

Flame machining is successful for producing gears of intermediate and large sizes. Templates are employed in some cases, while in others the desired torch movement is obtained from the cutting machine mechanism. An economical method for producing geared racks is that of flame-cutting the tooth outline along the major axis of a steel bar, thereby yielding two racks with a single torch cut.

Gear Milling. Cutting gear teeth in a milling machine is the most flexible method. Gears of all sizes, within the capacity of the machine, and of all pitches can be cut on a milling machine that is equipped with an index head. Furthermore, different gear styles such as spur, bevel, worm-wheel, and helical gears are regularly milled. Related items such as roller and silent chain sprockets, metric gears, and ratchets are also produced by milling. The milling machine performs equally as well with single and multiple gear cutters as it does with gear hobs. For the most part, the milling method is selected for use with single cutters for producing gears in small quantities.

The majority of modern spur gearing is designed with teeth of the involute shape or a modification thereof. A single cutter, such as is used in gear milling, produces a satisfactory gear tooth. Any standard involute gear cutter will cut a range of gear teeth. In order to cut any gear from 12 teeth to a rack, a series of eight cutters is necessary for *each pitch*. These cutters are numbered and their cutting ranges are as follows:

Cutter no.	Gear tooth range
1	135 teeth to rack
2	55–134
3	35–54
4	26–34
5	21–25
6	17–20
7	14–16
8	12–13

Where accuracy is desired on the high end of each range, it is recommended that cutters in the half-number size be used for obtaining better tooth form. Thus, for example, cutter no. $1\frac{1}{2}$ will cut gears from 80 to 134 teeth, inclusive.

Single-tooth involute cutters are available for either $14\frac{1}{2}$ or 20° pressure angles. The tooth form is obtained from the cutter shape. In gear milling, the full tooth depth and form are cut in a single pass. It is desirable on some work to employ a roughing cut ahead of the finishing one as a matter of increased production as well as of greater accuracy. Roughing cuts are made by gear *stocking cutters*. These cutters are generally characterized by steps on their side cutting faces. These steps may be placed on opposite sides of alternating teeth or on both sides of all faces. The cutters are designed to leave ample stock for the finishing cut, which can be made at high speeds since stock removal is not a problem.

Multiple cutters are made in sets to cut two or three teeth in a single pass; however, they are individual types in that they will only cut the number of teeth for which they are designed. Their design varies to the extent that the combinations as between roughing and finishing and between duplex and triplex are nonstandard. Roughing and finishing may be either separate or combined operations (Fig. 25-4).

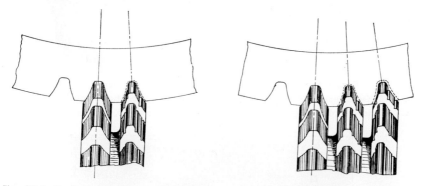

Fig. 25-4. Duplex and triplex multiple roughing gear cutters. (Courtesy of Michigan Tool Co., Detroit.)

Gear Hobbing. Hobbing is a method in which gear teeth are generated as the result of the combined rotating movement of the gear blank and the hob. It is shown diagrammatically in Fig. 25-5 for both complete and single-tooth generating action. The cutting element, or cutting tool, in the hobbing process is known as a hob. A hob is a threaded, gashed cutting tool that is essentially a fluted hardened steel worm equipped with proper clearances for cutting action. Single-thread (or start) hobs are most generally used, although where a high degree of accuracy is desired on gears of coarse pitch, a roughing cut is taken with double- or triple-thread hobs and the finishing cut with a single-thread hob. A single-thread hob cuts but one tooth, whereas a double-thread tooth cuts two teeth concurrently.

Gear hobbing can be visualized as the action of a rack and a gear when meshed: as the rack is moved in the direction of its major axis, the gear will rotate. In gear hobbing, an axial section of the hob is representative of the basic rack. Because of the lead or helix of the hob, succeeding axial hob sections advance this basic rack in the direction of the hob axis as it rotates. It can be seen that as the hob completes a full revolution, it will have advanced one full gear tooth.

Hobbing is a continuous cutting operation in which both the hob and the gear blank motion are rotative, with the added feature that feed is a

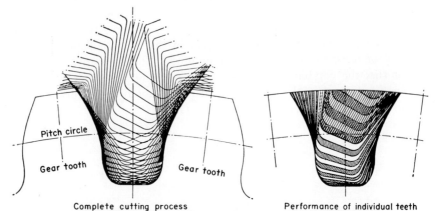

Complete cutting process   Performance of individual teeth

Fig. 25-5. Generating action of hobs. (From "Metal Cutting Tool Handbook," Metal Cutting Tool Institute, New York, 1949.)

Fig. 25-6. Typical spur gear hobbing operation. (Courtesy of Barber-Colman Co., Rockford, Ill.)

straight-line motion. A hob is capable of cutting any number of teeth within a given pitch. Furthermore, gears produced by a hob of a given pitch will mate perfectly. A typical hobbing operation is shown in Fig. 25-6, which shows a spur gear being cut. The resemblance of a spur hobbing operation to a worm and worm gear in mesh is quite striking. The hob is set to the helix angle of the thread in order that the path of the hob teeth, as they rotate, may be parallel with the teeth of the gear being cut.

Hobbing can be applied to cutting spur, helical, herringbone, and worm gears. This method is also employed for such forming as splines, ratchets, square ends, sprockets, cams, and, in fact, almost any contour that is based on a circle and that permits hob clearance while generating. Hobs for special work such as splines are designed to cut only one distinct part and are not to be confused with gear hobs for flexibility. The hobbing principle has been modified to the point where it is built into machine tools for turning shafts having several diameters or special shapes.

Gear Hobbing Machines

The selection of a gear hobbing machine affords a considerable choice of types and models. So far as design is concerned, there are two basic

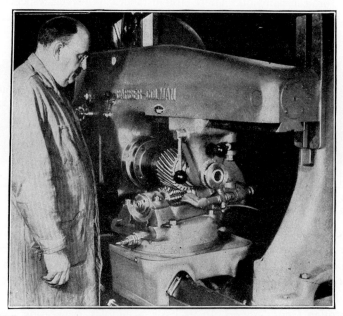

Fig. 25-7. Horizontal hobbing machine. (Courtesy of Barber-Colman Co., Rockford, Ill.)

types—the horizontal (Fig. 25-7) and the vertical hobbing machine. The capacity of a hobbing machine is governed by the maximum diameter of gear that it will cut; this is in turn modified by the pitch of the gear.

Hobbing can be likened to milling in that there are two operating principles—climb hobbing and conventional hobbing. It is frequently possible to stack gear blanks as a means of faster production. A typical production study shows seven gear blanks, 7.750 in. OD with 1-in. face, 8 pitch, 60 teeth being hobbed to semifinish at a rate of 21.8 min per load or 3.1 min per gear.

Vertical-spindle Hobbing Machines. In this design, as its name indicates, the construction is such that the spindle is vertical. The hobbing head attaches to the main column, the tailstock being movable on the outer column. The gear blank is held in a vertical position for the hobbing operation. Operating principles follow those of the horizontal types. Vertical hobbing machines are built as either single- or multiple-spindle units. Design and construction embody such features as automatic cycling, shifting hob head, centralized controls, and other details that promote rapid, accurate production.

Gear Shaping

A fundamental method of gear cutting is that of using a shaper equipped with a formed single-point tool and a template. This is an expedient for a repair job. There are instances, however, especially for

Fig. 25-8. Conventional gear shaper cutters. The one at the center is reversed in order to show its bottom, or cutting, face.

large gears, where a shaper or planer is similarly used. The small shop has the problem of cutting a bevel gear on a shaper owing to the lack of proper gear cutting equipment. Gear shaping is also applied to mass production; there should be no confusion on this point, since there are two widely different concepts involved.

Generating Gear Shapers. In its basic principles, generating gears can be likened to two gears in mesh, one of these being the cutter and the other one the gear blank. The cutter has a reciprocating motion and at the same time a slow rotation while the gear blank also rotates slowly in engagement with the cutter. The reciprocating motion of the cutter does the shaping. The cutter spindle is driven in relation to the gear blank spindle rotation so as to afford the correct ratio between the number of teeth on the cutter and those on the gear. There are examples of gear shaper operation in which the cutter merely reciprocates without rotating. Since this is a gear generating process, one cutter will produce mating gears of any number of teeth. Cutters are ground with a concave face that provides the necessary cutting edge (Fig. 25-8).

This principle of generating with a reciprocating cutter makes possible a substantial range of work. Internal gears, which prior to this development were difficult to produce, are readily cut by gear shaping. Spur gears, helical gears, herringbone gears, segment gears, contoured gears,

Fig. 25-9. Gear shaper designed to cut external as well as internal spur or helical gears. (Courtesy of The Fellows Gear Shaper Co., Springfield, Vt.)

face gears, splines, cams, hourglass worms, and profiles can all be cut by this method, although in some instances auxiliary equipment is necessary. Other unique possibilities include eccentric spur gears, three-lobed holes, square holes, irregularly shaped pawls, sprockets, ratchets, racks, interrupted gears, and gear segments.

Gear Shaping Machines. There is no counterpart to gear shapers among machine tools. In Fig. 25-9 the gear cutter is shown at the left with the two gears that are being cut mounted on their spindle in the center of the machine. The actual cutting operation can be noted as being one in which a single gear tooth is cut at a time. As the reciprocating cutter and the gear rotate, the cutter is fed into the work until correct tooth depth has been reached.

Shear-speed Gear Shapers. Another development in gear shaping machines is one that, primarily, reverses the principles involved in the previously discussed types. The shear-speed gear shaper cuts all gear teeth simultaneously. The gear blank reciprocates vertically. The cutter head is equipped with cutter blades that advance radially an equal amount with each workpiece stroke (Fig. 25-10). The cutter blades are retracted

Fig. 25-10. Shear-speed gear shaper cutter used showing cutter teeth retracted as at start of cut. Gears in foreground cut by this head. (Courtesy of Michigan Tool Co., Detroit.)

automatically in order to afford clearance for the workpiece. The entire operating cycle is automatic, including gear blank clamping. As a result, high production rates are readily achieved.

Bevel Gears

Bevel gears have individual features, for example, the pitch angle, pitch-cone apex, and face-cone apex. The tooth shape on bevel gears is such that their manufacture requires distinctive techniques.

Bevel Gear Blanks. A bevel gear is actually made in two separate machining phases. The first phase deals with the bevel gear blank. The design of the bevel gear blank must extend beyond mathematical and functional considerations and into the field of production problems. Such items as heat-treatment, mounting possibilities when cutting (which includes correct relation of hub and bore for rigidity), hub lengths for cutter clearance, and webbing require consideration. Locating surfaces are important to mounting the blank correctly in the gear cutting machine.

Bevel Gear Manufacture. Two different types of tooth generation are used in the production of straight bevel gears—the completing generator, with rotating cutters, and the two-tool generator, with two reciprocating cutting tools. On both types of generators, the tooth profile shape is produced by the generating method, in which a relative rolling motion takes place between the gear blank and the cutters or tools. The action is as though the gear blank being cut were rolling with a mating generating gear. In the case of the completing generator, the cutters represent a tooth of this mating gear, whereas with the two-tool generator the tools represent sides of adjacent teeth.

On the completing generator, the gear blank is mounted in a work spindle, which rotates in a time relationship with the cradle on which the cutters are mounted. A feed cam moves the work head and blank into cutting position, rough cutting the tooth, without roll, until the cut is just short of full tooth depth. The cradle, on which the cutter is mounted, and the work then roll to the bottom of the generating roll, rough shaping the tooth. The work is next fed into full depth, and a fast up-roll finish generates the tooth slot. At the top of the roll, the work backs out, and the cradle and work roll down again into the roughing position. During this short down roll, the blank is indexed.

In Fig. 25-11 at the left are shown two positions of the cutter at work; (a) at the beginning of the generating roll, and (b) at the end. Two-tool generators use a different cutting cycle but the same generating method just described. The two reciprocating tools represent the side of a tooth space of a generated gear as shown in Fig. 25-11, at the right.

Straight Bevel Gears. Straight bevel gears have lengthwise, localized tooth contact. This design permits small displacement of the gears under operating loads, without concentration of the load at the ends of the teeth, and also saves assembly time by permitting a tolerance in mounting the gears. Bevel gear cutting machines are available in a complete range whereby gears from $\frac{3}{16}$ to $35\frac{1}{2}$ in. in diameter can be cut. The gear cutting machines include the completing generators, which complete the gear from a solid blank. Two-tool generators use separate roughing and finishing cuts and a rougher as companion machines to the large two-tool generator.

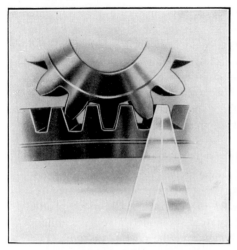 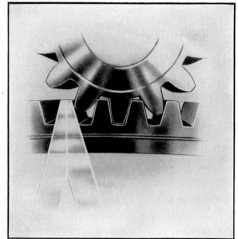

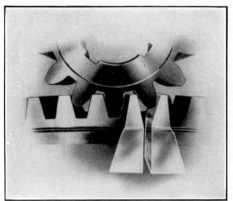 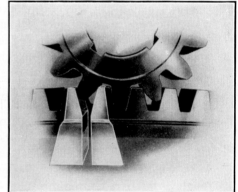

Fig. 25-11. Bevel gear generation. (Courtesy of Gleason Works, Rochester, N.Y.)

Spiral Bevel Gears. Gears in this classification have several type modifications of tooth shape and form. There are two main styles: in one category of spiral bevel gears the teeth are generated, while in a second style, termed formate, the gear is not generated but its mating pinion has generated teeth that are modified to suit the gear teeth, which have no profile curvature. Formate gears have the same appearance as generated ones except for a slight difference in the profile shape of the teeth.

Spiral bevel gears, except for the larger sizes which are cut on generating-type planers, are made on gear cutting machines that utilize a face-mill type of cutter having multiple blades extending from a slotted head in the direction of its axis. Cutting edges of the teeth are straight, yet tooth profiles of proper curvature result from relative rotation of the gear blank and the cutter spindle cradle. As this cradle returns to its starting position, the blank is indexed for the next tooth. There is considerable flexibility offered by these gear cutting machines, since hand of spiral, spiral angle, tooth bearing, and tooth size can all be varied by changing the relative position of the cutter and blank. Hypoid gears are

Fig. 25-12. Automatic hypoid gear generator. (Courtesy of Gleason Works, Rochester, N.Y.)

cut on these gear cutting machines with some adjustment in setup (Fig. 25-12).

Fabricated Gears

The great majority of cut gears are made from blanks that have been machined from forgings, castings, or bar stock. Material selection is based on cost and service requirements primarily. Where large gears are concerned, there is a tendency to replace castings with weldments (Fig. 25-13).

There are other types of gear blanks in which composite construction is used. A timing gear in which the gear face and web are cast aluminum alloy with a ferrous metal hub has proved successful in automobile motors. This construction is used to ensure quiet operation in the gear

Fig. 25-13. Gear blank weldment. Note three plate web members. (Courtesy of Western Gear Corp., Lynwood, Calif.)

train. There are other developments that achieve the same result by using nonmetallics for the gear teeth in conjunction with a metallic hub.

GEAR FINISHING METHODS

Gear Shaving. The gear finishing method is applicable to all types of spur and helical gears of both external and internal types. Its sequence in the manufacturing program is variable to the extent that shaving may either precede or follow heat-treatment. Most automotive shops shave gears prior to carburizing and hardening, a practice that is preferred by the gear-making industry generally.

Gear shaving is a machining process that produces fine, curled, hair-like chips; it is in no sense a cold-working process similar to burnishing. There are two basic principles around which gear shaving machines are designed. The most popular method employs a rotary shave cutter (Fig. 25-14), of which there are several styles. In the other design, a rack-type shaving tool consisting of a series of blades performs the necessary cutting action.

Rotary Shaving. In rotary shaving, the gear and cutter are mounted as intermeshing gears. The cutter has gashed teeth, but these do not extend to the root nor onto the crest; shaving action is confined to the sides and does not involve the periphery of the cutter. There are several principles of mounting the gear with respect to the shaving cutter. In one style these two elements are mounted on crossed axes in order to provide cutting action with a minimum of pressure. Stock removal results from axial motion of the cutting edges of the cutting teeth enhanced by the reciprocating motion between the cutter and the gear.

Additional rotary shaving methods include tangential shaving, which is a modification of the crossed-axis principle to the extent that the relative motion between gear and cutter is a tangential reciprocation of the cutter across the work. Narrow-faced gears are especially well adapted to this shaving method. In another method, the cutter and gear axes are

Fig. 25-14. A group of gear shaving cutters. These are individual cutters mounted for comparison. (Courtesy of National Broach and Machine Co., Detroit.)

parallel. Cutting action is obtained by reciprocating the cutter at a high frequency. Internal gears are shaved by this method.

Rack Shaving. The shaving, or generating rack, which is made up of individually replaceable teeth, is mounted on the shaving machine table. The gear is mounted on centers with its axis at an angle to the rack. As the rack reciprocates, the gear rolls with it, while at the same time it moves crosswise on the rack as a means of obtaining uniform rack wear. The gear is fed downward during the operation until its correct size has been reached. This method is most suitable for high production, since original tooling is somewhat more costly than with rotary shaving; yet rack tool life is so long that unit production costs are low. A rack of a given pitch will shave all gears of that same pitch and pressure angle.

Crown Shaving. The objective in crown shaving is that of shaping a tooth to provide a very slight crown at its center. This is accomplished by shaving the ends of the teeth, with the result that there will not be a concentrated load occurring there. Crown shaving can be accomplished by either rotary- or rack-type shaving machines.

Gear Shaving Procedures. In rotary gear shaving the procedure includes underpass shaving, traverse shaving, and traverpass shaving, which is a combination of the two other methods. Shaving cutter speeds are varied to suit the conditions of the gear as to material and hardness as well as finish desired. The usual speed, calculated for the pitch circle, lies between 300 and 400 sfpm for satisfactory results. Table feed is also a variable quantity, although a value of 0.010 in. per revolution of the gear can be regarded as a mean value.

Gear shaving concerns itself with tooth finish and not with gear diameter. The pre-shave cutting of a gear allows stock on the *thickness* of the tooth only. The amount of stock to be shaved varies with the diametral pitch: the coarser the pitch, the greater the amount. Thus gears of 2 to 4 diametral pitch allow 0.003 to 0.004 in. per tooth, while those of 16 to 18 diametral pitch have an amount of but 0.001 to 0.002 in. Uniform stock removal across the tooth is desirable for uniform cutter wear and best finish results.

Other Gear Finishing Methods

Gear grinding is applied where distortion is severe or a considerable amount of stock needs to be removed following the hardening operation. In common with precision grinding methods generally, gear grinding is capable of producing both an excellent finish and a high degree of accuracy. Critical gear installations frequently specify grinding for the method of finish. Gear grinding is considered to be the oldest method of precision gear finishing.

Gear lapping is a finishing method whose objective is that of correcting and removing small imperfections. Gear lapping machines are built in various styles and cover the complete range of gear requirements. Operating characteristics follow those common to conventional lapping machines.

Gear Tooth Honing. In order to remove nicks and other surface imperfections from hardened gears, the honing technique has proved successful. An abrasive-impregnated, plastic helical gear-shaped honing tool is run in mesh with the hardened gear in crossed axes relationship. The honing tool serves to drive the work gear at speeds reaching 1,000 sfpm. Concurrently it is traversed back and forth across the honing tool following a path parallel to the axis of the work gear while rotation is reversed. The honing tool is discarded when worn out, yet 5,000 to 8,000 gears are honed per unit.

Hardened gear honing improves the sound characteristics of the treated gears. Such improvement results from a combination of nick and burr removal coupled with minor tooth shape corrections and surface finish improvements.

Burnishing is a cold-working process that employs an extremely hard work gear in rolling contact with the gear being finished. Burnishing was formerly looked upon with favor, but it has been largely superseded by shaving. A burnished gear carries considerable residual stress, which is undesirable in connection with any succeeding heat-treatment.

Shot peening is sometimes used as a final finishing operation on gearing as a means of placing the outer layer of metal on the teeth in compression for better service life. This method is not considered a finishing one in the sense of attaining dimensional accuracy or surface excellence.

Gear Tooth Pointing. When gearing is designed for sliding engagement, it is desirable to point, chamfer, or round off the end of the gear teeth that are to mesh with each other. Among the several methods used for pointing are grinding and machining.

Gear Checking Equipment

No matter how carefully gears may be designed and manufactured, the possibility of error is always present. The variation permissible in gearing depends upon its

Fig. 25-15. Gear sound tester. Designed for operating gears at various loads and speeds. (Courtesy of National Broach and Machine Co., Detroit.)

end use. As loads and speeds are increased, the requirements for accuracy increase to the point where this characteristic becomes critical. There is a wealth of gear checking equipment available; included are instruments for bench-type checking as well as machinery for testing gears in operation.

The amount and character of the noise that a gear installation emits are a clue to its accuracy. Every pair of gears develops its own characteristic sound when in operation. Such sounds have been classified to the extent that an experienced inspector can interpret them as to source and cause. Several types of testing equipment have been developed for the purpose of screening gearing to eliminate noise (Fig. 25-15). The tester illustrated has a sounding box designed to amplify gear noises to the point where they can be recognized. It can be operated in the shop without interference from outside noises, since it is soundproofed to isolate the gearing sounds. The gear testing equipment termed "speeders" has several modifications of this principle built in.

Equipment for checking gear accuracy is all characterized by its precision potentials. Pitch distances, for example, are measured by gage blocks; in other designs, recording equipment is employed to chart run-

Fig. 25-16. A set of fine-pitch bevel gears. (Courtesy of Western Gear Corp., Lynwood, Calif.)

out, or wobble. Dial gages and sine bars are basic elements of other gear checking equipment. Master gears are another means for ascertaining gear accuracy.

Fine-pitch Gearing

A classification in which the diametral pitch is 20 or finer is known as fine-pitch gearing (Fig. 25-16). Considered from the standpoint of theoretical design, there is no characteristic distinguishing this from coarser pitch gearing of involute form. There is some difference in manufacturing procedures, since fine-pitch gears require special attention in such matters as clearance and top land dimensions. The concept of fine pitch includes spur, helical, and worm gearing. Complete specifications and engineering information on fine-pitch gearing are available in several standards published by the American Gear Manufacturers' Association.

ACCURATE GEARING

The demands placed upon manufacturing accuracy by national defense requirements are, in some cases, difficult to comprehend. When it is realized that missiles and aircraft must fly at tremendous speeds and for

Fig. 25-17. Ultracision hobbing machine for producing extremely accurate gearing. (Courtesy of Barber-Colman Co., Rockford, Ill.)

great distances with a degree of accuracy that is beyond our usual concept of precision, some idea can be had of the manufacturing control problem. The primary responsibility for success in this area must be accepted by the gear trains and components. In order to meet the control and tracking system requirements, gears accurate to 10 sec of an arc over nonadjacent teeth at any point of the profile, not just the pitch line, and concentricity within 0.000010 in. in a 4-in. diameter are needed. Such a degree of accuracy is being approached. When these requirements were released to the industry, it was found that in no country was there gear cutting equipment of such a high order of accuracy. One severe requirement was that the hobbing of the gear should be so accurate that no further finishing like grinding or shaving would be necessary.

The design and manufacture of the Ultracision hobbing machine called for entirely new concepts in manufacturing, in design, and especially in measurement. The resultant hobber (Fig. 25-17) embodies many new and novel ideas and features, not the least of which was the delivery of the machine from the manufacturer to the purchaser. While this equipment seems capable of meeting original engineering requirements, evidently the next problem will come from the miniaturization of gears that will be needed for more compact control units on future defense program items. Thus the importance of accurate gear production will be promoted further and precision manufacture will reach new horizons.

SURVEY QUESTIONS

25-1. If gears do not have cut or machined teeth, how are the teeth made?

25-2. Why is the selection of gear material critical?

25-3. In addition to metal, what other materials are used for gears?

25-4. What is the basic function of a gear?

25-5. Give an example of the use of spur gears on an engine lathe.

25-6. Give one reason for using helical gears.

25-7. As a machine designer, where would you incorporate herringbone gears?

25-8. What is the function of bevel gears?

25-9. Where in an automobile is hypoid gearing used, if at all?

25-10. Give at least two different functions for worm gear installations.

25-11. Give an application for a geared rack.

25-12. What determines the maximum diameter of a gear that can be cut in a milling machine?

25-13. What is the function of a stocking cutter?

25-14. What is a gear hob?

25-15. Are gear hobbing machines the same as milling machines?

25-16. On what type of equipment are the majority of gears produced?

25-17. How is it possible to cut a gear on a shaper?

25-18. Do gear shapers resemble metal shapers?

25-19. What is a shear-speed gear shaper?

25-20. What gears, if any, other than spur types, can be produced on a gear shaper?

25-21. What machine tools are used for the manufacture of bevel gears?

25-22. Where are spiral bevels used to best advantage?

25-23. Mention three different methods of making steel gear blanks.

25-24. What is the purpose of shaving a gear?

25-25. Is there any advantage to crown shaving?

25-26. What types of gear teeth are pointed?

25-27. What is the purpose of shot peening gear teeth?

25-28. How are gears checked?

25-29. Mention some equipment that uses fine-pitch gearing.

25-30. What has developed the necessity for production of "accurate gearing"?

Chapter 26

GRINDING AND FINISHES

Grinding is a machining method wherein metal is removed in the form of chips by means of a rotating grinding wheel. The latter is unique among cutting tools since it is, in effect, self-sharpening and at the same time possesses a multitude of cutting edges. Grinding is distinctive as a machining method in that it is a means of shaping extremely hard metallic materials. Grinding is also employed on all other metals common in engineering manufacture. It can also be used on hard and brittle nonmetals such as ceramics, plastics, and glass. In addition, grinding is the only method for machining some thin metallic workpieces that are difficult or impossible to hold in other machine tools.

Mass production has developed only as rapidly as have grinding techniques. True interchangeability manufacture resulted when grinding was capable of producing the required accuracy. While grinding is generally regarded primarily as a method of finishing, it is also capable of removing metal rapidly and at relatively low costs. Grinding is frequently in the rare position of applying the finish to workpieces that are the finished products of other machining methods. The precision built into machine tools results from their component parts being finished by grinding or a related method.

GRINDING WHEELS

Grindstones. Earliest records of grinding indicate that the grinding wheel was fashioned from a slab or block of natural sandstone. Those wheels were termed grindstones. Grindstones revolved slowly and the grinding operation was extremely time consuming. One salient drawback to grindstones was their tendency to wear out of round: no amount of dressing would provide a remedy, since the stone lacked uniform hardness throughout its cross section.

Natural Abrasive Wheels. The artificial grinding wheel, so termed in contradistinction to the natural grindstone, was introduced at the close of the Civil War. This wheel employed the natural abrasive *emery* for the cutting element. Emery is found in many countries including the United States (southern section). It obtains its cutting ability from the corundum and abrasive iron oxide contained in its composition. The corundum content ranges from 70 per cent to as low as 30 per cent, so that emery is a variable product. Emery wheels have been superseded by artificial abrasive wheels almost entirely. *Even though they have become obsolete, the term emery wheel continues to be applied, incorrectly, to grinding wheels.*

Corundum is a natural aluminum oxide containing variable amounts of impurities. Its high degree of hardness is the reason for its ability to perform satisfactorily in a grinding wheel. Quartz is another type of natural abrasive; however, it is not commonly used. Diamond is another natural abrasive; it is the hardest known substance and is used in some specialized grinding applications. Owing to its nature, it requires a distinctive bond, and diamond wheels must be used differently from conventional grinding wheels.

Artificial Abrasives

Natural abrasives lack uniformity and in consequence deliver erratic results. A realization of this motivated a search for an artificial abrasive whose quality could be controlled and whose cost of production would be reasonable. The quest for such a product led to the discovery of silicon carbide by Acheson around 1890. Jacobs is credited with inventing the process for making aluminum oxide in an electric furnace at about the same time. These two inventions provided the basis on which the grinding wheel industry has been developed.

Silicon Carbide. Silicon carbide (SiC) is a product of the electric resistance furnace. The furnace is charged with pure silica, petroleum coke, sawdust, and sodium chloride. The chemical reaction wherein silicon and carbon unite to form SiC is accompanied by the formation of CO, which escapes through the porosity caused in the furnace bath by the presence of the sawdust. The salt acts as a fluxing agent by forming chlorides with the impurities of the charge.

Silicon carbide particles are angular in form and fracture easily. They are harder than aluminum oxide but lack the latter's toughness. This abrasive is chosen for grinding hard materials of a brittle nature such as cemented carbides, ceramic materials, and cast irons. It is also favored for grinding materials of low tensile strength such as brass, bronze, copper, and aluminum alloys. There are many trade names applied to silicon carbide—Carborundum, Crystolon, Electrolon, "C" abrasive, Natalon, and Sterbon, among others.

Aluminum Oxide. Aluminum oxide (Al_2O_3) is produced in an electric arc furnace from bauxite. Bauxite contains ferric oxide, silica, and rutile, along with aluminum hydroxide. It is calcined prior to being charged into the electric furnace along with iron borings and coke breeze. The resulting melt is composed of approximately 95 per cent Al_2O_3, 3 per cent TiO_2, 1.5 per cent SiO_2, and 0.5 per cent Fe_2O_3.

Aluminum oxide crystals are tough and therefore do not tend to fracture readily. This characteristic makes them unsuited for grinding hard materials, since they tend to dull prior to fracture. They perform best when grinding tough materials such as the various grades of steel, wrought iron, and malleable cast iron. Modifications in the manufacturing process will alter the structure of the crystals and broaden their scope of applications. Aluminum oxide abrasives are known by such trade

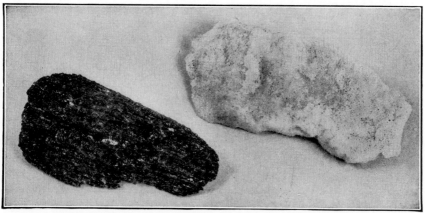

Fig. 26-1. Abrasive materials prior to crushing and grading: silicon carbide, dark in color; aluminum oxide, white. Note difference in structure.

names as Alundum, Borolon, Aloxite, Sterlith, "A" abrasive, Alowalt, and others.

Abrasive Grains. The artificial abrasives are recovered in lump form upon cooling from their molten state. The characteristics of the grains are noticeable upon solidification (Fig. 26-1) in that silicon carbide has a brittle grain whereas aluminum oxide is tough in comparison. The lumped material is sent through jaw crushers as the first step in size reduction. The resultant pieces are further reduced by being passed through steel sizing rolls.

Choice of grain size is governed by both the intended application and the finish desired on the ground workpiece (Fig. 26-2). Small amounts of impurities are added by some producers to color the finished abrasive

Bonding Types

A grinding wheel is composed of two components—the abrasive grain and its bonding agent. The bond in a grinding wheel acts to hold the grains in position and also to release them when they become dulled. There is no single bonding agent that will perform suitably for every grinding requirement; this accounts for the six different ones regarded as standard by the Grinding Wheel Manufacturers' Association. These six bond designations are V, vitrified; S, silicate; B, resinoid; R, rubber; E, shellac; O, oxychloride. Some variations and additions are employed by individual manufacturers as a means of developing a product of individual characteristics. A representative group of grinding wheel shapes is shown in Fig. 26-3.

Vitrified Bond. This is the most prominent of all bonding agents. It is also known as glass bond and porcelain bond. Basically this is a clay bonding agent with which other ceramic materials are mixed. The bond and abrasive grains are thoroughly mixed and processed as a batch. The wheels are then shaped and dried. A firing operation in a kiln is

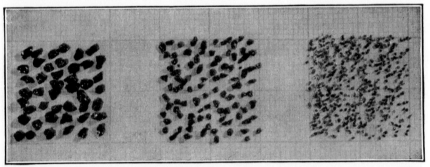

Fig. 26-2. Unretouched photograph of standard aluminum oxide abrasive grains on graph paper having 20 lines/in. (Courtesy of Pacific Grinding Wheel Co., Everett, Wash.)

the final operation in developing the bond strength. Vitrified bonds are strong and rigid.

Silicate Bond. This bond is composed of silicate of soda (water glass) combined with a metallic oxide, which, when baked, renders it insoluble in water. It is not a strong bond but it releases abrasive grains faster than the vitrified type. It is used for grinding edged tools and in other applications where operating temperatures must be at a minimum. Wheels above 36 in. in diameter are usually made with this bond.

Resinoid Bond. This is a plastic made of synthetic organic material. It has great strength and considerable elasticity; hence it is being employed to give the grinding wheel a wide range of properties. Resinoid bonded wheels cut rapidly and can be operated at high speeds.

Rubber Bond. This bond is a form of hard rubber and is used primarily for making hard, coarse snagging wheels, thin cut-off wheels, and finish wheels for producing fine finishes on hardened steels.

Grinding Wheel Structure. Wheel structure refers to the precise method of spacing the cutting units (abrasive grains) in the grinding wheel. It is obtained by exercising close control over the size and distribution of the pore spaces between the abrasive grains. The importance of structure shows itself in the performance of the grinding wheel, since it functions to provide chip clearances in the voids or pores. Structure is specified by a numerical series using the numbers from 0 to 15, inclusive. The lower numbers are used to designate the close, denser structures, while the higher ones indicate the more open, or more porous, structures.

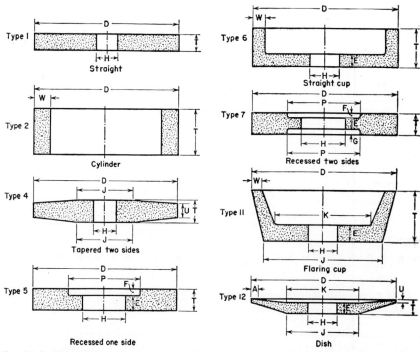

Fig. 26-3. Shape types of grinding wheels. (Selected from "Grinding Wheels," Simplified Practice Recommendation R45–57; The Grinding Wheel Manufacturers' Association, Worcester, Mass.)

Grinding Wheel Grades. The grade of a grinding wheel refers to its degree of hardness. This characteristic is dependent upon the bonding of the wheel, since the inherent hardness of the abrasive grains remains unaffected by both bond and grinding wheel manufacturing process. Grading is designated by letters in the following sequence:

Grade

Very soft.......... C, D, E, F, G
Soft............... H, I, J, K
Medium........... L, M, N, O
Hard.............. P, Q, R, S
Very hard......... T, U, V, W, X, Y, Z

These designations do not apply to a definite quantity; rather the reference is to a range of hardness.

Grinding Wheel Designations. Wheel selection frequently spells the difference between a successful grinding job and one that is unsatisfactory. A plan for grinding wheel designation as sponsored by the Grinding Wheel Manufacturers' Association is given in Fig. 26-4. This is a reliable guide to the selection of grinding wheels. However, all grinding

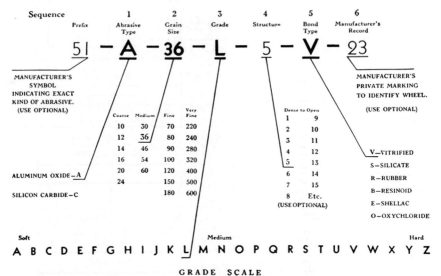

Sequence	1	2	3	4	5	6
Prefix	Abrasive Type	Grain Size	Grade	Structure	Bond Type	Manufacturer's Record

$$51 - A - 36 - L - 5 - V - 23$$

MANUFACTURER'S SYMBOL INDICATING EXACT KIND OF ABRASIVE. (USE OPTIONAL)

Coarse	Medium	Fine	Very Fine
10	30	70	220
12	36	80	240
14	46	90	280
16	54	100	320
20	60	120	400
24		150	500
		180	600

ALUMINUM OXIDE—A

SILICON CARBIDE—C

Dense to Open

1	9
2	10
3	11
4	12
5	13
6	14
7	15
8	Etc.

(USE OPTIONAL)

MANUFACTURER'S PRIVATE MARKING TO IDENTIFY WHEEL. (USE OPTIONAL)

V—VITRIFIED
S—SILICATE
R—RUBBER
B—RESINOID
E—SHELLAC
O—OXYCHLORIDE

Soft   Medium   Hard

A B C D E F G H I J K L M N O P Q R S T U V W X Y Z

GRADE SCALE

Fig. 26-4. Standard marking system chart. (From "Markings for Grinding Wheels," ASA B5.17—1949, The American Society of Mechanical Engineers, New York.)

Fig. 26-5. Grinding wheels shown with their respective abrasive grains. Coarse, medium, and fine grain sizes appear from left to right. (Courtesy of Norton Co., Worcester, Mass.)

wheel manufacturers do not adhere strictly to the chart designations, since some of them offer products whose characteristics do not conform exactly to those listed. Figure 26-5 gives examples of grinding wheels and their respective abrasive grain.

Grinding—A Cutting Action. Automatic self-sharpening is the accepted basic principle of the cutting action of the grinding wheel (Fig. 26-6). Each abrasive grain acts as a cutting tool that takes its individual chip from the workpiece. A definite relation exists between chip thickness and chip space. The former quality will in turn be affected by keenness

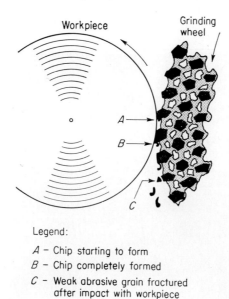

Legend:

A – Chip starting to form

B – Chip completely formed

C – Weak abrasive grain fractured after impact with workpiece

Fig. 26-6. Schematic sketch of the cutting action of a grinding wheel.

as well as depth of cut. Keenness results from the behavior of the bond, since a weak bond will release the grains readily, thereby causing the wheel to wear rapidly. A strong bond has the opposite effect and may not permit the release of grains until they become dulled to the point of losing their cutting efficiency.

Grinding Wheel Care and Operation

Dressing. Dressing, truing, and balancing are critical to all grinding wheels intended for precision grinding results. Dressing is necessary to relieve the "loading" of the wheel. The tools used for dressing and truing are of three general basic types: abrasive, diamond, and steel. There are several styles of each of these.

Truing. Truing refers to the treatment of a grinding wheel face by which it is shaped to grind a desired contour. Filleting is an example of the necessity for truing a wheel face. A given workpiece may require a series of different fillet sizes, all to be ground in a single setting; this can be accomplished by truing the wheel as required.

Crush Dressing. A hardened steel crusher, formed to the desired wheel-face contour, is brought in contact with the grinding wheel as it slowly revolves. This type of dressing readily brings the wheel face to desired shape. Crush dressing aids in rapid production of formed parts. A shortcoming of the use of crush dressing is a slight sacrifice in the quality of finish as compared to other types of dressing.

Grinding Fluids. Increasing attention is being given to the choice of fluid necessary for successful grinding results. Water was the original

Fig. 26-7. Coolant being delivered through grinding wheel to workpiece. (Courtesy of Gallmeyer & Livingston Co., Grand Rapids, Mich.)

fluid used in grinding. It has been largely superseded by soluble oils, since these fluids have splendid coolant action, prevent rusting, and possess lubricating qualities. Various types of oils are used for grinding, especially on thread grinding and similar contour work.

Grinding fluids keep the workpiece cool, thereby preventing surface cracks and distortion. They also aid materially in improving the surface, since chips are washed away, and there is some indication that a desirable lubricating action is present. Placing the grinding fluid at the contact surface is the aim of every coolant delivery system. In some grinding operations, there is a veritable flood of coolant delivered under considerable pressure to ensure proper coolant results.

A novel development is that of delivering the coolant directly through the grinding wheel to the point of use (Fig. 26-7). Specially designed open-structured grinding wheels, whose sides are sealed, are necessary for this technique. The grinding fluid is delivered to a hollow section at the hub and is caused to flow outward by the centrifugal force developed by the rotation of the grinding wheel.

Dry Grinding. Grinding with fluids, whatever their nature, is termed wet grinding. The majority of finish and precision grinding is of this

TABLE 26-1. MAXIMUM RECOMMENDED SAFE OPERATING SPEEDS*
(Speeds shown are in surface feet per minute)

Type of wheels	Vitrified and silicate bonded wheels			Organic bonded wheels		
	Soft	Me-dium	Hard	Soft	Me-dium	Hard
Type 1, straight wheels (including plate mounted and inserted nut wheels)...............	5,500	6,000†	6,500	6,500	8,000	9,500
Type 4, taper wheels..........	5,500	6,000†	6,500	6,500	8,000	9,500
Types 5 and 7, recessed wheels .	5,500	6,000†	6,500	6,500	8,000	9,500
Type 2, cylinder wheels (including plate mounted and inserted nut wheels)...............	4,500	5,500	6,000	6,000	8,000	9,500
Types 11 and 12, dish and flaring cup wheels...............	4,500	5,500	6,000	6,000	8,000	9,500
Type 13, saucer wheels........	4,500	5,500	6,000	6,000	8,000	9,500
Type 6, deep recessed cup wheels	4,500	5,000	5,500	6,000	7,500	9,000
Cutting wheels larger than 16 in. diameter....................	....	......	.....	....	....	7,500–14,000‡
Cutting wheels 16 in. and smaller	....	......	.....	....	....	10,000–16,000‡
Thread grinding wheels........	8,000	10,000	12,000	....	....	12,000
Automotive and aircraft crank grinding wheels (on standard machines).................	....	7,300	8,500			

* Abstracted from American Standard B7.1—1947, American Standards Association, New York.

† On precision machines vitrified wheels in medium grades may often be operated at speeds up to 6,500 sfpm.

‡ Depending on stability, design, and condition of machine.

type. However, a considerable amount of grinding is performed without the use of fluid on the workpiece or wheel by a method known as dry grinding. Most offhand grinding and snagging fall into this classification. There are instances where a change from wet to dry grinding has proved beneficial in eliminating defective work. Surface grinding frequently employs dry grinding, as does disk grinding.

Grinding Speeds. The speed of grinding is measured in feet per minute of the surface of the grinding wheel; grinding speed is stated in surface feet per minute. It is calculated by multiplying spindle revolutions by wheel circumference in feet. A usual speed of 6,500 sfpm is common to the majority of grinding operations; however, this is not to be regarded as a fixed figure, since both greater and lesser speeds are used. Cutoff wheels operate in the highest grinding wheel speed ranges and, in general, organic bonded wheels operate safely at speeds above the vitrified types. Workpiece speeds in cylindrical grinding are low in comparison with grinding wheel speeds employing a starting speed of 125 sfpm. A guide to safe grinding wheel speeds is presented in Table 26-1. It is recommended that this table be consulted in the interests of correct grinding results combined with safe operation.

GRINDING OPERATIONS

Tool and cutter grinding machines are designed primarily for sharpening tools and cutters that are cylindrical in cross section or that operate on the principle of rotation about a center. To be sure, linear cutters such as planer knives and die segments can also be ground on these machines when they are equipped with the necessary work-holding accessories. Among the tools ground on these machines such items as reamers and taps are in the majority; in the cutter classification hobs and milling cutters of a wide assortment of designs form the bulk of the grinding.

Cutter and Tool Grinding. Regardless of the elaborateness of the grinding equipment, there remains the necessity for skill and knowledge of a high order on the part of the operator if cutters and tools are to be correctly sharpened. Wheel selection is important in order to prevent cracking and heating, with subsequent loss of hardness. The grinding machine and its related equipment must be kept in good order and accurate alignment. Spindles must be free of vibration and table movement easy and smooth.

The position of the grinding spindle with respect to the work is a critical matter. Gear tooth cutters must be ground on a line normal to their horizontal axis when mounted in the grinding machine. Tooth rests should fit the teeth properly and care must be exercised in holding the tooth firmly against the tooth rest while grinding (Fig. 26-8). The most desirable procedure is that of having the tooth ground in contact with the rest. There is also the matter of cutter tooth position with respect to the grinding wheel, since the cut can be made either toward the cutting edge or the reverse. Both techniques have their respective advantages; however, the finer the finish on the cutting edge the longer the tooth will remain sharp. Frequently cutting edges are lightly honed immediately after grinding as a means of improving the cutting surface. Tool angles are ground to standards prevailing for the particular tool or cutter being sharpened. Information on this is available from cutter manufacturers as well as from ASA standards.

The condition of finish on any machined surface depends to a large extent upon the accuracy with which the cutting tool employed for machining has been ground. A cutter should never be used after it ceases to cut freely for the reasons that it will produce an inferior finish, it

Fig. 26-8. Tooth rest in position against the tooth being ground on a large end mill. (Courtesy of Norton Co., Worcester, Mass.)

may destroy the accuracy of the workpiece, and it will require increasingly more power. Sharp tools and cutters aid in economical production, as they do in improving quality of finish.

Grinding Cemented Carbide. Cemented carbides are used on both multiple-point and single-point cutters and tools. Inserted tooth milling cutters and similar tools are ground on tool and cutter grinding machines of the types previously described. Single-point straight-shank tools with carbide tips are ground offhand, for the most part, on specially designed grinding machines. These machines carry a grinding wheel at each end of the centrally mounted motor spindle. The motor should be reversible in order that both right- and left-hand tools can be ground. A roughing wheel is mounted on one end of the spindle and a finishing wheel on the other. Adjustable table rests, equipped with graduated dials for obtaining recommended tool-cutting angles, are adjacent to the grinding wheels.

The grinding wheels are mostly of cup shape, although straight wheels are more economical for grinding the steel shank of the tool. Silicon carbide grinding wheels of soft grade only should be used for grinding cemented carbides. Grinding wheel manufacturers are tending toward using a friable type of silicon carbide abrasive for this application. Diamond wheels are also recommended for this purpose but they are not as commonly employed as the silicon carbide ones. Especially fine finishes are obtained by finishing on an iron lapping disk charged with diamond powder.

Care is required for proper grinding results inasmuch as the tool is a composite of a steel shank and a carbide tip. It is recommended that the steel shank be ground on a separate wheel as a means of preserving the carbide grinding wheel. Grinding should be in a direction from carbide tip toward the shank. The tool should be rocked from side to side as a preventive against grooving the grinding wheel. Any necessary top dressing is always done prior to grinding the other tool faces.

PRODUCTION GRINDING

In its inception, precision grinding was considered supplementary to lathe machining. In general, the workpiece was turned on the lathe and the final sizing and finish were achieved by grinding. This concept of grinding has been expanded for several reasons, chief among them being the degree of finish grinding can produce and the fact that grinding is capable of machining material too hard to be turned in a lathe. The same situation applies to flat surfacing; grinding is capable of operations that cannot be achieved with the machine tools designed for flat surfacing.

Production grinding has gained increased stature as knowledge of its potentialities has broadened until it has become a serious competitor, in some areas, to the more traditional machining methods. Processing a workpiece must be studied today with a view toward grinding from the rough to the finished size. This transition has been materially helped by the ability of the foundry to produce castings of narrowing tolerances. The same situation applies to forgings and those other production methods which contribute the raw material of the machining department. In its own field, grinding is developing along lines familiar to other machine tools. Automatic operation and cycling, multiple cuts, and greater diversification in grinding machine and grinding wheel types have all contributed to the increasing attention being given to grinding as a general machining method rather than merely a method for finishing, as was formerly the case.

Production grinding is applied to external and internal surfaces as well as contouring in a variety of forms. Grinding machines can be classified on the basis of design types as:

Cylindrical...........	{ On center, Centerless, Chucking }
Internal.............	{ Chucking, Fixture, Centerless }
Surface..............	{ Horizontal, Vertical }
Specialized or individual	
Disk.................	{ Horizontal, Vertical }

Within these classifications, all design features, from manual to fully automatic operation, are available. Selection of a grinding machine is not unlike that of any machine tool, since there are modifying factors such as production requirements, workpiece size and shape, workpiece material, stock removal, finish requirements, and operation costs that need to be evaluated.

Cylindrical Grinding

This term had its origin in the fact that initially, grinding for a precision finish was performed on components of cylindrical shape. The meaning of the expression cylindrical grinding has been expanded to the point where the term is applied to tapers, cams, and external grinding of contours. It is understood that the workpiece is rotated in the same direction as that of the grinding wheel, but at a decidedly slower rate.

Work mounting or holding determines the type of grinding machine. The more flexible machines are those which hold the workpiece between centers, since they can accommodate a wider range of workpiece sizes. Such machines are specified as to capacity by two dimensions; 6 by 30 in., for example, means that the maximum workpiece would be 6 in. in diameter with a length of 30 in. The tailstock center is cut away in order that the grinding wheel may pass completely beyond the work. In some designs, a work-holding chuck is used in place of center mounting; however, this feature is employed only where required by workpiece shape.

A cylindrical grinding machine is equipped with a wheel head which carries the grinding element. A wheel spindle, whose bearing mounting is critical, carries the grinding wheel. The spindle is generally driven by multiple V belts from the motor, which is independently mounted in order to eliminate vibration from the wheel. Provision is made for traversing the workpiece across the wheel face in order that the workpiece length can be completely ground.

Table traverse can be operated manually but in production grinding automatic movement is general. Traversing is either by mechanical or by hydraulic means. It is said of the latter that there is less opportunity for vibration and in consequence design is tending in that direction. Table traverse is handled in an automatic cycle designed to eliminate the necessity for the operator to move any control levers during the grinding cycle.

The cylindrical grinding machine is equipped with an infeed whereby the wheel is fed into the work. The depth of cut for the wheel is a variable quantity and differs as between roughing and finishing cuts. Roughing cuts of 0.003 in. are taken, but on finishing this value is reduced to as little as 0.0001 in. Workpiece diameter is measured by micrometers or gages unless the grinding machine is equipped for automatic gaging. In the latter instance, infeed is included in the automatic operating cycle of the grinding machine.

In cylindrical grinding it is necessary to have a rigid work mounting in order to prevent deflection of the workpiece. A usual method, for pieces of any length, is to include steady rests that bear on the workpiece and support it. The forces from grinding wheel action tend to deflect the work outward as well as downward; hence the shoes in the rests must be positioned accordingly. It is also necessary to adjust these shoes after each cut in order to maintain a proper bearing against the workpiece.

There is a dwell time at each end of the traverse stroke in order to permit grinding the workpiece to size at its ends. It is here that the "spark-out" is noted: the volume of sparks emitting from the grinding operation is an indication of the depth of cut. When spark volume vanishes, it is evidence that the wheel is no longer cutting.

Cylindrical Grinding Techniques. Workpieces whose lengths are greater than the width of the wheel face are ground by traversing. There are occasions where the length to be ground can be accommodated without traverse movement. In such cases plunge grinding is employed; in this process the grinding wheel is moved into the work. Crankpin grinding is an example of the plunge-grinding technique. This procedure is used for grinding contours where the wheel has been dressed to suit.

Another interesting development in cylindrical grinding is that of making multiple or concurrent cuts (Fig. 26-9). On this job two different diameters are being ground simultaneously. Wheel diameters are maintained by a built-in truing device which, in turn, is operated by interchangeable flat cams. This particular job setup is indicative of the potentialities of multiple cuts—there are examples of several wheels grinding concurrently on a single workpiece.

Plain cylindrical grinding machines having a wheel slide or angle head causing the wheel to feed at an angle of 60° to the work axis, instead of the conventional 90°, are employed for grinding cylindrical surfaces and shoulders on a production basis. The grinding wheel is dressed so that its periphery can grind the cylindrical surface of the work and face-grind the shoulder simultaneously. By dressing the wheel periphery in multiple steps or by mounting several wheels on the spindle, it is possible to grind a number of different diameters and shoulders concurrently.

Cylindrical Grinding Machines. The conventional cylindrical grinding machine is referred to as a "plain" grinding machine. It is built primarily for grinding cylindrical shapes; however, it is not uncommon to

Fig. 26-9. 10 by 18 in. plain cylindrical grinding machine set up for grinding two diameters on an automotive part concurrently. (Courtesy of Cincinnati Milling and Grinding Machines, Inc., Cincinnati.)

equip these machines with attachments for cam grinding and other work of a similar nature. There are modifications of the basic design which have been developed for individual work classifications. An example is the gap machine, which has a gap in the bed to accommodate large flanges.

Roll grinders are built in an extremely wide size range for grinding rolls for many industrial uses. Rolling sheet in steel or aluminum requires rolls of considerable dimensions, especially in the category of back-up rolls. The paper industry also requires roll-grinding equipment as a critical part of its production machinery.

Other production-type cylindrical grinders include crankshaft grinding machines of many designs. Another example is that of piston grinding machines, which have an important part in automotive production, as do valve grinding machines employed for grinding valve seat inserts. Camshaft grinders for grinding cam faces as well as line bearings are well known to automotive production.

Cylindrical grinding machines, regardless of type, are designed and built for precision. Controls are equipped with dials for accurate setting and movement. Rigidity is incorporated in all critical members to ensure continued and long-lived accuracy. Refinements are continually being added; a striking example of this trend is the use of a strain gage connected with an electronic amplifier as a means of accurately aligning

Fig. 26-10. Universal-type cylindrical grinding machine. (Courtesy of Brown & Sharpe Manufacturing Co., Providence, R.I.)

the swivel table on either straight or taper work. The tendency toward fully automatic operation is increasingly apparent in cylindrical grinding machine design. Built-in sizing arrangements which control the entire grinding cycle, including rough and finish grind feeds and speeds, rapid traverse, and automatic sizing, provide a complete grinding service.

Universal Cylindrical Grinding Machines. Manufacturers refer to these grinding machines as universals; however, it seems desirable to include the term cylindrical in their descriptions, since they are primarily employed on that class of work. Grinding machines in this classification are distinctive in that they are equipped with a headstock carrying a rotating center and that, in addition, the headstock swivels (Fig. 26-10). The wheel head is of special design; it can also swivel. On some makes, the grinding wheel can be mounted in any one of three different positions on its spindle. The combination of swiveling headstock and wheel head makes this classification of grinding machines truly universal in operation. Internal grinding is also done on this type.

Internal Grinding

This method of grinding is confined to finishing holes or bores. It is capable of producing excellent surfaces with a high degree of accuracy. Its development has been such that it has replaced some reaming operations for reasons of economy as well as of excellence of finish. Precision

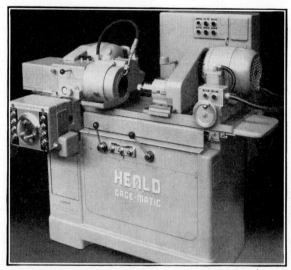

Fig. 26-11. Gage-matic internal grinding machine built with automatic grinding cycle. (Courtesy of The Heald Machine Co., Worcester, Mass.)

within 0.00025 in. is readily attained, while limits as close as 0.0001 in. lie within the capacity of internal grinding. Here, as in other types of grinding, hard materials can be finished to desired accuracy; distortion in bores and holes of heat-treated workpieces are corrected by this grinding method. Internal grinding machines are designed and built to take their place in any production program requirement.

Chucking-type Internal Grinders. In this type the workpiece is held in a chuck mounted in the work head. Several design modifications exist on the various features of internal grinding machines (Fig. 26-11). The work head is a typical example, since the work spindle rotates in some models, while in others it is stationary. It may have a reciprocating motion, or the grinding element may reciprocate. Either work head or wheel head or both may be equipped with cross slides. The table may or may not traverse, and its movement can be manually or mechanically operated, or both.

Internal Grinding Techniques. Accepted procedure for grinding bores in relatively small work is that of bringing the grinding wheel into contact with the entire internal surface by rotating the workpiece with its axis parallel to that of the grinding wheel. For better visibility, grinding contact is made on the side away from the operator. Plunge grinding is used for producing contoured internal surfaces, but straight bores are not plunge-ground.

Large workpieces are mounted on a face plate for grinding in a planetary type of internal grinding machine. The grinder is designed to provide the grinding wheel with rotation about its own axis as well as to travel the wheel in an orbit whereby it can contact the entire surface of the bore. The workpiece, in this case, is held stationary. Both wet and dry grinding find application over the range of internal grinding.

Internal grinding has been developed on the automatic-cycle principle to the point where the operator is required only to load, start, and unload the machine. The various modifications embodied in these automatics follow the dictates of the grinding job requirements. There are few application limitations for internal grinding, since straight, taper, and contoured bores are ground without difficulty. Production machines for multiple operations are also available.

Centerless Grinding

This method is different from cylindrical grinding, since here the workpiece is not supported on centers. This omission is of advantage in many respects, chiefly in the elimination of the centering operation, resulting in lower costs. Also, a more accurate cylinder can be generated on slender workpieces, since there is no axial thrust from the centers. Centerless grinding is admirably suited to repetitive production work because, once the job setup is made, the operator can load while the previous piece is being finished. Shafting, rods, and bars of stock lengths are ground by the centerless method on the one hand, while workpieces whose length is less than that of the grinding wheel face are examples of the other extreme.

There are three conventional methods for advancing the workpiece in centerless grinding; these are termed through feed, end feed, and infeed. A given grinder design incorporates one of these principles; the methods are not used interchangeably on a single grinding machine or with the same workpiece. To these three methods must now be added a fourth one, which is known as the rotary infeed.

The operating principle of cylindrical centerless grinding employs three basic elements—the grinding wheel, the regulating wheel, and the work rest blade in a fixed relationship (Fig. 26-12). The grinding wheel, traveling at a speed ranging around 6,500 sfpm, contacts the workpiece, whose rotation is in the opposite direction. A regulating wheel of the same rotation, whose speed varies from 15 to 300 rpm, bears on the opposite diameter of the workpiece. The result of these movements is that the workpiece and grinding wheel are traveling in the same direction at their contact line; however, since the workpiece is rotating at a slower rate, there is relative motion, which causes the grinding effect. A work

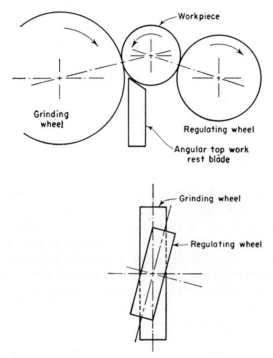

Fig. 26-12. Diagram of centerless grinding operating principle.

rest or blade supports the workpiece, thereby holding it in its correct geometric position. The centers of the grinding and regulating wheel are in a plane, but the workpiece center is above this horizontal. Lowering the center of the workpiece has the effect of reducing its diameter, while raising it has the opposite effect.

The regulating wheel is placed at an angle with the workpiece axis in order to impart feed. This wheel is an abrasive one that is dressed by means of a built-in diamond dresser. Its face is dressed concave for the purpose of ensuring line, rather than point, contact with the workpiece. Workpiece feed rate is a function of the inclination of the regulating wheel axis, together with its diameter and speed of rotation.

Infeed Centerless Grinding. This method is actually a form of plunge grinding. There is no feed of the workpiece, whose length is less than the width of the grinding wheel face. By installing segmented wheels, a variety of diameters can be ground simultaneously. This method is commonly employed on workpieces having one surface to be ground, such as bolts or shouldered pieces. In setups of this type, it is usual to contour the regulating wheel as well as the grinding wheel to fit the design of the surface to be ground.

Centerless Internal Grinding. A somewhat specialized application is that of internal grinding of workpieces whose outside surfaces have been cylindrically ground. However, where suitable applications are found, this method is highly satisfactory. The operating principle of centerless internal grinding machines is based on supporting the workpiece exterior between two pressure rolls, while the regulating wheel forms the third point of contact. In consequence, the truth of the internal grind depends entirely on the accuracy of the external surface. There are examples of this method being built into grinding machines with fully automatic cycles.

Surface Grinding

Machining and finishing of flat surfaces that are free from projections and of a size not to exceed machine capacity belong in the field of surface grinding. While this grinding method is capable of producing accurate surfaces, it is, nevertheless, of interest on first operation work as well. Its common application is that of precision grinding.

Surface grinding machines are classified according to spindle treatment as horizontal or vertical types. As a general thing, the vertical spindle surface grinding machine mounts a cup wheel as its grinding element, whereas the horizontal one is equipped with a straight wheel. Machine size influences wheel type in that segmented wheels are conventional for large vertical machines.

Magnetic Chucks. The workpieces are usually held by magnetic chucks, either directly or indirectly. Nonmagnetic materials are mounted in fixtures which may or may not be held magnetically. Magnetic chucks are built in a variety of styles, depending on the type of work they are to accommodate (Fig. 26-13). They are a satisfactory holding device provided the workpiece facing surface is relatively flat; if it is not, the use of shims or wedging is necessary, but neither is entirely satisfactory. A source of direct current is required for chuck operation; further equipment includes demagnetizing accessories. These chucks must be used with care to prevent overheating. Magnetic chuck development has been successful in perfecting a permanent magnet type; these do not require a source of direct current.

where a flat surface is required. Work mounting is either directly on the table or on angle plates.

Disk Grinding

A distinctive method of metal removal wherein a disk rather than a wheel is the grinding element is of interest to every work type from snagging castings to precision finish. This method has frequently been termed surface grinding, a phrase that, while accurate, may lead to some confusion with other surface grinding methods.

Disk grinding uses an abrasive disk that is fastened to a steel disk mounted on the grinding machine spindle. Fastening is either done

Fig. 26-15. Offhand grind of a shaper tool. (Courtesy of Tool Laboratory, University of Washington, Seattle, Wash.)

mechanically, by bolting, or it is done by gluing the abrasive disk to the metal one. Abrasive disks are in no sense similar to the sanding disks familiar to the woodworking shop. On the contrary, abrasive disks are made similarly to grinding wheels; however, the former may have steel wire or other strength-reinforcing agencies incorporated in them. The large sizes are generally of segmented construction for ease of both manufacture and mounting.

Disk Grinding Machines. Disk grinding is no longer an offhand grinding process. The degree of finish, production, and precision obtainable by disk grinding is directly related to the design of the disk grinding machine. Horizontal and vertical, single and multiple spindles, conventional and single-purpose, automatic and manual operation, and combinations thereof have all appeared in disk grinding machines.

Offhand Grinding. The general metalworking shop would find itself hard-pressed without offhand grinding. This method finds manifold uses, from tool grinding to dimensional work (Fig. 26-15). In the toolroom there are many examples of resharpening tools by this method. Precautions against overheating the workpiece and placing undue pressure on the grinding wheel are necessary, and choosing the correct wheel is vital. Safety considerations in offhand grinding include the proper positioning of the work rest to prevent the workpiece from wedging and *grinding on the face and not the side of the wheel.* Eye protection is basic, as is the use of wheel guards. The grinding wheels must be balanced and should be dressed as occasion demands.

Fig. 26-16. Snagging a gray iron casting on a conventional grinding wheel stand. (Courtesy of Norton Co., Worcester, Mass.)

Snagging. This is the rough grinding method whose chief application is the removal of metal in volume in the shortest possible time. Removing casting fins, gates, risers, and scabs is a common application for snagging. The method is applied as a first operation in a host of other applications on forgings, weldments, cutoff bars, shapes, and plates.

Most snagging is done on conventional grinding stands carrying a wheel at each end of the spindle (Fig. 26-16). Straight wheels are used, and they attain considerable size for large work. Snagging is also done by bringing the grinding wheel to the workpiece with swing-frame or portable-type grinders. Snagging is primarily a manual grinding operation and, with labor costs looming more important, automatic machines are an intriguing possibility.

ABRASIVE BELT GRINDING

The use of abrasive paper glued into an endless belt which then becomes the abrasive element of a grinding machine is finding increased application. This is a development from the original idea of polishing and buffing with abrasive paper or cloth. Several different types of machines are currently available for abrasive belt use. A conventional design (Fig. 26-17) has a vertical belt travel provided with suitable backing to carry the grinding thrust. This method is capable of producing excellent surfaces but is not regarded as a volume metal removal process. Abrasive belt grinding is performed dry for most applications, although there are some specially prepared materials designed for use with the wet method.

Fig. 26-17. Abrasive belt grinding machine. (Courtesy of Tool Laboratory, University of Washington, Seattle, Wash.)

Abrasive Belt Equipment. A coated abrasive belt that is mounted on a polishing lathe and back-stand idler (Fig. 26-18) is capable of performing either offhand rough grinding or polishing. A basic difference between this setup and a grinding wheel exists; although the radiums of the working area is no greater here than on the grinding wheel, the belt has a much longer working length, permitting it to cut cooler at higher speeds. Downtime for changing an abrasive belt is practically insignificant, since flanges, spindle nuts, or guards need not be removed. All that is required is to move the idler pulley forward slightly, remove the old belt, and replace it. Because the belt is flexible it can be used to grind compound curves or contours in molded, cast, or forged components. Another advantage is that when the belt is used over a soft contact wheel, the flexible belt will give under pressure and conform to the shape of the work being held against it. The behavior of a belt over a flat platen deserves especial mention since the flexibility of the coated abrasive belt permits straight-line finishing over the full area of flat surfaces.

Fig. 26-18. Back-stand type abrasive belt grinding and polishing machine. (Courtesy of Behr-Manning Co., Troy, N.Y.)

Fig. 26-19. Jet compressor blade polishing machine complete with control panel and five #50-95 abrasive tape polishing heads. (Courtesy of Hammond Machinery Builders, Inc., Kalamazoo, Mich.)

Applications. The design and construction of the contact wheel decidedly influence abrasive belt performance. Many wheel types are in use, such as cog-tooth rubber wheels, compressed canvas wheels, and heavy-duty canvas wheels, among others. Thus, a rubber X serration will promote stock removal in rough grinding to much better advantage than a plain face rubber wheel.

Noticeable strides have been made in contour polishing and grinding. In this area, such items as surface finishing turbine jet blades are noteworthy (Fig. 26-19). There are several designs of airfoil grinders using the abrasive belt principle.

Machine tools in many categories are being developed for abrasive belt use. Among these are centerless grinders, which remove metal at the rate of 1 lb/min, with an abrasive belt 9 in. wide by 14 ft long, when grinding seamless stainless steel tubing. Another application is that of flat sheet grinders. These are used for finishing titanium alloy and stainless steel sheets, the abrasive belt being as much as 50 in. in width by 20 ft long. Abrasive belt equipment has been developed for fully automatic operation such as surfacing aluminum ingots prior to forging. Additional applications are appearing to the point where abrasive belt grinding and polishing can no longer be classified as a secondary operation. On the contrary, this technique has moved into the ranks of basic machining operations.

FINISHES

In discussing finishes, it is intended to refer not to the dimensional requirements but rather to the condition of the surface insofar as its roughness is concerned. Such expressions as surface roughness and surface finish are common; yet it is contended that the term surface finish is an erroneous one, since each of the words composing that term has a distinct meaning. That the term has considerable standing is shown by its use as the title of a standard.[1] The definitions in that standard are largely based on information in American Standard B46.1—1955, "Standard of Surface Roughness, Waviness, and Lay."[2]

Definitions applying to the more common terms used in a discussion of finishes are abstracted here from the above standards:

Surface—The surface of an object is the boundary which separates that object from another substance or object.

Nominal Surface—A two-dimensional boundary of separation which is absolutely true and smooth and whose shape and extent is defined by a drawing or descriptive specification.

[1] "Surface Finish, Standard," Society of Automotive Engineers, Inc., New York, 1945.
[2] American Standards Association, New York.

Surface Qualities—The physical characteristics of a surface, such as roughness, waviness and flaws.

Roughness—That deviation from nominal surface evidenced by minute contiguous irregularities occurring on the nominal surface. Roughness in itself does not alter the trueness of a surface.

Roughness Number—A physical measurement in RMS microinches which represents the maximum permissible degree of roughness of the surface to which it is applied except that, where two numbers are used, the larger shall be the maximum and the smaller the minimum permissible degree of roughness.

Microinch (μin.)—One millionth (0.000001) part of the U.S. Standard linear inch.

RMS—The square root of the mean of the sum of the squares of the height (in microinches) of the irregularities. This value can be calculated but is usually read from a meter or instrument made for measuring surface roughness.

Waviness—That deviation from nominal surface evidenced by recurrent irregularities having the form of waves. These deviations are usually of greater magnitude than surface roughness, which may be superimposed on waviness.

Flaws—Irregularities which occur at one place, or at relatively infrequent intervals in the surface; *e.g.*, a scratch, ridge, hole, peak, crack, or check.

Lay—The direction of the predominant surface pattern.

The significance of these definitions is that they emphasize the ability of the designer to communicate his desires to the shop by means of standard drawing symbols. The standard drawing symbols are published in the Standards, as are scales for roughness and waviness.

The chief sources of surface roughness are the feed marks or ridges caused by cutting tool or grinding wheel and the minute particles from the built-up edge shed on the surface in the process of machining. The degree of roughness is the direct result of the machining operation, since any given single machining method is capable of producing differing results.

In the surface-finishing methods in common use the primary objective is the removal of the metal film on the workpiece surface that is variously termed fragmented, amorphous, noncrystalline, and/or smear metal. The concept of finish concerns itself with this metallic layer, which is not considered a homogeneous part of the base metal. When this layer is removed from a surface, an excellent finish of high quality results. *The extent of this metal layer is variable.* The dulling of a cutting tool or grinding wheel will cause imperfect cutting action: the base metal will be torn rather than cleanly cut, and increased surface roughness will result.

This condition explains the variations in finished size of components subjected to identical machining and finishing processing. The range of surface roughness characteristics derived from various production methods is shown in Fig. 26-20.

Surface Roughness Measurement. An accomplished mechanic will frequently depend upon his sense of feel in estimating surface quality by drawing the fingernail over a surface. A more scientific version of this procedure substitutes an instrument for the fingernail.

One such instrument, known as a profilometer, employs a small diamond-tipped aluminum stylus mounted between two button anvils at

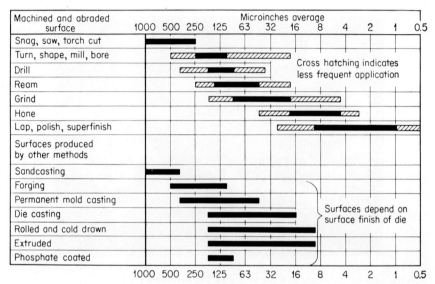

Fig. 26-20. Surface roughness obtained by various machining and other manufacturing methods. (Courtesy of Brush Instruments, Cleveland.)

the end of a handle. When this assembly is drawn along the surface, the diamond tip moves vertically with an amplitude determined by the surface roughness. This mechanical motion is transformed into an electrical current, which can be read directly in microinches on a meter of the instrument. This instrument can also be equipped with a recorder. It is common practice to use these instruments directly at the machine tool for control purposes.

Another instrument for measuring surface roughness is known as the Surfindicator. It employs a hand-operated pickup together with a meter graduated in microinches. The pickup contains a 0.0005-in. tip radius conical diamond stylus, affording excellent penetration of the surface irregularities produced in finishing. Mechanical motion of this stylus is electronically averaged and transferred to the meter dial for direct reading. One major advantage is that surface finishes can be checked while the component remains in the machine tool (Fig. 26-21).

Measurement of surface roughness is only meaningful to the degree to which it is understood and utilized. It does not follow that every mating surface, regardless of material or function, should approach zero micro-inch roughness. The ideal finish is that one which will permit the optimum oil film to be maintained under both load and operating conditions for a given application.

Honing. Honing is essentially an abrading procedure that is applicable to all metals and to many nonmetals such as plastics, rubber, ceramics,

Fig. 26-21. The Surfindicator is used to check machined finishes without removing the piece from the machine. (Courtesy of Brush Electronics Co., Cleveland.)

and glass. The abrading, or cutting, element is known as a hone. It is composed of an abrasive material bonded to shape in a manner similar to grinding wheel construction. Hones are graded and identified by a standard code sponsored by the Grinding Wheel Manufacturers' Association.

Honing can be accomplished manually, but in production, honing machines are usual. The honing unit consists of one or more honing sticks mounted in an adaptor with a suitable mandrel. This unit is free to float and, in the case of internal honing, follows the existing hole. The finish surface pattern is that of a crosshatch which is the natural result of hone travel during its operation. The severity of the finish pattern is a function of hone fineness and pressure. The latter is, in turn, dependent upon the hardness and toughness of the material being honed but will range from 150 to 450 psi.

The widest application of honing deals with internal, cylindrical applications; however, other surface geometry, including flats, is also honed. Honing machines are built for every type of application. Their development includes production designs of multiple-spindle type. Honing is regarded as a precision finishing method capable of closely controlled accuracy.

Lapping. Lapping is a method of finishing whose objective is that of refining the geometrical accuracy and surface finish by means of a loose abrasive. In order to accomplish its purpose, an element known as a lap is charged with abrasive powder whose vehicle can be either grease, oil, or a soap and water compound. The workpiece is then subjected to the action of the abrasive-charged lap, whose motion is dictated by the geometry of the surface being lapped. The relative motion between the workpiece and the lap is not positive in the sense that a definite path is followed. Rather, the action is a floating one in which there is a guiding action designed to prevent a repetitious path as a means of uniform treatment of the workpiece surface.

The lap element is generally a close-grained gray cast iron, although practically all the usual engineering metals, such as copper-base alloys, lead, tin, and aluminum alloys find specialized application. Copper, for example, is used primarily as the material for diamond lapping. Non-metals such as wood, felt, and leather also are suitable for lap elements, especially on hardened steel surfaces. Metallic laps are prepared by rolling or pressing the abrasive into them.

Abrasive powders are graded as to fineness and are further classified as soft, medium, or hard. They are employed for polishing gems and are worked in connection with soft laps. Lapping abrasives are procurable in stick form similar to those common in buffing operations.

Lapping is either a manual or a machine process. Flat surface hand lapping is relatively easy. The flat lap is charged uniformly with abrasive over its entire surface area and then moved over the workpiece surface in a figure-eight motion with slight pressure application. In production work, lapping is carried on as a mechanical process. Lapping machines are built primarily to suit a specific job (Fig. 26-22).

Lapping is also applied to specialized applications such as gear lapping, spherical lapping, centerless lapping, and lapping gage block surfaces. The latter are processed by means of non-rotating laps. Excellent surface quality is provided on small parts by employing an oscillating-spindle lapping machine wherein the piece is frequently lifted from the rotating lap member.

Superfinishing. An innovation termed superfinish had its beginning in 1936. Its objective is that of removing amorphous metal resulting from previous machining methods, regardless of type. It is capable of reducing

Fig. 26-22. Lapping machine, showing use of one-piece work holder for cylindrical lapping. (Courtesy of Norton Co., Worcester, Mass.)

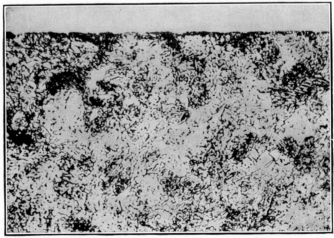

Fig. 26-23. Superfinish profile $\times 750$, microinch 8 to 10 on C-1095 steel. (Courtesy of Chrysler Corp., Detroit.)

surface roughness and lessening inequalities in surface geometry (Fig. 26-23).

Superfinishing is an abrading process in which the abrasive element is in the form of a stone or stick. The stone is given an oscillating traverse while in contact with the rotating workpiece. This operation uses slight pressure, on the order of 20 psi, while work rotation ranges from 50 to 60 spfm—the workpiece, meantime, being flooded with lubricant. Superfinishing is not intended primarily as a dimension-changing process; it is designed for stock removal averaging 0.0001 to 0.0002 in. on a diameter. However, an unlimited choice of surface patterns ranging from a mirror finish to 30 microinches rms may be applied.

Fig. 26-24. Superfinishing machine for all bearings on the crankshaft shown. (Courtesy of the Gishold Machine Co., Madison, Wis.)

Superfinishing machines in a variety of designs, of which Fig. 26-24 is an example, are available to industry. This is a machine and never a manual method. It is used in the automotive industry for such components as tappets, crankshaft bearings, clutch plates, brake drums, bearing races, and many others. Production potentials are high with machines adapted to specific parts. By way of example, brake drums are completed at the rate of 150/hr on a single-spindle machine, while tappet bodies are superfinished at the rate of 720/hr on a 12-spindle machine.

Vapor-blast Finishing. Another method for surface finishing is that of employing a wet blast carrying an abrasive material. Compressed air at 85 psi drives the abrasive-carrying liquid through the gun nozzle at a rate that causes a vapor blast to result. Various types and sizes of abrasives are used, depending on the finish desired. Castings are processed with a 40-80 quartz or silicon carbide abrasive, whereas a machined surface may go to the extreme of a 1,200 mesh "Novaculite" abrasive in a process also termed liquid honing.

This finishing method is indispensable for such applications as contoured dies where tedious hand processing has been standard practice. Another application is that of de-burring small, intricate parts where featheredges remain from previous machining. It is satisfactory for use on glass and plastics, but owing to its nature its action is not as rapid as that of other finishing methods.

Buffing and Polishing. Mention must be made of these two time-honored methods of producing surface finishes. They are not intended as dimension-attaining methods but are useful in achieving eye-pleasing finishes. Buffing and polishing are performed by several different methods and are applied to metal and nonmetals.

SURVEY QUESTIONS

26-1. How is metal removed in the grinding operation?

26-2. Is grinding confined to metals or can other materials be so processed?

26-3. How has grinding contributed to interchangeability of parts manufacture?

26-4. Are grindstones used in mass production?

26-5. Mention some of the natural abrasives that have been used in grinding wheels.

26-6. In what equipment are artificial abrasives made?

26-7. What are the two most common abrasives used in grinding wheels?

26-8. Of what importance are abrasive grain sizes?

26-9. Why does a grinding wheel resemble foundry molding sand?

26-10. What is the purpose of bond in a grinding wheel?

26-11. Are grinding wheels standardized?

26-12. What is a vitrified bond?

26-13. Why are different types of bonds used in grinding wheels?

26-14. Are all grinding wheels of the same degree of hardness?

26-15. What is meant by dressing a grinding wheel?

26-16. What purpose does grinding fluid serve?

26-17. Is the surface speed of a grinding wheel critical?

26-18. What is the objective of cutter grinding?

26-19. On what type equipment are milling cutters ground?

26-20. On what type equipment would the taper on an automobile axle shaft be finished?

26-21. Give some examples of cylindrical grinding applications.

26-22. How are automotive pistons finished?

26-23. Give an example of internal grinding on an automobile motor.

26-24. Is centerless grinding the same as cylindrical grinding?

26-25. What is meant by plunge grinding?

26-26. What types of surfaces are generally produced with surface grinding?

26-27. What are magnetic chucks?

26-28. What is a grinding element that is used in disk grinding?

26-29. What is meant by offhand grinding?

26-30. Is abrasive belt grinding confined to flat surfaces?

26-31. What is a backstand grinder?

26-32. Are all finishes produced by grinding?

26-33. What is meant by surface roughness?

26-34. What is the purpose of lapping?

26-35. What material is generally used for making a lap?

26-36. Are any abrasives used in lapping?

26-37. What is the objective of superfinishing?

26-38. Where is vapor-blast finishing used?

26-39. Is honing confined to metal finishing?

26-40. Give an example of a component that is finished by buffing.

Chapter 27

TRANSFER AND
SPECIAL MACHINES

A development that is proving to be the beginning of a new trend in engineering manufacture is that of the automatic transfer machine. This principle is being applied to machining components whose production requirements are impressive. There appears to be no standard terminology applying to this new method. Among the terms used to designate these machining lines are automatic transfer processing machines, automatic processing machines, transfermatics, transfer machines, and process-through machines. Basically this equipment is composed of several individual machine tools arranged in accordance with a predetermined machining sequence yet integrated into a composite whole. The result is machining on the production line principle.

A beginning was made by assembling several multiple-spindle machine tools into a line. The workpiece was successively machined in each one in accordance with the chosen sequence of operations. Drilling and tapping were the primary considerations of these early machines. The workpiece was loaded, clamped, and transferred manually from one station to the next. Continuing study and investigation resulted in the successful completion of a transfer machine in which both clamping and transferring became automatic functions of the machine. Essentially this achievement formed the basis of the automatic transfer machine in its present state of development.

This equipment demonstrated its ability to machine aircraft engine cylinder heads for both the B-17 and the B-29 heavy bomber program in World War II. One transfer machine built for this program had 81 stations and its total length was 200 ft. The experience gained in wartime applications has served as a basis for further development of the automatic transfer machine for peacetime production requirements.

Automatic transfer machines are individual in the sense that they are built to meet specific requirements. In the automotive industry, where

500

design changes are continually being made, it may be necessary to write off the cost of an automatic transfer machine over a model year whereas in another industry, in which design modification is less frequent, a greater period of time might be allowed for amortizing the investment. It is possible to modify existing stations on automatic transfer machines to accommodate revisions in workpiece design.

TRANSFER MACHINES

The first transfer-type machines were confined to drilling and tapping operations. These operations continue to be in the forefront; however, related ones have been added, including rough, semifinish, and finish boring, facing, chamfering, reaming, countersinking, counterboring, and rough and finishing milling.

Individual machine tools that form part of an automatic transfer machine may be of conventional design insofar as operating principles are concerned. Multiple-spindle drilling machines are an example. Obviously design and construction modifications are frequently necessary in order to integrate the individual unit into a transfer machine.

Another production accomplishment is that of processing two workpieces simultaneously. Such a procedure is possible where parts are of a size to permit double mounting on a single work-holding fixture. There is little that is fundamentally new from a machining viewpoint in the automatic transfer machine. Their distinguishing characteristics are those of integration, synchronization, and workpiece handling.

Machine Operation. It is incorrect to assume that these machines are automatic to the point where the human element can be completely eliminated. These machines operate by electrical and hydraulic circuits. Not only is the human element needed; it must be of the highest skill, intelligence, and resourcefulness since any down time is critical with production rates high. Even though push-button controls and signaling devices are built into most automatic transfer machines, they cannot operate without supervision and care.

Machine Achievements. Transfer machines are at their best for heavy production runs. They are not suitable for every type of manufacture nor are they confined to machining operations. The A. O. Smith Co. automobile frame plant at Milwaukee, Wis., furnishes an example of long standing of the application of a variation of the automatic transfer machine principle to the fabrication of steel strip. Metal stamping with automatic transfer presses was presented in Chap. 12, together with illustrations of requisite equipment. A somewhat similar development has occurred in production foundries where castings are produced on another variation of the process-through principle including sand conditioning systems, machine molding, conveyor pouring, mechanical shakeout, and flask return.

Irrespective of the end product, the objective in all these developments is that of achieving greater production at lower cost. This major accomplishment is traceable to the elimination of lost time in workpiece movement. As material-handling time is decreased, man-hour requirements are lowered in direct proportion. In order to understand the progress that has been made by this innovation, the following cases, whose data have been provided by the respective machine tool manufacturers involved, are included.

Process Machines

Process machines are designed for specific applications and are capable of a wide variety of machining operations. The automotive industry is a fruitful field for such applications because of its substantial production requirements. A process machine capable of machining V-8

Fig. 27-1. A 10-station machine for processing V-8 engine blocks. (Courtesy of The Ingersoll Milling Machine Co., Rockford, Ill.)

motor blocks at a rate of 108/hr is shown in Fig. 27-1. Among the machining operations performed are those of finish-boring the assembled cam bearing liners and crank bearings, which are held to an accuracy of 0.001 in. in both diameter and alignment. Other simultaneous operations consist of milling the banks, boring distributor holes, and also boring and chamfering the cylinder holes. It is obvious that this process machine is capable of contributing substantially toward low-cost production.

Transfermatics

Sectionized Automation. In order to prevent loss of production during periods of down time, sectionized automation has been introduced. This new advance is based upon the division of a transfer machine (Fig. 27-2) into definite sections in order to permit shutdown of some of the operations without interrupting the automatic cycle of the others.

A basic feature of this equipment is the Toolometer, which programs the actual behavior of the cutting tools within a given section. These units are mounted to program the operation of all tools. Every time a part is produced, the hands of the Toolometers, which are electrically interlocked with the machine cycle, index counterclockwise. When one of the hands reaches its zero position the section of the machine which it governs becomes inoperative. The tool setup man changes the dull tool, together with any other Toolometers that are almost ready for replacement. Then he manually rotates the Toolometer hands to their starting

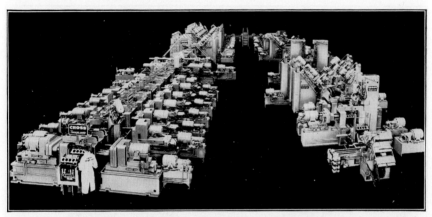

Fig. 27-2. A five-station sectionized transfer machine tooled for machining V-8 motor blocks. (Courtesy of The Cross Co., Detroit.)

positions, thus establishing new programs for the fresh tools. The section now automatically returns to operation in sequence with the other sections. Preset tools eliminate the need for trial cuts and machine adjustment.

This sectionized automation operates as follows: If, for example, it is necessary to shut down section 3 to change one of the tools, as indicated by the Toolometer, sections 1, 2, 4, and 5 continue in full automatic operation. The operator continues to feed parts into section 1. The cylinder blocks coming out of section 2 are banked up in front of section 3, while the parts banked behind section 3 are fed into section 4. After the toolsetter replaces the dull tool with a fresh one, he resets the Toolometer and section 3 returns to automatic operation in sequence with other operations.

Statistical information on this machine includes the following: This line performs 555 operations on V-8 cylinder blocks; it produces 100 pieces/hr at 100 per cent efficiency, with 104 pieces in process simultaneously and each part handled in seven different positions.

It covers 265 drilling operations, 6 milling, 21 boring, 56 reaming, 101 countersinking, 106 tapping, and 133 inspections. Additionally, there are 104 stations: 1 for loading, 53 for machining, 7 for part handling, 6 for mechanical inspection, 36 for visual inspection, 1 for unloading. On this machine, grouping and programming of tool changes plus the availability of preset tools drastically reduce machine down time.

Case Studies of Transfer Machines

Steering Gear Housing. An example of machining on an automatic transfer machine is that of the steering gear housing casting shown in

Fig. 27-3. Three views of steering gear housing after being machined. (Courtesy of Greenlee Bros. & Co., Rockford, Ill.)

Fig. 27-3. This is a gray iron casting, which, for the purpose of machining, is mounted on work-holding pallets as shown in Fig. 27-4. The machining is done in an automatic transfer machine where each operating cycle is fully automatic, with the exception of depressing a push button to start the cycle. After the operator has placed the work-holding fixture in the loading station the sequence of functions during a normal automatic cycle is:

1. Depress cycle start button.

2. All work-holding pallets advance from their respective operations, including the movement of the work from the loading station into the first operating station.

3. At the completion of the transfer of the work, the elevating dowel pins raise and enter the bushings in the work-holding pallet, and each pallet is hydraulically clamped in the pallet-locating fixture ready for operation.

Fig. 27-4. Two views of a Greenlee work-holding pallet for steering gear machines; one view shows the pallet empty and the other with the steering gear housing intact. (Courtesy of Greenlee Bros. & Co., Rockford, Ill.)

4. The transfer mechanism return to its starting position, ready for the next cycle.

5. When all work-holding pallets are properly located and clamped, all operating units advance, perform their operations, and return.

6. After all operating units have returned, all the work-holding pallets are released and the locating pins withdrawn. The cycle is then completed and a white light appears on the operator's control cabinet to indicate that the machine is ready to start the next cycle.

All functions of the machine are hydraulically operated and electrically interlocked so that the units must advance, perform their operations, and return before the fixtures can be released and the transfer bar become operative. Similarly, all fixtures must be transferred to each successive position and be clamped solidly before the operating units can advance and perform their operations. In the event that any of the func-

tions listed in the sequence fails, the automatic cycle of the machine becomes inoperative.

Failure of the clamping, unclamping, transfer, or operating units to
perform during any part of the cycle can be readily detected and the
trouble located immediately by a system of lights shown on the panel
above the push buttons on the operator's control cabinet.

At all of the six stations providing for removal of the work-holding
pallets and at the final gaging station, the operator can stop the machine
during removal or gaging for safety purposes. By again depressing the
start button, the machine will go back into automatic cycle.

Fig. 27-5. 33-station and 4-station automatic transfer machines to perform operation on
steering gear housing. View from load station of machine. (Courtesy of Greenlee Bros.
& Co., Rockford, Ill.)

This completely automatic transfer machine (Fig. 27-5) performs a
total of 114 operations with 128 tools. There are 26 working stations, 3
idle stations, and 6 checking stations, all equipped with a total of 32
heads. The total length of the machine is 219 ft. The specifications include 73 electric motors totaling 581 hp, 42.2 miles of electric wire, 280
limit switches, 183 indicating lights, and 5,500 ft of hydraulic tubing.

The operations that are performed are the following:

8 milling	2 bore and face	2 recess and chamfer
18 boring	10 bore and chamfer	20 chamfer
48 drilling	2 recessing	24 tapping

The production on this equipment is estimated at 228 pieces/hr at 100
per cent efficiency, or 184 pieces/hr at 80 per cent efficiency. This unit

is typical of the automatic transfer machines that are helping the manufacturing industry increase production at lower unit cost.

Universal Joint Spider Forgings. Another type of transfer machine is shown in Fig. 27-6. This machine is designed in a rectangular pattern as a means of saving floor space as well as completing a cycle whereby the

Fig. 27-6. Transfer-type machine of rectangular pattern design (Courtesy of W. F. & John Barnes Co., Rockford, Ill.)

Fig. 27-7. Lower view is of the transfer pallet wherein the universal joint spiders are mounted for machining. Upper view shows a testing fixture. (Courtesy of W. F. & John Barnes Co., Rockford, Ill.)

pallets are returned to the loading station. A distinctive feature of this machine is the production of symmetrical components, as the opposed heads at each station perform the same operation. The pallets in Fig. 27-7 are designed for holding four identical workpieces during the machining cycle. This transfer machine combines the operation on two ends of the spider of four pieces at each work station. The forged steel universal joint spiders are drilled, chamfered, and hollow-milled in a continuous cycle at a gross rate of 766/hr. Positioning and clamping of pieces in pallet transfer fixtures permit straight-through operations without unclamping or repositioning the workpieces. Rough broaching the forgings is the only preliminary operation.

A further refinement in the tooling design includes power clamping of workpieces in the fixture, and automatic unclamping and unloading after

Fig. 27-8. Automatic transfer machine for valve bodies. There are 26 work stations included. (Courtesy of Baker Bros., Inc., Toledo, Ohio.)

all machining operations are completed. Pallets are then returned to the operator at the loading station. There is one station that washes the chips away prior to return of the pallet for reloading. This machine has 17 stations and occupies a floor space totaling 2,576 sq ft.

Valve Bodies. The increasing flexibility of the automatic transfer machine concept can well be illustrated by the following example, which is designed for machining valve bodies. Its flexibility is demonstrated when it is understood that this installation has a capacity for valve sizes from ⅜ to 2 in., inclusive. The completed transfer machine is composed of six standard units together with five special ones. The assembly of these units results in 26 work stations, of which the first one is used for loading. The operations for the various stations consist of drilling, counter-boring, and facing, reaming, tapping, and broaching. These operations follow one another in a sequence that gives the unit a productive capacity ranging from 103 ⅜-in. valve bodies to 50 2-in. valve bodies per hour at 10 per cent production. The layout of the machine is on the rectangular principle, whereby work carriers are delivered to the work station as noted in Fig. 27-8. A study of that installation shows the electrical control panels at the rear, while the operating pulpit is shown at the front with the operator at the controls.

INTEGRATED-INTERLOCKED LINE

A further extension of the mechanization potential, which at the same time permits the manufacturer great latitude in the utilization of standard machine tools, is developing substantially. This sort of tooling will operate whether 2, 3, 4, or 50 machine tools are assembled into one production line. Such advancement has been most successful in the larger shops, for the reason that more equipment is available; also, the type of operation lends itself best to large-scale production.

The actual setting up of the line consists of hooking suitable machine tools together with necessary chutes, feeder lines, and automatic gaging and sizing equipment to deliver a constant high production potential. The challenging part of this development is the inviting cost picture. There are installations in which the line establishment costs but 15 to 20 per cent above the actual machine tool cost. Also, the line equipment, or much of it at least, is already in the shop and therefore is familiar to the operating personnel, which means higher operating efficiency.

When the integrated-interlocked line is installed and operating, it does resemble the transfer-through equipment insofar as production is concerned. However, there is this difference—standard machine tool equipment predominates. In consequence, individual machine tools can be removed and set up individually should such procedure become desirable.

An example of the achievement that this concept is capable of can be appreciated from the production of 1,200 pinion gears/hr. The line utilizes feedback, automatic sizing, integrated gaging, parts washing, and spiral storage units. The actual manufacturing process utilizes 62 machine tools, 5 parts washers, and 4 storage units. Automatic equipment is electrically controlled and completely separate from the machine toolbuilders' electrical panels—a design that was introduced as a means of simplifying the electrical interlock.

The trend toward automatic transfer installations is not confined to machining alone. On the contrary, sheet metal presses of the transfer type are well established. In the foundry there are integrated molding and pouring units designed on this basis. In short, where production volume is sufficiently great to warrant attention to automation, the automatic transfer principle is providing a competent answer.

SURVEY QUESTIONS

27-1. What are the criteria for installing transfer machining equipment?

27-2. List at least three alternate designations for this type of installation.

27-3. In what industry are automatic transfer machines used predominantly?

27-4. Mention one of the first installations of transfer machining equipment.

27-5. How do sectioned transfer machines differ from other types?

27-6. What is a basic difference between machining on a transfer machine and doing the job in some other manner?

27-7. Why does the design of automatic transfer machines include a rectangular pattern in some instances?

27-8. Are the individual units in a transfer machine standard machine tools?

27-9. Should an automatic transfer machine line be installed in an airframe manufacturing plant?

27-10. Wherein do automatic transfer lines and numerical control equipment differ basically?

Chapter 28

MACHINING AND CUTTING TOOLS

In the terminology of metal cutting, both the machine tool and the cutting tool used in that machine are designated as "tools," and this causes some confusion. By way of definition, a cutting tool has a cutting edge, single or in multiple, which is used to produce the machined surface on the workpiece being processed in a machine tool. The cutting tool is a most important governing factor in machine tool development.

Machining Research. Scientific studies in machining were begun in 1880 by Frederick W. Taylor at the Midvale Steel Company in Philadelphia. The results of his research were presented in December, 1906, as part of his inaugural address as president of the American Society of Mechanical Engineers. This monograph, "On the Art of Cutting Metals," is a learned paper of outstanding brilliance and completeness.[1] He acknowledges the contributions to these studies by his colleagues, White, Gantt, and Barth, among others. The monograph is of such fundamental importance to an understanding of the subject of metal cutting that it is recommended to every student interested in this field.

Some of the discoveries and developments made by Taylor and his associates have, with the passing of time, proved of fundamental significance. Barth led this group of investigators in the application of mathematics to the physical experimental data which resulted in the perfection, about 1901, of a slide rule for calculating machine tool operating data.

A significant discovery in cutting tools occurred in the period 1898–1900, during which the Taylor-White Process of heat-treating chrome-tungsten steels was perfected. This development, supplemented in 1906 by the discovery that small vanadium additions to chrome-tungsten steels improved red-hardness and tool life, gave industry modern high-speed steel. The introduction of these steels proved revolutionary: they were given

[1] *Trans. ASME*, Vol. 28, pp. 32–350, 1907.

universal application for cutting tools for machining metals as well as nonmetals.

The research in cutting metal has been shared by many investigators in several countries; this work belongs to no one group of men. Engineering literature is replete with the names of researchers in metal cutting. Prominent among these are Klopstock and Schwerd in Germany; Rosenhain and Sturney in England; Boston, Gilbert, Ernst, Martellotti, Merchant, Schmidt, Trigger, and Chao in the United States.

Fundamental Factors. The solution of the problem of machining a given component involves many variables; however, the shape and type of cutting tool, its composition, the capacity of the chosen machine tool, and the properties of the component are of major importance. There are other pertinent factors affecting any machining problem, such as production and cost requirements, personnel, available equipment, and plant layout.

The microstructure of metal being machined is critical insofar as tool wear is concerned. It has been demonstrated that steels of different analyses, but with similar microstructures and microconstituents, develop similar tool life. However, metals having the same hardness value but differing microstructures will show a variation in tool wear.

Hot Machining. Machining metals at elevated temperatures has been under study for some time. It seems evident that one of the virtues of these studies will be the possibility of machining high-strength steels. When strengths reach 2,500,000 psi and higher, the material being machined approaches the hardness and strength of the cutting tool with attendant difficulties. A solution is that of reducing the shear strength of the material by hot machining. This can be accomplished by introducing induction heating at the tool face. Heating need not penetrate more than the depth of the cut in order to decrease the strength of the chip. The design requirements of missiles and supersonic aircraft demand steels of properties that can only be machined through development of new and different techniques.

TOOL CUTTING ACTION

The generally held belief that a cutting tool working in metal acts similarly to a wedge used in splitting wood has been shown to be inaccurate as a result of research studies by Hans Ernst.[2] In place of the so-named theory of splitting, the concept of metal shear has been evolved. To make it possible for the cutting edge of the tool to enter the metal being machined, a force needs to be applied along that edge which is equal to the forces tending to hold the crystals within the metal together.

[2] "Physics of Metal Cutting," American Society for Metals, Cleveland, 1938.

With the application of this force, the metal ahead of the cutting edge is placed in shear. This shear stress reaches a maximum value along a shear plane that is approximately perpendicular to the face of the tool. The location of the shear plane varies as does its size or the shear area. Among the pertinent factors are the shape and geometry of the cutting tool.

A further factor is that of friction between the chip and the face of the cutting tool. Friction can be lessened with light cuts that yield thin chips; however, that is not an efficient procedure for maximum metal removal. In like manner, a low relative velocity between the chip and the face of the cutting tool is inefficient when viewed from the standpoint of metal removal. Two alternatives remain—the use of a lubricant between the chip and the tool face and the improvement of quality of the surface on the cutting tool face. Insofar as the former is concerned, it is apparent that a cutting fluid should be selected with extreme care, since it serves the dual function of coolant and lubricant. The surface condition of a cutting tool will change with use. It may be honed to a smooth finish but as a result of chip abrasion the surface soon roughens in service.

Another approach to the reduction of friction between chip and tool is that of additives in the metal being machined. The free-machining steels feature the inclusion of sulfides—and in some cases of lead—as a means of lowering the friction coefficient. Obviously, lower power requirements parallel lower frictional forces. In addition, better surface quality is obtained on the workpiece, since greater freedom from built-up tool edge is a natural result.

Cutting Fluids

In tool cutting action, as in many other metalworking methods performed at ambient temperatures, high temperatures tend to develop as a result of surface and internal friction. Unless these temperatures are controlled, there will be interference with the flow of metal as well as the deleterious effect of temperature on the metal. In order to meet this situation, cutting fluids in a wide variety of types have been developed. Such fluids have the dual function of lubricating and cooling simultaneously. Basically, these fluids are of two general types: one, in which the oil is used without dilution, and the second type, known generally as soluble oil, in which the oil is mixed with water. In addition to these two types of oils, water is also used as a coolant. An early use of water as a coolant can be traced back to the grindstone. However, water has the disadvantage of rusting the surfaces that it contacts, and also it has slight lubricating value. In order to meet these shortcomings, additives such as soda ash and alkaline salts are combined with the water.

Undoubtedly, soluble oils or compounds have the widest application in machining. They are compounded from soaps and oils together with emulsifying and wetting agents, such as detergents. Cutting oils are of various types, although straight petroleum and oils of animal origin are among the most common. To this group can be added the compounded oils, which have been developed for certain properties. Chief among these are the sulfurized oils that have proved highly successful in preventing the welding of chips to the cutting tool. It has been well established that sulfurized oils need to be selected for specific applications; in other words, there is no such thing as a general-purpose sulfurized oil.

Since machining requirements vary over a wide range of materials and energy input, it is necessary to study individual applications in order that proper coolants may be used. As the studies increase in scope, new items such as CO_2 and some types of wax have been introduced.

Chip Formation

The science of metal cutting has developed the facts on chip formation to the point where three basic types are classified; these classifications are recorded in the literature[3] and are accepted as basic, irrespective of the type of machining operation used—broaching, drilling, milling, turning, or any other.

In the process of metal cutting, energy input is spent in three ways: (1) the majority of the energy is converted into heat in the chip; (2) additional energy causes residual stresses in the chip and the workpiece; (3) about one-third of the energy is spent in friction of the chip rubbing against the tool.

The ability of the tool to form chips properly has a profound effect upon tool life as does the interface temperature between the tool and the chip. A proper coolant can be of great help in this connection, since its lubricating qualities will aid in the reduction of friction. Another way to reduce temperature is to increase the shear angle, thereby lessening friction.

Type 1 Chip. This type, termed the discontinuous, or segmented, chip (Fig. 28-1), is commonly found in the machining of brittle metals such as gray cast iron. The chip consists of individual segments of varying size, which may or may not adhere to each other and which may leave the tool in the form of particles. Segments result from the actual fracturing of the metal ahead of the tool cutting edge. The surface quality on the workpiece is usually fair; long tool life and low power consumption are further characteristics. This chip type can also be obtained when ductile materials are machined at low speeds; such procedure is not conducive to long tool life, and a poor surface quality results.

[3] Ernst, Hans, and M. E. Merchant: "Chip Formation, Friction and Finish," Cincinnati Milling Machine Co., Cincinnati, 1941.

Type 2 Chip. This classification refers to the continuous chip without built-up tool edge (Fig. 28-2). It is the ideal chip to obtain when machining ductile metals. The chip is formed by the continuing deformation of the metal ahead of the tool without fracture and is accompanied by smooth flow of the chip over the tool face. It results in an excellent surface on the workpiece. This chip is best obtained when machining at high speeds. On brass, this chip can be obtained at practically any cutting speed. It does pose the problem of chip disposal; this drawback can be overcome by grinding a groove, termed a *chip breaker*, on the face of

Fig. 28-1. Type 1 chip: discontinuous or segmented chip. (Courtesy of Cincinnati Milling and Grinding Machines Co., Cincinnati.)

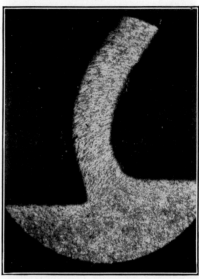

Fig. 28-2. Type 2 chip: continuous chip without built-up tool edge. (Courtesy of Cincinnati Milling and Grinding Machines Co., Cincinnati.)

the cutting tool. Attention must be given to this detail as a safety precaution for the operator.

Type 3 Chip. The basic characteristic in this classification is a continuous chip formed with built-up tool edge (Fig. 28-3). In effect this chip is similar to type 2 except for the built-up tool edge, which is a mass of metal that adheres to the tool face. This mass is formed as the result of high resistance to sliding of the chip along the tool face. The mass increases in size until it becomes unstable under the influence of the cutting pressure, when a part or all of the mass may break away. A part of the broken-off built-up edge may pass over the cutting edge into the work, resulting in a rough surface. The built-up edge, as shown in the type 3 chip, is one cause of rapid tool wear. The pieces which are built up and then slough off are extremely abrasive and increase wear substantially. It is conceded that the chief cause of surface roughness can be traced to built-up edge effect. The elimination of this difficulty is achieved by reducing the high frictional resistance between the chip and the tool edge. Regardless of chip classification, the fundamental mechanism of metal cutting in machining is the same; differing results are traceable to material composition and to tool behavior in the given job.

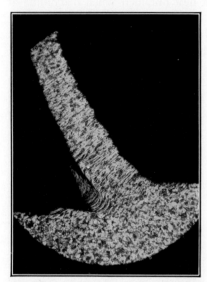

Fig. 28-3. Type 3 chip; continuous chip with built-up tool edge. (Courtesy of Cincinnati Milling and Grinding Machines Co., Cincinnati.)

SINGLE-POINT TOOLS

A single-point tool is a cutting tool for use in a lathe, turret lathe, planer, shaper, boring mill, or other machine having one face and one continuous cutting edge which produces the machined surface.[4] Such a tool can either be made in one piece, with the cutting edge an extension of the shank, or it may be in the form of a bit that is clamped in a toolholder. In either case the actual cutting face may be in the form of an inserted tip; in some special cases the cutting tip may be built up by welding through the use of a weld rod of desired composition. Tool bits offer the advantage of ease of interchangeability and low cost.

Single-point Tool Designations

In Fig. 28-4 is shown standard terminology. Adoption of this method of designation will do much to eliminate the misunderstandings that frequently occur in tool design. The tool bit shown is a right-cut one suitable for turning soft steel. The magnitude of the elements of the tool bit as shown in the key is established for a particular usage. The functions of these elements are outlined in the following paragraphs.

Rake Angles. These angles include back rake and side rake. The back rake angle lies between the face of a tool and a line parallel to the base of the holder. Positive rake exists when the face slopes downward from

[4] American Standard B5.22—1950, American Society of Mechanical Engineers, New York.

the point toward the shank; if the slope is reversed, the tool has negative back rake. The side rake angle lies between the face of the tool and a line parallel to its base.

The rake angles exert a greater effect on the cutting efficiency of a metal-cutting tool than any other angles. Their combined effect is to

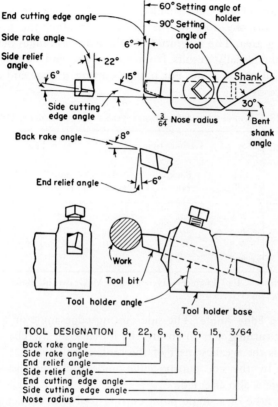

Fig. 28-4. Single-point tool designations showing a tool bit in a 30° left-bent shank and 15° tool-bit angle toolholder. (From American Standard B5.22—1950, American Society of Mechanical Engineers, New York.)

facilitate the flow of the chip over the face of the tool and also to influence the shear angle. Rake angles for cemented carbide tools are generally of lower magnitude than high-speed-steel cutting tools. The brittle nature of cemented carbides necessitates rigid support for the cutting edge. Negative back rake tends to absorb impact loads resulting from interrupted cuts.

Relief Angles. Relief angles provide the necessary clearance to permit the tool to enter the work. In the absence of relief angles, the tool would merely abrade the workpiece. Relief angles should be held to a minimum in order to prevent weakening the cutting edge. Generally speaking, relief angles from 5 to 10° are satisfactory; the exact amount depends on the diameter of the workpiece as well as the feed and cutting tool material (Table 28-1).

End Cutting Edge Angle. This angle is measured between the cutting edge on the end of the tool and a line normal to the side edge of the straight portion of the tool shank. It should be held to a minimum in order to support the nose of the tool and conduct the heat from the critical cutting area. The magnitude of these angles ranges between 8 and 15°. Chattering usually results from having the end cutting edge angle either too small or too large. For plunge cutting, a large end cutting edge angle is a necessity.

TABLE 28-1. REPRESENTATIVE SINGLE-POINT TOOL ANGLES, DEGREES*

Material	Carbide tips			High-speed steel		
	Side relief	Back rake	Side rake	Side relief	Back rake	Side rake
AISI 1020	6–8	0	3	12	16.5	14
Cast iron	6–8	0–4	2–4	10	5	12
Al alloy	6–8	10–20	10–20	12	35	15
Cu alloy	6–8	0	4	10	0	0–4

* Abstracted from "Tool Engineers Handbook," McGraw-Hill Book Company, Inc., New York, 1949.

Side Cutting Edge Angle. The side cutting edge angle on a single-point tool used for turning acts to absorb the initial load, thereby relieving the nose, which is the weakest part of the tool, of this shock. Chip thickness is controlled by the side cutting edge angle, and chip distribution over the entire edge is also effected.

Nose. The nose of a single-point cutting tool is critical, since it is generally the weakest part of the tool. It is actually an extension of the cutting edge and as such is called upon to dissipate much of the heat generated by the cut. Since it is small, the tendency to overheat and break down is always present. The quality of the finished surface is largely dependent upon the shape of the tool nose. In some instances a sharp point is desirable because of its ability to minimize chatter. A rounded nose makes for a stronger tool and one more capable of withstanding the heat generated by the cutting action.

Single-point Tool Types. There are many classifications of single-point tools, based on tool shape or specialized application. Among those best known are radial tools, straight tools, goose-necked tools, roughing and finishing tools, curved cutting edge tools, square-nosed tools, dove-tailing tools, cutoff or parting tools, boring tools, knurling tools, form tools, radius tools, skiving tools, and recessing tools. Life tests for single-point tools are established in American Standard B5.19—1953.[5]

CUTTING TOOL MATERIALS

High-speed Steel

The principal alloying elements are tungsten and molybdenum, along with chromium, vanadium, and sometimes cobalt. These elements impart the property of red-hardness, which means that when these steels are correctly heat-treated, they retain their original hardness at temperatures at which they approach visible redness.

Carbon content governs the initial hardness of high-speed steel; the alloying elements develop properties other than hardness. A range of from 0.65 to 0.80 per cent carbon gives the best combination of hardness, cutting ability, and resistance to shock. Shock resistance is best met with lower carbon contents; dies, punches, and similar impact-type tools are made from such steels. Cutting tools requiring high hardness, such as tool bits used where length of tool life and cutting ability are of paramount importance, are made from high-carbon, high-speed steels.

Designations. High-speed steels are generally designated by a ratio, as 18:4:1; the analysis corresponding to this ratio is 17 to 19 per cent tungsten, 3.5 to 4.5 per cent chromium, and 0.75 to 1.25 per cent vanadium. This particular type, along with 18:4:2 and 14:4:2, is most popular.

High-speed tool steels are being designated by code numbers sponsored by the Joint Industry Conference, known as the JIC. With this codification, analyses can be expected to follow rather definite patterns. It is possible, for example, by using the JIC code number, to specify cobalt-tungsten 18-4-2-8 as T-5, which is a decided simplification.

High-speed Steel Tools. Every category of cutting tool used in the machine shop is obtainable in high-speed steel. The range extends from taps to broaches and from tool bits to hobs. Such tools are purchased ready for use, although high-speed steel is also obtainable as bar stocks and blanks as well as extended sections of every conceivable geometry. Fully heat-treated high-speed steel will show a working hardness of Rockwell C 62-65 and a compressive stress approximating 400,000 psi.

In an endeavor to increase high-speed steel tool life, a post-treating process using steam has been developed. It is accomplished in a furnace which circulates steam by forced convection, resulting in the deposition of a porous oxide film (Fe_3O_4) on the tool surfaces. The film is tightly adherent and is 0.0001 in. thick and blue-black in color. It affords cor-

[5] American Society of Mechanical Engineers, New York.

rosion resistance and is of sufficient porosity to retain cutting oil successfully. Some substantially increased tool life has been reported by this
treatment; it is applied to all styles of high-speed tools, such as taps, drills,
broaches, milling cutters, and others.

Cast Alloys

There is a series of materials employed for metal-cutting tools that is
produced entirely by casting. The range of analysis includes 25 to 35
per cent CR, 4 to 25 per cent W, 6 to 20 per cent Mo, 1 to 3 per cent C;

Fig. 28-5. Turning steel with cast-alloy cutting tools. (Courtesy of Crucible Steel Company
of America, New York.)

Mn and Si are always present as deoxidizers. Additives such as Va, B, Ta,
and Co are present in some types. Considerable interest is being displayed
in tool bits of these cast-alloy tools, which are available in ground-bit
and ground-tipped tool types. They have strengths above the high-speed
steels, and a hardness of Rockwell C 60-62. Such tools are, generally
speaking, intermediate between high-speed steels and cemented carbides
in application as well as initial cost. An example of the application of
cast-alloy tool bits is shown in Fig. 28-5.

Cemented Carbides

A most significant advance in cutting tool materials has been provided by cemented, or sintered, carbides. These materials were originally

developed for use in drawing lamp filament wire where diamond dies had previously been used. This development occurred between 1920 and 1930; improved compositions and manufacturing methods have continued to broaden the scope of cemented carbide applications (Fig. 28-6). The use of cemented carbides is not confined to cutting tools but

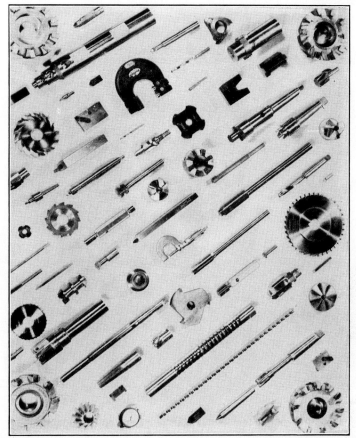

Fig. 28-6. Selection of tools and component parts made from cemented carbide. (Courtesy of Metallurgical Products Division, General Electric Co., Detroit.)

holds interest in the machine shop for components requiring extreme hardness and wear resistance, such as lathe centers, micrometer anvils, gage points, and others.

Cemented carbides are classified on the basis of their chemical composition. The largest grouping, known as the CQ series, is composed of W, C, and Co. The other classifications refer to those containing Ti, Ta, and Cb in addition to tungsten carbide and cobalt in a variety of formulations. Since there are a number of cemented carbide producers, a system of product identification has been developed wherein specific analysis within a given series is delineated. In the CQ series, identification number CQ1 refers to 88.25 W, 5.75 C, and 6.0 Co.

It is obvious that from the extensive array of carbides now available every conceivable type of machining can be met. In addition, these materials are also making vital contributions in many other areas, such as combatting surface wear, impact resistance, corrosion resistance, high-temperature service, deflection, deformation, and resistance to galling

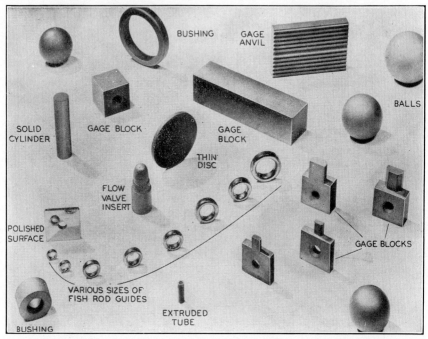

Fig. 28-7. Cemented carbide components for diverse applications. (Courtesy of Metallurgical Products Division, General Electric Co., Detroit.)

(Fig. 28-7). It is paramount that the proper grade be selected for a given application.

Processing. The manufacture of cemented carbides is similar for all types. The carbides are generally formed by heating a mixture of tungsten oxide or powder with a measured amount of carbon powder, such as lampblack, in a hydrogen atmosphere; there are other methods of forming carbides as well. The carbides are then crushed, milled, and screened in powdered form. The cobalt constituent, which is the binder material, is likewise prepared as a powder.

The selected ingredients for a given composition are pressed into the desired end product shape. This procedure takes a number of forms, including a unique one wherein a powder charge is set off in a sealed chamber as means of pressure development. Following the forming operations, the blanks, which are usually soft, on the order of graphite in a lead pencil, are then placed in a furnace and sintered in vacuum.

Cemented Carbide Cutting Tools. Cemented carbide tipped tool bits are so generally used that the insert blanks, or tips, have been standardized.[6] Sintered tips are generally brazed to suitable tool-bit shanks (Fig. 28-8). However, this procedure is not limited to such tools; milling cutters,

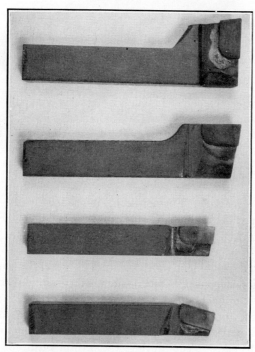

Fig. 28-8. Cemented carbide tipped lathe tool bits of several designs. Note that carbide insert is brazed to the tool bit.

twist drills, broaches, and many others, including mining and woodworking tools, are built in a similar manner. Copper is frequently used as a braze metal because of its relatively high melting point. An innovation is eliminating the tool bit as such and clamping the carbide pieces directly in a specially designed holder (Fig. 28-9), of which there are several types. There are distinct advantages connected with this method of holding the carbide; no machining is necessary for fitting the insert to the shank, nor is a brazing operation required. Grinding is done less frequently, since the carbide inserts can be indexed several times before

[6] American Standard B5.36—1957, American Society of Mechanical Engineers, New York.

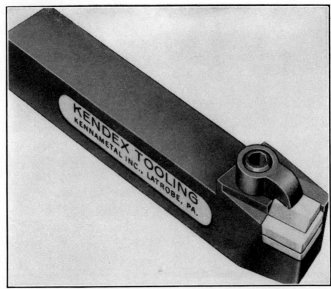

Fig. 28-9. Kendex tool with spare button insert showing chip breaker and clamp. (Courtesy of Kennametal, Inc., Latrobe, Pa.)

regrinding is necessary. Furthermore, it is frequently economically feasible to discard the carbide insert when drilled.

Ceramics

In any new development, nomenclature is generally confusing. This situation applies here since terms such as ceramic oxides, cemented oxides, cermets, and ceramics are used. It seems more nearly accurate to refer to these tools as oxide rather than ceramic. In the tools under discussion, the particles or crystals are held together solely by grain growth, which takes place during the manufacture of the material. There is no binder addition as in cemented carbides. Aluminum oxide in the form of microscopic crystals under 7 microns is necessary in order to develop high density in the tools. The oxide is highly inert chemically and has no tendency to weld to common metals; further, it gives complete resistance to oxidation at elevated temperatures.

Advantages of Ceramic Oxide Tooling. These tools have been in use and under investigation for quite some time, resulting in the developing of considerable experience. Superiority for ceramic tools has been claimed as follows: (1) They machine faster than with carbides; (2) for a given metal volume removal there is less wear than with carbides, and less down time; (3) they machine a wide variety of materials, doing both roughing and finishing operations; (4) they cut hardened steels that carbides cannot; (5) they give a superior finish—in many cases the grinding can be eliminated (Fig. 28-10); (6) there is no tendency to weld or to form a built-up edge; (7) ceramic tools do not require a coolant.

Cutting Tool Design. Ceramic tools are stronger in compression than in tension. In consequence, tools should be ground so that maximum cutting forces are in compression. Negative rake augmented by a heavy negative land in the leading edge is considered the best tool geometry. Ceramics cannot be brazed as satisfactorily as can carbides, which means that a clamp-type toolholder is usually employed. Ceramic tools are mainly

Fig. 28-10. Finishing cut with oxide tool. (Courtesy of the Sintox Corp., Allentown, Pa.)

used in the form of throwaway inserts; since extreme rigidity is desirable, a thicker insert proves best. The geometry of the inserts shows triangles, squares, cubes, or circles. Chip breakers are advisable here as with other single-point cutting tools.

Operating Conditions. Inasmuch as improvements are being offered continually, there are no fixed values for cutting speeds. There seems to be little point in publishing tables for speeds and feeds which are obsolescent in an extremely short time. Because of the absence of welding during turning, much less heat is generated than with carbides; as a result, ceramics operate at higher cutting speeds. Another factor is the ability of these tools to withstand high temperatures. As a result, ceramics are operated at from two to ten times the speed of carbide. An average value would place the cutting range somewhere between 1,000 and 1,500 fpm.

Insofar as feeds and depths of cut are concerned, it has been suggested that for clamp-type tools the depth of cut be 0.150 in. and the feed be 0.015 in. per revolution. The usual precautions are important in that these tools do not perform well in intermittent cuts, nor can standard performance be expected from machine tools that lack rigidity. Ceramic tools can be ground; however, certain precautions are necessary. It is essential to use bonded diamond abrasive wheels, with the grinding being done under coolant.

It is evident that ceramic oxide tools are capable of increasing production rates, which means, of course, decreased costs. Since these tools continue under development, some little time will be required before their adoption becomes widespread and their abilities become known. The cost of ceramic tool bits is relatively modest, which should help in getting these tools adopted to production programs.

Diamond-tipped Tools

Because of their extreme hardness, diamonds are used to advantage as specialized metal-cutting tools. They are difficult to mount and will chip or fracture under certain conditions of interrupted cutting. Their outstanding ability to hold size and finish for an extended production run makes them especially valuable for boring and finishing nonferrous and nonmetallic engineering materials.

ULTRASONIC MACHINING

This is a dependable and practical method for shaping hard materials quickly and economically to close dimensional tolerances and surface finishes. The actual cutting is performed by abrasive grains that are carried in a recirculated liquid that flows between the workpiece and the tool. Ultrasonic machining employs the same abrasive types and grit sizes used in commercial grinding wheels. The principal abrasives are aluminum oxide, boron carbide, and silicon carbide. A tool stroke of a few thousandths of an inch, oscillating linearly approximately 20,000 times/sec, drives the abrasive grains. The shape of the tool develops or governs the exact bombardment pattern of the grit against the workpiece. The extremely rapid motion of the tool face produces cavitation of the abrasive liquid, driving the abrasive grains against the workpiece. The turbulent action also serves as a pump, producing a circulation of the liquid for washing out the minutely cut particles. The high velocity with which the grit bombards the workpiece machines away microscopic particles without perceptible heat. The equipment, termed Cavitron, used for this method is shown in Fig. 28-11. It consists essentially of an electronic generator that converts 110- or 220-volt 60-cycle alternating current to high-frequency power. The transducer converts electrical energy into mechanical energy, causing the tool to oscillate linearly at ultrasonic frequencies. The maximum workpiece diameter that can be machined in a single cut is determined by the power output of the generator and the transducer.

Tooling for Ultrasonics. Alloy steel is the preferable tool material, although brass and hard copper are satisfactory on some applications. The shape of the form tool must mate the surface to be machined; there is practically no limitation on the profile. Tool size is governed by the degree of accuracy and the type of finish required. The cutting tool is usually mounted to the toolholder by brazing, but occasionally it may

Fig. 28-11. Cavitron, the ultrasonic machine tool, showing electronic generator at left and transducer as the machine head. (Courtesy of The Sheffield Corp., Dayton, Ohio.)

be held mechanically. Machining rates are governed by the hardness or density of the workpiece material, as well as the coarseness of the abrasive grains. Tool cross-sectional area is limited by the power capacity of the transducer. These units are built in several capacities, the largest capable of machining a hole 3½ in. in diameter; sizes range down to 0.006 in. in diameter.

Finish and Accuracy. The precision and finish of ultrasonic machined surfaces depends on the size and finish of the tools as well as the abrasive. In roughing operations, a 25 microinch finish may be obtained with 280 grit. Tolerances of 0.002 in. are generally obtained with 280 grit and tolerances of 0.0005 in. or better may be obtained with finer abrasives as secondary operations. Maximum precision and finish are obtained by the use of more than one tool and more than one grit size for any individual profile cut.

The different basic types of machining that can be performed include drilling, tapping, broaching, shaving, slicing, dicing, and engraving. The materials that can be machined include ceramics, gem stones, ferrite, aluminum oxide, glass, and many others. Ultrasonic machining is accomplished on probably the safest type of machine tool, since there are no hazardous moving parts or exposed electrical circuits.

MACHINING PERFORMANCE

Research on chip formation has resulted in shifting the machining of metal from an art to a science. Continuing study is providing further knowledge of machining fundamentals. In order to secure the best possible results in machining, it is imperative that the cutting tool be correctly ground both as to keenness and surface finish, and that it be rigidly supported in its machine. Heat generated by the machining action must be minimized and dissipated rapidly.

SURVEY QUESTIONS

28-1. Define the term "machine tool."

28-2. What is a cutting tool?

28-3. Who was the pioneer in research on metal cutting?

28-4. What was his connection with the American Society of Mechanical Engineers?

28-5. To what does the Taylor-White Process relate?

28-6. In what areas will hot machining be of significance?

28-7. Who developed the theory of metal shear in connection with cutting tool action?

28-8. Why is the selection of a cutting fluid of fundamental importance?

28-9. What is the basic material in cutting fluid?

28-10. Explain the term "soluble oil."

28-11. How is CO_2 being used in the machine shop?

28-12. Which of the three chip types gives the greatest difficulty with tool wear?

28-13. How are tool bits mounted in a lathe?

28-14. List six angles that must be correct in a properly ground single-point lathe tool.

28-15. To what does the designation 18:4:1 refer?

28-16. Wherein does the heat-treatment of high-speed differ from plain carbon steel tools?

28-17. Should the cast-alloy metal-cutting tools be considered as ferrous materials?

28-18. Give the composition of at least one of these types.

28-19. Mention some of the attributes of cemented carbide materials.

28-20. Is there any difference in grinding cemented carbide single-point tools as compared with high-speed steel tool bits?

28-21. What are ceramic tools?

28-22. Give at least two advantages for ceramic tooling.

28-23. How do ceramic tools compare with carbides from the viewpoint of cutting speeds?

28-24. Is there any difficulty in using diamond-tipped tools?

28-25. In what area does ultrasonic machining apply?

28-26. Is the equipment used in ultrasonic machining similar to standard machine tools?

28-27. How does ultrasonic machining compare in cost with other methods?

28-28. What would be the correct tool material for machining a diesel crankshaft cast from ductile iron?

Chapter 29

MEASURING

Not all components that are used in engineering manufacture have machine-finished surfaces. There are other methods for developing suitable surfaces, as shown in Fig. 26-20 (page 493). When a design can use another method, thereby eliminating machining, lower manufacturing costs will result. Machining a component requires a second operation with its consequent cost increase. It should be the objective of designers and manufacturing personnel to eliminate second operations in the interests of economy. To this end such concepts as die castings, no-draft forgings, and extrusions should be given greater consideration because of their potential for providing functional surfaces.

The objective of every machining operation is that of bringing an end product to dimension or to a desired surface condition or both. A finished machined component is one that meets specifications as to dimensions and surface quality alike. Surface quality was discussed in Chap. 26; measurements will be surveyed here.

It is the duty of the design department to establish the desired degree of accuracy and to convey these requirements to the production department. The best means of securing accuracy is coordination between these departments. There is no point in specifying accuracy that is either impossible or too costly to achieve. Frequently the machine tool equipment necessary to produce the requested accuracy is not available; then, too, the specified precision may be beyond the requirements of the end product, resulting in unnecessarily high cost. With the increased use of standards for fits, surfaces, and quality, carelessness in dimension design should be eliminated. In this connection it is suggested that "Limits and Fits for Engineering and Manufacturing"[1] be consulted for standard dimensioning procedures in order to develop uniform practices throughout the engineering industries. If such uniformity were achieved, much

[1] American Standard B46.1—1955, American Standards Association, New York.

of the confusion that inevitably accompanies contract manufacturing would be eliminated and absolute interchangeability of competitively manufactured products would be established.

Variability. There can be no such thing as an absolute dimension in manufacturing. In recognition of this situation, tolerances are, or should be, included in every precision measurement. Tolerances are necessary to overcome the variability that is inherent in all phases of manufacturing. Materials vary in composition and properties; machine tools are subject to the vagaries resulting from temperature changes during prolonged operation as well as to deterioration from usage. Cutting tool behavior is the greatest single source of dimension variability, since tool wear and tool slippage are constant occurrences. Obviously, artisanship is a variable quality. Regardless of how well a design is conceived and prepared, it must be processed, and therein lie the problems of manufacturing.

Measurement Levels. The degree of precision that is necessary for the proper functioning of a particular component must be recognized by the designer. There are several approaches to, or available means of, making measurements. It is desirable to establish some arbitrary classifications in order that measuring instruments, equipment, and tools can be studied. Common usage divides measurements at three levels, viz., non-precision, semi-precision, and precision.

Another classification of dimensional measuring is a grouping by method; a distinction is made as between direct measurements on the one hand and comparative measurements on the other. Direct measurements are made on the workpiece in order to determine its actual dimensions and size. A direct measurement involves the human equation, since the recorded result is obtained by reading or interpretation.

Comparative measurement means that the dimension under consideration is compared with a standard. This method of measurement is highly regarded for inspection purposes in production manufacture. It is capable of producing accurate results provided the measuring equipment is maintained at a high level of precision: any comparison is only as trustworthy as the accuracy of the standard of comparison.

Emphasis is necessary in the matter of the accuracy of the measuring equipment. *Never take the accuracy of any measuring equipment for granted.* It is always sound procedure to check the zero reading, or similar features, of any measuring equipment prior to employing it for dimensional measuring. The higher the level of precision desired, the more important this precaution becomes. That industry recognizes this necessity is shown by the use of such devices as periodic checking against standards and of constant-temperature workrooms, where precision fits for guaranteed interchangeability are produced. Gaging rooms are held at constant temperature and humidity conditions as a means of eliminating variability and of increasing precision.

DIRECT MEASUREMENTS

Every toolmaker and machinist equips himself with a complement of precision measuring tools as his "tools of the trade." The extent of this tool collection is usually in direct proportion to his skill, since as his ability grows he is called upon for an increasing diversity of performance. In recognition of this situation, a wide range of standard and special measuring equipment is available. Some of the basic types will be reviewed here since a knowledge of their uses is fundamental to the student of engineering manufacture.

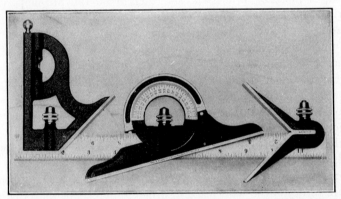

Fig. 29-1. Combination set with 12-in. blade, combination stock, center head, and reversible protractor head. (Courtesy of The L. S. Starrett Co., Athol, Mass.)

Steel Rules. The basic measuring tool is a steel rule, frequently termed a scale. Rules are available in individual lengths from 1 to 72 in. The face of the rule is marked with graduations along each of its four edges. Graduation marks varying from 0.0005 to 0.010 in. in width are either etched or milled into the rule, which is made of heat-treated steel. The four scales on a steel rule follow a series of graduation designations. A rule equipped with no. 4 graduation means that the scales on that rule are graduated into 64ths, 32ds, 16ths, and 8ths of an inch, respectively. Many combinations are available, including fractions and hundredths in addition to metric scales.

Steel rules are available in several designs including flexible, stainless, end graduated, shrink, pocket, hook, and others. A favorite type for general shop measurements is one that is grooved longitudinally on one face. This groove is used as a guide for the several heads that can be clamped to the rule, which acts as a blade (Fig. 29-1). The most versatile of these accessories is the combination head, which when clamped to the blade forms a square. The other leg of the head provides a 45° angle and the head also has a level that can be used for checking vertical as well as horizontal surfaces. The combination head can be clamped at a graduation to mark off a fixed distance for gaging purposes when setting an inside caliper. Another accessory shown in Fig. 29-1 is termed a center head. It is used to locate the center of round bar stock on any relatively true circular workpiece. The legs of the head are tangent to the circle and, since the blade bisects the leg angle, its edge passes through the center of the circle. It is only necessary to scribe two

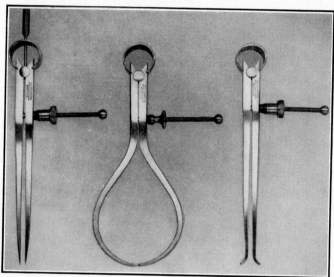

Fig. 29-2. Spring divider, outside spring caliper, and inside spring caliper. (Courtesy of The L. S. Starrett Co., Athol, Mass.)

lines on the circle at different positions; their intersection is the center of that circle. A reversible protractor is also available for clamping to the blade. Double protractors and inclinometers are other useful accessories. However, the conventional combination set consists of a combination head, or stock, a center head, and a reversible protractor head. This set is indispensable for layout work in the toolroom or die shop, as it is for direct measurements in machining operations.

Calipers. An outside caliper measures outside diameters, while the inside type is used for measuring bores and hole diameters. Such calipers are usually made with a spring joint (Fig. 29-2), but there are two additional styles, known as the firm-joint (in this, friction holds the caliper setting) and the lock-joint (held by means of a locking screw). There is considerable skill required to make an accurate reading with a spring-joint caliper. The user must develop a "feel" for the caliper. Since the joint has a spring and the caliper legs are not stiff, it is possible to force a caliper over a workpiece even though its setting is too small. The setting should be such that the weight of the caliper will just carry its points over the workpiece without any effort on the part of the mechanic. An outside caliper is read by placing one leg against the end of an accurate steel rule and reading the rule graduation at the other leg point.

Inside calipers are distinguished by the fact that their leg points face outward. They are inserted in the bore or hole and the adjusting nut is loosened until the leg points contact the wall. Here again a delicate sense of feel is necessary for accurate measurement. After a caliper has been adjusted to the hole diameter, its setting is read by placing it on a steel rule. Both rule and caliper leg can be placed against a finished surface as a means of alignment, or the combination stock can be set at a full inch blade graduation, one caliper point placed against it, and the measurement read at the other caliper leg point.

A workpiece should never be calipered while it is rotating; inaccurate readings will result, and there is danger of accident. Another precaution is that of placing the caliper exactly normal to the workpiece surface. If a caliper is accidentally dropped, its setting should be rechecked immediately.

Several other styles of calipers are available, including thread, Yankee thread, keyhole, transfer type, forging, double, and hermaphrodite—the last with one leg as a divider point and the other resembling an inside caliper leg. Dividers are generally included as a tool related to calipers. All the calipers mentioned thus far depend upon the ability of the user for accuracy of measurement and are not considered precision measuring instruments.

Micrometer Calipers. The best-known and most generally used precision direct-measuring tool is the micrometer caliper. It is available in many styles and also in outside and inside types. The measuring principle is the same for all. They are graduated to give readings in one-thousandths of an inch; when equipped with a vernier, readings are made to ten-thousandths.

Outside micrometer calipers are generally made to cover a range of 1 in. (Fig. 29-3). The small size reads from 0 to 1 in. and the next size from 1 to 2 in., which means that the zero reading for the 1- to 2-in. size is at 1 in. An exception to this design is the tubular frame micrometer caliper. It has several spindles that can be inserted to cover a wide range of diameters.

The micrometer principle of measuring has been in use for approximately a century. The micrometer caliper is almost universally referred to as a "mike." This instrument consists of a C frame that is usually a forging. The fixed measuring surface, termed the anvil, is located inside the outer frame end. The movable measuring surface is the end of the spindle, which is threaded at its opposite end and attached to the thimble. The micrometer barrel has graduations on its outer surface and is equipped with a spindle nut in its bore. As the thimble is turned, the spindle advances or retracts, depending on the direction of thimble rotation.

The principle of measurement is based on the fact that the spindle thread has a pitch of $\frac{1}{40}$ in., which equals the decimal fraction of 0.025

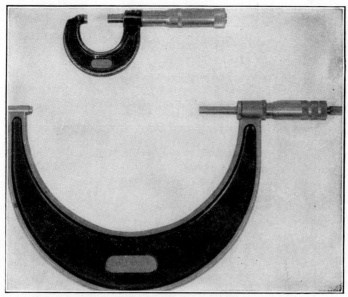

Fig. 29-3. Outside micrometer calipers. Upper view shows caliper with 0- to 1-in. range while lower one has a 5- to 6-in. range and is equipped with ratchet stop.

in. Turning the thimble one revolution advances the spindle 0.025 in. The barrel is graduated, with each mark thereon representing one revolution of the thimble, i.e., 0.025 in. Every fourth graduation, $0.025 \times 4 = 0.100$ in., carries a digit starting from zero. The micrometer reading in *tenths* can be made by noting the highest digit uncovered on the barrel. Each uncovered graduation beyond the digit equals 0.025 in. If three graduations are uncovered, for example, the reading equals the number of tenths plus 3×0.025 in. $= 0.075$ in. However, a full space graduation is rarely encountered; usually a fractional space results. This is read directly from the thimble edge, whose periphery is divided into 25 equal spaces, each one totaling 0.001 in. In order, therefore, to make a micrometer reading, it is necessary to read the highest full number uncovered on the barrel scale, add the number of *full* spaces between that number and the thimble edge, and finally add the number of spaces on the thimble scale for the total reading (Fig. 29-4).

There is possibility for error, since varying pressure can be applied when bringing the spindle into contact with the workpiece. This difficulty is solved by placing a ratchet at the outer end of the spindle. Another design that provides accurate readings is shown in Fig. 29-5. This micrometer caliper employs a built-in dial indicator as a means of

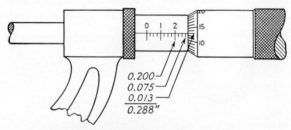

Fig. 29-4. Micrometer caliper reading.

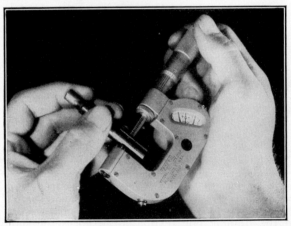

Fig. 29-5. Indicating micrometer caliper. (Courtesy of Federal Products Corp., Providence, R.I.)

eliminating human error and pressure variations. The micrometer shown is also equipped with a vernier, thereby giving readings accurate to within 0.0001 in. Regardless of type or style, a micrometer caliper will only read accurately when it is in proper adjustment. Prior to using a micrometer *always check its zero reading with a gage block or other standard measure.*

Types of Micrometer Calipers. Because of its precision, the micrometer caliper has been adapted to fit many varied applications. Thread micrometers are commonly used for measuring screw threads. Some of the specialized ones include hub, tube, paper gage, sheet metal, inspector's gage, and depth types. Micrometer calipers are also available in direct reading styles.

Vernier Calipers. Vernier tools are precision measuring instruments capable of a degree of accuracy on the order of 0.001 in. The vernier is named after Pierre Vernier, by whom it was invented in 1631. The vernier caliper (Fig. 29-6) is not as commonly used in America as it is in Europe, since the micrometer has greater appeal here. The vernier is used with a scale that is graduated into 40ths, or 0.025ths of an inch.

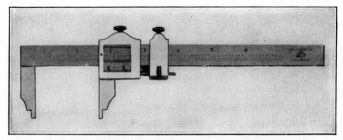

Fig. 29-6. Vernier caliper graduated for English measure.

Fig. 29-7. Dial gages and dial indicators of various styles and calibrations.

The vernier has 25 divisions which are numbered at every fifth division and which equal, in extreme length, 24 divisions on the scale or 24×0.025 in. $= 0.600$ in. Therefore, one division on the vernier equals $\frac{1}{25}$ of 0.600 in. $= 0.024$ in. This results in a difference of 0.001 in. between a division on the vernier and a division on the scale.

Dial Gages. Dial gages are direct-reading instruments whose application is always associated with precision measurements. Dial gages are used in a great variety of indicators and other instruments for measuring and checking. In order to meet these varied requirements, dial gages are built in several styles (Fig. 29-7) and in different calibrations. Dial gages carry either 0.001-, 0,0005-, or 0.0001-in. calibrations. The scales on the dials can be had in various styles and arrangements, and it is usual to have movable dials which permit zero alignment. The utility of dial gages is not limited to measurement, since they are reliable for checking workpiece setups and alignment. A further application is that of checking the accuracy of machine tools on spindle concentricity and bed-way alignment.

QUALITY CONTROL GAGING

The means of controlling dimensions in production belong to the province of gaging. There are a number of gaging systems and, as noted later in the chapter, there are many different types of gages available. Basically, however, the gaging falls into three categories which are referred to as pre-process gaging, in-process gaging, and post-process gaging. This concept includes more than merely the physical method of manipulating the gage, since gaging can be tied in with the actual machining process. When this is done and the machine is tooled or equipped with feedback control, such rigging is beamed toward automatic production.

Pre-process gaging, as it applies in feedback control, refers primarily to the positioning of the workpiece prior to the machining operation, which, in some instances, includes surface preparation. Such procedure fits in closely with some subject matter in Chap. 18. The axial positioning on the table is frequently referred to as "flagging."

In-process gaging means exactly what the term implies, *i.e.*, gaging is done while the component is in process. This gaging concept continuously measures the workpiece during its entire machining cycle. When it is used in connection with feedback control, of course, it functions to initiate the correction of any errors that are revealed.

Post-process gaging refers to inspection gaging of the component after it has been finish-machined. Obviously, this has a dual objective: in the first place, it is a matter of quality control, and secondly, it serves as a means of machine control. Any discrepancy that post-process gaging uncovers can immediately be corrected in the machine setup. Taken together then, these gaging categories are of basic importance in developing control, both dimensionally and in the process itself. Quality control depends upon such vigilance for its effectiveness.

COMPARATIVE MEASUREMENTS

Precision and high-precision measurements are usually made by comparative means. The actual measurement resolves itself into a deviation from the selected standard measure. For genuine interchangeability, the same basic standard should be employed throughout all industry.

Gage Blocks. The idea of a gage block, as a *precision standard*, was conceived by C. E. Johansson, who produced the first set in Sweden in 1896. The 81 individual blocks that comprise a standard set are generally made from AISI 52100 steel that has been suitably finished, hardened, and stabilized (Fig. 29-8). An innovation is the production

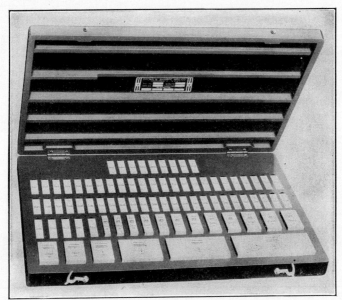

Fig. 29-8. A set of Johansson gage blocks containing 81 individual blocks. (Courtesy of Brown & Sharpe Manufacturing Co., Providence, R.I.)

of gage blocks of solid carbide. This construction is said to make the life of the block longer than that of the steel types. A standard set of 81 blocks as shown is made up of the following sizes:

One ten-thousandth series 0.1001–0.1009 in., inclusive—9 blocks
One-thousandth series 0.101–0.149 in., inclusive—49 blocks
Fifty-thousandth series 0.050–0.950 in., inclusive—19 blocks

This set makes it possible to develop dimensions in increments of 0.0001 in. from 0.100 to beyond 10 in. through combinations of suitably sized blocks.

Gage blocks, frequently termed jo-blocks, are produced by several sources, many of which have introduced design and manufacturing innovations. Gage blocks are generally made in decimal sizes, but there are fractional sizes available. The degree of precision varies with the different classifications, yet at 68°F class AA blocks have a tolerance of only ±0.000002 in. When such gage blocks are carefully wrung together, their cohesion is said to be more than thirty times that ascribable to atmospheric pressure.

Cylindrical Plug and Ring Gages. It is desirable to have standard

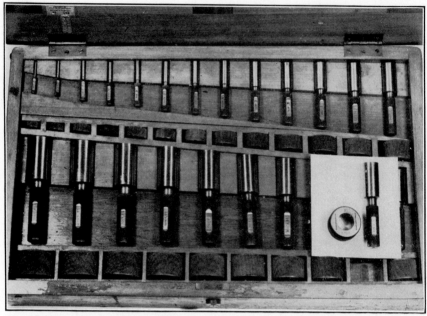

Fig. 29-9. A set of B & S plug and ring gages ranging from ⅛- to 1½-in. diameter by ¹⁄₁₆-in. increments. Note typical gage pair in insert. (Courtesy of Gaging Laboratory, University of Washington, Seattle, Wash.)

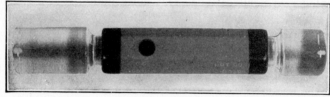

Fig. 29-10. Plug gage of "go" and "no go" type equipped with removable glass gaging members.

gages for circular measurements, since they will facilitate checking the working gages. In common with other precision gages, these are stabilized and have a high degree of accuracy at a working temperature of 68°F. The plug gage is used for gaging holes and bores, while the ring gage is for checking outside diameters (Fig. 29-9).

Plug and ring gages are conventional inspection tools. Formerly they were universally made of steel and suitably heat-treated and finished; for protection against hard usage or measurable wear, steel gages are frequently chromium-plated. An interesting innovation has been that of making the gaging members of glass (Fig. 29-10). The plug gage shown has both "go" and "no go" gaging members fitted with tapers in a plastic holder to make possible the replacement or renewal of the gaging members. The go and no go members are ground to meet the upper and lower tolerance limits.

Snap Gages. A snap gage has two sets of gaging points in tandem, so that it is possible to gage an outside diameter with a single motion of the

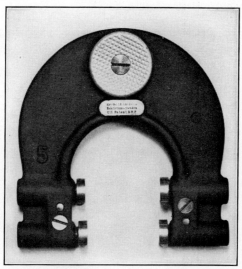

Fig. 29-11. Snap gage of the "go—no go" type that has a measuring range from 1.000 to 1.250 in.

hand, in contrast to the procedure with a plug gage, whose ends must be reversed. Snap gages are usually single styles so designed that the gaging points have a range of adjustment. Snap gages of this type are set by gage blocks to the sizes desired (Fig. 29-11). There are fixed snap gages that do not have the adjustable anvil feature. Design changes and innovations include a snap gage with dial attachment for reading exact diameters within the tolerance range.

Supermicrometers. This instrument is, in effect, a gaging machine of precision on the order of 0.0001 in. at 68°F (Fig. 29-12). It has a capacity range that permits the checking of components and gages in the range from 0 to 10 in. The gaging anvils are set by means of individual gages.

Fig. 29-12. Supermicrometer with four 1-in. circular gages in position. (Courtesy of Gaging Laboratory, University of Washington, Seattle, Wash.)

Fig. 29-13. Operator checking seven dimensions simultaneously on a special aircraft bolt in a Sigmatic gaging machine. (Courtesy of Pratt & Whitney Co., West Hartford, Conn.)

Visual Gages. There are numerous visual gage designs that are used primarily for parts inspection. The principle of operation varies with different design types. These instruments are commonly referred to as comparators. The upper gage point is lowered onto the part manually and the size deviation is read on the dial, which is graduated for both plus and minus tolerances. The basic dimension is set by means of standard gages. Another type of visual comparator employs a lighted scale for the readings. Instruments of this design are frequently termed electrolimit gages.

Multiple-reading Electric Gages. The gages in this classification have been developed for inspection work in mass-production industries. The

Fig. 29-14. A Precisionaire gage checks all eight bores on V-8 blocks in a single reading. In a simultaneous operation, this gage classifies and stamps all bore sizes, thereby permitting selective piston assembly. (Courtesy of The Sheffield Corp., Dayton, Ohio.)

basic feature of these gages is their capacity to measure accurately several dimensions simultaneously. There is some difference in their operating details as between different makes; however, as a rule, green and red lights are arranged to flash a go and no-go signal (Fig. 29-13).

Air Gages. Compressed air is employed in a series of gage designs that operate on two basic principles. One, known as the pressure type, is based on the idea of varying air pressures, while the other one, termed the flow type, operates with varying air velocities at constant pressure.

The latter principle has proved most adaptable owing to inherent advantages. When a column of air flows under constant pressure, it will have the same velocity at every point in its length. This feature gives this gage great flexibility, since the distance of the gaging spindle from the instrument is of no consequence.

Air gages have been expanded from the single unit for measuring bores to multiple units capable of several simultaneous measurements. In addition, gages of this design are used for checking straightness, squareness, parallelism, concentricity, bell mouthing, and other conditions. Their operation is fully automatic, and the readings are instantaneous (Fig. 29-14). They find wide adaption in production tooling.

PRECISION MEASUREMENTS

The necessity for accuracy in gages is fundamental to the program of interchangeability of parts manufacture. A master standard should be adopted by management, and all essential measuring tools, gages, and instruments should be calibrated to the established master standard. Such calibration is not difficult since it can readily be done by measurement with light rays through the use of optical flats in combination with a monochromatic light source.

Measurement with Light Rays. The equipment necessary for measuring with light rays consists of a set of optical flats, a set of master reference gages, and a source of monochromatic light. It is desirable to have a steel working flat available since it can be used for checking gages other than gage blocks, thereby preserving the optical flats.

Optical flats are flat disks made from fused quartz, pyrex, or clear white glass in a variety of diameters and thicknesses. The best thermal stability and wearing properties can be attained in the fused quartz flats. Only one face of the flat need be accurately flat, although the opposite face is made approximately parallel. Optical flats should be given extreme care both in use and storage in order to prevent scratches and nicks.

The light source used in this measuring method must be of a single wave length. A light bulb shielded by a special selenium diffusion glass is frequently used. The diffusion glass serves to cut out all the wave lengths of the violet, blue, green, yellow, and orange light. It transmits a red wave length whose equivalent measuring unit is 12.5 millionths of an inch per dark band, which equals 8 bands to the ten-thousandths inch.

The monochromatic light source is passed through an optical flat resting on a surface whose flatness is to be checked. When a deviation from absolute parallelism exists between the surface being checked and the optical flat, there will be interference between the light bands that will show as alternate light and dark spaces (Fig. 29-15). The number and shape of these alternate spaces accurately show the nature of the surface being examined.

When plug gages, for example, are checked, they are placed with a master standard of the desired dimension on a working flat. They are then covered with an optical flat and placed in the monochromatic light source for checking interference bands. The number of these bands is an accurate measure of the gage deviation from the master standard. Measurements made by this method are read in millionths of an inch. Temperature conditions must be constant at 68°F for effective control.

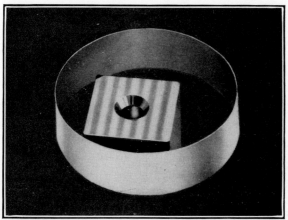

Fig. 29-15. Optical flat checking a Hoke gage block. The straight interference bands indicate true flatness. (Courtesy of Pratt & Whitney Co., West Hartford, Conn.)

Optical Measurement. The continuing requirement for greater precision has been met, in part, by the development of a high-precision coordinate measuring machine (Fig. 29-16). This new optical device offers a decided improvement in measuring technique since it is a direct-reading instrument, which eliminates errors associated with indirect measuring equipment. The machine is capable of precision measurements with an accuracy of 0.00005 in. It further allows the operator to take direct readings of 0.00005, 0.0001, 0.001, 0.01, 0.1, and 1 in., in one observation through the microscope. The machine is equipped with two microscopes suited for the two coordinates. The different measuring operations are illuminated by diascopic and episcopic illumination. The direct measurements possible with this machine are extremely reliable, very simple, and eliminate spindle and personal measuring error.

Spectroscopy. The accuracy of light-wave measurements in millionths of an inch can be exceeded. Developments indicate that the unit of measurement has been extended to angstroms. Since an angstrom unit is slightly less than 4 billionths of an inch, it is obvious that new concepts of precision are possible. The atomic pile has contributed a minute amount of special mercury that, when combined with a spectroscope and an interferometer, can measure to less than a billionth of an inch. This scientific development gives new and fuller meaning to precision measurements.

Radioisotopes. Mention was made in Chap. 1 of the potentialities of radioisotopes as measuring devices. This technique or science is developing continually to the point where there now are manufacturing gages

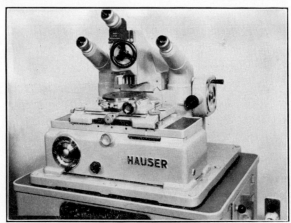

Fig. 29-16. Optical precision measuring machine. (Courtesy of Henri Hauser, Ltd., Bienne, Switzerland.)

employing the isotope principle. Some of these have been incorporated in production tooling. This development can be expected to increase and intensify as the techniques become better understood.

SURVEY QUESTIONS

29-1. Give an example of a second operation on a weldment.

29-2. Who should be responsible for the degree of accuracy on a machined part?

29-3. How is it possible to increase manufacturing costs through accuracy?

29-4. Mention some sources of variability in a forged piston.

29-5. Where are comparative measurements used?

29-6. How can the accuracy of a 3-in. micrometer caliper be checked?

29-7. Suggest some of the features that would be incorporated in a gaging room.

29-8. What is the meaning of a no. 4 graduation as applied to a steel rule?

29-9. Give three applications for a combination stock.

29-10. Where can a center head be used to advantage?

29-11. Explain the term "caliper feel."

29-12. Mention a practical application for a transfer caliper.

29-13. Write the fractional pitch of a micrometer caliper screw.

29-14. Can a vernier measure as accurately as a micrometer?

29-15. When, if ever, is it desirable to use a dial gage on an engine lathe?

29-16. What is meant by "flagging"?

29-17. Mention at least two applications for jo-blocks.

29-18. How many blocks comprise a standard Johansson set?

29-19. What type of fits are checked with plug gages?

29-20. Can a 1-in. plug gage enter a 1-in. ring gage of the same set?

29-21. Mention some advantages to using a snap gage.

29-22. What is the function of a supermicrometer?

29-23. Give some applications for air gages.

29-24. Where is an optical flat used?

29-25. Of what degree of precision is spectroscopy capable?

REFERENCES FOR MACHINING SECTION

Chaps. 15–29

"Broaches and Broaching," 1944, by Burden, Broaching Tool Institute, New York.

"Designing for Production," 1957, by Niebel and Baldwin, Richard D. Irwin, Inc., Homewood, Ill.

"Dimensions and Tolerances in Mass Production," 1954, by Buckingham, The Industrial Press, New York.

"Grinding Practice," 1950, by Colvin and Stanley, McGraw-Hill Book Company, Inc., New York.

"Introduction to Electronic Analogue Computers," 1955, by Wass, McGraw-Hill Book Company, Inc., New York.

"Machine Tools for Engineers," 1950, by Hine, McGraw-Hill Book Company, Inc., New York.

"Machine Tool Operations, Part II," 1954, by Burghardt and Axelrod, McGraw-Hill Book Company, Inc., New York.

"Machinery's Handbook," 1948, The Industrial Press, New York.

"Manufacturing Processes," 1957, by Begeman, John Wiley & Sons, Inc., New York.

"Mechanical Engineers' Handbook," 12th ed., 1950, by Kent, John Wiley & Sons, Inc., New York.

"Metal Cutting Tool Handbook," 1949, Metal Cutting Tool Institute, New York.

"Metal Cutting Principles," 1954, by Shaw, Massachusetts Institute of Technology, Cambridge, Mass.

"Metal Machining," 1953, by Doyle, Prentice-Hall, Inc., Englewood Cliffs, N.J.

"Metal Processing," 1951, by Boston, John Wiley & Sons, Inc., New York.

"Metrology and Gauging," 1957, by Parsons, Macdonald & Evans, London.

"Modern Methods of Gear Manufacture," 1950, National Broach and Machine Company, Detroit.

"The New American Machinists' Handbook," 1955, by LeGrand (ed.), McGraw-Hill Book Company, Inc., New York.

"Tool Engineers' Handbook," 1949, American Society of Tool Engineers, McGraw-Hill Book Company, Inc., New York.

"Treatise on Milling and Milling Machines," 1951, Cincinnati Milling Machine Company, Cincinnati.

Chapter 30

WELDING BASICS

Historical

The welding of metal through employing elevated temperatures complemented by pressure has been practiced since antiquity. There appears to be no definitely known date of origin for any of the basic welding processes. The Dura wrought-iron objects which were found in Syria by the Fine Arts Department of Yale University in cooperation with the French Académie des Sciences, as a result of their excavations in the early 1930's, included specimens of welded rings. These discoveries indicate that hammer welding was known as early as the second century A.D.[1] The carved iron pillar at Delhi, India, whose total height is 23 ft 8 in. and whose outside diameter varies from 16.4 to 12.05 in., Thomas Turner states, "consists of malleable iron of great purity, and was made about A.D. 400, by welding together discs of metal."[2]

It was in 1778 that Peter Townsend was commissioned to make, for the sum of £5,000, a chain that would reach across, in the Hudson River, from Constitution Island to West Point and would act as a barrier against the British fleet. This chain was made from 2½ in. square wrought-iron bars at the Stirling Iron Works located at Chester, Orange County, N.Y. Each link was approximately 2 to 3 ft in length and weighed upward of 140 lb; the total weight with fastenings was about 180 tons. The chain was made by using 17 forges continuously, employing 60 men in an operation that could well be termed the first mass-production metal-manufacturing job in the United States. The chain was hauled in sections to the assembly site, where it was joined by further welding, supplemented by clevises.

The necessary buoyancy was imparted to the chain by attaching it to supporting logs that were, in turn, held against the current by suitable anchors. There are links of this chain displayed at Raynham Hall, Oyster

[1] Higgins, John W.: The Iron Age of Dura Craftsmanship, *The Iron Age*, Vol. 135, No. 2, pp. 13–15, 75, Jan. 10, 1935.
[2] "Metallurgy of Iron," 2d ed., p. 4, Charles Griffin & Co., Ltd., London, 1900.

Bay, N.Y., and at the U.S. Military Academy at West Point, as well as at various museums (Fig. 30-1).

The origin of arc welding is obscure. The consensus of historians on this subject is that electric arc welding was originated in Europe. N. Slavianov is credited with originating the idea of metallic arc welding, a revision of the carbon arc method. He was given an award at the Chicago world's fair in 1893 for an exhibit of a "Process of Electric Welding." Prominent among other early investigators in the field of electric arc welding was Sir Humphry Davy in England.

Fig. 30-1. Section of the great chain, 1,700 feet long, which was stretched across the Hudson River. (Courtesy of United States Military Academy, West Point, N.Y. Department of the Army photograph.)

The development of oxyacetylene welding was hampered by a lack of knowledge of the behavior of these gaseous mixtures. The explosive potential of acetylene when mixed with air or oxygen retarded the development of suitable apparatus. Edmond Fouché was granted a patent in the United States on November 11, 1902, covering a welding blowpipe; Fig. 30-2 is taken from a copy of this patent. Fouché was associated with Émile Picard and Eugene Bournonville in the Société Acétylène Dissous in France. It was in 1901 that Bournonville installed the first plant in America for generating and compressing acetylene gas in portable cylinders as dissolved acetylene.

The original work in electric resistance welding was done in America by Elihu Thomson. His experiments, dating as early as 1883, were re-

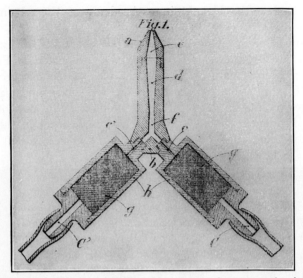

Fig. 30-2. Sketch of the Fouché blowpipe taken from patent drawing.

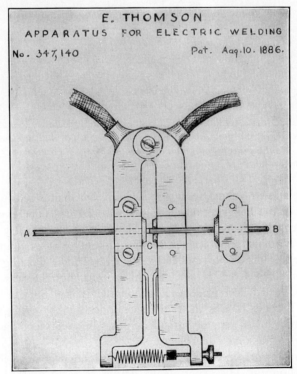

Fig. 30-3. Original patent of electric resistance welding.

ferred to by himself as dealing with the "art or process of electric welding." A sketch of his apparatus, patented on August 10, 1886, is shown in Fig. 30-3. This equipment was used for butt-welding the wires shown as *A* and *B*, with the resultant weld located at *C*.

This brief historical sketch of the early developments in welding would be incomplete without mention of the achievements of Dr. Hans Goldschmidt. It was in 1895 that he succeeded with his experiments in Thermit welding. His discovery was based on the reduction of iron oxide into metallic iron by aluminum. However it was not until 1897 that a patent was granted, and the process was introduced into America in 1902.

WELDING NOMENCLATURE

There are many variables entering into the concept of welding. By way of example, welding methods can be assessed from the metallurgical viewpoint or from the heat source. Techniques, methods, and procedures have all formed the basis for segments of welding terminology. Continued usage of a welding expression has, on occasion, resulted in a traditional inference. The case of the term fusion welding is an illustration. Even though the term fusion welding has been recognized over the years as designating a basic process, it is no longer accepted as a correct expression.

Standardization of Nomenclature. The desirability and advantages of uniform terminology in welding have been recognized by engineering and manufacturing alike. Lack of standardization in this regard has led to the introduction of expedients. This has been the normal result of the rapid expansion of welding both as to process development and as to applications.

The American Welding Society from time to time issues standards covering welding nomenclature. A study of these standards shows that their revision has always been in the direction of greater clarity and simplification. The latest revision, the work of the Committee on Definitions and Charts, has been embodied in two standards:

1. "Master Chart of Welding Processes and Process Charts" (A3.0-49)
2. "Standard Welding Terms and Their Definitions" (A3.1-49)

The Master Chart of Welding Processes is presented here as Fig. 30-4. This chart diagrams all the currently used welding processes in one concise, logical arrangement. The standard that includes the Master Chart has three appended pages devoted to Process Charts. The first of these pages of Process Charts covers forge, flow, gas, induction, and Thermit welding; the second deals with arc welding; and the final one is devoted to resistance welding processes. The charts interpret the characteristics of each process under twenty-four headings.

The Process Charts omit brazing, which appears on the Master Chart. This situation raises the question of the fundamental concept of brazing;

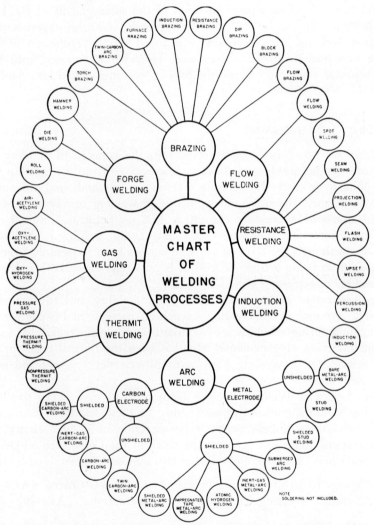

Fig. 30-4. Master Chart of Welding Processes. (American Standard A3.1-49, American Welding Society, New York, 1949.)

this process is considered to be predicated on capillary action and, except for processing temperature range, is similar to soldering. The demarcation temperature between brazing and soldering has been established at 800°F by this standard. The other processes on the Master Chart are established primarily by the manner of heating.

Cold Weld. There has been considerable divergence of opinion in connection with the formal definition of the term weld. While it has always been assumed that a weld is made at an elevated temperature, it is known that some metals can be joined while at room temperature through the use of pressure alone.

Anthony Sowter, working with associates in the research laboratories of the General Electric Co., Ltd., Wembley, England, developed a promising system of consistent cold pressure welding. This technique applies especially to such metals as aluminum and copper through carefully controlled surface condition preparations, die design, and applied pressure. The process has been successfully employed and is used in an increasing degree in this country (Fig. 30-5). Cold pressure welded joints are unaffected by age or temperature change. Since processing is completed without the addition of heat they are unique in welding and applications exist where this development is proving extremely useful.

Fig. 30-5. Typical examples of closures made by the Koldweld method without the use of sealing compound. (Courtesy of Utica Drop Forge & Tool Co., Utica, N.Y.)

Definition of a Weld. The standard definition for the term weld is: "A localized coalescence of metals wherein coalescence is produced by heating to suitable temperatures, with or without the application of pressure, and with or without the use of filler metal. The filler metal either has a melting point approximately the same as the base metal or has a melting point below that of the base metal but above 800°F."[3] It should be noted that the expressions pressure weld and non-pressure weld have been rendered obsolete by this revised standard definition.

Welder or Weldor. Some clarification is necessary of the terms used when referring to the worker who actually makes a weld, especially since the terminology used in labor contracts has been indefinite to the point of becoming controversial. There is some sentiment in favor of the

[3] Standard Welding Terms and Their Definitions," American Standard A3.0-49, American Welding Society, New York, 1949.

use of the term *weldor* in preference to *welder*. The reasoning behind this trend is that the term welder can, according to some interpretations, refer either to the worker or to the welding machine.

The standards definition considers the terms synonymous, defining them as "one who is capable of performing manual or semiautomatic welding operations." A *welding operator*, on the other hand, is understood to be one who operates machine or automatic welding equipment.

WELDING PROCESSES

The Master Chart (Fig. 30-4) recognizes eight fundamental welding processes, each of which has one or more subdivisions. Those represented by one or only a few modifications will be discussed here, while each of the more diversified processes will be the subject of a subsequent chapter. The sequence of the welding processes in the treatment that follows has no significance beyond being a convenient alphabetical arrangement.

The point has repeatedly been made in earlier chapters that metal products are produced by casting or by mechanical work; in other words, they are either cast or wrought. This must be kept in mind when welding either cast or wrought products, since in some welding processes the resultant weld metal is actually a casting, while in those welds where pressure or impact is used in the welding procedure a modification of the cast structure of the weld results (Fig. 30-6). There is the difference, however, that the deposited weld metal has a higher cooling rate than a sand casting, and modified cast structure results.

Welding processes cannot be divided on the basis of their application either to cast products on the one hand or wrought products on the other. Some processes do fall into one or the other division; others have but minor use in the one field and major applications in the other; while gas and arc welding as well as brazing are commonly used on both categories of metal products. In fact, brazing was the only method that could be used universally until the comparatively recent development of torch and arc welding.

Flow Welding. Castings were formerly repaired through the expedient of bolted or riveted straps or patches. A repair of this kind required skill and ingenuity of a high order. The author remembers seeing a repair on a broken cast-iron automobile crankcase that involved affixing some 40 assorted pieces to a copper plate, which was in turn fashioned and riveted to the remainder of the crankcase in a manner that resulted in an oil-tight job!

Another approach to repairing castings was that of "burning on"—a job that was generally assigned to the foundry. Burning-on was the method from which flow welding was developed; these two terms are used interchangeably.

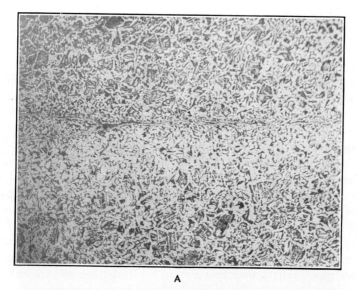

A

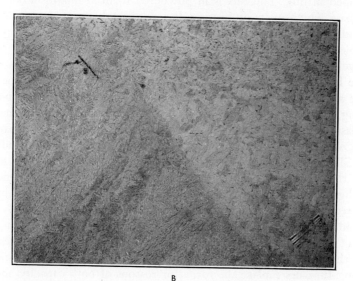

B

Fig. 30-6. A, metallic arc weld in mild steel with E4510 electrode, ×112. B, forge weld in mild steel, ×80.

The technique used in flow welding is that of embedding the broken parts, properly aligned, in molding sand or other suitable investment. Provisions for flowing molten metal around the fracture are included in the mold. The actual welding operation consists of pouring molten metal, whose flow is directed through suitable gating arrangements, past the casting fracture. After an interval sufficiently great to bring both edges of the break to fluidity, the stream of molten metal is stopped off. The casting is permitted to cool prior to its removal from the mold. Chipping and grinding follow, to smooth the weld to shape.

Forge Welding. One of the most beloved poems in American literature is "The Village Blacksmith," in which Longfellow so graphically portrays one of the artisans by whose skillful hands forgings and weldments have been wrought throughout the ages. The shortcomings of forge welding are its relatively narrow field of application and its lack of adaptability. Forge welding enjoyed its greatest popularity in joining wrought iron and mild steel. It has been responsible for some remarkable achievements, notable both for magnitude and for complicated shape.

The technique of making a forge weld depends somewhat upon the type of joint: for the most part, a lap joint is used. The two bars to be welded are first scarfed (tapered) in a manner that will result in a normal thickness throughout the length of the welded section. After scarfing and fitting, the faying surfaces are heated to pronounced redness, when they are momentarily withdrawn from the forge fire and sprinkled with or dipped in flux. The flux is in powdered form, primarily a borax or a silica base which melts on heating. It acts as a solvent of any oxides present and protects the surfaces from further oxidation by the forge blast. The pieces are then replaced in the forge fire and the air blast is opened to develop rapid heating to welding temperature.

The blacksmith gages proper welding temperature by the appearance of the scarfed surfaces. When these surfaces are just below the point of flowing, corresponding to a high state of plasticity, he shuts off the forge air blast and rapidly removes the pieces from the fire. The parts are struck violently against the anvil in order to free the scarfs of adhering scale. The parts are next placed on the anvil with the scarfs mating. Once the scarfs have been matched, the smith grasps his hammer and rains light, rapid blows on the joint, to be followed by blows of increasing intensity until the weld is completed.

In addition to the manual method of forge welding, other modifications of this basic process include the use of power hammers, presses, or rolls; these are especially useful as the size of the weldments increase. Heating furnaces replace the forge for reasons of both capacity and control. On repetitive work, dies are used in a power hammer much as they are used in the production of drop forgings.

Among the modifications of forge welding, butt-welded pipe deserves particular mention. The skelp, from which the pipe is to be made, is sheared to form a tong hold on the skelp end. Skelp is charged into a furnace, where it is brought to welding temperature. A device similar to a drawbench is located on the delivery end of the furnace. The actual welding of the skelp into pipe is accomplished by drawing the skelp through a collar known as a welding bell; this operation forces the edges together into a butt weld (Fig. 30-7). The welding bell is slipped over a pair of tongs which grip and pull the skelp from the furnace by dropping the handle end of the tongs into the moving drawbench chain. The entire operation is speedily done, with production of 1-in. pipe approaching 700 20-ft lengths/hr.

Induction Welding. This welding process derives its name from the heating source used. Limitations are placed on broader use of induction welding because of the relative scarcity of induction heating installations in manufactories generally. Potentially rapid processing is a favorable factor that should develop increasing interest in induction welding.

Thermit Welding. Fundamentally, Thermit is a mechanical mixture of powdered aluminum and iron oxide. In order to develop desired characteristics in the final weld metal, various elements, such as manganese,

Fig. 30-7. Steel skelp drawn through welding bell, thereby forming longitudinal weld in pipe, (Courtesy of Carnegie-Illinois Steel Corp., Pittsburgh.)

nickel, molybdenum, and carbon, are added to the Thermit mixture in varying combinations. This mixture is ignited by means of a magnesium fuse or powder. The resulting chemical reaction

$$8Al + 3Fe_3O_4 = 9Fe + 4Al_2O_3$$

is of about 30 sec duration, regardless of the quantity of Thermit used, and develops a temperature approximating 5000°F.

The Thermit welding operation is not unlike flow welding, the Thermit reaction supplying the required molten weld metal. The parts to be welded are given proper joint preparation by chipping, flame cutting, or grinding. The joint must be open throughout its entire area. The pieces are placed in alignment and secured to prevent movement prior to and during welding. The joint opening is filled with wax and a reinforcing wax band is built to the shape desired by the weld metal. When the wax has been worked to proper shape, a mold box is placed around the wax pattern. The box is then filled and rammed with molding material similar to steel molding sand.

As the mold is made, suitable gates and risers are placed in position. These are withdrawn upon completion of the mold, and heating torches, for drying the mold and melting out the wax, are brought into play. Preheating is continued until the casting weld faces reach full redness. The Thermit mixture, held in a conically shaped crucible equipped with a tapping pin at its apex, is ignited and upon completion of the reaction the crucible is tapped, which permits the molten metal to flow into and fill the mold. A typical Thermit weld is pictured in Fig. 30-8.

Thermit welding is applied to fabrication and repair of heavy sections. An outstanding achievement was the welding of stern frame castings for aircraft carriers and other craft. Stern frames were cast in sections and

Fig. 30-8. Completed Thermit weld shown at right while a second weld, at left, is waxed up ready for the mold box. (Courtesy of Thermex Metallurgical Co., Lakehurst, N.J.)

welded; some of these welds were made in cross sections reaching to 40 in. in one dimension.

Welding Symbols

With the increased application of welding, the necessity for standardized design has arisen, and this has led to the development of welding symbols. The American Welding Society has sponsored the symbols shown in Fig. 30-9. These symbols are used throughout the designing and welding industry in America. They are not used universally as yet, but revisions are being considered whereby welding symbols for both the United States and Great Britain would be standardized.

There have been several revisions of the welding symbol code, and to avoid confusion, only the current code should be used. The student is urged to become familiar with the basic elements in the welding symbol code.

A unique development, and one that appreciably increases the flexibility of the welding symbol code, has been issued by the AWS; nondestructive testing symbols can now be included or superimposed upon the welding symbols on a design drawing. This procedure is detailed in American Standard A2.2-58, and for the first time offers such a dual approach.

ADHESIVE BONDING

Any method or technique that can improve the scope and efficiency of joining has profound meaning. Progress in this direction has been made with the application of spot welding as a replacement for rivets. Further advances have come about through the introduction of adhesive bonding. This development provides the means for making joints in many categories and especially in areas that are entirely new.

Bonding Materials. Adhesives are capable of making a joint of sufficient strength to resist normally applied loads. The preponderance of the adhesives used as bonding metals either to themselves or to other engineering materials can be classified as:

1. Thermosetting resins
2. Thermoplastic resins
3. Silicone resins
4. Elastomers

The former are discussed in Chap. 3. Elastomers are elastic in nature, as exemplified by both natural and synthetic rubbers. Owing to the elastic behavior of these adhesives, they are used in non-structural applications since they lack the rigidity demanded by structural applications. These materials are frequently used as an additive in thermosetting plastics as a means of reducing brittleness and increasing shock resistance.

Bonding Practice. Adhesive bonded joints must be correctly engineered to obtain desired end results. Included in this program are such basic considerations as the selection of adhesive material coupled with joint geometry, loading, ambient temperature and humidity conditions, among others. Actual processing follows the procedures applicable to brazing or welding. Surface preparation requires strict attention both as to cleanliness and roughness condition at the instant of adhesive application, which is done by brushing or spraying. Adhesives are also available in tape forms that are convenient for flat or curved surface application.

After an adhesively bonded joint has been assembled it must be cured. Such curing combines air drying with stoving or baking. Temperature and time control is vital to success; variability must be eliminated completely.

Industrial Applications. Adhesive bonding has been significantly successful in joining metals to nonmetals, as exemplified by brake shoe lining in automobiles. It is the answer in those areas where temperatures are objectionable during joining. An outstanding example is that of joining heat-treated materials when fabricating sandwich-type construction. Insulation and leakproofing are further application areas. When extremely thin metals are to be joined, adhesives supply a reliable solution.

The application possibilities are expanding continually because of the potential of adhesive bonds. When weight saving is a consideration, these joints are an answer, as they are for lowered production costs.

SURVEY QUESTIONS

30-1. Describe an ancient welding application.

30-2. What is considered to be the first example of mass production in metal fabrication in this country?

30-3. Who invented the gas welding torch?

30-4. In what country was resistance welding invented?

30-5. Who is responsible for the standardization of welding nomenclature?

30-6. How many basic welding processes are recognized as standard?

30-7. Is it possible to use cold welding for reclamation repair?

30-8. Spell the term applying to the artisan who performs welding.

30-9. Explain if flow welding can be used in pressure vessel fabrication.

30-10. What is a forge?

30-11. How is a ¾-in. galvanized steel pipe made?

30-12. Are Thermit and flow welds made in the same manner?

30-13. Where, if at all, is Thermit welding used in structural steel fabrication?

30-14. State several advantages to using welding symbols.

30-15. List the different types of grooves that are covered by weld symbols.

30-16. When weld symbols are used, how is the weld metal shown, if at all?

30-17. How can an arc weld be distinguished from a resistance weld by the use of weld symbols?

30-18. How is it possible to show direction of welding with symbols?

30-19. Explain if there is any difference between arc and gas welding symbols.

30-20. Wherein does adhesive bonding differ from resistance welding?

30-21. Mention an industry or product wherein adhesive bonding has considerable application.

30-22. Describe any method other than adhesive bonding that can be successfully used for joining dissimilar metals.

Chapter 31

ARC WELDING

Arc welding is defined as "a group of welding processes wherein coalescence is produced by heating with an electric arc or arcs, with or without the application of pressure and with or without the use of filler metal."[1] The approach to applied arc welding—and the terminology most commonly heard—is based on type of current, electrode, shielding, and manipulation. Both direct current and alternating current are used and in some methods both d-c and a-c arcs are used to complement each other. The manner of manipulating the arc during welding may be manual, semiautomatic, or fully automatic.

DIRECT CURRENT

M-G Sets. A substantial amount of d-c welding uses motor-generator (m-g) sets as a means of converting power-line alternating current of high voltage and low amperage into direct current of suitable characteristics for arc welding. Such welding machines are available in ratings from 150 to 600 amp and, for the most part, are single-operator sets. A typical arc welding machine, in which the d-c welding generator is driven by an a-c motor, is shown in Fig. 31-1. For field work and in those situations where a satisfactory power-line source is unavailable, d-c welding generators are driven by gas engines or diesel motors (Fig. 31-2). The load on these motors is such that they must have ample reserve power, coupled with the ability to respond instantly to fluctuating power demands.

Direct-current Generators. The development of welding electrodes has shifted the emphasis in generator characteristics. Formerly there was considerable interest in voltage recovery time from the dead short resulting from arc starting, but now that electrode shieldings are capable of residual ionization, there is less necessity for instantaneous voltage recovery.

Direct-current welding generators are designed to produce "drooping

[1] "Standard Welding Terms and Their Definitions," American Standard A3.0-49, American Welding Society, New York, 1949.

Fig. 31-1. Portable motor-generator (m-g) welding machine, d-c type. (Courtesy of Lincoln Electric Co., Cleveland.)

Fig. 31-2. Portable engine-driven d-c welder, equipped with self-adjusting voltage control. (Courtesy of the Harnischfeger Corp., Milwaukee.)

characteristics" for the static VA curve plotted for an individual design. These curves, of which Fig. 31-3 is an example, show the relation between voltage and amperage for a given terminal voltage. It is of interest to note the degree of change in current values (amp) for any change in arc voltage. If 25 volts is taken as a representative value for a welding arc, it can readily be seen that when the arc shorts (zero voltage) there is but a very slight increase in amperage. This is of practical importance, since the arc length, which controls the voltage, is continually varying. This variation in arc length is due to a combination of manipulations plus the conditions in the arc stream of metal globules. The steeper the VA curve, the less will be the amperage fluctuation during welding.

The above explanation refers to the *static* characteristics of the welding generator. When this generator is welding, the results encountered are not actually those of the curve. However there is evidence to indicate that the static curve characteristics point the way to the performance that can be expected under operating conditions.

A check on operating power source performance can be obtained by photographing the transients of the welding circuit during operation. This can be accomplished by connecting an oscillograph into the welding circuit. A comparison between different d-c

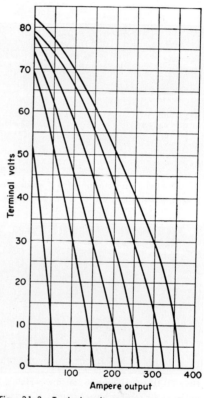

Fig. 31-3. Typical volt-ampere curves for a d-c welding generator. (Courtesy of Harnischfeger Corp., Milwaukee.)

sources as between m-g and rectifier types is shown by the accompanying oscillographs in Figs. 31-4a and 31-4b.

Welding generators can be designed to deliver a wide range of characteristics, for example, arc voltage remaining constant while current varies, or the reverse. The type of excitations used can be an external source, cross field, or third brush. Of greater practical importance is the matter of control of the welding current. The two best-known systems are the single control, in which the weldor manipulates one knob, and the dual control, which offers individual regulation of both open-circuit voltage and current.

Rectifier Type Direct Current. A serious competitor to the M-G set d-c arc welding machine is developing through the increasing popularity of the rectifier type. In this equipment (Fig. 31-5) three-phase a-c current is taken from the line through a selenium-type rectifier, although silicon rectifiers have also been developed for this use.

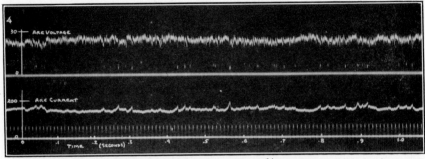

Fig. 31-4(a). Oscillograph of d-c welding current using ⅛-in. electrode high-density current in vertical weld; m-g set for d-c power source.

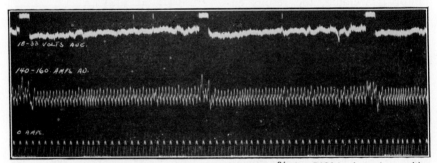

Fig. 31-4b. Oscillograph of d-c welding current using ³⁄₁₆-in. E6016 electrode, positive polarity; d-c rectifier power source. (Courtesy of A. O. Smith Corp., Milwaukee.)

In a selenium cell the thin layer of selenium lies between front and back electrodes. Though neither electrode nor the selenium itself is an asymmetric conductor, the barrier layer between the selenium and the front electrode acts as a unidirectional element for the electric current. The selenium cell has better overload characteristics than any other rectifying element now known. It is able to withstand severe current overloads for short times without sustaining damage. It is easy to detect when a selenium stack has failed, because of the foul odor, a feature which silicon and other rectifiers do not have. Selenium rectifiers show very little aging, *i.e.*, increased forward voltage drop with time. Transformers can be provided with taps to increase the a-c voltage input after 20,000 to 50,000 hr of operation if necessary. The selenium cells are generally used below 1,000 cycles per second, because of their high inherent shunt capacity. Power factor at line frequency of 60 cycles is essentially unity for the rectifier alone, and usually the associated circuit elements are the determining factor in the over-all power factor.

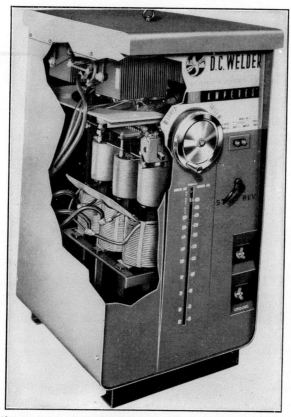

Fig. 31-5. Rectifier type d-c welder showing construction details, with rectifier located at the top. (Courtesy of A. O. Smith Corp., Milwaukee.)

The rectifying equipment is placed in the transformer cabinet; the latter is provided with suitably designed cooling, usually by a fan. In addition, a complete series of operating controls, including remote switching, is mounted on the front panel. There is much to be said for this type of d-c welding current source. Among its advantages are quiet operation and low maintenance owing to the absence of moving parts other than the cooling fan. A further advantage is the ease of paralleling—the possibility of connecting several units in parallel in order to develop current outputs in excess of the capabilities of a single machine; such flexibility has obvious advantages.

The duty-cycle rating on this type equipment is 60 per cent, which means that the welding current is on 6 min and off 4 min in each 10-min interval. Rectified d-c current is of a pulsating nature, which produces a higher metal deposition rate coupled with denser welds because of a higher spray to globule metal transfer ratio. There is also a high current response factor, since voltage recovery is substantially faster than in the m-g sets. Additional advantages include such items as low no-load power consumption and a higher electrical efficiency. Lower first cost or initial investment is also a decisive factor favoring rectifier-type equipment.

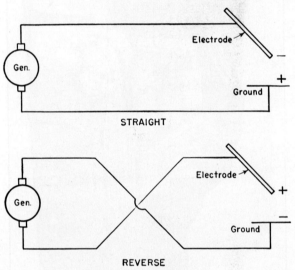

Fig. 31-6. Schematic drawing of straight and reverse polarity connections for a d-c welding generator.

A comparison of m-g welding current with that of d-c rectifier type is shown graphically in Figs. 31-4a and 31-4b. The pulsating nature of the d-c rectified current is readily recognized from Fig. 31-4b. The voltage curves are quite similar in each case.

Polarity. The outstanding feature of d-c welding equipment is its unidirectional current flow. The terminals on the welding current circuit are positive (anode) and negative (cathode), respectively. As a result the welding circuit can be connected with the electrode negative or positive, depending on the procedure requirements. Straight polarity refers to the work being positive (electrode negative). Reverse polarity is the opposite connection, or the one in which the work is negative (electrode positive). The polarity connections are sketched in Fig. 31-6.

The significance attached to polarity arises from the fact that in an arc composed primarily of iron (unshielded electrodes), greater heat is liberated at the anode. This preponderance of heat at the anode is attributed to the electrons flowing at high speed from their cathode source, bombarding the anode area. The ratio of heat distribution is generally considered to be 2:3 at the anode to 1:3 at the cathode. Consequently the base metal, being of greater volume, is connected at the anode in order to give it the benefit of greater heat input. When shielded electrodes are used, this situation may be altered by reason of the action of certain of the components in the shielding.

ALTERNATING CURRENT

The use of alternating current for welding is not a recent development. C. J. Holslag,[2] among others, championed this system with enthusiasm. It failed of general acceptance because of the practical operating difficulties of both striking and maintaining an arc when only bare or lightly coated electrodes were available. The introduction of shielded electrodes and their subsequent and continuing functional improvement have caused an increasing interest in a-c welding, to the point where this method has surpassed the d-c method for steel production welding.

Fig. 31-7. Transformer-type a-c welding equipment. (Courtesy of Harnischfeger Corp., Milwaukee.)

Welding Transformers. Alternating-current welding installations generally employ a welding transformer as the source of current. A representative welding transformer is pictured in Fig. 31-7. Regulation of welding current output is obtained by manipulating suitable controls on the front panel. Essentially the a-c welding transformer is designed to receive single-phase power of line voltage and transform it into welding current of relatively lower voltage and stepped-up amperage. Provision for adjusting the welding current is a feature of all welding transform-

[2] "Arc Welding Handbook," McGraw-Hill Book Company, Inc., New York, 1924.

ers. The design of this feature varies with different manufacturers; such ideas as taps taken from the windings, movable coils or cores, and combinations of these are incorporated. Built-in power factor correction and a cooling fan are other features of the welding transformer.

Alternating-current Welding. The characteristics of welding current from an a-c source are different from those of the d-c type. In a-c welding there is a reversal from positive to negative equal to the number of cycles of that current; there is no difference in heat distribution as between the terminals of the welding circuit. A further feature is that alternating current does not build up a magnetic field surrounding the electrode (conductor) to the degree that this phenomenon occurs in a d-c welding circuit. As a result, a-c welding is relatively free of the magnetic disturbance, or arc blow, that proves so annoying in d-c welding, especially where high amperage is needed or where weldment design requires the placing of metal in a position causing magnetic disturbance in the welding arc.

Direct- and Alternating-current Welding Compared

The outstanding feature of d-c welding is its polarity potential. This is especially important in welding nonferrous alloys. Further advantages claimed for direct current are arc stability and ease of manipulation. It is also noteworthy that on motor-generator sets a much better line-load situation is obtained from a three-phase motor, which makes the set more desirable than in the case of the transformer.

One of the criticisms cited against m-g sets for d-c welding is that the rotating members, commutators, and other rotating parts create a maintenance problem. When the weldor is changing electrodes or is taking care of other tasks, the machine is running and power is being consumed in overcoming the friction load of the set, resulting in added over-all cost of operation.

Alternating-current transformers, when they are equipped with proper power factor correction, are the most efficient of the arc welding current sources. This equipment costs considerably less per unit than does direct current. It requires less floor space and is lighter in weight and more easily moved. The major advantage of a-c welding arises from insignificant arc blow; because of this, heavier welding currents are used and more rapid welding is obtained.

An undesirable feature of a-c welding is the possibility of power-line unbalance occasioned by single-phase load. This situation can be improved by the installation of other motor-driven equipment to afford a balanced line load. The former objection to a-c welding with its high arc striking voltage has been largely overcome through the introduction of shielded-type electrodes.

Even though a-c and d-c welding currents are different, there is some difference in the current source equipment. However, these divergent welding current sources are brought together in a single equipment which is available as a combination a-c or d-c power source. As noted in Fig. 31-8, it bears a very close resemblance to the transformer-type welders.

METAL ELECTRODE WELDING

Carbon electrodes have largely been replaced in arc welding procedures by metal types. Metal electrodes were originally pieces of bare wire, which proved extremely difficult to manipulate owing to arc instability. Remedial measures included dipping, dusting, or painting the wire with a thin coating of ferric or calcium compounds. These electrodes were known as light-coated or sulcoated and were used with d-c straight polarity. They were unsatisfactory for a-c welding. Welds made with this electrode do not

Fig. 31-8. Combination a-c/d-c welding current transformer. (Courtesy of Miller Electric Manufacturing Co., Appleton, Wis.)

have a heavy slag coating; rather there is a light oxide deposit that is readily removed by brushing. The absence of a slag deposit has proved of value in those applications where freedom from slag inclusions is critical. Light-coated electrodes continue to be used in automatic arc welding.

Shielded Metal Electrodes

Although shielded or heavy-coated electrodes have come into general use in comparatively recent years, the basic idea is not entirely new. Benardos introduced electrodes of many shapes and with various types of shielding before the turn of the century; some of these are shown in Fig. 31-9.

Specifications comparing filler metal have been developed by the American Welding Society in chart form under the AWS A5.0-57 code designation. In addition, there is a complete range of codes covering filler metal and welding electrodes and rods of all types. These codes have been developed by the American Welding Society in conjunction with

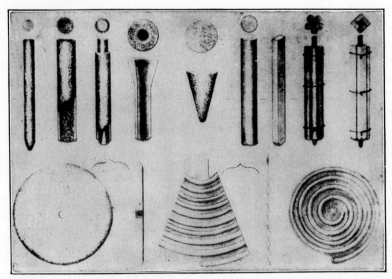

Fig. 31-9. Shielded electrode types of the latter part of the nineteenth century.

TABLE 31-1. MINIMUM TENSILE STRENGTH AND DUCTILITY REQUIREMENTS FOR
ALL-WELD-METAL TENSION TEST IN THE AS-WELDED CONDITION

AWS-ASTM classification no.	Tensile strength, minimum, psi*	Yield point, minimum, psi*	Elongation in 2 in., minimum, per cent
E4510	45,000	Not specified	5
E4520	45,000	Not specified	5
E6010	62,000	50,000	22
E6011	62,000	50,000	22
E6012	67,000	55,000	17
E6013	67,000	55,000	17
E6015	67,000	55,000	22
E6016	67,000	55,000	22
E6020	62,000	50,000	25
E6024	67,000	55,000	17
E6027	62,000	50,000	25
E6030	62,000	50,000	25

* For all classifications of electrodes except E45xx, for each increase of one percentage point in elongation over the minimum, the yield point or tensile strength or both may decrease 1,000 psi, to a minimum of 60,000 psi for the tensile strength and 48,000 psi for the yield point.

the American Society for Testing Materials for the most part. Sixteen such codes have been issued, with additional ones in preparation. Undoubtedly, the one of greatest interest is A5.5-54, entitled "Specifications for High Tensile and Low-alloy Steel & Covered Arc-welding Elec-

TABLE 31-2. ELECTRODE CLASSIFICATION*

Electrode classifica-tion no.	Type of coating or covering	Capable of producing satisfactory welds in position shown†	Type of current
	E45 series—Minimum tensile strength of deposited metal in non-stress-relieved condition, 45,000 psi
E4510 E4520	Sul-coated or light-coated	F, V, OH, H H-fillets, F	Not specified, but generally d-c, straight polarity (electrode negative)
	E60 series—Minimum tensile strength of deposited metal in non-stress-relieved condition, 60,000 psi or higher
E6010	High cellulose sodium	F, V, OH, H	For use with d-c, reversed polarity (electrode positive) only
E6011	High cellulose potassium	F, V, OH, H	For use with a-c or d-c, reversed polarity (electrode positive)
E6012	High titania sodium	F, V, OH, H	For use with d-c, straight polarity (electrode negative), or a-c
E6013	High titania potassium	F, V, OH, H	For use with a-c or d-c, straight polarity (electrode negative)
E6015	Low hydrogen sodium	F, V, OH, H	For use with d-c, reversed polarity (electrode positive), only
E6016	Low hydrogen potassium	F, V, OH, H	For use with a-c or d-c, reversed polarity (electrode positive)
E6020	High iron oxide	H-fillets, F	For use with d-c, straight polarity (electrode negative), or a-c for horizontal fillet welds; and d-c, either polarity, or a-c, for flat-position welding
E6024	Iron powder, titania	H-fillets, F	For use with d-c, either polarity, or a-c
E6027	Iron powder, iron oxide	H-fillets, F	For use with d-c, straight polarity (electrode negative), or a-c for horizontal fillet welds; and d-c, either polarity, or a-c, for flat-position welding.
E6030	High iron oxide	F	For use with d-c, either polarity, or a-c

* Abstracted from "Tentative Specifications for Mild Steel Arc-welding Electrodes," American Welding Society and American Society of Testing Materials, 1955.

† The abbreviations F, H, V, OH, and H-fillets indicate welding positions as follows: F, flat; V, vertical; H, horizontal; OH, overhead; H-fillets, horizontal fillets. For electrodes $\frac{3}{16}$ in. and under, except in classification E6015 and E6016, which are $\frac{5}{32}$ in. and under.

trodes," which serves the steel welding field completely. It is suggested that the pertinent codes be consulted in every case prior to the choice of electrodes or filler metal for a given application. Such specifications give information on electrode classification, mechanical properties, and welding current in addition to other critical information.

The classification number is devised in such a manner that the first two digits indicate the minimum tensile strength of the weld metal in pounds per square inch. For example, electrode E6010 specifies a tensile strength of 62,000 to 70,000 psi with a yield of 52,000 to 58,000 psi. The entire series of electrodes in the E60 classification is for mild steel welding and specifies a minimum tensile strength of deposited weld metal in non-stress-relieved condition of 62,000 psi, as noted in Table 31-1.

The types of shielding used on these various electrodes, together with the welding position in which they are to be used, are shown in Table 31-2. The shielding materials used by the different manufacturers for the electrode classifications given above are a matter of individual formulation. The coating composition of mild steel metallic arc welding electrodes under AWS electrode numbers is given in Table 31-3.

TABLE 31-3. TYPICAL COATING FORMULATIONS FOR AWS ELECTRODE CLASSES

Coating material	Amount, per cent				
	E6010	E6011	E6012	E6013	E6020
China clay...............					
Cellulose..............	21.0	16.0	4.0	12.0	2.6
Charcoal.............					
Asbestos..............	10.5	....	....	....	6.9
Titanium dioxide........	10.5				
Ferromanganese.........	5.3	5.3	8.0	5.6	10.3
Potassium titanate	....	18.9	....	12.3	
Zircon.................	....	....	....	13.8	
Zirconia................	....	6.6			
Talc...................	....	8.3	10.0	7.7	
Calcium carbonate.......	....	6.5	3.0	2.7	2.6
Manganese dioxide......	....	....	....	....	2.6
Silica flour.............	....	1.6	....	....	2.6
Rutile.................	....	....	39.0	10.3	8.6
Glycerin..............					
Feldspar..............	....	....	10.0	14.3	21.6
Magnetite..............	....	....	....	....	6.9
Dextrin................	....	....	1.0		
Alumina................	....	....	....	2.7	
Sodium silicate..........	52.7	36.8	25.0	....	35.3
Potassium silicate........	....	....	....	18.6	

Electrode shieldings serve a multiple function. First, they are used to prevent atmospheric contamination of the arc stream. Second, by depositing a slag on the weld bead they shield the freshly made weld from the atmosphere. Third, the generation of combustion products in the arc aids in penetration of the weld. Finally, ingredients in the coating act as ionizing agents in the arc stream. This last feature is of especial importance with electrodes used for a-c welding. Alloying elements and base metal, as in the case of iron powder, can be introduced into the weld metal from the shielding. Electrode development has been rapid and of decided utility. The initial revision was that of the low-hydrogen type, which has been widely accepted. Its chief virtue is that of producing weld metal that is relatively free of underbead cracking caused by hydrogen liberated from cellulosic shieldings. This progress was followed almost immediately by the inclusion of substantial amounts of iron powder in the electrode shielding. The unique properties and general acceptance of the initial iron powder type electrode have set a standard for operational characteristics. It is now believed that the development of the low-hydrogen iron powder electrode has reached a point where equal advantages are obtained over the conventional E7015 and E7016 as are obtained by the E6024 over the E6012 electrode.

The formulations for coatings of these electrodes are detailed in Table 31-4.

TABLE 31-4. COMPARISON OF COATINGS ON THE $\frac{3}{16}$-IN. ELECTRODES TESTED*

Distinguishing constituents	Conventional E7016			E7016 modified with 30% iron powder		E7016 modified with 50% iron powder	
	(1)†	(2)	(3)	(4)	(5)	(6)	(7)
$TiO_2 + ZrO_2$, %	27.0	28.0	28.0	6.0	5.0	12.0	17.0
$CaO + MgO$, %	25.0	27.0	26.0	30.0	28.0	8.0	11.0
Powdered iron, %	4.5	4.0	4.5	30.0	31.0	51.0	48.0
Ratio CaO/TiO_2	0.93	0.96	0.93	5.0	5.6	0.67	0.65
Moisture, %, as received	0.19	1.50	0.48	0.20	0.19	0.10	0.13
Coating, %	23.5	25.0	24.0	31.0	31.0	49.0	54.0
Optimum welding amperage in flat position	225	225	225	250	250	280	280
Maximum welding amperage in flat position	250	250	250	275	300	350	325

* Smith, Rinehart, and Kelton: Properties and Applications of Low-hydrogen Iron-powder Electrodes, *The Welding Journal*, April, 1956.

† Indicates electrode number.

Coating of Electrodes. The shielding materials are compounded dry and then mixed with some type of liquid binder, generally sodium silicate. This mixture is worked in a pugmill or similar mechanical mixer. When the coating material reaches the consistency of stiff mud, it is transferred to the electrode coating machine for extrusion onto the base wire.

The wire used for the various electrodes does not vary in chemical composition. The electrode core wire is produced in the wire mill in the form of coils. These coils are straightened and cut to lengths which vary with the diameter. The core wires are then transferred to the extrusion press, where the coating is extruded onto them. Among the necessary precautions is making sure that the coating is concentric with the wire. Figure 31-10 shows one type of electrode extrusion press in operation. It should be noted that the coating is extruded over the entire length of the

Fig. 31-10. Extruding shielding on core wire in the production of shielded electrodes. (Courtesy of the Hydraulic Press Manufacturing Co., Mount Gilead, Ohio.)

electrode. As the electrode travels toward the oven, the coating is brushed off the end for holder gripping.

The method of producing shielded electrodes varies with different manufacturers. In some cases electrodes are extruded to double length, being cut in half later. The rate of production of electrodes is a function of the type of extrusion press used. Production rates in excess of 900 electrodes/min have been reported.

Electrode Color Code. A color code for identifying electrodes has been developed and published as an NEMA specification entitled "Standard for Arc-welding Electrode Identification."[3] The markings occur as spot, end, or group colors which occur either at the end or on the center grip, depending on electrode type.

[3] National Electrical Manufacturers' Association, New York, 1959.

Burn-off Characteristics. The metal electrode is consumed in arc welding because of the heat of the arc, which causes it to melt and transfer across the arc to the base metal. Here it unites with the melted base metal to form the molten pool of weld metal. Transference across the arc is characterized by various-sized globules, particles, and vaporized metal. The phenomenon of metal transfer is influenced by the rate at which the electrode tip melts or burns off. Variability in burn-off will give non-uniform results in the weld deposit. Welding speed is an equally pertinent consideration: faster burn-off means higher rates of weld metal deposition. Burn-off rates vary with the different electrode classifications, and there are variations between electrodes within a given classification.

MANUAL ARC WELDING TECHNIQUES

Preliminaries. Before striking the arc, certain precautionary measures are necessary. The weldor needs to be equipped with suitable clothing to protect him from the rays and the heat emitted by the arc. Proper eye protection must be provided; welding face shields and hoods must be equipped with filter lenses that are free of cracks. Cover glasses should be free of spatter. Ventilation of the welding area must be adequate at all times.

The welding equipment also requires attention. The leads from the welding machine must be fully insulated against current leakage; this important consideration is too frequently overlooked. Ground connections should give solid contact to eliminate resistance, thereby ensuring maximum welding current flow. The electrode holder should be free of weld spatter and should be constructed so as to give firm contact with the electrode. Machine settings should be checked prior to striking the arc.

Striking the Arc. The arc is established by contacting the electrode with the work and promptly separating it from the work by a distance equal to the desired arc length; this maneuver closes the welding circuit and establishes the current flow. A straight vertical movement is difficult to master, since hesitation on contact will cause the electrode to freeze to the base metal. Should sticking occur, a sharp sidewise twist of the electrode will break it free. On the other hand, a too vigorous withdrawal of the electrode from its initial contact will draw out and extinguish the arc.

A second method of arc striking is to move the electrode as if striking a match, drawing the electrode across the base metal. There is less possibility of a stuck electrode when the scratching method is employed. Once the arc is kindled, it can readily be guided to its required position.

Contact arc welding, a different technique from the previously described ones, employs an extremely simplified arc initiating technique.
Welding electrodes having heavy additions of iron powder in the coating
are the basis of this method. When electrode contact is made, a current
flows through the shielding because of its iron powder content, which
is sufficient to establish the arc. Once the arc is kindled, the electrode
can be dragged along the intended welding path and actually no arc
needs to be held at all. The electrode coating melts at a rate considerably
slower than that of the core wire, with the result that a cup is formed in
the shielding which acts to protect the arc stream from atmospheric contamination. Because of the characteristics of this type electrode, the

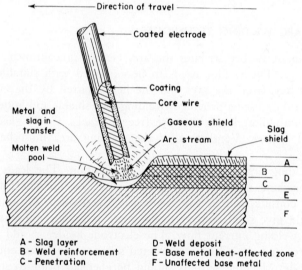

Fig. 31-11. Diagrammatic sketch of shielded electrode during welding operation. (From
"Welding Metallurgy," 2d ed., American Welding Society, New York, 1949.)

actual weld metal pattern has a deep center penetration flattening out to
shallow edges.

Maintenance of a proper arc length is dependent upon a continuing
downward movement of the electrode as compensation for the melting
of its tip by the arc. Failure to follow this procedure will result in an
increasing arc length, and ultimately, no arc at all. The electrode is
consumed by this downward movement into the arc until it becomes
too short for further welding. The remainder of the electrode, called the
stub, is removed from the electrode holder and replaced by another
electrode.

Once the arc is established, the base metal becomes fused in the actual
welding operation. The electrode is held at an inclination to the work in

the direction of weld travel. The behavior of the arc is diagramed in Fig. 31-11. The electrode is moved along the line of welding at a speed that will give a smooth uniform weld deposit. Electrode movement will vary with the position of welding, *i.e.*, flat (down-hand), horizontal, vertical, or overhead (Table 31-2). The practice of weaving the electrode is generally followed; however, there is considerable divergence of opinion on the pattern such movements should take. Procedures should be definitely established in order to remove this important feature of welding from the sphere of the weldor's discretion.

Restriking the Arc. The arc can be broken through faulty technique, wind interference, or accident. The arc must be broken when the electrode has been consumed. A satisfactory procedure for restriking the arc is to kindle it at the forward end of the weld crater, following this by a movement back across the crater, and forward again as welding continues. If the interval during which the arc is extinguished is sufficiently great to permit the slag to congeal, welding must be stopped until the slag has been removed in order to prevent the possibility of slag inclusion or entrapment.

Breaking the Arc. There are two accepted methods of breaking an arc. When the electrode is to be changed and the weld continued from the crater, it is customary to shorten the arc and move the electrode rapidly sidewise out of the weld crater. The second method consists of holding the electrode stationary until the crater becomes filled, following this by a gradual withdrawal of the electrode.

Weld Positioners. This presentation of arc welding has been devoted to such things as power sources and electrodes and arc technique. While these are basic considerations, when actual welding cost is calculated, they total only a fraction thereof. The major factor in welding cost is labor and overhead. In order to reduce these, especially labor costs, while at the same time improving weld quality, the actual welding operation itself must be considered. It is accepted that the best weld quality results when a weld is made in the down-hand position. Frequently, specifications call for welds to be made down-hand in order to ensure quality. Another significant factor is the lessening of fatigue on the part of the weldor when he can weld in the down-hand position.

Equipment known as weld positioners has been designed as a solution to this problem. A weldment can be clamped thereon and positioned so that the welds are always in the down-hand area. Weld positioners were originally rather humble equipment but have become imposing installations (Fig. 31-12). The positioner shown is of 80,000 lb capacity with a variable-speed table rotation of 0.0135 to 3.1 rpm through 360°. The table elevates by power, lowers 5 ft, and tilts 135°.

The weldment shown on the positioner is the frame of a 9 cu yd power shovel. The weldment weighs 59,000 lb, is 12 ft wide by 35 ft long by 3½ ft in thickness. Prior to the installation of this positioner, this weldment required 32 crane lifts and needed many stringer beads, mostly three-pass welds. Crane lifts have been reduced to nine, while down-hand welding has permitted replacing the usual first-pass stringer bead with heavy welds and reduced many welds from three passes to one or two. Ease of positioning also has made practical increased use of automatic welding. A cost study on this job shows that there is a saving of 90 hr in welding time alone. It is obvious from this case that weld

Fig. 31-12. Weld positioner of 80,000 lb capacity shown mounting a 59,000 lb power shovel frame weldment. (Courtesy of Harnischfeger Corp., Milwaukee.)

positioners play an important part in the production of economical and acceptable weldments.

Jigs and Fixtures. It is always well to study any weldment from the viewpoint of proper tooling. The job should be tooled with suitable fixtures or jigs in order to preserve alignment and also, of greater importance, to control distortion. Any well-engineered weldment should be given such consideration. In order to inaugurate a program that will produce end products in line with specifications, it is also necessary to evaluate the welding program itself. Included therein are such important items as sequence, welding positions, electrode selection, and welding current source and magnitude. Since labor costs are the overwhelming consideration every device should be called upon to make labor just as effective as possible. A proved way of doing this is through the use of jigs, fixtures, and positioners.

SURVEY QUESTIONS

31-1. Does arc welding add filler or weld metal?

31-2. What are the different ways of manipulating an arc?

31-3. Explain the expression "m-g set."

31-4. What is the actual function of an m-g set?

31-5. Sketch a "drooping characteristic" static VA curve.

31-6. What is the purpose of dual control?

31-7. If there is a d-c welding current source other than an m-g set, explain its basic design.

31-8. Why is duty cycle of importance when purchasing a welder?

31-9. If there is any difference between the current from an m-g set and that from a rectifier, explain why.

31-10. Is arc polarity important?

31-11. What is the source of a-c welding current?

31-12. List any profound advantages for a-c arc welding.

31-13. A newly organized shipyard is about to purchase its welding equipment. Specify the type that would prove most satisfactory for them.

31-14. What electrodes preceded metallic types?

31-15. Mention some electrode classifications other than shielded ones.

31-16. Discuss the reason for selecting E6010 over E6012 for a given job.

31-17. Give an "E" number for an iron powder class electrode.

31-18. What is the most generally used binder in electrode shielding?

31-19. How is the shielding affixed to a metallic electrode?

31-20. Is there any positive method of electrode identification as to class?

31-21. In what manner does "burn-off" influence welding costs?

31-22. State the necessary personal preparations that must precede arc striking.

31-23. What is an electrode holder?

31-24. How should an arc be struck or kindled?

31-25. Of all possible welding positions, which one, if any, is best? Why?

31-26. Where should weld positioners be used?

31-27. Mention some of the purposes for using a welding jig.

31-28. Explain the term "welding sequence."

31-29. Suggest some effective methods for controlling distortion during welding.

Chapter 32

GAS WELDING

Gas welding is the term applied to those processes in which the necessary heat for coalescence is provided by a gas flame or flames. The requisite gases are mixed in a blowpipe, also termed torch, whence they issue as a combustible gaseous mixture; this, upon ignition, provides the necessary welding heat. There are always two gases in the mixture: one is combustible and the other serves to speed and support combustion, thus promoting high flame temperature. Since by far the major part of gas welding is performed by the oxyacetylene process, it will be considered in some detail.

OXYACETYLENE FUNDAMENTALS

Oxyacetylene welding was described by Le Châtelier in 1895 in a paper read before the Académie des Sciences in Paris. He stated that the combustion of a gaseous mixture composed of equal volumes of acetylene and oxygen exceeded by 1000°C the temperature of the oxyhydrogen flame. Another fundamental contribution to the oxyacetylene process was the invention in the United States by Thomas L. Willson, in 1892, of a commercial method for manufacturing calcium carbide as a raw material for the production of acetylene.

Calcium Carbide. The electrochemical industry is the parent of calcium carbide. This material, referred to in the trade as carbide, is dark gray in color and of a stonelike consistency. It is produced in an electric arc furnace, of the type shown in Fig. 32-1, from a basic charge consisting of lime and coke. The temperature within the furnace is sufficiently high to cause the following reaction:

$$CaO + 3C = CaC_2 + CO$$

The purity of the raw materials in the charge is of extreme importance, since only high-grade calcium carbide will produce acetylene gas of superior quality.

The molten calcium carbide is tapped from the furnace and permitted to cool and solidify. It is then broken for screening and grading, in accordance with such designations as lump, egg, nut, etc. (the nut size is 1¼ by ⅜ in.). After grading, it is packed in sheet steel drums for storage or shipment. The drums must be tightly sealed to guard against moisture penetration.

Calcium carbide is a safe material to store or transport. It will not burn nor will it deteriorate. It will not explode. All these statements hold only if the material is kept moisture-free. A violent action occurs when calcium carbide is mixed with water. This reaction is accom-

Fig. 32-1. One type of arc furnace used for the production of calcium carbide. (Courtesy of Lectromeld Furnace Division, McGraw-Edison Co., Pittsburgh.)

panied by the evolution of acetylene gas, which has a characteristic odor. Calcium carbide, on the other hand, is an odorless substance. If, then, an odor is noted in the vicinity of carbide storage, it acts as a warning that acetylene gas is present.

Acetylene Gas

Acetylene gas, C_2H_2, is one of a number of hydrocarbon gases; it is produced by the action of water on calcium carbide:

$$CaC_2 + 2H_2O = C_2H_2 + Ca(OH)_2$$

Acetylene is composed of 92.3 per cent C and 7.7 per cent H by weight. A distinctive feature of acetylene gas is its endothermic property, which is equal to 228 Btu/cu ft.

Generation of Acetylene. Acetylene gas for welding is produced in acetylene generator equipment. Generators are of two basic designs. The least-used method is that in which water is dripped onto a large volume of carbide. The term drip generator has been applied to this design, which is used primarily for small lamp applications. The difficulty encountered in this type is that as the water is added to the carbide, considerable quantities of heat are developed. The heat, in turn, acts to increase the temperature of the carbide, which may become high enough to cause dissociation of the acetylene into its components, with further release of heat.

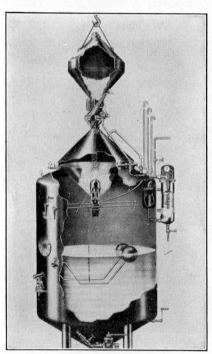

The heat difficulty was overcome by building a generator on the principle of dropping carbide into a large volume of water, so that reaction temperatures could be controlled. A generator of this design is shown in Fig. 32-2. Charging is regulated in order to maintain a constant pressure of acetylene independent of the volume being withdrawn from the generator.

The National Board of Fire Underwriters exercises strict jurisdictional control over the design and manufacture of acetylene generators. Capacities for water and carbide are specified, as are other constructional features including gas withdrawal rate and safety devices.

Fig. 32-2. Industrial-type acetylene generator in cutaway view showing carbide supply at top. (Courtesy of Linde Air Products Co., New York.)

Generators are further divided as to operation, between low- and medium-pressure systems. Portable generators are popular where small volumes of acetylene are used, while large industrial establishments have permanent installations.

Compressed Acetylene. Inasmuch as many users of acetylene gas do not require a volume sufficient to warrant the installation of generator equipment, they find it expedient to purchase the gas rather than to produce it. In the early years of the industry, the term dissolved acetylene was widely used. This expression originated from the construction of the acetylene cylinders, wherein the gas is actually held in solution in acetone (CH_3—CO—CH_3). Claude and Hess[1] discovered that at pressures exceeding 24 psi, dissociation starts at one point in the gas volume and spreads very rapidly through the entire volume, causing a complete breakdown of the acetylene accompanied by a tremendous increase in temperature and pressure.

In 1896 basic patents were granted on the revolutionary idea of compressing acetylene in the small voids that result from inserting a porous filler in the acetylene storage cylinder. In a later development, acetone was poured into the porous lining in order to fill all voids. Acetone has the property of dissolving approximately twenty-four times its own volume of acetylene for each atmosphere of pressure.

Acetylene Cylinders. The construction of acetylene cylinders is governed by regulations of the Interstate Commerce Commission. The cylinders in most common use for welding have an acetylene capacity of approximately 275 cu ft at 250 psi pressure at 70°F. Cylinders are varied as to physical form, both domed- and recessed-head types being used. There is a base band encircling the bottom of the cylinder as a protective device for safety in handling. Several fusible plugs that melt at 220°F are located in both the top and the bottom of the cylinder as an additional protective measure. Regulations do not generally permit the use of a valve handwheel; instead a wrench is necessary to open the cylinder—a precaution against tampering. A safety link is usually provided in the valve stem as a means of preventing valve damage from rough treatment.

The cylinder contains some type of porous filler material to provide the cells which hold the acetone. There are several classifications of filler materials—loose fillers, semi-supported fillers, and self-supporting fillers. Examples of loose fillers are raw silk, kapok, granulated charcoal, and infusorial earth mixed with treated wood chips. Loose fillers lack adhesive properties and are forced into the cylinders in a predetermined amount. Asbestos blocks are the leading type of semi-supported filler.

Self-supporting fillers are composed of grains or fibers, or both, joined together by binding agents into a monolithic, porous body, Charcoal and infusorial earth with asbestos fibers bound together with zinc or oxychloride cement are examples of this type of filler (Fig. 32-3). Inasmuch as the acetylene gas in a cylinder is dissolved in acetone, the pressure gage is inadequate for showing gas content. The gas volume is determined by weight, using a constant of 14.5 cu ft/lb at 70°F.

Precautions. Regulations forbid any but the supplier to fill acetylene cylinders.

[1] Claude, George, and Albert Hess: "Sur un nouveau mode d'emmagasinement de l'acétylène," Académie des Sciences, Paris, 1897.

One cylinder should never be filled from another for any reason whatsoever.

Open flame should be kept away from acetylene cylinders.

Acetylene gas mixed with air in volumes from 3 per cent upward forms an explosive mixture.

Acetylene cylinders can only provide gas in a volume that the acetone will yield; therefore the valve should be opened only partially. Failure to observe this precaution will result in drawing liquid acetone into the welding apparatus, causing it to foul. Cylinders should always be used in an upright position.

Copper tubing should never be used as an acetylene line. Brass or a copper-base alloy is the proper material. Iron or steel pipe is entirely satisfactory for distribution mains and laterals.

Oxygen

This gas is familiar to every engineering student. It is obtained by fractional distillation of liquid air, of which it forms about 20 per cent by volume. The boiling point of oxygen is —297.2°F, while nitrogen boils at —320.5°F. When the two liquids are mechanically mixed, they can be separated by reaching and holding the temperature at which one will vaporize; this is the basis of oxygen production. Oxygen is compressed in cylinders for industrial distribution.

Oxygen Cylinders. Cylinders for the distribution of oxygen are manufactured and maintained under the regulations of the Interstate Commerce Commission. Cylinders are of various sizes; the most common size in the gas welding shop has a capacity of 220 cu ft at 2,000 psi pressure at 70°F. The cylinders are of one-piece construction, being produced by piercing a billet section, as shown in Fig. 32-4.

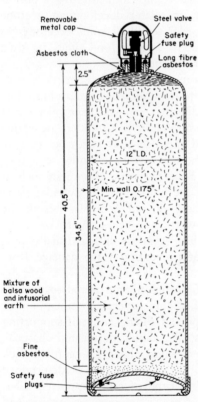

Fig. 32-3. Diagram of the cross section of a conventional acetylene cylinder. Acetylene capacity approximately 275 cu ft at 250 psi pressure and 70°F; water capacity approximately 4,021 cu in. (Courtesy of Air Reduction Sales Co., New York.)

Every oxygen cylinder has a series of numbers and letters stamped on its dome. The inscription ICC-3A refers to Interstate Commerce Commission regulation 3A governing the manufacture and maintenance of cylinders. The serial number and the initials of the owning company are then given. The series of figures below these are the date of manufacture and the dates of testing. Each cylinder must be tested at five-year

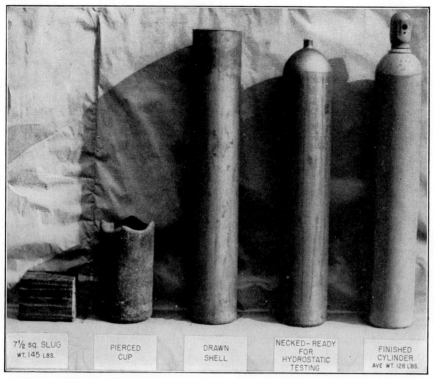

| 7½ sq. SLUG WT. 145 LBS. | PIERCED CUP | DRAWN SHELL | NECKED- READY FOR HYDROSTATIC TESTING | FINISHED CYLINDER AVE WT. 128 LBS. |

Fig. 32-4. Successive operations in the production of a standard oxygen cylinder. (Courtesy of Taylor-Wharton Co., Easton, Pa.)

intervals as a precautionary measure, and the month and year of each test are stamped on the cylinder.

Oxygen cylinders are equipped with valves designed to be opened fully when in service. Many designs have an upper seat which acts to prevent leakage along the stem when the valve is fully open. The valve body has a frangible disk designed to release the contents of the cylinder in case excessive pressures should be built up, as in the event of a fire. A protective cap covers the valve and prevents damage to this vital part of the cylinder assembly.

GAS WELDING EQUIPMENT

Regulators. The pressure of a full oxygen cylinder at room temperature is 2,200 psi, while the acetylene cylinder carries a pressure of 250 psi. These pressures are too high for any welding operation. In order to reduce the pressures, a piece of equipment known as a regulator is attached directly to the gas cylinder.

Regulators are obtainable for acetylene as well as oxygen. However, regulators are not the same for the two gases, since cylinder pressure for oxygen is almost ten times that for acetylene. Regulators can be distinguished from one another by noting the scale on the gages of the regulators or by checking the threads for the hose connection.

A regulator is a reduction valve operating on the diaphragm principle. The regulator has a T handle which, when turned clockwise, loads a

Fig. 32-5. Double-stage gas regulator shown at left and single-stage at right. (Courtesy of Smith Welding Equipment Corp., Minneapolis.)

spring as desired by the weldor. The spring pressure is such that the diaphragm reacting against it will permit gas of the predetermined pressure to pass through to the hose.

Insofar as the design of the regulators is concerned, there are two general types (Fig. 32-5). The one described above is known as a single-stage regulator; another is the double, or two-stage, regulator. The advantage of the two-stage regulator is that it makes a more accurate compensation for pressure loss in the cylinder resulting from gas consumption. In this design the first stage is generally an automatic one, while the second stage is controlled by the aforementioned T handle.

Another respect in which regulator design offers two alternatives is the gage; some designs use a single gage, while others use two. With the single-gage regulator it is possible to read only the pressure on the welding line; there is no means of determining cylinder pressure. When there are two gages on the regulator, one gage shows the cylinder pressure and the other one will read at zero until the desired gas pressure has been established by turning the T handle. It must be remembered that as the volume of gas in the cylinder is consumed, cylinder pressures drop, which may, in the case of a single-stage regulator, make it necessary for the weldor to readjust the regulator to maintain the desired line pressure.

Before a regulator is attached to a cylinder, the cylinder valve, with the opening facing away from the weldor, should be "cracked," *i.e.*, opened slightly and immediately closed. This is done in order to free the regulator attachment seat of any foreign matter. The regulator is attached by means of a union nut, which should be drawn up snugly.

Welding Hose. The gases are conducted from the regulators to the torch by means of hoses specially made for this purpose. As a warning, the hose on the acetylene cylinder is red, indicating inflammable gas.

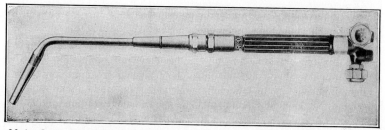

Fig. 32-6. Conventional oxyacetylene welding torch. (Courtesy of Bastian-Blessing Co., Chicago.)

The hose used for oxygen is either dark green or black. There is also available a twin hose in which both hoses are bound into one. Hose connections are arranged with a connecting nut on each end of the hose. In order to prevent a crossover on hose connections, the acetylene hose is always equipped with a left-hand thread, while the oxygen hose has a right-hand thread. As a further distinguishing characteristic, the acetylene hose nut has a groove machined in it, whereas the oxygen one is plain.

Torches. The construction of the welding torch and all its features vary with different manufacturers (Fig. 32-6). Essentially a torch consists of the base or butt, of which the gas connections are an integral part. Gas flow is regulated by a needle valve on each gas inlet. The base of the torch is joined permanently to the body, which serves as the handle and contains single passages for oxygen and acetylene.

The torch head houses the mixing chamber, in which the two entering gases are blended into the oxyacetylene mixture that issues from the torch tip, where combustion occurs. The tips are of different design and construction insofar as appearance and mechanical details are concerned. Each tip has an appropriate gradation based on the size of the orifice at its open end (Fig. 32-7). A given tip is designed to weld a joint of specific thickness; correct choice of tip is essential to proper welding results. The employment of a tip that is too small or one that is too large will result in improper welding conditions and prove costly in both gas and labor.

Basic Torch Design. Welding torches are designed either for *low-pressure* or for *medium-pressure* operation. Design details for these two types of operation are different. There are no high-pressure welding torches; in the early period of oxyacetylene welding these proved too dangerous and were discarded. There is one torch designed to function

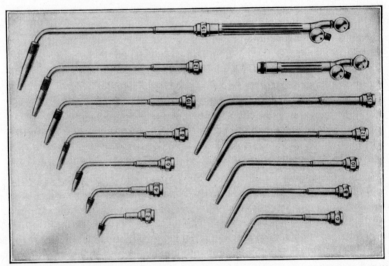

Fig. 32-7. Oxyacetylene welding torch and interchangeable tips. (Courtesy of Harris Calorific Co., Cleveland.)

on both the low- and the medium-pressure system. An acetylene generator or torch which operates at a pressure below 1 psi is of the low-pressure type, whereas those operating at pressures up to 15 psi are in the medium-pressure category.

The low-pressure torch employs a low acetylene pressure, using the oxygen pressure to aspirate the acetylene in an action similar to that of a Bunsen burner.

The medium-pressure torch, on occasion referred to as an equal-pressure torch, operates with both gases at the same pressure. The gas pressure is relied upon to cause flow of the combustible mixture through the tip. Pressures vary with tip sizes; each different tip size requires pressure adjustment for that particular size. Manufacturers' recommendations should be followed as to tip sizes and pressures.

Oxyacetylene Welding Flames. Since there are two gases combined in the combustion mixture in the torch, three flame conditions are possible:

1. Neutral or normal flame (gases correctly proportioned)
2. Carburizing or reducing flame (excess acetylene in mixture)
3. Oxidizing or cutting flame (excess oxygen in mixture)

These three flames are distinctive in appearance, in sound of operation, and in temperature (Fig. 32-8). For most welding applications the neutral flame is best, although both of the other types are employed in

Torch Flames	NEUTRAL	OXIDIZING	CARBURIZING
	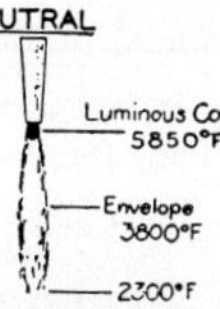 Luminous Cone 5850°F Envelope 3800°F 2300°F	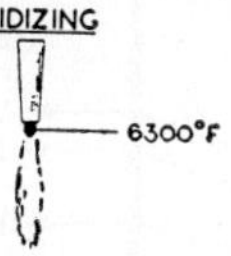 6300°F	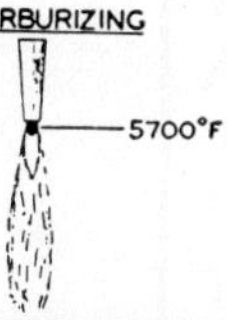 5700°F
Ratio Oxygen	1.04-1.14	1.15-1.70	0.85-0.95
Acetylene	1	1	1
Effect on Metal	Metal is clean and clear, flowing easily.	Excessive foaming and sparking of metal.	Metal boils and is not clear.

Fig. 32-8. Oxyacetylene flame characteristics under different gas ratios. (Courtesy of Air Reduction Sales Co., New York.)

specific instances. Figure 32-9 embodies the recommendations of the International Acetylene Association.

The chemistry and heat balance of the neutral oxyacetylene welding flame are as follows:

$$
\begin{array}{lll}
 & & Btu/cu\ ft \\
\text{Primary combustion} & C_2H_2 + O_2 = 2CO + H_2 = & 287 \\
\text{Secondary combustion} & 2CO + O_2 = 2CO_2 \quad = & 641 \\
 & H_2 + \tfrac{1}{2}O_2 = H_2O \quad = & 277 \\
\text{Endothermic} & = & 228 \\
\hline
 & & 1433
\end{array}
$$

Primary combustion employs one volume each of C_2H_2 and O_2; these gases are supplied directly from the cylinders or gas lines. Their combustion represents the inner core of the flame (Fig. 32-8). The highest flame temperature ccurs at the tip of the inner cone; hence the tip of this cone should be held just off the metal for best results in welding.

The oxygen necessary for secondary combustion is obtained from the ambient atmosphere and totals $1\frac{1}{2}$ volumes. Secondary combustion is present as the outer or enveloping flame. Its importance in welding is twofold: it acts as a preheating medium and also prevents oxidation

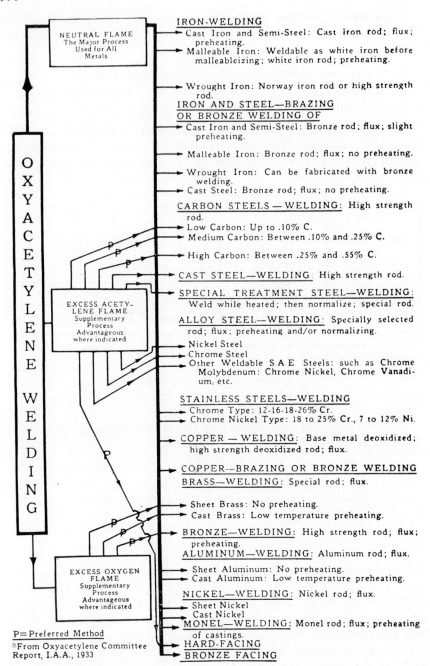

Fig. 32-9. Oxyacetylene welding applications. (Courtesy of International Acetylene Association, New York.)

of the weld, since it consumes the oxygen of the surrounding air. Correct flame adjustment, coupled with proper torch manipulation and welding techniques, delivers the high type of work of which gas welding is capable.

Weld Rods. In some types of joints, such as edged or flange-edged, or flange joints, welding can proceed without addition of an external source of weld metal. Gas welds made without the addition of weld metal were formerly termed autogenous welds. When, however, a veed or similar joint is to be welded, it is necessary to add weld metal from a source referred to as a welding rod. Information on gas welding rods is given in specification A5.2-46 issued by the American Welding Society.

APPLIED GAS WELDING

The groundwork for making a gas weld consists of proper joint preparation on the metal to be welded. The weldor then selects the tip that is correct in size for the joint and adjusts the regulator pressures in accordance with the recommended values for the particular tip chosen. The torch is lighted by opening the acetylene valve very slightly. After the acetylene gas is ignited, greater volume is turned on until the acetylene flame, which is a very deep yellow, just leaves the tip of the torch. The oxygen valve on the torch is then opened and oxygen is fed into the flame until the desired flame condition has been achieved.

The actual welding operation consists of heating the base metal until a molten pool forms. The welding rod is immersed in the pool and thus melted. The flame should bring the edges of the joint to a molten state ahead of the puddle. The weldor moves the torch from side to side in a rippling motion.

Gas welding can be performed with either the forehand or the backhand method. In the case of a right-handed weldor, using the forehand method means that the weld will start on the right and progress toward the left. This procedure results in the torch flame pointing in the direction of welding, thereby giving considerable preheat to the joint. Backhand welding is just the reverse. The welding starts at the left end of the joint and proceeds toward the right. Steel is welded without the use of flux; cast iron, brass, and aluminum require flux. Flux is added by heating the weld rod and dipping it into the flux, or by sprinkling flux onto the joint, or, as is frequently done in the case of nonferrous metals, the flux is made into a liquid paste that is brushed on both the weld rod and the joint. The addition of flux serves the purpose of removing oxides and preventing their formation. It also aids in some instances by giving a "wetting" action to the molten weld metal.

Oxyhydrogen Welding

The Master Chart of Welding Processes shows that oxyhydrogen is a significant gas welding process. Hydrogen, when burned with oxygen, delivers a flame temperature of 4622°F, which is considerably below that of the oxyacetylene flame. Because of low flame temperature, oxyhydrogen welding is applied primarily to low-fusion-point metals. There have been instances where this flame was desirable because of the absence of any carburizing action such as can result from an improperly adjusted oxyacetylene flame.

Manifolds and Distribution Systems

Portable oxygen and acetylene cylinders are used primarily in jobbing-type welding. The volume of gas available from a single cylinder is limited for a given time interval. Production welding frequently requires gas in considerable volume because of the number of torches operating simultaneously. In order to supply this demand it is customary to connect several cylinders to a common line. Essentially these lines are headers equipped with requisite threaded connections and valved to permit adding or closing off the connected gas cylinders as circumstances demand. These headers, together with their accompanying valves and gages, are known as manifolds.

Acetylene manifolds are connected to flash-back arresters, which in turn lead to the distribution system. Large users of acetylene employ generators as the gas source; however, the oxygen is supplied from manifolded cylinders or, in some large installations, from high-pressure oxygen-tube trailers. The welding stations are equipped with single-gage regulators, inasmuch as line pressures established at the manifolds are usually above torch needs. The piping comprising welding gas distribution systems should have welded joints and should be painted in colors to meet safety regulations.

SURVEY QUESTIONS

32-1. Mention another term or name for a welding torch.

32-2. What is the predominant gas welding method?

32-3. How is calcium carbide related to gas welding?

32-4. In what way does geography affect the source of calcium carbide?

32-5. Why is acetylene regarded as a distinctive gas?

32-6. How can the presence of acetylene gas be detected?

32-7. Who has jurisdiction over the design of acetylene generating and transporting equipment?

32-8. Explain the term "compressed acetylene."

32-9. If acetylene and oxygen cylinders are unlike, wherein do they differ?

32-10. Discuss any precautions governing the withdrawal of acetylene from its cylinder.

32-11. What safety devices are built into oxygen cylinders?

32-12. Other than by the gages, how can oxygen regulators be distinguished from acetylene ones?

32-13. What purpose do two gages serve on a welding gas regulator?

32-14. Explain the advantage of twin hose, if any.

32-15. Why are torches designed to accommodate different size welding tips?

32-16. What gas pressure is critical when using a low-pressure torch?

32-17. An AISI 3135 coupler is to be welded. What type of welding flame is best here?

32-18. An automobile water jacket has burst because of freezing. How should the broken pieces be welded in order to gain a satisfactory repair?

32-19. Wherein do weld rods differ from welding electrodes, if at all?

32-20. From whence does the total oxygen supply for a torch flame come?

32-21. What is backhand welding?

32-22. Is flux necessary for gas welding all metals? State any exceptions.

32-23. Give one specific application for oxyhydrogen welding.

32-24. When are manifolds necessary to a gas welding installation?

32-25. A gasoline service structure is to be welded from A7. What would be the most satisfactory and economical welding method for its construction?

Chapter 33

BRAZING AND
BRAZE WELDING

The joining of ferrous metals as well as the copper-base alloys by a nonferrous filler metal was undoubtedly one of the earliest welding processes. Under the specification "Standard Welding Terms and Their Definitions,"[1] terminology has been adopted to include all the metals that lend themselves to this type of joining. *Brazing* is defined in this standard as "a group of welding processes wherein coalescence is produced by heating to suitable temperatures above 800°F and by using a non-ferrous filler metal, having a melting point below that of the base metals. The filler metal is distributed between the closely fitted surfaces of the joint by capillary attraction."

Braze welding is defined in the same standard as "a method of welding whereby a groove, fillet, plug or slot weld is made using a non-ferrous filler metal, having a melting point below that of the base metals but above 800°F. The filler metal is *not* distributed in the joint by capillary attraction. (Bronze Welding, formerly used, is a misnomer for this term.)" Note that the parenthetical sentence is part of the standard definition. These definitions are included here in order to clarify the terms as used in this chapter.

BRAZING

Brazing is classified into eight types on the Master Chart of Welding Processes.[2] Each of these types refers primarily to a heating method. Other classifications can be made on the basis of filler metal and, to a lesser extent, of base metal. Again, brazing processes are, on occasion, catalogued as high-temperature or low-temperature.

The use of the word brazing can be misleading. Originally it may have been derived from the idea of using pulverized brass or brass spelter.

[1] American Standard A3.0-49, American Welding Society, New York, 1949.
[2] American Standard A3.1-49, American Welding Society, New York, 1949.

594

This limitation is no longer valid; copper and copper-base alloys do not monopolize the field of braze filler metals, since aluminum, magnesium, and the silver-base alloys are also included.

The Bond. A brazed joint is one that is processed by employing a temperature which is at least 100°F below the melting point of the base metal. The base metal is not brought to fusion where it could form an alloy with the molten braze metal. Conjecture arises at once over the exact nature of bond. The question is best answered by a microscopic examination of the area (Fig. 33-1). The example shown displays some diffusion at the interface of the brazing and base metal resulting in a narrow area of intermediate composition. The braze metals are chosen for their affinity to the base metal. Braze metals must diffuse rapidly

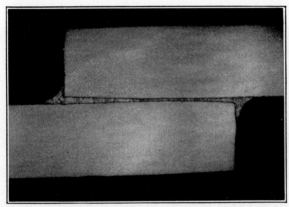

Fig. 33-1. Micrograph of brazed bond on steel sections. (Courtesy of American Brass Co., Waterbury, Conn.)

into the base metal, thereby creating an alloy of a relatively low melting point. The success or failure of a brazed joint is dependent upon the proper interbonding between the metals composing the joint.

Braze Metals. The braze metals employed with ferrous materials are primarily of copper or silver base. The copper-base brazing alloys have higher melting points than those containing silver. Commercially pure copper is used as a brazing alloy even though temperature has to reach 2050°F; this is the highest temperature for any brazing operation. There are many copper-base brazing compositions; some meet the standard specifications, while others have been developed on an individual basis.

The second classification of braze metal used in joining ferrous materials of all types, whether the joint is of the same or dissimilar metals, comprises the silver-base alloys. These materials are receiving deserved attention on a broad scale as they become better known and their potentialities are better understood. One deterrent to wider acceptance is the belief that because they contain silver they are too costly to use in engineering manufacture. Actually the reverse is true when silver brazing alloys are specified and correct procedures are established. These alloys have a flow point range between 1175 and 1600°F. These braze metals find greater acceptance in joining stainless steels than do the copper braze ones.

The brazing alloys are procurable in the form of sheet, strip, wire, and powder or granules. Sheet that is only a few thousandths of an inch thick is available as a standard commercial product. A desirable procedure is to place thin braze metal sheet or rings in a joint as a means of proper distribution. The use of wire for ringing a circular joint is also common practice.

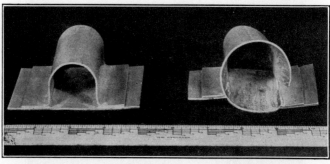

Fig. 33-2. Aluminum brazed specimen using brazing sheet before and after destructive testing. (Courtesy of Welding Laboratory, University of Washington, Seattle, Wash.)

Another class of brazing alloys is used with aluminum alloys. Brazing aluminum alloys differs from other brazing applications only in the choice of the braze metal. Some alloys have been developed specifically for this purpose. The chief one is 4043, also specified as ASTM B85; this alloy is composed of 5 per cent Si and the balance Al. It has a flow range between 1070 and 1165°F. Composite sheet made up of 3003 core material clad on one side with a brazing alloy is termed no. 11 brazing sheet, whereas cladding on both sides is known as no. 12 brazing sheet. The use of this composite sheet greatly simplifies brazing procedures. Figure 33-2 shows a braze made with such a sheet, bent in U shape, to a plain sheet of 3003 Al alloy.

Brazing Paste. The major part of copper brazing is done in furnaces. Brazing copper is generally supplied in the form of rings, foil, slugs, metalizing, or electroplate. Another means for supplying the copper braze metal is brazing paste. It is maintained that the ease with which the paste can be applied simplifies the entire brazing operation. Applicator units have been developed which permit the paste to be extruded in a number of forms, such as rounds, ribbons, flats, etc., thereby facilitating its placement at the desired location in the joint.

Fluxes. The use of flux on a brazed joint is mandatory inasmuch as the necessity of protecting the base metal from oxidation at brazing temperatures is always present. Flux must dissolve any oxides which are present and also prevent the formation of oxides. It must also be liquid at brazing temperatures in order to flow over the joint surface.

Fluxes used for brazing are of various compositions, since their behavior is a combination of chemical and mechanical action. Common borax has long been a stand-by in forge welding. It has some use in brazing, but its application is limited because it does not have the property of dissolving the oxides of aluminum, chromium, or beryllium. When borax is used as a flux, it should be made into a paste by dissolving it in alcohol; water is useless for this purpose since it will evaporate at operating temperatures, leaving crystalline borax.

The composition of brazing fluxes can be quite complex. Some of the ingredients used are boric acid, phosphates, and halogen salts. Fluorides are generally present in fluxes used for brazing aluminum. Fluxes are available as powder, as paste, and as liquid. Flux is usually painted on the surfaces to be brazed, since this results both in full coverage and in even distribution.

The possibility of entrapped flux on large areas is always present. A research project on this problem was undertaken at the University of Washington.[3] The specimens used in this project were $7/8$-in.-diameter C1035 cold-drawn steel. After butt brazing, the specimens were machined to standard 0.505-in. tensile test bars and subjected to the tensile test. Most brazed joints proved unsound owing to flux inclusions. A solution was found by vibrating the joint to eliminate entrapped flux.

Joint Design. Since brazing depends on capillary attraction for its success, joint clearance should be designed to promote this action. The general principle governing braze joint design is to have the smallest possible clearance in the joint. Experience gained on many brazing specimens indicates that with grade 12 alloy, there was little difference in joint strengths, when loaded in tension, so long as the clearance in the joint did not exceed 0.015 in. Above that value, joint strengths lessened in direct proportion to joint clearance.

Shear-type joints are preferable, since they permit variation in joint surface area to meet design requirements. They have also proved superior from the standpoint of corrosion resistance. A joint design that permits the use of pressure during the brazing operation will give superior

[3] Crane, C. H., and T. J. Bauer: "Silver Brazed Joints," graduation thesis in Mechanical Engineering, 1946.

results. Joint design means little if the ordinary precautions of surface cleansing and surface finish are overlooked. The use of carbon tetra-chloride on the joint surface prior to flux application will remove oil, grease, and foreign matter and provide a clean surface for subsequent processing. Examples of joint designs are shown in Fig. 33-3.

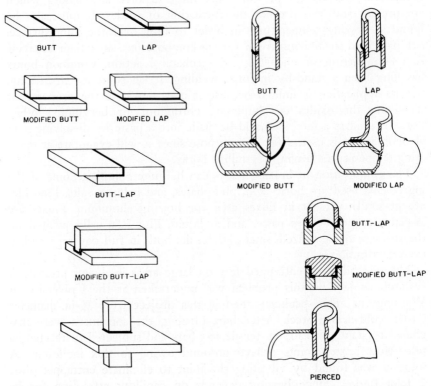

BUTT   LAP

MODIFIED BUTT   MODIFIED LAP

BUTT-LAP

BUTT   LAP

MODIFIED BUTT   MODIFIED LAP

BUTT-LAP

MODIFIED BUTT-LAP   MODIFIED BUTT-LAP

PIERCED

Fig. 33-3. Basic development of joint designs common to brazing. (Courtesy of Handy & Harman, New York.)

Brazing Method

There are several methods of applying heat for brazing. The selection of the method to be used will be dependent on such factors as base metal, braze metal, joint design, part size, and production requirements. Most satisfactory results are achieved by assembling the joint with the braze metal in place prior to heating. This recommended procedure often requires the use of holding fixtures or other clamping devices. However, the pressure that such devices exert on the joint contributes to the superior results that are obtained.

Torch Brazing. Torch brazing employs the use of a gas torch as the source of heat. A welding torch is commonly used for flexibility. Braze

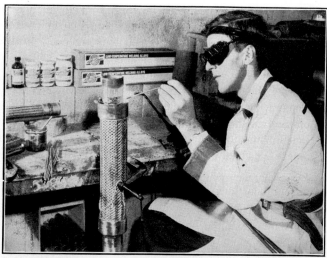

Fig. 33-4. Torch brazing operation on a vibration eliminator that must withstand 550 psi bursting pressure. (Courtesy of the All-State Welding Alloy Co., White Plains, N.Y.)

Fig. 33-5. Stationary torch brazing of heat exchanger parts. (Courtesy of Handy & Harman, New York.)

metal is added in the form of wire (Fig. 33-4). The difficulty in this particular application is to prevent burn-through on the flexible bronze hose.

A second application of torch brazing is shown in Fig. 33-5. In this setup, multiple-flame torches are used. These form a permanent installation into which the product to be brazed is moved. On this particular job the flame time of 45 sec is controlled by a timing device that shuts off the gas. There are 32 joints brazed simultaneously in this operation.

Induction Brazing. The principle of induction heating is being applied to brazing where the product is produced in quantity. Where so employed, it is necessary to develop heating coil equipment of a shape and size to accommodate the component to be brazed. It is for this reason that induction brazing does not offer the versatility of the torch system;

Fig. 33-6. Preparing a part to be induction-brazed. Note threads on base which require that no braze metal spill. (Courtesy of Handy & Harman, New York.)

however, when an installation has been properly made, much more accurate control can be had by induction brazing. An example of induction brazing is shown in Fig. 33-6. The braze metal is in the form of a ring about to be set in position prior to placing in the induction heating fixture. The equipment is operated by means of a foot switch, and through electronic controls the time and temperature are held within close limits.

Furnace Brazing. Furnace brazing is used on assemblies, and the entire operation is frequently mechanized by using a conveyor-type furnace. The sections to be joined are assembled with the braze metal in position. Clamping fixtures may or may not be necessary, depending upon the individual job.

There is a considerable amount of copper hydrogen furnace brazing. The hydrogen atmosphere maintained within the furnace eliminates the use of flux. This system of brazing has had a great deal to do with the development of carbide-tipped tools, the single-point as well as the more elaborate types. When a single-point tool is being tipped with a carbide insert, the tool material is milled out to accommodate the insert. The braze metal is then placed between the carbide piece and the tool and wired into position. This assembly is placed in the controlled hydrogen atmosphere of the furnace and brazing is completed. Brazing alloys used for such work are either silver- or copper-base.

Dip Brazing. The idea of using a molten bath as a source of heat for brazing has two aspects. In one instance the bath is composed of some type of salts, which serve merely as a source of heat. The advantage, of course, is that any assembly immersed in the molten salt bath will attain a uniform temperature.

In the other system of dip brazing, the molten bath is composed of filler metal. The part to be brazed, having previously been fluxed, is dipped into the molten bath and the filler metal enters the joint, thereby completing the brazing operation. This system is used for such specialties as joining wire ends and is not employed on parts of any size.

BRAZE WELDING

Braze welding consists of a gas torch welding operation in which the weld rod is of copper base, although copper-base electrodes are available for arc use. The composition of the weld rod is such that its melting point is well below that of the material on which it is used. By way of example, one of the well-regarded braze weld rods has a melting temperature of 1650°F. When this is used in connection with a ferrous metal, savings can obviously be effected, since welding time is shortened and less heat is required.

There are some instances in which ferrous materials have been braze-welded in construction. There have been some cast-iron pipelines assembled with braze-welded joints. Galvanized sheet steel can be braze-welded with ease and at the same time retain the corrosion resistance of the original sheet. Examples can be found in motorcar construction, where sheet steel stampings are joined by braze welding.

Braze welding is of greatest utility in connection with reclamation and repair. The soundest procedure for reclaiming a broken malleable cast-iron part is braze welding. This is true both from the metallurgical and from the mechanical standpoint. Cast-iron parts are frequently repaired with braze welding. This method has become so general in the repair shop that steel parts are also being braze-welded.

Applied Braze Welding

Joint surfaces must be clean and free of grease. They should then be placed in proper alignment prior to heat application. An important consideration for making a sound braze weld is the careful fluxing of the joint. Fluxes are generally in powdered form. They are added to the braze weld by sprinkling on the surface, both before and during the welding operation. Further flux can be added by heating the braze rod

Fig. 33-7. This huge glass manufacturing roll, warped by heat-treatment, was saved by overlaying the end shaft with bronze weld metal (top). The finished surface of the end shaft machined to concentric dimensions, evenly built up with no distortion or warping of giant expensive roll (bottom). (Courtesy of the Eutectic Welding Alloys Corp., New York.)

and dipping it into the flux, causing the latter to flow and form a coating on the rod.

Heating of the base metal is most generally done with the gas torch. The chief precaution is to see to it that the base metal is not overheated and at the same time receives sufficient heat. The temperature should be such that the braze weld rod will melt and flow when it is rubbed against the heated base metal.

The best way of making a braze weld is to coat the surface of the joint with braze metal in a procedure referred to as tinning. This is merely a very light or thin coat of braze metal. When tinning is done correctly, the braze welding operation becomes a very simple one. One difficulty, especially in braze welding cast iron, is preventing the formation of "whirlpools" in the molten weld metal. When these do appear, their cause can usually be traced to the presence of scale or slag inclusions. It is then necessary to heat that area and puddle the metal with a weld rod, freeing the inclusion so that it can float to the surface. Braze welding is frequently the preferred method for repairing mechanical parts (Fig. 33-7).

EFFECTING ECONOMIES THROUGH BRAZING

Brazing or braze welding can be a decided step in the direction of lowered production costs. These processes have for the most part been

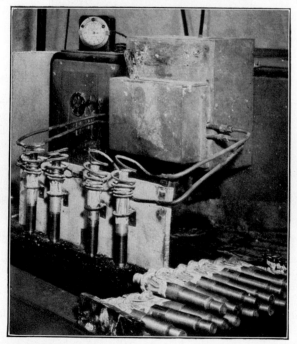

Fig. 33-8. Induction brazing shaft assembly used in brazing collar to shaft. (Courtesy of Handy & Harman, New York.)

regarded as a specialty associated primarily with joining small, light-gage metal parts. The potentialities of these processes for lowering production costs on heavier members have frequently been overlooked. The design shown in Fig. 33-8 is but one example of the possibility of breaking down a member into smaller components that will be the basis of a brazed assembly. Smaller components are made with less material and frequently with a substantial saving in labor and material costs.

The problem of producing a crankshaft for a 2 by 2-in. air compressor was solved in a satisfactory manner by a brazed assembly. Samples of crankshafts so produced were tested in torsion and the results were well above design values. Another important saving resulted from the elimination of substantial investment in forging dies and forging equipment. The

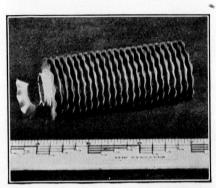

Fig. 33-9. Heat exchanger tube with radiating fins brazed to main tube.

Fig. 33-10. Broken milling cutter at left repaired by silver brazing shown at right. (Courtesy of Handy & Harman, New York.)

brazed design offered flexibility without the risk of obsolescence of expensive tooling.

The heat exchanger tube shown in Fig. 33-9 is another example of production brazing. This tube is made by winding the radiating fin metal as a helix on the base tube. The junction between them is brazed to give a solid joint with high heat conductivity. An example of the reclamation of broken tools is shown in Fig. 33-10. It is evident that such repair work can effect considerable economies both through the re-use of the tool and through the saving that can be realized by reducing lost time in the shop.

SURVEY QUESTIONS

33-1. How is braze metal classified?

33-2. Is there any molten metal present at the braze joint interface?

33-3. Should a broken surveyor tape be repaired by braze welding or by brazing?

33-4. How can the strength developed by a brazed joint be accounted for?

33-5. If brazing is successfully used with nonferrous metals, give an example.

33-6. Precisely where is brazing sheet used?

33-7. List the components or materials necessary to making a brazed joint.

33-8. Give an example of production copper brazing.

33-9. If there is a place for borax in a brazing operation, explain its function.

33-10. Wherein, if at all, do braze joint designs differ from arc welding ones?

33-11. Why is brazing critical to the modern machine shop?

33-12. Of all of the different brazing operations, which is most flexible? Why?

33-13. How is a brazing fixture used?

33-14. If brazing can be adapted to production line activity, give a specific example.

33-15. What is the derivation of the term "induction brazing"?

33-16. Outline a procedure that will produce a welded joint between cast iron and mild steel.

33-17. Develop the least complicated routine for repairing a crack in a section of a wall-type cast iron hot water radiator.

33-18. If brazing is preferable to arc welding a broken side milling cutter, state the reasons.

33-19. How should a broken auto bumper be repaired for lasting service?

33-20. Explain if there is any difference between silver brazing and silver soldering.

33-21. Just what does "tinning" mean in brazing?

33-22. If brazing is used as a production method, name some components so treated.

33-23. Is braze or gas welding the more economical in reclamation of cast iron?

33-24. What is the general physical form of braze metal prior to use?

Chapter 34

RESISTANCE WELDING

FUNDAMENTAL FACTORS

Resistance welding is defined as "a group of welding processes wherein coalescence is produced by the heat obtained from the resistance of the work to the flow of electric current in a circuit of which the work is a part, and by the application of pressure."[1] A feature of resistance welding is that all the welding covered by this term involves the use of pressure. From this it is obvious that there is no such thing as manual resistance welding; on the contrary, all resistance welding is done in some type of resistance welding machine. There is some portable equipment; however, the work done by this equipment is not analogous to manual welding by other methods.

Since welding machines are necessary to resistance welding, the range of work that can be resistance-welded is narrow. Resistance welding is thought of primarily as a process for joining comparatively light gage metal parts. An exception is the flash butt welding of sections attaining diameters of several inches.

Heat Origin and Distribution. Heat used in these welding methods is generated by the resistance of the parts to be welded to the passage of the electric current supplied by the welding machine. The heat for resistance welding is expressed by the formula

$$W = I^2Rt$$

where W = heat, watt-sec
I = current flowing through the weld, amp
R = resistance, ohms
t = time, sec

The salient features of a typical spot welder are shown in Fig. 34-1. The pieces to be welded are lapped and in position under the electrodes of the welding machine. Power supply is brought in through a timer,

[1] "Standard Welding Terms and Their Definitions," American Standard A3.0-49, American Welding Society, New York, 1949.

then passes through a transformer equipped with current regulator; provision for applying pressure to the electrodes is also included.

The temperature gradient on a spot-welding operation is shown in Fig. 34-2. The temperature varies considerably through the weld section. The flow of heat in a resistance weld is affected by several factors;

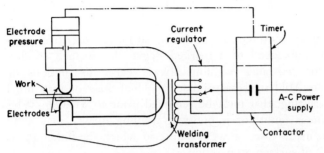

Fig. 34-1. Diagrammatic sketch of spot welder circuit. (From The Welding Journal, August, 1945.)

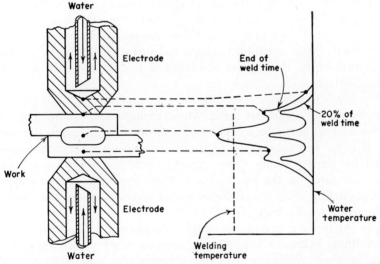

Fig. 34-2. Temperature gradient diagram for a spot-welding operation. (From The Welding Journal, August, 1945.)

prominent among them is the electrical resistance of the materials being welded. This means that materials of high heat and electrical conductivity will be difficult to weld in that they will require high welding currents. They also make it necessary to provide electrode material capable of carrying the required currents. Silver and copper are not readily welded, yet certain of their alloys present no difficulty because of their lower conductivity. Aluminum, whose conductivity is about 60 per cent of that of annealed copper, is readily welded but current requirements are high. The high-strength aluminum alloys, prominent in aircraft construction, have a conductivity equal to about one-half that of commercially pure aluminum, a fact that makes them well adapted to resistance welding. Other commonly used engineering materials—such as nickel alloys, steel, magnesium, and, especially, stainless steels—are also readily weldable.

The contact resistance at the faying surfaces is a critical consideration, since it is influenced to a marked degree by surface conditions. Procedures for resistance welding always carry instructions on surface preparation. Mild steel has mill scale, which may or may not be aggravated by rusting, that must be removed prior to welding. When surface preparation is faulty or is omitted, welding quality may suffer. There have been many cases of weld failure in which the difficulty was caused by neglect of surface preparation.

Welding electrodes require care in both selection and maintenance; contact resistance between them and the weldment must be held to a minimum. The tendency for the electrode contact surface to pick up metal from the weldment is always present. The degree of pickup is governed by such factors as composition, temperature, surface condition, and pressure. Strict attention to shape and surface condition of electrode tips is mandatory if excessive resistance is to be avoided at the outer contact surfaces.

Heat losses in resistance welding vary in proportion to the heat conductivity of the weldment metal. Metal of high heat conductivity will remove heat from the local weld area at a rate detrimental to the operation. It is for this reason that high current values are invariably accompanied by short welding times. Another heat loss arises from cooling water circulated in the electrodes. If they were permitted to operate without cooling, their temperatures would increase rapidly and electrical conductivity would drop.

Heat distribution across the weld is important for proper welding results. In a weldment consisting of two or more pieces, they should arrive at their respective welding temperatures simultaneously. This requisite is the same as in any welding operation. When this desired condition is fulfilled, there will be mutual diffusion, as between the weldment parts, and a sound weld will be formed. It is readily understandable that welding dissimilar metals is an extremely difficult matter, since with different fusion points, differing heating periods are indicated.

Power Supply. The unbalance in the power line caused by the operation of conventional single-phase resistance welding equipment (Fig. 34-3) has become a source of concern. The difficulty arises from the fact that a conventional single-phase welder operates at a power factor in the range of 30 to 60 per cent and has a high kva demand that is of short duration. A single-phase load connected to a three-phase power line causes unbalanced conditions in the latter which result in voltage disturbance in all three phases. One result of this unbalance is the flickering of lights when the welder is operating.

Another shortcoming in the operation of single-phase resistance welding equipment of the spot welder type arises from the introduction of the material to be welded into the throat of the machine. When material

Fig. 34-3. Foot-operated, single-phase, conventional-type spot welder. (Courtesy of The Taylor-Winfield Corp., Warren, Ohio.)

is thus placed, impedance is increased and the current passing through the secondary circuit is decreased. In procedures where spot welds follow along a welded joint, causing the weldment to move into the throat, each succeeding weld is made with decreasing heat because of the increasing impedance. Current compensating devices can be installed to maintain a constant current in the welding circuit; however, such further installations increase the amount of the original investment and tend, in a measure, to complicate the operation.

Power-line Loading. The difficulties of line unbalance occasioned by single-phase equipment are capable of a variety of solutions. All these embrace problems in electrical circuit design. One solution is the use of three-phase machines. These are of two general types—frequency converter and rectifier. In the frequency converter machines, the transformer has three primary windings, connected to the three phases of the power supply through control tubes. A single secondary supplies welding current of a lower basic frequency. The power factor of any electrical circuit is inversely proportional to the frequency; hence the net result of a frequency converter machine is to increase the power factor and decrease the kva demand. The current is taken from all three phases of the supply lines and the resulting power factor of such a machine is in the 80 to 90 per cent range.

Another type machine is the rectifier type. In this case, the three-phase supply voltage is transformed down to welding voltage, then rectified to direct current for welding. This results in a power factor of 90 per cent or better.

Alternating-current Heat Control. Since the welding current in single-phase a-c circuit is equal to the secondary voltage of the welding transformer divided by the impedance of the secondary circuit, it can be changed by varying any of these values. Impedance cannot be readily changed because its value depends on the dimensions of the secondary loop circuit coupled with the resistance of the weldment in the circuit and the resistance of the secondary leads. Varying the secondary voltage offers a better and more exact means of controlling the welding current. A simple means for varying secondary voltage is the use of taps, controlled by a tap switch, on the primary winding.

Equipment is available for changing the voltage to the primary of the welding transformer. The autotransformer is equipped with taps whereby its output voltage is varied. This output is connected to the primary of the welding transformer; the resultant hookup is capable of modifying the secondary transformer welding voltage and thus of varying the heat in the welding circuit.

Electronic Control. Heat control is also possible through the installation of electron tubes in the circuit ahead of the welding transformer. The two types of tubes used for this purpose are the ignitron and the thyratron. These tubes are rectifiers, passing current in one direction only. Two of these tubes connected back to back act as a contactor controlling the current to the welding transformer. When current is permitted to flow, voltage is applied to the primary and the secondary of the welding transformer; when, on the other hand, no current is permitted to flow, welding voltage is also shut off.

A further function of electron tubes is the effect that the timing of the welding current has on the effective voltage. Delaying the current start at each half cycle results in the current becoming discontinuous, and the current wave is an interrupted sinusoidal one. The range of current control, where this method is used, is governed by the power-line voltage as well as the type of tubes used in the control unit. Thyratrons are capable of control from 20 to 100 per cent on 440 volts and 40 to 100 per cent on 220 volts. When heat control is used, thyratrons become triggers to fire the ignitrons. Another feature of heat control is the use of "slope control." This permits the heat control to be applied on a sliding scale. "Up slope" permits an increasing application of heat while "down slope" permits a decay of welding current. Up slope is helpful in reducing electrode pickup, while down slope reduces weld cracks on some, especially nonferrous, materials.

THREE-PHASE DESIGNS

The practical disadvantages resulting from connecting single-phase resistance welding machines to three-phase power circuits have resulted in the development of means for overcoming these difficulties. The expedient of using a motor-generator set seems attractive until costs and

Fig. 34-4. Aircraft-type spot welder with 150-kva three-phase transformer equipped with Dekatron three-phase frequency converter control, which utilizes impulse-counting circuits for precise and consistent timing of all functions. (Courtesy of Precision Welder and Flexo-press Co., Cincinnati.)

operating features are evaluated. A more feasible approach to the solution of this problem has been that of the storage of electrical energy. The two possibilities for stored energy are the electrostatic type and the electromagnetic type.

In general the characteristics of resistance welding machines using stored energy embody much lower kva demand, hence sometimes lower welding costs. These welding machines are capable of discharging very high current values in short intervals of time. Stored-energy welders are of greatest interest for welding materials of high electrical and heat conductivity, for example, aluminum alloys.

DRY DISC RECTIFIER WELDERS

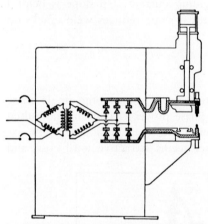

Fig. 34-5. Schematic diagram of a dry disk rectifier-type three-phase welding machine. (Courtesy of The Taylor-Winfield Corp., Warren, Ohio.)

Three-phase Welders. Developments in this area have produced equipment such as that in Fig. 34-4 where an installation complete with controls is seen. These machines are equipped for aluminum, stainless steel, and inconel welding under governmental specifications MIL-W-6858 as well as MIL-W-6860. A somewhat similar design is shown schematically in Fig. 34-5. The physical and mechanical features of the machine are essentially the same as shown in Fig. 34-4.

CONTROLS AND ELECTRODES ON RESISTANCE WELDERS

Time Controls. The importance of proper timing is indicated by the fundamental heat equation, in which the time t is a factor. The methods used for timing control are varied to suit the particular welding job. In spot welding, the timing allows for a continuous flow of current for a given interval, which is repeated with each spot weld made. The timing interval is commonly expressed in cycles of the basic frequency, as: 5 cycles of a 60-cycle current.

Seam welding presents a different problem, since a continuity pattern is essential. The electrodes for seam welders are in the form of disks or wheels which contact the work continuously. Welding current is timed by adjusting both "on" and "off" time as the seam proceeds through the welding wheels. The welding current is interrupted with electronic tubes even though the initiating switch is closed.

Still another basic timer is used in connection with pulsation welding, a process in the spot weld category which consists of repeated heating and cooling periods. The number of repetitions depends primarily on the type of material being welded and its thickness. When a sequence has been developed as to on and off times, this sequence is repeated for each similar weld. The timing device must, therefore, control three elements, viz., on time, off time, and the number of repetitions.

Resistance welding procedures directed toward heat-treatment of the weld call for a variable timing sequence. There are "on," or heat, times of differing lengths with subsequent "off," or cool, times also of variable lengths. Such timing devices are assembled from available standard timers.

Timing devices are classified as synchronous and nonsynchronous. The former initiates welding current at a precise point on the a-c wave, while the latter initiates the current at any point on the wave. Thus the inrush current on a nonsynchronous control is variable, while it is constant on a synchronous control.

Another development is "counting tubes" which actually count the cycles of an a-c wave.

Pressure Controls. The basic spot welder is equipped with a treadle or a manually operated lever as the pressure device. The total resistance R in the fundamental heat equation is composed of several factors: the specific resistance of the material being welded, the contact resistance between electrode and work, and the contact resistance at the faying surfaces. The specific resistance of the material is an inherent physical property that is unaffected by pressure; however, the remaining two resistances are influenced by the pressure applied to the electrode. A high pressure will tend to compact the weld pile, with the result that resistance will be lowered and greater current will flow. It would appear desirable to use a low pressure and thus gain increased resistance. Practical results do not bear out this reasoning, for sparking and electrode sticking develop when low pressure is used. Electrode deterioration and poor welding generally are other results of too low pressure.

Applied pressure is of importance, yet when any appreciable dwell time is incorporated in the sequence, the actual contact resistance decreases. The phenomena involved in this situation are traceable to such sources as metal film behavior and even plastic flow as well as other physical properties of the weldment metal. In considering welding pressures or forces, due consideration must be made of the pressures required to fit the two pieces together, as in the case of stampings.

Manual Pressure Devices. Foot-pedal mechanisms are an ideal solution, since they permit freedom of movement to both hands for guiding the weldment materials. Many existing designs employ some principle of mechanical advantage as a means of multiplying the actual foot pressure.

The rocker arm type, in which the upper electrode moves in an arc, is a widely used design; spring action is built into these linkages for flexibility of movement. The pressure potential of foot-operated mechanisms is relatively low and they are not generally found on production equipment.

Mechanical Pressure. Closer pressure control and lessened operator fatigue are achieved by the substitution of power for manual pressure operation. Motorized pressure mechanisms are also capable of higher pressures and for that reason offer an advantageous production potential. Design details of these types feature the use of a cam system for actuating the rocker arm of the resistance welding machine.

Hydraulic Pressure Systems. As the capacity and size of resistance welding machines increase, it is to be expected that design features will follow those found satisfactory in related equipment. Hydraulic controls are becoming more common on large resistance welders in which a multiplicity of electrodes are incorporated. Resistance welding machines of the type considered here are specialized production equipment in that they are designed for single-purpose application.

Hydraulic cylinders are located to permit the mounting of the electrodes directly in the piston rods. The pressure potentials are high, and close control is possible.

Pneumatic Pressure Systems. The introduction of air-operated pressure applications has fostered the development of a resistance welding machine known as a press welder. The unique feature of this design is that the movable electrode holder travels in a vertical slide, thereby causing straight-line motion instead of the arc travel of the rocker arm types. This design feature results in close electrode alignment.

Air-operated pistons are capable of flexible pressure control through suitable valves and air-line pressures. Electrodes are advanced and retracted by introducing air pressure on alternate ends of the piston. Cushioning of electrode impact is another feature of air-operated pressure systems. Air operation is used on rocker arm welders in a variety of arrangements.

Electrodes for Resistance Welding. The importance of proper electrode selection and application can be gathered from the standard specifications that have been developed for guidance in their selecting. The Resistance Welder Manufacturing Association (RWMA) has sponsored electrode specifications in which group A covers the copper-base alloys and group B the copper-tungsten alloys. Each group is subdivided into classes which define application in respect to equipment use as well as weldment material.

Both the physical and the electrical requirements of electrodes vary with the type of materials to be welded, as they do with the welding machines in which they are to be used. Spot welders predominate, with the result that standardization has been introduced. These electrodes are made with no. 1 or no. 2 Morse tapers for friction fit in the electrode holder. The electrodes are equipped with a blind hole for water cooling. Electrode operating temperatures profoundly affect performance, since electrical conductivity is a function of temperature as it is of composition. The principal purpose of electrode cooling is to prevent annealing,

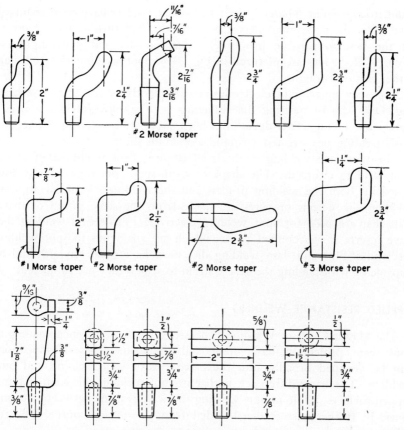

Fig. 34-6. Special spot welding electrode designs. (Courtesy of SMS Corp., Detroit.)

consequently reducing "mushrooming" and spreading contact surface. The choice of electrode shape and material depends on the work to be welded. Material of high conductivity requires high current and electrodes capable of delivering that current.

Composite, or faced, electrodes are available for meeting specific welding conditions. The facing may cover the entire welding tip, or inserts may be used. Copper-tungsten alloys are favorite facing materials for welding stainless steels and brass. The facings are brazed to copper backing, with the latter forming the electrode body. Electrode contours carry such designations as pointed, dome, flat, and offset. Electrode point dimensions are critical, since if a $\frac{3}{16}$-in.-diameter point is permitted to wear to $\frac{1}{4}$-in. diameter, the weld area will be almost doubled, requiring a substantial increase in welding current.

Electrodes of a variety of shapes are available to meet clearances and seam locations. Electrode holders are influenced by similar considerations, to the point where straight and offset holders have been standardized. The fit, or seating, between electrodes and their holders must be of the best to provide proper electrical contact and water-tightness. Typical electrodes are pictured in Fig. 34-6. Spot welding electrodes are either cast or wrought.

Improper behavior of electrodes can frequently be traced to overheating. One way of meeting this difficulty is to employ refrigeration as a means of cooling. This device has been successfully used in connection with welding heat-treated wrought-aluminum sheet.

The resistance welding methods all employ some modification of the spot welding electrode. The shape or form such contactors take is governed by both the welding process and the weldment material. In seam welding the wheels or rings are made from the same group of materials that are used for spot welding electrodes. Projection welding dies have inserts at the contact points which are analogous to spot welding electrodes. Butt and flash welding dies must have great strength and be capable of withstanding the severe strain to which they are subjected.

APPLIED RESISTANCE WELDING

The Master Chart of Welding Processes[2] classifies resistance welding as spot, seam, projection, flash, upset, and percussion. These classifications can be grouped broadly into the categories of spot welding and butt welding. The basic difference is that in spot welding the seam requires lapped surfaces, while in butt welding the weld is made between abutting faces. In neither case is metal added from an outside source. The resultant weld, therefore, adds no weight to the weldment.

Product Design

Products designed for resistance welding should be developed for the greatest possible simplicity in joining. The welding requirements should be geared to the use of conventional resistance welding machines as a measure to eliminate difficulties that arise from the use of complicated current-carrying components. The unencumbered welding machine dis-

[2] American Standard A3.1-49, American Welding Society, New York, 1949.

penses with involved problems of placing as well as removing the product. Standard electrodes are preferred, since they do not require elaborate water passages and connections.

Resistance welds must be made in short time intervals, since substantial currents, meaning high heat values, are used. The heating time is of short duration as a precaution against warping or burning the weldment. These requisites indicate the reason for the popularity of resistance welding on light-gage material. Heavy weldments with high heat requirements are not adapted to resistance welding as a general rule. There have been some examples of plate welding but such cases are rare. Resistance welding can be used to best advantage by designing a product of sheet metal that requires little surface preparation and is of a shape affording ready access to the weld locations.

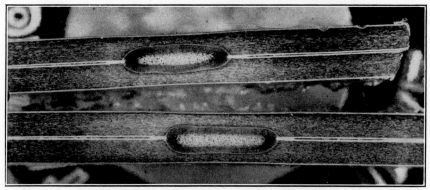

Fig. 34-7. Cross section of spot welds, ×10; 0.040-in. 2024-T3 Alclad aluminum sheet.

Spot Welding. The resistance welding principle finds its widest application in spot welding and its many variations. Where controlled welding has been established, the operation of the machine is automatic once the initiating switch has been closed. There remains, however, a substantial amount of spot welding in which there is slight attention paid to control conditions.

A properly made spot weld results in a "nugget" that, in cross section, approaches the geometry of a sharpened ellipse (Fig. 34-7). The properties of the nugget are a function of the weld program as well as material, kind, and thickness. The ideal spot weld will show penetration evenly divided between the sheets when the latter are of the same thickness and material.

One feature of the spot welding operation is the resultant shrinkage, which is at maximum value normal to the weld. Surface indentations result largely from weld shrinkage, with electrode marks acting as a contributing factor. The latter can be avoided by using one large electrode contact surface, thereby keeping the dimpling effect on one side of the welded joint. Where dissimilar materials or materials of different gages are to be welded, it is common practice to use electrodes of contrasting diameters as a means of obtaining differential heating as between the two members.

Electrode contacts are designed for both direct and indirect operation. In the usual type of the former setting the electrodes are so placed that they face each other, *i.e.*, one is above the other. The indirect setting,

Fig. 34-8. Multi-electrode, multi-transformer spot welder for welding hood panel reinforcements tooled to move parts automatically in cadence with production line. (Courtesy of National Electric Welding Machines Co., Bay City, Mich.)

on the other hand, places *both* electrodes on the same side of the joint, separated by a space interval. The welding current travels down through one electrode, then across in a copper shorting block, and up through the second electrode. Setting up such an arrangement requires exact knowledge of welding conditions; care must be taken to prevent the contacted sheet from acting as a shunt for the welding current. Indirect spot welding is not to be confused with multiple spot welding, where several spots are made simultaneously. Some ingenious spot welding machines have been developed as production equipment using the principle of multiple spot welding (Fig. 34-8).

The welding cycle of spot welding machines is varied from a single complete welding operation through pulsation and program welding. Pulsation welding means the reapplication of welding current to a given spot, thus lowering the amount of welding current required. Program welding is applied where heat-treatment of the spot weld is necessary, as in hardenable steels and heat-treatable aluminum alloys. Program welding includes the welding operation plus any post-treatment that the material requires.

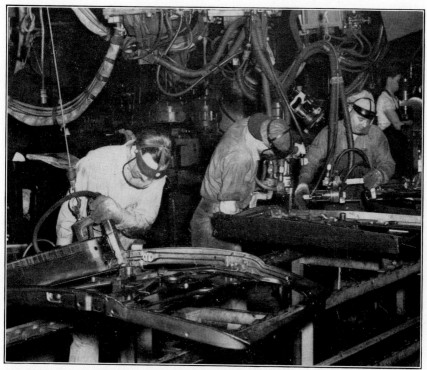

Fig. 34-9. Typical portable welding equipment of the gun-welder type shown welding automobile body parts. (Courtesy of The Budd Co., Philadelphia.)

The spot welder can be brought to the work by means of portable, or gun-type, equipment. The welding element (Fig. 34-9) is portable and is applied at the point of welding, which lends flexibility; the transformer and control equipment have a more stationary mounting. The design of the gun, which is equipped with electrodes, an application mechanism, and water-cooling lines, does not follow a given pattern. The "push" gun type does, in effect, shoot a weld, since its operation is reminiscent of a firearm. Other design types are the scissors, the pinch, the "C" (after C clamp), the swivel, etc. The designations refer to the method of operation or construction of the welding gun.

Spot welding has attained such widespread acceptance in industry as to justify the development of procedure standards. Table 31-1 is included here as an example of the data contained in "Recommended Practices for Resistance Welding (Tentative)."[3] This standard also con-

TABLE 34-1. SPOT WELDING LOW-CARBON STEEL*

Thickness T of thinnest outside piece, in. (Notes 1, 2, 3, and 4 below)	Electrode diameter and shape (Note 5 below) or		Net electrode force, lb	Weld time (single impulse), cycles (60 per sec)	Welding current (approx.), amp	Minimum contacting overlap, in.	Minimum weld spacing, in. (Note 6 below)	Diameter of fused zone (approx.), in. D_w	Minimum shear strength, lb	
									Ultimate tensile strength of metal	
	D, in., min.	d, in., max.							Below 70,000 psi	70,000 psi and above
0.010	3/8	1/8	200	4	4,000	3/8	1/4	0.10	130	180
0.021	3/8	3/16	300	6	6,500	7/16	3/8	0.13	320	440
0.031	3/8	3/16	400	8	8,000	7/16	1/2	0.16	570	800
0.040	1/2	1/4	500	10	9,500	1/2	3/4	0.19	920	1,200
0.050	1/2	1/4	650	12	10,500	9/16	7/8	0.22	1,350	
0.062	1/2	1/4	800	14	12,000	5/8	1	0.25	1,850	
0.078	5/8	5/16	1100	17	14,000	11/16	1 1/4	0.29	2,700	
0.094	5/8	5/16	1300	20	15,500	3/4	1 1/2	0.31	3,450	
0.109	5/8	3/8	1600	23	17,500	13/16	1 5/8	0.32	4,150	
0.125	7/8	3/8	1800	26	19,000	7/8	1 3/4	0.33	5,000	

Notes:
1. Type of steel—SAE 1010.
2. Material should be free from scale, oxides, paint, grease, and oil.
3. Welding conditions determined by thickness of thinnest outside piece T.
4. Data for total thickness of pile-up not exceeding $4T$. Maximum ratio between two thicknesses 3/1.
5. Electrode material, Class 2, minimum conductivity, 75 per cent of copper; minimum hardness, 75 Rockwell B.
6. Minimum weld spacing is that spacing for two pieces for which no special precautions need be taken to compensate for shunted current effect of adjacent welds. For three pieces increase spacing 30 per cent.
* From American Standard C1.1-50, American Welding Society, New York, 1950.

tains data covering the following: pulsation-welding low-carbon steel; spot-welding stainless steel; pulsation-welding stainless steel; spot-welding annealed nickel, monel, and inconel; and spot-welding hardenable steels (quench and temper method).

[3] American Standard C1.1-50, American Welding Society, New York, p. 4, 1950.

Seam Welding. Welding wheels, or a wheel and a plate, replace the electrodes of a spot welder in seam welding machines. A mechanical drive is provided for the welding wheels. In some designs both wheels are driven, while in others one wheel is driven and the other is an idler. The work is moved forward between the welding wheels at a rate varying from 2 to 50 fpm, depending on such modifications as welding current and material type and thickness. Figure 34-10 shows a diagram of a seam in addition to a spot welding cycle.

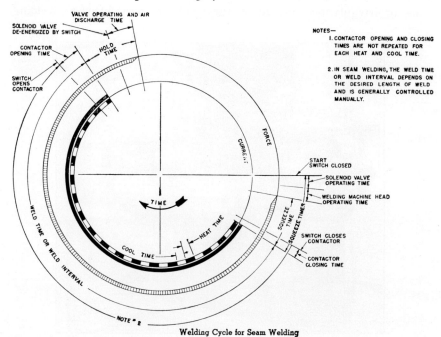

Fig. 34-10. Diagram of welding cycle for seam welding. (From American Standard A3.0-49, American Welding Society, New York.)

Seam welding machines are designed on several basic principles. The relation of the wheels to the machine determines the type. If the plane of the wheels is parallel with the throat of the machine, it is a longitudinal type. The circular type has its wheels 90° from the throat (Fig. 34-11). It is used for welding bottoms into drums and similar jobs. A seam welder wherein the welding wheels can be adapted to both of the previous requirements is referred to as a universal. The mechanism used for driving the welding wheels also gives rise to design types; examples are the gear drive and knurled drive. In the case of the latter, the welding wheels are friction-driven by a knurled wheel, which in turn derives its motion directly from a motor.

The seam welding considered thus far has involved lap joints, which are similar to spot welding. There is a further classification of seam welding, known as the butt seam, which is used for welding the longitudinal seam in tubing. The tubing is rolled with an open seam and is guided by that opening into the welding machine. Pressure is exerted from the sides in a closing action on the seam, where the welding wheels supply the necessary current for completing the weld.

Projection Welding. This method of welding is another modification of spot welding. The location of the welds is predetermined by projections or irregularities formed on the weldment parts prior to welding.

Fig. 34-11. Tandem seam welders welding center seams in automobile gas tanks. A similar setup welds the other two seams. Production on a straight-line installation is 600 pieces/hr. (Courtesy of Pontiac Division, Progressive Welder Sales, Co., Pontiac, Mich.)

The projections act as contact points for localizing the weld. In consequence the welding machine is equipped with flat-faced electrodes or dies rather than the usual type of spot welding electrodes. The number of welds that can be made simultaneously is governed by the number of contact surfaces or points that are located within the die area. No previously made welds are in this area, since their presence would act as a shunt for the welding current. This is not to be taken to mean that all projection welds are of the multiple type; there are single ones as well.

Projection welding machines are generally built similarly to press welders. In fact some types are of a design that permits them to be used for either spot or projection welding with only slight equipment changes in shifting from one system to the other. There are also examples of projection welding machines constructed as production or specialized equipment. These designs are predicated on the requirements for a particular welding job and as a result bear slight resemblance in appearance to the standard type of machine. Figure 34-12 shows one example of a production projection welding machine. This equipment is rated at a capacity of 1,000 plates/hr welded to conveyor chain links used in bottling machines.

Fig. 34-12. Discharge side of projection welding machine, showing plates welded to chain links. (Courtesy of Thomson Electric Welder Co., Lynn, Mass.)

Flash Welding. Flash welding is also referred to as flash butt welding. In this method of resistance welding, the weld occurs between abutting surfaces or faces of the parts to be joined. The method has been successful on all materials that can be spot-welded and it also is used for welding dissimilar metals. The shape and size of the weldment parts are of slight consequence, since flash welds are used on sheet metal as they are on bar stock to considerable thicknesses. The all-steel automobile body exemplifies the flash welding technique for joining its component stampings. The flash remaining after welding, when removed, leaves a joint so expertly made that from outward appearance it cannot be detected. In the automotive industry flash welding is a generously used method of joining parts of all categories. It is chosen because of its potential in the direction of lower manufacturing costs. As an example, the splined end of a drive shaft is flash-welded to the central portion and then the drive pinion is flash-welded to the opposite end of this weldment. Thus the drive shaft comprises three parts joined by two flash welds. The saving in material, labor, and machine time of this welding method over making the part from a single piece of steel is a major one. In fact flash welding has been so completely accepted in automotive construction that standard regulations have been established for its application.[4]

The welding heat results from the flashing action, which is produced by forcing tightly together the surfaces or faces to be welded, as a means of establishing current flow in local areas. This heat concentration in small areas causes localized melting, with the result that molten metal is violently expelled by current behavior. There is a pronounced showering of sparks and molten metal particles during the flashing period (Fig. 34-13). The flashing cycle is continued for a period governed by pressure and welding current conditions. The objective is to heat both pieces to a distance back from the weld face and in an amount that will bring the affected surfaces to a high degree of plasticity.

Upset Welding. This process holds the distinction of being the forerunner of all the resistance welding methods. The original patent for resistance welding covered substantially what is now termed upset welding. Upset welding is unique in that the abutting surfaces are subjected to continuing pressure throughout the entire welding operation. The weld faces are pressed together prior to the release of the welding current. The pressure continues for the duration of the welding current plus an additional time increment following the cessation of current. The magnitude of the pressure may be variable through the welding cycle, starting with a low value as a means of initially increasing contact resistance. Welding heat is generated entirely by the resistance to current flow. The upset weld is the nearest approach to the forge weld. The parts are heated by the passage of a current, rather than in a forge. When the proper temperature is reached, the parts weld or fuse together under the action of the forge force.

Percussion Welding. Resistance, in the usual sense, plays little part in percussion, or, as it is sometimes termed, percussive welding. The welding heat in this process results from an arc discharge of extremely short duration. The arc is kindled between the faces of the weldments' parts. The current for the arc is obtained from stored electrical energy. The term stored electrical energy is not to be confused with a similar one

[4] "Recommended Practices for Automotive Flash-butt Welding (Tentative)," American Standards D8.1-46, American Welding Society, New York.

used in connection with spot welding for the reason that no welding transformer is included in the welding circuit.

Arc duration is on the order of 0.001 sec, whence power expenditure reaches 200 kw. Because of this design the heating effect on the weldment parts is confined to a thin zone on the surface. Immediately upon discharge of the arc, the weldment parts are brought together with percussive force in an action that causes weld completion. Two distinctive

Fig. 34-13. 2,000-kva dual-transformer automatic hydraulic flash welder for welding steel rings to 24-in. width and 3-in. thickness. (Courtesy of Swift Ohio Corp., Detroit.)

characteristics of this process are that (1) dissimilar metals can be welded, since welding heat arises from an arc discharge and resistance plays no part; (2) the pieces to be welded must be individual ones and completely separated (for instance, a closing joint in a ring could not be welded by the percussion welding process). Owing to the nature of the heating process, there is no flash formed at the weld interface.

Welds made by this method are confined to parts of relatively small cross section, among these being wire, rod, and tubing. The possibilities for welding dissimilar metals are interesting when it is realized that, by way of example, brass has been welded to magnesium and stellite to bronze valve stems. Percussion welding is limited primarily to such fields, since it cannot compete with flash welding on the basis of economy.

SURVEY QUESTIONS

34-1. Does resistance welding deal with molten metal?

34-2. How does the flexibility of resistance welding compare with torch welding?

34-3. If resistance welding is used on steel structures, explain requisite procedures.

34-4. How is welding heat generated in resistance welding?

34-5. What is the usual basic power supply?

34-6. Give the origin of the term "spot welding."

34-7. Explain "temperature gradient" as the term applies to spot welding.

34-8. Why does 304L stainless steel spot-weld more readily than does 5052 Al alloy sheet?

34-9. Why is contact resistance important in spot welding?

34-10. Wherein, if at all, do spot welder electrodes differ from metal arc types?

34-11. What effect does the depth of throat in a spot welding machine have on welding current?

34-12. How does a rectifier-type spot welder affect power-line loading?

34-13. Describe one method for controlling welding current in spot welding.

34-14. What different types of electron tubes are used in heat control?

34-15. Of what further function are electron tubes capable?

34-16. Mention the different power characteristics or types used in resistance welding.

34-17. How is the welding current interval controlled in resistance welding?

34-18. What dual function does pressure serve in spot welding?

34-19. List the different pressure systems or types used in resistance welding.

34-20. Discuss a specific welding operation or application that would require the use of faced electrodes.

34-21. How are electrodes seated in a spot welding machine in order to ensure watertightness?

34-22. Mention a design criterion for products intended for resistance welding.

34-23. Does weld shrinkage exist to the point of causing difficulty in resistance welds?

34-24. How, if at all, can surface indentation be eliminated in spot-welded components?

34-25. Give a specific example for the use of multiple spot welders.

34-26. How do portable spot welders tend to improve the versatility of resistance welding?

34-27. If seam welds are distinguishable from spot welds, explain the characteristic making this possible.

34-28. Describe the basic design of a circular-type seam welder.

34-29. Where, on an auto body, would flash welds be expected to be used?

34-30. What preparation is needed for projection-welded joints?

34-31. What other basic type of welding does upset welding approximate?

34-32. How are the longitudinal (body) seams in a "tin" can made?

34-33. Why is resistance welding omitted or bypassed in welded steel ship hull construction?

34-34. State at least two advantages for resistance welding over riveting in airframe construction.

34-35. Why are resistance welds never used on or with cast iron?

Chapter 35

AUTOMATIC AND
SPECIALIZED WELDING ARCS

Automatic arc welding finds its broadest field of application where production demands are high. This concept of arc welding lacks the versatility and portability characteristics of the manual type. On the other hand, where production requirements justify the installation of automatic arc welding, the resulting costs are extremely favorable and the welding quality is high.

There are several modifications of manual arc welding that are of interest. These all employ some type of shielding or some arc operating principles that have been derived from the basic welding arc. In some instances, these specialized welding arcs are manually operated, while in others they have developed as fully or semiautomatic equipment.

AUTOMATIC ARC WELDING

Automatic Bare Electrode Arc Welding. The original interest in automatic arcs was for equipment which merely performed the metallic arc welding function. Mechanically, equipment is primarily built for d-c operation and the electrode is of the bare wire type. The chief difference between manual and automatic is that closer control is possible with automatic equipment by the elimination of the human equation; as a result, higher welding speeds and better weld results are achieved.

The electrode wire is supplied in coils. It is fed automatically through the welding head at a rate to maintain a constant arc length. This wire, although termed bare, actually has a light arc stabilizing or a dust coating on its surface. In some types the electrode wire is knurled in order to increase the flux holding capacity of the surface and also to aid in securing a positive drive through the wire feeding rolls of the welding head.

The quality of the weld metal deposited by this process is not equal to that obtained where more positive shielding is employed, because of the tendency to porosity and brittleness. These shortcomings are to be expected; there is slight protection of the arc stream or the deposited metal from the atmosphere, so that iron nitrides and oxides form readily. This tendency is not so great as to impair the serviceability of the weld in most applications.

In order to obtain satisfactory welds, reasonable precautions must be exercised on edge preparation as well as on fit-up. One reason for the favorable cost aspect of this method of welding is the fact that, since no shielding material is used on the electrode, there is no slag deposit on the finished weld and no time is required for slag removal. On occasion automatic bare metal arc welding has been specified as a means of eliminating all possibility of entrapped slag from the final weld.

Shielding Systems. The principle of the shielded electrode is detailed in Chap. 31, where tables of shielding formulations are included. That concept of shielding belongs primarily to manual arc welding, although the early work in automatic shielded arc welding followed a similar pattern.

The evolution of automatic shielded arcs has developed into new shielding concepts and new shielding systems. These follow two basic ideas, either that of solid materials, which are added at the time of welding, or the use of a gas that is inert to the arc welding procedure. A further modification of this concept is the use of both solid and gas shielding in an arc simultaneously. Since the automatic shielded arc has so many derivations, it is also possible to find those systems in which flux shielding is included in the welding wire and gas shield is also employed. In short, it can be said that just about every combination has been introduced except the possible use of a liquid.

Research by the author has shown interesting results with liquid applied as a vapor. However, the liquid must be chosen with extreme care, since some, though they appear suitable because of their chemical composition, will develop a noxious gas as a by-product of arc action. The choice of shielding gas is not as yet standardized, although helium, argon, and carbon dioxide are the leading ones. These gases are used singly or in combination, or in connection with another gas acting as a booster or catalyst. There is a marked difference of opinion between our own scientists and those abroad with respect to inert-gas shielding insofar as gas choice and use are concerned.

Automatic Shielded Metallic Arc Welding. As the use of shielded electrodes in manual arc welding developed and the nature of the weldments produced by that means became better understood, interest centered in developing automatic equipment to perform similar work. The problem was to find a means of making electrical contact in an automatic arc head through electrode shielding.

One attempt employed an automatic head, which incorporated a device for wrapping a previously impregnated tape around the bare metal wire just prior to entering the arc. The tape was made of a combination of textile and fine copper wire woven in open mesh; it was saturated with a shielding solution whose composition varied with the requirements of the weld. This idea proved to be a versatile one, since the shielding could be changed merely by inserting a different tape into the welding head. Its primary application was on light gage material or as a sealing bead for submerged melt welding.

Submerged Melt Welding. A significant improvement in metal arc welding appeared with the advent of the submerged or hidden arc. The basic principles of this system are illustrated in Fig. 35-1. The welding electrode is bare wire; it may or may not be copper-coated and is available in a variety of diameters supplied in coils. The automatic welding

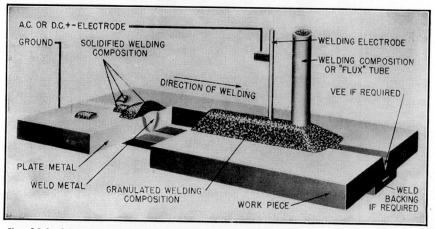

Fig. 35-1. Schematic drawing showing the principles of operation of the submerged melt welding process. (Courtesy of The Linde Air Products Co., New York.)

head is similar to the one used with automatic bare metal arc welding. The main point of difference is that with submerged arc welding a granular material, variously referred to as melt or flux, is fed into the weld by gravity in an amount sufficient to submerge the arc completely. Figure 35-2 illustrates the pertinent features of a d-c submerged arc welding head design; the flux tube is shown, as well as the hopper, the wire reel from which the bare weld wire is fed, and the operating controls.

The operating characteristics of submerged arc welding are different from those of all other arcs. Here the arc burns beneath a blanket of granular flux or melt where it is invisible. The operator needs no eye protection from arc rays although he should have the protection of clear glass as a safety precaution.

There are two basic submerged arc welding methods, both subject to modifications, such as the use of twin or dual arcs instead of the single arc for increased welding speed. There are also revisions whereby the arc can be oscillated in order to weave a wide pad or weld deposit. The one pictured in Fig. 35-1 operates on alternating as well as direct current, whereas the equipment shown in Fig. 35-2 is for direct current only. There are some differences in operation between the two; however, they deliver fundamentally the same welding result.

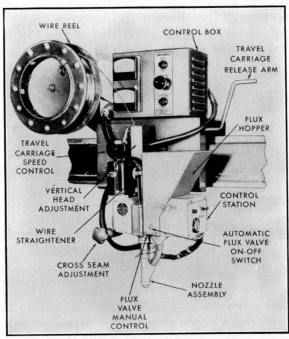

Fig. 35-2. Self-propelled Lincolnweld submerged arc welding equipment. (Courtesy of Lincoln Electric Co., Cleveland.)

Operation—The arc is struck beneath the granular melt, or flux; as the welding proceeds, this covering material leads the arc in order to submerge the latter through its period of operation, thereby effectively excluding the atmosphere. As the welding continues, some of the granular material becomes fused, while the excess remains unaffected. The latter is picked up by a vacuum device and returned to the hopper for re-use.

The fused material is visibly red at the time of welding; however, upon cooling it changes to a dark color and has a glasslike consistency which can readily be brushed from the weld. It is interesting to note that the fused material, or slag, forms a substantial blanket over the deposited weld metal, thereby both shielding it and aiding in the control of its cooling rate.

Submerged arc welding is capable of producing welds of unusually high mechanical properties both in strength and ductility. Furthermore, the process has yielded excellent results on low-alloy, high-strength structural steels, firebox, stainless, and other special steels (Fig. 35-3). Test data indicate that in many instances these welds show properties equal to, and in some instances higher than, those of the base metal. The results, of course, are influenced by the type of wire and melt used in welding.

Fig. 35-3. Submerged arc welding of spherical heads 60 in. in diameter from 2⅞-in. thick plate for use on Braun spherical head Freedwater heater (patent pending). (Courtesy of C. F. Braun Co., Alhambra, Calif.)

Welding speeds obtainable from submerged arc welding are spectacular, especially when compared to previous accomplishments. For example, butt welds are made at a rate of 10 to 12 in./min in 1-in. steel plate (Fig. 35-4). These welds are completed in one pass, which is of significance since it means much higher over-all welding speed. Moreover, the addition of filler metal is small with submerged arc welding because of the high currents used. There is considerable melting of the base metal, which means that joint preparation need not be as open as in the case of other types of automatic arc welding.

Granular Melt—The composition of the granular shielding material is confidential with the producer, although it is a product of the electric

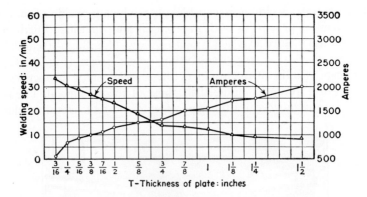

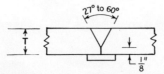

Type of welding groove for one-pass butt weld

Fig. 35-4. Typical relationships of welding speed versus plate thickness in low carbon steel material for submerged arc welding. (Abstracted from "Automatic Arc and Gas Welding Processes," American Welding Society, No. D7.2-48T.)

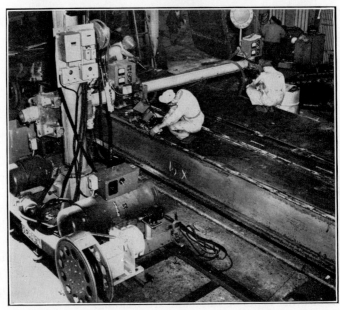

Fig. 35-5. Welding freight car bottoms at American Car & Foundry Co., using two submerged melt heads simultaneously by mounting them on a traveling gantry. (Courtesy of Lincoln Electric Co., Cleveland.)

arc furnace. There has been much experimental work in connection with developing this granular shielding material. Some of the early experiments used river sand, among other things. The size of the granules exerts an effect on the operation and welding results. The appearance of the welding bead is influenced by the size of the granules used.

Submerged arc welding is used in the down-hand position; because of this limitation, some extremely ingenious welding fixtures have been devised. Supplementary equipment is not limited to weld positioners; it includes many examples of gear developed for increasing the speed of welding on large as well as complicated equipment. Figure 35-5 is by no means a standardized application; it is used here to give an indication of the elaborateness of some of the installations used in connection with submerged arc welding.

SEMIAUTOMATIC ARC WELDING

Semiautomatic welding has made substantial progress in the past few years. It is generally expected that this type of welding will replace as much as 50 per cent of the manual welding now practiced. The development goes beyond shielding types and includes power source as well. Some manufacturers refer to this development as semimanual. Since these methods cannot control as large a molten metal pool as properly equipped automatic arcs, the welding current requirements are usually within the range of the larger welding machines designed for manual arc welding.

The current source for semiautomatic welding is known as "constant potential," wherein relatively small changes in arc length, and hence arc voltage, result in decided changes in the arc current. Whereas the "constant current" arc described under manual arc welding, Chap. 31, is easily controlled, the "constant potential" arc is self-controlling and intolerant of outside changes. Because of this design, a small increase in arc length, and hence voltage, results in a large decrease in arc current and electrode burn-off rate. A decrease in arc length and voltage results in a large increase in arc current and resultant burn-off rate. No time-consuming sampling-type control circuit is required here and filler wire feed is accomplished with a simple adjustable feed motor. This arc is easily kindled because of its electrical characteristics. The advantage of the semiautomatic method is increased flexibility (Fig. 35-6). The apparatus approximates manual arc welding in use, except that the welding must be done in the flat position.

The electrode wire, supplied in coils, is fed into the weld automatically. A low-pressure air system flows the melt from the tank to the welding gun, from whence it issues to cover the arc completely although it does not flow ahead of the arc, thereby permitting the seam to be viewed.

The travel of the welding gun along the seam is also automatic. The gun is an L-shaped tube approximately 1½ in. in diameter. A small electric motor drives a knurled steel wheel that rides the work and propels the gun at any preset speed up to 70 in./min; in consequence, the weldor needs merely to guide the gun. Welds are made without edge preparation in plate thicknesses up to ½ in., and it is also possible to make fillet welds. Every advantage of the submerged arc principle is retained in this method, which also has the versatility that manual manipulation contributes.

Fig. 35-6. Semiautomatic submerged melt gun with automatic wire and melt feed used in welding a hoist drum. (Courtesy of Lincoln Electric Co., Cleveland.)

Submerged Type. Insofar as shielding is concerned, both flux as well as gas are used individually in some designs and in combination in others.

Among the systems that belong in the latter category are those in which a continuously fed wire electrode is magnetically coated with flux and the arc is shielded by a flow of carbon dioxide gas. Such welds can be made at a speed as much as three to four times faster than manual arc welding with shielded electrodes.

A somewhat different approach employs a continuous flux cored electrode fed through gun equipment to the welding arc. At the same time, the arc and weld zone are shielded by a carbon dioxide gas atmosphere fed through the gun (Fig. 35-7). The methods described here have the

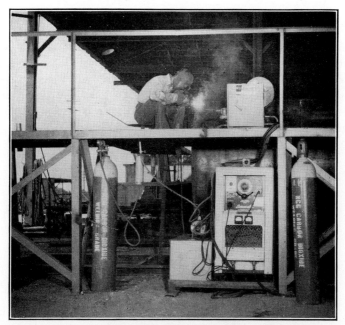

Fig. 35-7. Dual-shield submerged arc employing flux cored electrode in combination with CO_2 gas shielding shown here on tank welding. (Courtesy of National Cylinder Gas Co., Chicago.)

advantage of all-position welding in contrast to submerged melt, which must be performed down-hand.

SPECIALIZED WELDING ARCS

Whenever an arc welding method proves itself, it is but a question of time until it is developed for automatic operation; hence it seems logical to assume that every manual arc welding process has its automatic counterpart. It is difficult to make a clear-cut distinction between those processes that should be referred to as automatic and those that are manual.

Inert-gas Shielded Arc Welding. The principle of shielding an electric arc with an inert gas, in which the arc is maintained through a nonconsumable electrode, was patented as early as 1930. Since that time there have been many important developments.

One outstanding feature is the absence of welding flux (Fig. 35-8). Thus, expense is saved in initial cost and by freedom from the necessity for removal after welding. Further, there need be no fear of residual flux, with its corrosive potentials, remaining anywhere in the weldment —a genuine contribution to the welding of such metals as aluminum and stainless steels. Another important factor results from the area of the weld being comparatively small; as a result heating concentration is such as to eliminate many of the distortion difficulties. In welding stainless steels a narrow heat zone means less possibility of carbide precipitation.

The equipment used in inert-gas shielded arc welding consists of a power source, a cylinder of compressed gas equipped with proper regulators, and an electrode holder or torch. There is also equipment for automatic operation.

Fig. 35-8. Argon shielded arc welding of stainless steel jet engine components. (Courtesy of Linde Co., Division of Union Carbide Corp., New York.)

The use of straight polarity permits higher current values, inasmuch as the heat distribution in the arc results in greater heat on the base metal rather than on the electrode. As noted in Table 35-1, current values will vary with the diameter of the electrode. Reverse polarity is of interest because of the behavior of the electrical characteristics of the arc, especially when welding such materials as aluminum alloys, which readily form surface oxides. Reverse polarity tends to break through these oxides, giving a clean weld; however, welding speeds are considerably less, which means that welding quality is gained at a definite sacrifice of welding speed.

Alternating current is widely used in connection with this process. It was discovered early that the oxide layer on some metals acted as a rectifier, with the result that alternating current was converted to what amounted to half-cycle, pulsating, direct current of straight polarity. Welds made by alternating current resulting in this rectification were of poor quality, containing oxide inclusions. High-frequency current was superimposed on the welding current as a means of overcoming this difficulty. This afforded only partial relief, since the welding circuit then actually carried a d-c component along with the alternating current. The trend in welding circuits is toward using high frequency imposed on the welding circuit only for starting the arc.

TABLE 35-1. CURRENT RANGES FOR TUNGSTEN ELECTRODES, AMPERES

Electrode diameter, in.	a-c without d-c component		a-c unbalanced (argon)	d-c straight polarity (helium)	d-c reverse polarity (either gas)
	Helium	Argon			
0.010	......	Up to 15	....	Up to 6	
0.020	......	10–20	....	15–25	
0.040	......	20–30	....	20–50	
$\frac{1}{16}$	25–30	30–80	40–120	50–150	10–20
$\frac{3}{32}$	30–50	60–130	100–180	100–250	15–30
$\frac{1}{8}$	40–80	100–180	150–225	200–300	25–40
$\frac{3}{16}$	50–150	180–300	250–325	275–350	40–80
$\frac{1}{4}$	60–250	250–400	300–450	300–450	80–125

Shielding Gas. Helium and argon are the inert gases used for shielding. They are used singly as well as in various combinations. Helium is conducive to higher arc voltages than argon. Hence there is more heat when helium is used, arc watts being the product of voltage and amperage.

In addition to these two inert gases, hydrogen is used for arc shielding in the atomic hydrogen process. Shielding gas types have been expanded to include chemically active carbon dioxide, which was first introduced in England.

When a filler wire containing excess amounts of deoxidizers, such as manganese or silicon, is used in conjunction with CO_2, a ductile weld will result. The advantage of this system is high welding speed coupled with low-cost shielding; d-c reverse polarity is general here. The invitingly low cost of CO_2 has led to intense research in attempting to adapt this shielding to wider use. One promising development is that of using a dual-gas shielding with argon as the inner core and CO_2 as an envelope.

Nitrogen has not as yet been established as a satisfactory shielding material.

These gases are available in quantity and are supplied in compressed-gas cylinders. Regulators used on the cylinders should be of the flow-meter rather than the straight pressure-reduction type because the volume flow is critical for proper welding and as a means of saving gas. The gas is conducted to the arc torch through a conventional hose.

Argon mixed with a small volume of oxygen is proving of value because of the better arc penetration that results. This gas mixture can be purchased compressed in cylinders, or two separate cylinders—one each of argon and oxygen—can be manifolded and the correct gas volume metered from each and used only with consumable electrodes.

Tig and Mig. With the development of inert-gas shielded arc welding, two basic design principles have emerged. In one design, the electrode, usually of tungsten, acts to maintain the arc without itself becoming molten. This is known as a nonconsumable type and has been designated as "TIG," tungsten inert gas.

The tungsten electrodes are coded under AWS specification A5.12-55 on the basis of chemical analysis. There are four classifications ranging from pure tungsten through tungsten-thorium alloys to tungsten-zirconium. Each of these analyses offers some advantage for a particular requirement. For example, the tungsten electrode with zirconium added has some advantage when using high-frequency alternating current for welding aluminum. Thoriated-tungsten electrodes are especially desirable for d-c straight polarity welding with helium.

The reverse concept is one using a consumable electrode for starting and maintaining the arc. The electrode is consumed during welding and is the source of weld metal. In consequence, this system has been labeled as "MIG," metal inert gas. Wire compositions have been developed especially for this application. The composition for the most part is about the same as the base metal, with allowance added for loss in the arc. The wire is available either as single drawn or as stranded types. A modification of the MIG process is that in which a cold wire attachment is used, thereby inserting another source of weld metal into the arc. This is of especial advantage for built-up surfaces. While these classifications are unofficial insofar as specifications are concerned, they are proving most useful and descriptive.

Tungsten Inert Gas. The torch used for TIG welding is rather complicated. The detailed construction varies with different manufacturers, although the over-all design is more or less similar. Water cooling is provided at the electrode and shielding cup. The inert gas issues through the shielding cup, which is of ceramic material or stainless steel.

There is no provision for adding weld metal from the arc torch; instead, such material is provided from a separate source in the form of a weld rod (Fig. 35-9).

The progress made in both development and applications of this process tends to indicate that further development can be expected. Magnesium, aluminum alloys, and stainless steel have been the principal benefactors thus far. However, the entire category of "hard-to-weld metals" will be welded satisfactorily as the adaptability of this process is extended.

Consumable Electrode Inert Gas. In this equipment the electrode is a bare metal wire that functions concurrently as both electrode and filler

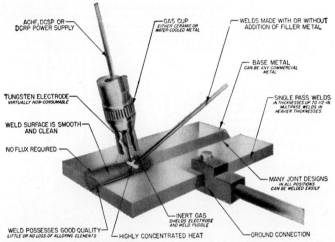

Fig. 35-9. Essentials of the tungsten inert gas (TIG) welding process. (Courtesy of Linde Co., Division of Union Carbide Corp., New York.)

metal, MIG (Fig. 35-10). The weld or electrode wire is fed into the arc automatically from a reel on which it is coiled.

Other features of the equipment follow the general design of inert-gas arc equipment. The mobility of the welding gun is of distinct advantage for welding in all positions as it is for welding fillets. The equipment is characterized by the use of direct current and argon gas for shielding. It is also available in automatic models for production work. There is some evidence of weld spatter, since this is a metal arc welding method. An automatic welding operation is shown in Fig. 35-11.

Tags and Mags. Inasmuch as neither hydrogen nor CO_2 is an inert gas, the previous terms TIG and MIG seem to be inexact. It has been suggested that in their stead the terms TAGS for tungsten arc gas shielding and MAGS for metal arc gas shielding methods should be used. This nomenclature is indicative of the rapidity with which the gas shielding welding processes are moving forward.

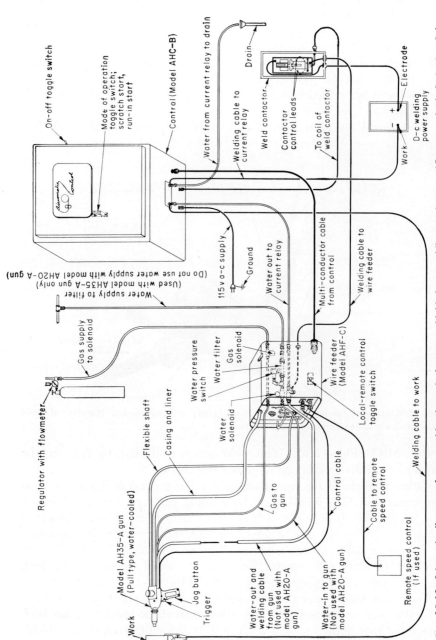

Fig. 35-10. Schematic diagram of consumable electrode inert-gas shielded arc welding equipment. (Courtesy of Air Reduction Sales Co., New York.)

Electric Arc Stud Welding. End welding stud bolts by an electric arc process was successfully realized in the latter years of the 1930 decade. Stud welding is now regarded as an accepted method. Its definition by the American Welding Society is "an arc welding process wherein coalescence is produced by heating with an electric arc drawn between a metal stud, or similar part, and the other work part until the surfaces to be joined are properly heated, when they are brought together under pressure, and no shielding is used."[1]

Fig. 35-11. Welding 0.062 gage Al wing tanks with automatic consumable electrode argon shielded arc. (Courtesy of Air Reduction Sales Co., New York.)

Equipment for stud welding consists of a source of direct current, a time control device, and the stud gun. The latter is equipped with a chuck for holding the stud during the welding cycle. Studs are of many designs; at one end they are threaded, blank, or contoured, depending on their use. The opposite, or base, end of the stud, which is the end where the welding occurs, contains flux held beneath a metal cap that gives the base end a conical appearance. A ceramic ferrule fits the welding end of the stud in a way that prevents the spatter of molten metal at the time the weld is actually made. The ferrule also functions as a mold which causes the molten metal at the base of the stud to be cast into a convex fillet.

[1] "Standard Welding Terms and Their Definitions," Standard A3.0-49, American Welding Society, New York, 1949.

Welding procedure consists of fixing a stud in the gun chuck, placing a ferrule in position around the stud, and then setting the stud on its desired location. The welding cycle is automatic and is controlled by the timer in the circuit. Depressing the gun trigger draws the stud away from the base metal, thereby establishing an arc and causing melting. After sufficient melting has occurred, a spring in the stud gun releases, forcing the stud into the pool of molten metal. This entire operation is automatic; it proceeds to completion upon the pressing of the gun trigger. A stud welding cycle is extremely fast, being on the order of $\frac{1}{20}$ sec for a $\frac{1}{8}$-in.-diameter and $\frac{3}{4}$ sec for a $\frac{3}{4}$-in.-diameter stud.

Fig. 35-12. Welding threaded studs with a Nelson stud gun. Note ceramic ferrules positioned on welded studs. (Courtesy of Gregory Industries, Lorain, Ohio.)

Studs are used for many types of fastenings, but threaded ones are in the majority. Figure 35-12 shows a stud gun in operation. Corrugated metal roofing is fastened by driving the sheet down over a welded stud and then riveting the latter.

Firecracker Welding. The principle of making an arc weld with the electrode stationary has been considered for some time, abroad as well as in the United States. This technique has been termed firecracker welding, undoubtedly from the fact that the actual welding operation simulates the burning of a fuse on a firecracker.

The technique, in the case of a lap weld, consists of placing a shielded electrode along the length of the joint. One end of the electrode is connected to the power source. After the electrode has been put in place, it is covered by a holding strip, which is usually copper. This acts to hold the electrode in position and also to cool the electrode, which will become overheated if it is too long. Once the assembly is in position, the arc is started by contacting the electrode with the base metal by means of a piece of carbon or similar material. The length of the arc will be equal to the thickness of the shielding on the electrode. There is difficulty in starting the arc, since there is a tendency for the electrode to stick immediately following the kindling of the arc.

Research conducted on this process at the University of Washington led to a solution of the problem of arc starting through tapering the electrode so that the end starting the weld presented but a very small volume of metal. The setup for firecracker welding has been varied by different researchers. Some have included strips of paper in order to increase the shielding on the electrode.

The results obtained were entirely satisfactory in the experiments referred to above. The penetration and soundness of these welds show the excellent fusion obtained. There has not been very much application of this technique in American industry.

Electrode Techniques. With the development of heavily coated electrodes, there has been some interest in new manipulation techniques, among them the deep fillet technique. In this method of welding the proper electrode is held close to the work; a high welding current and fast travel speed, used with alternating current, form a combination delivering good penetration.

A similar development has recently been offered in the form of contact welding electrodes. It is claimed that they merely need to be touched to the base metal and moved along the joint without any attempt to maintain a given arc length. The disadvantage of the contact electrode is its high cost.

SURVEY QUESTIONS

35-1. Where does automatic arc welding fit into manufacturing?

35-2. Describe "bare electrode" welding.

35-3. Wherein do shielding concepts differ in automatic as compared with manual arc welding?

35-4. Mention the most widely used types of shielding gases.

35-5. Suggest a specific application for submerged melt welding.

35-6. Discuss any major limitations to the use of submerged arc welding.

35-7. How is arc shielding accomplished in the submerged type welding?

35-8. Suggest some advantages to the use of semiautomatic submerged arc welding.

35-9. Where are flux-cored electrodes used?

35-10. Suggest any advantages to the use of dual-shielded arc welding.

35-11. List the equipment for an inert-gas welding station.

35-12. What effect, if any, does polarity have in inert-gas welding?

35-13. Why is it impossible to use oxygen regulators with inert gas?

35-14. What makes filler-wire composition important to CO_2-shielded welding?

35-15. If inert-gas welding is suited to structural steel welding, give some advantages or reasons.

35-16. Explain the operation of nonconsumable electrode welding.

35-17. How is argon treated in order to improve weld penetration?

35-18. Give the composition of "TIG" electrodes.

35-19. List some advantages of TIG welding over oxyacetylene torch welding.

35-20. Can MIG and TIG welding be used interchangeably with equal results?

35-21. A longitudinal weld is to be made in a 304L stainless steel tank designed with a butt joint. Specify the best engineered weld here.

35-22. If MIG is not confined to welding wrought metals, give an exception.

35-23. Suggest the most satisfactory method of welding the butt joints in the deck plating of an oil tanker.

35-24. Discuss the possibility of welding hull plate joints with an automatic submerged arc.

35-25. Does stud welding qualify as a shielded arc method? Why or why not?

35-26. How can stud welding be of utility in welding structural steel?

35-27. Suggest an economical application for firecracker welding.

35-28. A boiler drum is fabricated from 2-in. plate by welding. What welding method should be used in order to develop specification welds?

35-29. Is a submerged melt weld a multiple-pass type or not? Why?

35-30. What advantages does contact electrode type welding offer over other manual ones?

35-31. The designer is considering both spot welding and TIG for a weld in 5056 Al sheet. Which of these two methods will give the weldment with least weight? Why?

35-32. Which type—a submerged-arc weld or an inert-gas-arc weld—is easier for the weldor to make? Why?

Chapter 36

AUXILIARY TORCH AND ARC APPLICATIONS

The flexibility of both the torch and the arc has led to the development of applications which cannot be considered as strictly in the category of welding methods. The utility of these two sources of heat has been a factor in such developments as flame shaping, hard surface overlaying, and heat bending, among others. Torch and arc progress has been such that they are now regarded as inseparable from any broad welding program.

Flame shaping is closely related to welding. Engineering design is

Fig. 36-1. Diesel engine base being fabricated from flame-cut steel sections. Note weld positioner for rotating weldment. (Courtesy of Electromotive Division, General Motors Corp., La Grange, Ill.)

employing welded flame-shaped components to an increasing degree (Fig. 36-1). The edge preparation for welding plate is largely a matter of using flame shaping. Arc cutting is gaining in interest for those applications where the flame cannot be used or is ineffective. Materials such as the stainless steels and armor plate are leading examples. Both the torch and the arc have broad application in demolition and in scrap metal preparation.

Hard surfacing, in which both the arc and the torch are used, is accepted as routine by the industry. This process closely resembles welding in that metal is deposited on a base by the combination of a rod and a portable heat source. A further parallel is the recently introduced automatic arc equipment for hard surfacing. This has proved of great value in reclamation, as it has in processing components designed to withstand wear and abrasion.

Flame straightening is widely recognized in shipbuilding, where it has been developed further than in other applications. It is the purpose of this chapter to discuss all these related processes, since they are inseparable in any welding program.

FLAME SHAPING

Flame shaping is not an exact term inasmuch as the flame is an adjunct rather than the primary element in this method. There is some basis for the statement that flame shaping is more accurately described as oxygen shaping, since the basic process, as well as its many modifications, relies upon oxidation for its success. The major application of flame shaping is that of severing steel either at random or for contouring to dimension; consequently such terms as flame cutting and oxygen cutting are also commonly applied to this method.

Theory of Oxygen Cutting. All metallic materials are, in greater or less degree, subject to oxidation. The intensity of oxidation is dependent upon and related to such variables as composition, time, environment, surface condition, and temperature. In general the ferrous group, except for those alloys specially compounded for corrosion resistance, are preeminently sensitive to oxidation at ordinary temperatures. Mild steel is known to rust as the result of contacting oxygen borne in air and water. This reaction is characterized by the appearance of a red-brown surface overlay resulting from the combination of oxygen and iron and is expressed in the formula

$$2Fe + 3O = Fe_2O_3$$

Oxidation, or rusting, is a continuing process which causes gradual disintegration of the metal being attacked. The speed of this attack is a function of oxygen concentration as well as of temperature.

Pure iron, if heated to its kindling temperature and then subjected to a stream of pure oxygen, will burn violently. This phenomenon is the basis of the use of the shop term "burning" in reference to oxygen cutting. While this shop term may be natural enough, its use is to be discouraged on the ground of inaccuracy, since oxygen-cut steel and burnt steel are not remotely related. The equation given above indicates the necessity for purity of the elements concerned. Any impurities present will tend to retard the reaction; this applies especially to oxygen.

Fig. 36-2. Manual torch cutting operation. (Courtesy of Victor Equipment Co., San Francisco.)

The reaction between iron and oxygen occurs at kindling temperature, about 1600°F, as follows:

$$3Fe + 2O_2 = Fe_3O_4 + 26{,}691 \text{ cal}$$

The resultant material is black oxide of iron.

The fundamentals of flame shaping consist of heating the metal to its kindling temperature, then directing a blast of oxygen against the heated area, thereby causing rapid oxidation to occur (Fig. 36-2). The success attained is a function of the composition of the base metal. Oxygen cutting cannot be used to shape nonferrous metals, cast irons, or stainless steels. All of these are, in demolition and in emergency repair work, melted by a torch flame. Preheating is the term applied to the procedure of bringing metal to its kindling temperature.

Preheating Flames. A concentrated heat source capable of high temperatures is important to flame cutting. The accepted means of accomplishing preheating is the use of a combination of a combustible gas mixed with oxygen. In theory any combustible gas should be satisfactory for preheating; however, there are practical considerations such as metal composition, gas cost and availability, and heating time that must be considered. Frequently the choice of a preheating gas is predicated on local conditions.

TABLE 36-1. PROPERTIES OF SOME COMBUSTIBLE GASES*

Characteristic	Acetylene C_2H_2	Hydrogen H_2	Methane CH_4	Ethane C_2H_6	Propane C_3H_8	Normal butane C_4H_{10}	Iso-butane C_4H_{10}	Manufactured gas	Natural gas
Cubic feet of gas lb (60°F)....	14.3	187.7	23.64	12.594	8.6	6.5154	6.5154		
Btu/cu ft......	1,503	323.9	1,008	1,764	2,505	3,274	3,274	550	1,000
Btu/lb.........	21,572	60,810	......	22,216	21,500	21,331	21,331	20,050	21,496

* Compiled from various sources.

Properties of some of the better-known combustible gases are shown in Table 36-1. The matter of gas selection revolves around relative values. If rapid preheating time is of importance, as it is when numerous pieces are to be cut, then that gas giving the highest flame temperature should be selected. Where cuts of greater duration are the rule, preheating time loses much of its significance.

The combustion equation for acetylene gas (C_2H_2) is given in Chap. 32. Similar equations for propane, butane, and hydrogen follow:

	Oxy-propane flame	*Btu/cu ft*
Primary	$C_3H_8 + 1\frac{1}{2}O_2 = 3CO + 4H_2$	430.5
Secondary	$3CO + 1\frac{1}{2}O_2 = 3CO_2$	961.5
	$4H_2 + 2O_2 \quad = 4H_2O$	1108.0
		2500.0

1 volume C_3H_8 requires $5O_2$
Flame temperature, 5300°F

	Oxy-butane flame	
Primary	$C_4H_{10} + 2O_2 \quad = 4CO + 5H_2$	574
Secondary	$4CO + 2O_2 \quad = 4CO_2$	1282
	$5H_2 + 2\frac{1}{2}O_2 = 5H_2O$	1385
		3241

1 volume C_4H_{10} requires $6\frac{1}{2}O_2$
Flame temperature, 5300°F

Oxyhydrogen flame *Btu/cu ft*

$$H_2 + \tfrac{1}{2}O_2 = H_2O \qquad\qquad 275.1$$

Flame temperature, 5400°F

Comparison of the values resulting from combustion of these four gases shows that the oxy-butane mixture has the highest Btu per cubic foot potential but is capable of only a 5300°F flame temperature. It also reveals that the volume of oxygen required for primary combustion is greatest for butane and lowest for hydrogen. Another consideration worthy of note is that the oxyacetylene flame is most easily adjusted, a fact of considerable significance where carbon pickup on the edge of the cut is a critical consideration.

Fuel Gases Used for Cutting. Acetylene gas, while it has much to recommend it as a preheating gas, is not preeminent. There is much that can be said for other gases, especially for those in the liquefied petroleum gas field. Coke oven gas finds favor as a fuel for preheating in steel

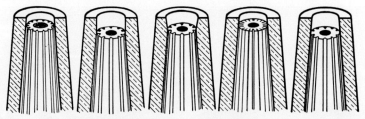

Fig. 36-3. Sketches showing recessed tips used with liquefied petroleum, manufactured and natural gas. (Courtesy of Harris Calorific Co., Cleveland.)

mill cutting operations. This gas can be used as manufactured or mixed with blast furnace gas or included in a combination of gases, depending on local conditions. Natural gas has proved itself as a satisfactory fuel for gas cutting. Its chief limitations are geographical, since no attempt is made to transport this gas in any other form than bulk pumped through distribution pipe lines.

Propane and butane, singly or in combination, are distributed as liquefied gases and, as such, find application as fuel for oxygen cutting. These gases are commonly merchandised under proprietary trade names. The addition of an "odorant" is practiced as a means of calling attention to and locating any leaks or gas escapement. Liquefied petroleum gases intended for industrial use, in contradistinction to those sold for domestic purposes, are primarily propane. Liquefied petroleum gases have a lower flame propagation speed than does acetylene gas. Because of this fact, recessed-type torch tips are necessary (Fig. 36-3). The design of these tips is varied to suit different gas characteristics. Manufacturers of oxygen cutting torches are in a position to supply recessed tips that will fit their standard torches.

Metallurgical Changes. There is some evidence indicating that a carbon pickup develops at the flame-cut surface. To avoid this, close attention must be given to flame composition during both the preheating and the cutting period. The increase in carbon near the surface even when hydrogen is the fuel gas indicates that circumstances other than flame conditions exist. The reasons for this carbon gain are that the carbon content of the plate back from the cut is lower than the original analysis,

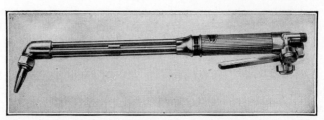

Fig. 36-4. Manual cutting torch. (Courtesy of Bastian-Blessing Co., Chicago.)

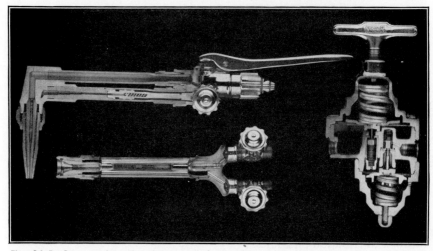

Fig. 36-5. Cross section of welding torch body with cutting conversion unit shown above; regulator at left. (Courtesy of Victor Equipment Co., San Francisco.)

indicating that a carbon migration is promoted by the heat of the cut.

Cutting Torches. The torch or blowpipe equipment used for flame cutting is designed for manual or machine operation. The former type (Fig. 36-4) is equipped with an angular head, while machine torch heads are commonly of a straight design. A manual cutting torch is similar to a welding torch but it is larger and of heavier construction. Further, in addition to the needle valves at the base for regulation of gas flow, there is a third valve, or trigger, for releasing the stream of cutting oxygen. The location of the third valve varies with different manufacturers although its function is the same in all cases.

There is a separate channel for the delivery of the cutting oxygen, which is always through the central part of the tip, regardless of tip design. Figure 36-5 shows the path of travel of the cutting oxygen as well as of the preheating gases. These views are of acetylene equipment as seen from the flush tip ends. The preheating gases are delivered through a series of ports located in a concentric circle surrounding the

Fig. 36-6. Reducing scrap ingots to charging box size with a heavy-duty machine cutting torch. (Courtesy of Linde Air Products Co., New York.)

central oxygen orifice. The number of preheating ports varies with the size of the piece to be cut; a greater number of preheating flames results in faster heating. The conversion units shown in Fig. 36-5 are attached to a welding torch body as a replacement for the welding head when it is desired to change over from welding to cutting without changing the torch body. A reconverted torch is satisfactory for maintenance and repair but for production and heavy cutting an integrated cutting torch is best from an operational as well as a cost viewpoint.

The machine cutting torch is of straight-line construction with the tip

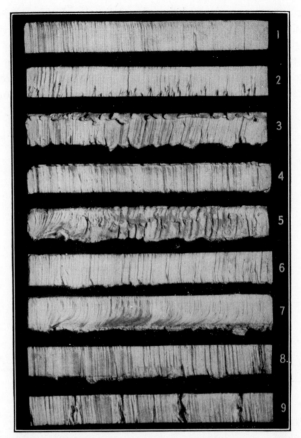

Fig. 36-7. Common faults occurring in hand cutting. (From "The Oxy-acetylene Handbook," Linde Air Products, New York, 1943.)

1. This is *a correctly made cut* in 1-in. plate. The edge is square and the draglines are essentially vertical and not too pronounced.

2. *Preheat flames were too small* for this cut: cutting speed was too slow, causing bad gouging at the bottom.

3. *Preheat flames were too long:* top surface has melted over, cut edge is irregular, and there is an excessive amount of adhering slag.

4. *Oxygen pressure was too low:* top edge has melted over because of the too slow cutting speed.

5. *Oxygen pressure was too high* and *nozzle size too small:* entire control of the cut has been lost.

6. *Cutting speed was too slow:* irregularities of the draglines are emphasized.

7. *Cutting speed was too high:* there is a pronounced break to the dragline and the cut edge is irregular.

8. *Blowpipe travel was unsteady:* cut edge is wavy and irregular.

9. *Cut was lost and not carefully restarted:* bad gouges were caused at the re-starting point.

as an extension of the body. Machine cutting blowpipes are constructed for heavier service and differ from the manual models on this account. Extremely heavy-duty cutting blowpipes reach massive proportions; because of their capacity they are water-cooled at the tip (Fig. 36-6). It is sometimes necessary, when heavy cutting is undertaken, to supply cutting oxygen through lines separate from those used in preheating.

Applied Cutting. Regardless of whether the cutting torch is guided manually or mechanically, the fundamental principle of cutting is the same: heating a spot or edge to kindling temperature and then causing an oxygen stream to impinge thereon. Preheating time can be lessened by choosing a corner or edge in preference to a mass of metal as a target. The device of using a chisel to raise a sliver of metal from a heavy

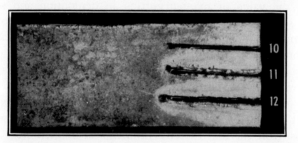

Fig. 36-8. Plan view of torch cuts in steel plates. (From "The Oxy-acetylene Handbook," Linde Air Products, New York, 1943.)

10. *Correct procedure was used* in making this cut.

11. *Too much preheat was used* and *nozzle was held too close to the plate:* a bad melting over of the top edge occurred.

12. *Too little preheat was used* and *flames were held too far from the plate:* the heat spread opened up the kerf at the top; the kerf is too wide at the top and tapers in.

section as a means of rapid preheat will save both time and gas. Once the stream of cutting oxygen is released, rapid oxidation occurs, forming a kerf through the metal in a manner similar to the action of a ripsaw on lumber. The slag from the kerf assists in carrying the cut forward. However, when plates of any thickness are being cut, the cut does not remain perfectly normal to the plate surface, since it does not penetrate the full plate thickness instantaneously. As a result, the kerf cross section assumes a curved shape with the bottom of the cut showing some lag —in cutting terminology, drag. The amount of drag is of small consequence on straight-line cuts, but it is important when contouring is being done or curves are being produced. The amount of drag can be modified by controlling the speed of cut and the gas pressures.

Cutting can be so closely controlled that properly cut plates compare favorably in dimensional accuracy with those produced by machining. The common errors in cutting are shown in Fig. 36-7, where sections of 1-in. plate have been subjected to some of the variabilities arising in applied cutting; the caption explains the error in each case.

The illustrations in Fig. 36-7 pertain to the vertical cross section of the kerf. Plan views of plate cutting are given in Figure 36-8. Careful study of these two figures, together with their accompanying explanations, will familiarize the student with the principles of controlled cutting. Selection of the correct size and style of cutting tip and oxygen pressure should follow the manufacturer's recommendation. The choice of tip size is governed by the type of material to be cut, its surface condition, and its thickness.

Flame shaping is largely confined to mild steel plates because of their adaptability to this process and the welding operations that follow. However, the value of oxygen cutting in demolition and scrap preparation is so great that it seems safe to refer to it as one of the most valuable tools in industry. Cast iron is never shape-cut; rather it is cut into sections which are utilized for furnace charges. Cutting cast iron with a torch is difficult, since extremely wide kerfs are necessary in order to circumvent the graphitic carbon constituent. An expedient is to feed a steel rod into the cut in order to provide a greater volume of slag and higher temperature. Another device is to place a steel waster plate on the cast-iron surface, thereby utilizing the molten steel slag as the agency for melting through the cast iron. Somewhat similar ideas have been employed where copper-base alloys required demolition.

Machine Oxygen Cutting. There are many designs of mechanical equipment used for flame shaping. This equipment had its inception in the idea of replacing manual operation with a more precise mechanical movement. The development of machine oxygen cutting equipment has proceeded to the point where automatic operation is accomplished. Equipment development has followed along three basic types, designed respectively for straight-line cuts, circles and contours, and profiling. Each type is available as single- or multiple-torch equipment.

Production cutting frequently employs a template, or profile, for a tracer guide. The method of holding the tracer element to the guide varies. In some cases friction is depended upon to perform this function; a more positive means is the use of a magnetized element for contacting the steel template. Electronic control of the tracer element has made possible the use of wooden templates or drawings for a guide. The light beam, which governs the tracer head movement, follows the drawing line or template edge, as the case may be. When electric-eye tracing is available, it is possible to use the drawing as a guide, thereby eliminating the expense and the time required for template construction. Electric-eye tracing has proved satisfactory for quantity production from a given drawing, thereby inaugurating a speedy and economical flame-cutting routine (Fig. 36-9).

The flame cutting of circles is performed with equipment that uses the idea of guiding from a point located at the center of the circle. The cutting torch (or torches) is mounted on a tractor driven by an electric motor. The motor is arranged with a variable drive for optimum operating speeds. The radius arm of the machine is adjusted to fit any circle within the range of the equipment.

Straight-line work constitutes the major part of automatic flame cutting. Plates are cut to size or edges straightened or beveled with automatic equipment (Fig. 36-10).

Fig. 36-9. Electronic tracer-type multiple-torch flame cutting machine. Note tracing device at left with three torches cutting simultaneously. (Courtesy of Air Reduction Sales Co., New York.)

The various arrangements possible for edge preparation are manifold. It is possible, for example, to set up two torches for concurrent cutting: the leading one is slanted for the desired bevel cut and is followed by a vertical torch that takes off the toe of the bevel and leaves a vertical root for the weld.

Computer-controlled Flame Profiling Machine. Flame profiling has seen significant development in the shipbuilding industry as it has in the fabrication of machine bases, frames, and mechanical equipment generally. The actual procedure starts with a design drawing. The implementation of the design can follow several different methods, as described in this chapter. An extension of currently accepted methods has come about through the introduction of the techniques discussed in Chap. 18. The

Fig. 36-10. Straight-line cutting with tractor-mounted torch. Tractor speed is variable as is torch position. (Courtesy of Air Reduction Sales Co., New York.)

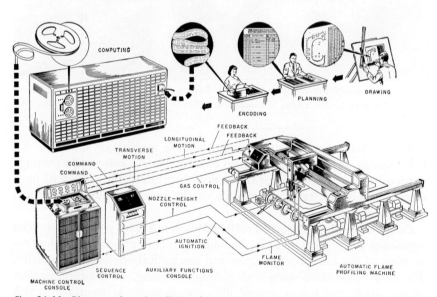

Fig. 36-11. Diagram of an installation for a computer controlled flame profiling machine. (Courtesy of British Oxygen Gases, Ltd., London, England.)

adaption of numerical control to flame profiling introduces economies and degrees of accuracy unobtainable by any other known methods.

The equipment and procedures are much the same in flame profiling as they are in machine tools operated by numerical control. A flow chart of an installation of an automatic flame profiling machine is detailed in Fig. 36-11. The part to be profiled may be designed in the usual manner; however, the dimensions should be specified as positions relative to the system of axes rather than as linear measurements. The planning sheet is developed wherein programming is critical. Programming consists of such basic profiling information as cutting speed, kerf width, preheat time, etc. Operating routine is the one familiar to numerical control of machine tool equipment. The sequence control is designed to care automatically for:

1. Gas control
2. Preheat flame ignition
3. Flame height sensing
4. Flame monitoring

In Fig. 36-12 the various controls are shown, including the flame ignition electrode, together with other accuracy-promoting instrumentation.

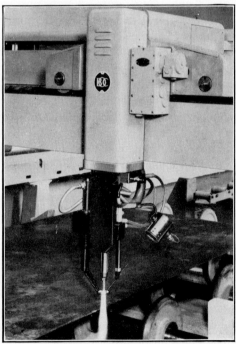

Fig. 36-12. Cutter head automatically flame profiling steel plates. (Courtesy of British Oxygen Gases, Ltd., London, England.)

Stack Cutting. Duplicate plate or sheet parts can be produced economically by flame shaping. There is no necessity for making an expensive die when production requirements are not sufficient to warrant it. Instead, the sheet steel or plates are stacked and the desired shape is flame-cut through the entire stack thickness. A precaution that must be observed is making sure that the sheets in the stack contact firmly; otherwise the cut will be arrested on passing through one plate or sheet.

Specialized Cutting Applications

Powder Cutting. Flame-cutting stainless steel has been difficult because the material is specially made to resist oxidation and when melted a tenacious chromium oxide is formed. There have been expedients tried for solving this problem, such as waster plates and increased tip sizes coupled with high gas pressures; however, none of these proved entirely satisfactory. A completely new and successful approach to flame-cutting stainless steel introduces a powdered material into the cutting stream.

Iron powder is used in another method. The powder is blown through the cutting tip by air or nitrogen under pressure. Upon issuing from the tip, the powder enters the preheating flames and burns, with a resulting increase in the flame temperature. Torch tips require additional orifices through which the powder stream can issue prior to entering the flame. Auxiliary equipment for placing the powder under pressure and separate lines for carrying it to the torch are requirements of this method.

A different approach to powder cutting consists of introducing a dry flux into the oxygen stream. The action of the flux is considered to be chemical rather than thermal like that of the iron powder. The flux is blown into the cutting stream, where it reacts to produce a very fluid slag stream that results in cutting speeds and quality comparable to mild steel cutting. Figure 36-13 illustrates the stack cutting of stainless steel sheets by the powder method.

Arc Cutting. The principle of arc cutting is merely that of melting a path through the base metal. There is no comparison in quality of cut between torch cutting and arc cutting. The latter produces a very rough kerf and one that is difficult to hold to alignment. Arc cutting has been successfully used on copper-base alloys and other metals that are not easily severed with a cutting torch. It is a ready means of accomplishing demolition work where a torch is unsatisfactory.

Arc cutting has commonly been done with a hard carbon or graphite electrode using direct current, although alternating current has also been employed. The cut is made upward on heavy material in order to keep the bottom of the kerf in the lead. Metal electrodes, both plain and

Fig. 36-13. Stack cutting twelve 10-gage type 304 stainless steel sheets by powder cutting method. (Courtesy of Linde Air Products Co., New York.)

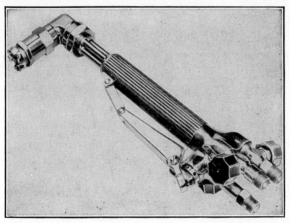

Fig. 36-14. Underwater cutting torch. Note the three gas connections at base of torch. (Courtesy of Bastain-Blessing Co., Chicago.)

shielded, are used for arc cutting. Shielded electrodes will function adequately, but their cost may be a deterrent. Soaking a gas-type shielded electrode in water will speed up the cutting operation.

Underwater Cutting. An underwater cutting torch is similar to a standard cutting torch, with the addition of a skirt over the tip (Fig. 36-14) and an additional line to supply compressed air to the skirt or cap.

Acetylene gas is used for shallow depths, but on jobs of depth greater than 25 ft, hydrogen is used as the fuel gas because pressure requirements are beyond the safe limits for acetylene.

The tip skirt, or sheath equipped with end vents, is placed against the work and air is turned in. The air acts to hold the water away from the flame and at the same time supplies the secondary oxygen necessary to sustain the preheating flames. The torch can be lighted prior to descent, or an electrical spark-plug arrangement can be incorporated in the tip for lighting the preheating flames. Underwater cutting is also accomplished with an electric arc, using a shielded electrode.

Arcair Process. A novel process of gouging and cutting with an arc is termed the arcair process; this is essentially the melting of metal with

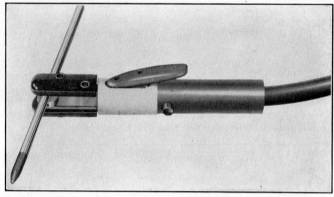

Fig. 36-15. Arcair metal cutting and gouging torch with mounted graphite cutting electrode. (Courtesy of Arcair Co., Bremerton, Wash.)

an electric arc and the mechanical removal of the molten metal by means of a high-velocity air jet. Since it does not depend on oxidation, it is used successfully on metals which do not readily oxidize, such as stainless steels and copper alloys. Its application to structural steel is especially effective for gouging and removal of weld backing beads.

The torch consists of an external air nozzle which provides a stream of air which is parallel to the electrode and which is maintained in position even though the direction of the electrode is changed. A valve is provided to control the air "on" and "off," and a coaxial cable to supply the current and air (Fig. 36-15).

Carbon electrodes are usually used with d-c reverse polarity at high current values. Speed of travel is approximately 24 in./min for a 3/8-in. groove, but it will vary with the depth and type of cut. The surface is extremely smooth; though some carburization is present, it is confined to a very thin layer.

SURFACING

Surfacing is defined as the "deposition of filler metal on a metal surface to obtain desired properties or dimensions."[1] Obviously this definition is subject to some variation in interpretation, since the term deposition can be understood to refer to either coalescence or a mechanical bond.

Hard Facing. The term hard facing is applied to those welding processes in which a surfacing material is applied for the purpose of increasing resistance to abrasion or corrosion or both. This development is also referred to as hard surfacing, especially where the object is to produce an edge or surface capable of resisting abrasion. Oil drilling tools were among the first kinds of equipment to be given this treatment. Hard surfacing is applied to either new or worn parts. An especially broad area for this process is the equipment used by contractors, such as dipper teeth and blading for graders. The useful life of surfaces on switch frogs and crusher liners has been prolonged by overlaying the wearing area with some type of hard-surfacing material.

TABLE 36-2*

Operating requirements	Service and/or production conditions	Recommended surfacing material
Extreme impact...............	Build up and joining 13% Mn steel	Austenitic Mn steel
Severe impact...............	Slight deformation permissible	Pearlitic steel, chrome base, Cr-Mo base
Impact and abrasion..........	Tough, hard deposits of alloy steels that can be forged and heat-treated	Martensitic steels
Impact and abrasion at elevated temperatures	Frictional wear, seizing, galling, and softening to 1100°F	High-speed steels, die steels
Elevated temperatures, corrosion abrasion, some impact	Resistance to hot-gas corrosion up to 2000°F	Cobalt base with high chromium and tungsten
Severe abrasion with light impact	Ball mill liners	Ni-Cr irons, Cr-Mo irons
Severe abrasion under light loads	Plowshares, sand chutes	Austenitic high-chromium irons
Extreme abrasion............	Sharp cutting edges	Tungsten carbide

* Abstracted and compiled from manufacturers' publications.

The development of surfacing materials has kept pace with the broadening demand, with the result that there is now an extensive selection of materials available for every condition of service and method of application. The information in Table 36-2 is included as a guide to the selection

[1] Standard A3.0-49, American Welding Society, New York, 1949.

of proper hard-surfacing materials. The tabulation shows that surfacing materials include many highly alloyed steel types as well as carbides and nonferrous compositions, some of which were discussed in Chap. 4.

Hard facing cannot be applied indiscriminately to all metals; this applies especially to the nonferrous group. The light metals are not suitable because of their low melting points. Copper-base alloys are rarely considered for hard-surfacing treatment, since they also have melting points below those of the surfacing materials. Monel metal is an exception in that it is readily adaptable to hard surfacing.

As a general rule those steels which are readily weldable offer no

Fig. 36-16. Power shovel bucket being repaired and hard-faced manually. (Courtesy of Stoody Co., Whittier, Calif.)

difficulty for hard surfacing (Fig. 36-16). When, however, carbon contents increase, precautions such as preheating and postheating are necessary as a means of avoiding cracking and shrinkage difficulties. The more complex steel compositions, such as high-speed and stainless types, require individual consideration as to procedures and techniques.

Hard facing is not confined to engineering manufacture. The petroleum industry offers a diversity of applications. Processing industries where eroding materials are handled offer outlets for overlay work. Agricultural equipment, especially plowshares and other items of tillage equipment, is one of the prominent subjects for hard facing.

Application Procedures. Hard-surfacing materials are supplied in the form of weld rods and electrodes. They are, therefore, applied to the base metal by any of the commonly known welding methods. The original method of application was by the use of a gas torch with the hard-facing material in the form of a weld rod. There is a considerable amount of knowledge required for best results, since heats range from melting of the base metal down to temperatures just below or approaching fusion.

Deposits vary in thickness considerably, a minimum layer being $\frac{1}{16}$ in. When heavy build-up is necessary, it is common practice to use a low-priced material for the backup material, and to top it with a high-quality surfacing.

Fig. 36-17. A crusher mantel mounted on a positioner for rotation under automatic head that is depositing high-chrome wear-resistant facing. (Courtesy of Stoody Co., Whittier, Calif.)

Hard-surfacing materials are available in electrode form suitable for application by arc welding. Some of these are solid electrodes, either bare or shielded. Others are in the form of tubing in which the surfacing material is in fragments held within the tube. This scheme solves the problem of physical form preparation of such materials as the carbide types and permits the use of particles whose cost is substantially lower than those requiring more elaborate preparation.

A noteworthy achievement in arc application of hard surfacing (Fig. 36–17) has been the automatic arc. Hard-surfacing material in wire form is supplied in coils for use in an automatic arc welding head. Where the entire operation can be mechanized, genuine savings in over-all costs are possible.

Soft Facing. Not all overlay work is done with materials designed to increase surface hardness. On the contrary, there is considerable application for copper-base alloys as surfacing materials. Primarily the use of bronze overlays is restricted to areas subject to wear by friction. In some instances, built-up surfaces are repaired by bronze. There are examples of shafts being built up oversize and then machined to bearing diameter. An interesting application of bronze is the resurfacing of valve seats in a motor block. Bronze overlays are not confined to wearing surfaces, since these have properties of corrosion resistance that can be exploited. Another application can be found in resisting erosion, as in valve seats or drawing dies. Monel has proved itself as a facing material in steam turbine casings where steam-flow action causes erosion.

SPRAYED METAL COATINGS

Metalizing lends itself to two main fields of application. One is metal-sprayed coatings designed for improving surface conditions, as for cor-

Fig. 36-18. Crankshaft bearing being built up by metal spraying process. The spray gun is mounted on a lathe carriage. (Courtesy of Metallizing Co. of America, Chicago.)

rosion and temperature resistance; maintenance and repair comprise the second. Sprayed coatings for decorative effects on such diverse materials as wood, glass, and ceramics are a further category. A significant development in promoting metalizing stems from the adaption of standardized symbols for metalizing (AWS Code C2.6-57T). With these symbols it is now possible to indicate on a design exactly what is desired in the way of metalizing.

Equipment. A spray gun is the essential part of a metalizing installation. The spray gun serves as a device for atomizing the coating material and then delivering it through a nozzle in the form of a spray possessing sufficient velocity to cause impact on contact with the bare surface (Fig. 36-18). The gun is serviced by a source of heat—either oxyacetylene or some other combustible gas, such as propane or hydrogen. The material to form the metal spray is commonly fed to the gun as wire; there are instances where powder is used, but in these cases distinctive equipment is necessary. Compressed air is connected to an air turbine in the spray gun as a means of feeding the wire; it also serves to atomize the molten metal and blow it out through the nozzle.

Nozzles and attendant equipment are available in a range of sizes that will accommodate wire diameters up to and inclusive of ⅛ in. The

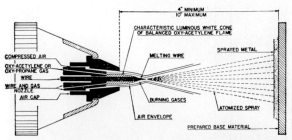

Fig. 36-19. Wire nozzle and air cap cross section of one type of metal spray gun. (Courtesy of Metallizing Engineering Co., Inc., Westbury, N. Y.)

speed of wire feed is controlled by a needle valve in the turbine air line or by a governor. Nozzles must be selected to operate with the particular type of fuel gas in use (Fig. 36-19). Operation of the spray gun is continuous with the metalizing wire being fed into the gas flame where it is melted. The molten globules are atomized by the compressed-air jet operating at 60 to 70 psi, and blown out through the orifice in the nozzle.

Preparation of Surface. The surface to be sprayed must be properly prepared. All foreign matter must be removed as a preliminary to subjecting the surface to some form of roughening treatment. The surface texture must be such that it will offer anchoring points for the spray particles. It is important to note that the *bond between the spray coating and the surface metal is mechanical.* This being the case, every effort must be made to have surface roughness of such a character that when the spray strikes it will adhere firmly.

Several methods of surface preparation are general; of these, grit blasting offers the least complications. The choice of method is dependent upon the shape and size of the part to be sprayed. Circular components, such as shafting, are mounted in a lathe, and a coarse, rough thread is cut on the surface (Fig. 36-20). When this treatment fails to produce proper keying points, it is common practice to run a knurling tool over the thread crests in order to flatten them in a manner that leaves an undercut effect on the part.

Another technique consists of using an electric arc to roughen the surface in place of either a blast or a machining operation. There is a metalizing wire which requires no surface preparation—it can be sprayed directly on any clean area.

Fig. 36-20. Preparing surface for metal spray operation by using a 50° threading tool ground with negative rake to push out base metal rather than remove it. (Courtesy of Metallizing Co. of America, Chicago.)

Spraying Procedures. Metal coatings should be sprayed in light layers with the gun nozzle held 4 to 10 in. from the surface. The desired thickness is obtained by applying a sufficient number of layers. This procedure is preferred to applying a single heavy layer, since heavy layers are subject to stratification difficulties. Spraying can be done by manual manipulation with the smaller, portable guns; when heavier equipment is used, the gun is mechanically mounted.

The metalized surface can be finished by machining to dimension. Components that have been machined undersize are built up by metal spraying. A sprayed metal surface reacts differently from solid material to machining operations. Tool positions, feed, and speeds are different for machining sprayed surfaces.

Metal Spray Applications. The field of application for metalizing is being extended constantly. Substituting powder for wire makes it possible to use coating materials that cannot be produced as wire. Powder spraying is accomplished by equipment so constructed that the powder is drawn into the nozzle by suction. The base material need not be metallic. For example, the plating that was formerly used for carbon brushes has been supplanted by spraying with copper.

Sprayed metal coatings are used for joining, in what amounts to a brazing operation. The faying surfaces are sprayed with the bonding

Fig. 36-21. Powder spray equipment operates without using compressed air. (Courtesy of Metallizing Engineering Co., Inc., Westbury, N.Y.)

metal; surfaces are assembled and placed in a furnace, where temperatures are raised to the flow point of the sprayed metal. The resultant weld is on occasion referred to as a spray weld. This development, as well as the method of using hard-surfacing materials for wire and of making hard-faced overlays by metal spraying, is known to the industry.

Armor-plated Plastic Dies. The use of plastic dies is rather a conflicting one in the metal forming field. Actually, plastics generally cost more than metals for the same job, although the reverse can also be true. The secret lies in the ability of plastic dies to be made so much more cheaply than metal ones. The limitation on the use of plastic dies has been the small production, in the area of 10 to 20,000 stampings. However, this has been overcome by armor plating such dies with a metalized spray, to the point where their life is extended over 100,000 pieces. It is claimed that the spray coatings add somewhere between 5 and 10 per cent to the total cost of the dies. A further claim advanced for the sprayed plastic dies is the porous nature of the coating, which aids in holding lubricant during the operating production cycle.

Ceramic-sprayed Coating. The impact of ceramics upon engineering manufacture is presented in Chap. 4. Recently, the requirements for high-temperature-resisting surfaces has led to the investigation of ceramic coatings. This has been successful since equipment and techniques have been developed for spraying powder (Fig. 36-21). Among the more important coating materials are aluminum oxide, zirconium silicate, and stabilized zirconium. These hard, crystalline refractory oxides offer important advantages. They are both thermally and electrically insulating. Their hardness, chemical inertness, and stability in combustion temperatures provide high resistance to excessive heat, abrasion, erosion, and corrosion. Their high melting points and low thermal conductivities reduce the temperature of the underlying materials and permit high operating temperatures. The melting point of these oxides reaches 4500°F, which compares to 2600°F for some types of stainless steels. The development of these oxide coatings has been patented and a license is required for their use.

CONTRACTION

The author makes no claim for originality in the matter of employing contraction as a tool for correcting distorted or bent sections in ductile metal members. On the contrary, he recognizes the pioneering work in this field done by Joseph Holt and published in a copyrighted pamphlet more than a decade ago.[2] However, the author has had considerable experience with the Holt method, working individually as well as with the originator of this technique for contraction bending.

Heat Bending. The basic principle in using contraction as an easy means of causing metal to move is that of upsetting a section in such a manner and in such a position that subsequent cooling will cause contraction to be effective at a chosen point or region. A member is heated differentially so that expansion is confined and as a result the area of elevated temperature cannot elongate but upsets. Heating must follow a carefully chosen pattern, since a member cannot be heated completely across its section lest no upsetting action occur. The heated area is of a

[2] Holt, Joseph: "Contraction as a Friend in Need," Seattle, Wash., 1938. Permission has been granted the author for use of any material appearing in this publication.

conformation that permits the remainder of the cross section being straightened to remain at normal temperature. The cool section acts as the restraint which causes the upsetting behavior of the heated area. Figure 36-22 shows diagrammatically the manner in which a flat steel bar can be bent by the application of these principles.

Initial heating is applied at point *A*, located approximately one-third the distance in from the edge *DE*. When using a welding flame, it should be positioned so that it points toward *BC* or in the direction in which the heat is to travel. *Heating should be done rapidly and uniformly* by moving the flame in a sidewise path over a triangular area

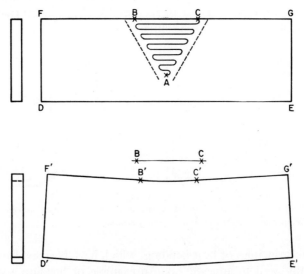

Fig. 36-22. Heat bending applied to a flat bar of uniform cross section. Top, primary heat-affected area within dotted lines. Continuous line shows path of torch flame and area of upset.

whose apex is located at *A* and whose base is formed by *BC*. Special care should be exercised in heating, since failure to confine the heated area will defeat the entire objective. If, for example, the heat effect is permitted to wander from point *A* toward the edge *DE*, the entire bar will elongate and the desired positioned upsetting effect will be nullified because the area of the bar adjacent to the edge *DE* will not act as a restraining force against elongation. There must be a portion of the metal remaining at a temperature lower than the heated area if localized upsetting is to occur.

After the triangular area is heated rapidly, the heat source is withdrawn. The metal within the heated area cannot expand longitudinally owing to the restraint of the cooler metal adjacent to the edge *DE*. In consequence, edge *FG* has not elongated; rather, the area bounded by *A, B, C* has expanded into itself, causing increased thickening or upsetting of the metal in that area. Upon cooling, this critical area will contract, causing a shortening of the edge *FG* to the length *F'G'*. Obviously this shortening causes the entire bar to bend toward that edge.

The amount of bending resulting from a single heat application is dependent upon the temperature of both the heated and the restraint area. As a general rule, several small and rapid heat applications are preferable to one extended effort. Good results follow from the correct placing of heats and control of temperatures, and these are matters requiring the exercise of judgment. There is no point in heating steel to scaling temperature; as a matter of fact, a black heat, in contradistinction to a red one, will suffice for some applications.

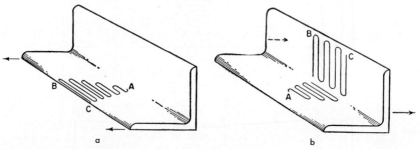

Fig. 36-23. Heat bending applied to equal-leg steel angles. Arrows indicate direction of bend upon cooling after heat has caused upsetting action.

The basic principles of heat bending, which have been explained above, apply equally well to any section. An example of bending a steel angle is sketched in Fig. 36-23*a* and 23*b*. In Fig. 36-23*a*, one entire leg acts as the restraining metal in a manner that will cause the angle to be bent toward edge *BC*. Figure 36-23*b* shows the angle bending in the opposite direction. Only the metal adjacent to *A* can act as restraint here, since the heated area extends across the remainder of the section. It might prove desirable to use a second torch on leg *BC* in order to meet the basic requirement of rapid heating.

Heat Straightening. The greatest utility of the heat bending process lies in straightening bent members. Potential applications are legion for this method. Considerable recognition has been given this method in straightening bent members of highway bridges damaged by blows or through the action of floods. It should be borne in mind that straightening is accomplished entirely by heat, employing the principles explained in this section.

A disastrous fire in two hangars at McChord Air Force Base, Washington, left these steel structures in severely warped and twisted condition (Fig. 36-24a). There was genuine concern about having to rebuild these hangars completely at a substantial cost. However, these structures have now been reclaimed by heat straightening methods (Fig. 36-24b). The result has proved to be a decided monetary saving to the government. Furthermore, the period during which these hangars were out of

Fig. 36-24a. Twisted steel structures in McChord Air Force Base fire-swept hangars.

Fig. 36-24b. Steel structures in McChord Air Force Base hangars, shown in Fig. 36-24a, following flame straightening. (Courtesy of U.S. Air Force, McChord Air Force Base, Washington.)

service was greatly lessened. Undoubtedly, this was the largest heat straightening job ever attempted and carried to successful completion.

Obviously, judgment of a high order is needed on a straightening job, since improperly placed heat applications can lead to disastrous results. It should be stressed that experience must be gained by a thorough grounding in fundamentals on simple members before complicated applications are attempted.

The use of heat straightening is not confined to structural steel members. The machine shop and assembly floor frequently have need of this method. Distorted castings of ductile metal offer a further field of application. In every instance it is essential that heat be applied at the correct location.

Small heats give closer control and better results. Heating a large area will frequently result in complete failure, since no restraining area remains. A cool restraining area is as necessary to success as is the heating feature of the heat straightening method.

SURVEY QUESTIONS

36-1. How are flame shaping and arc welding complementary?

36-2. On what design of welded joints is edge preparation necessary?

36-3. Give a broad application for arc cutting or severing.

36-4. Flame cutting uses two gases; which of these cannot be replaced?

36-5. Fundamentally, what is the basis of flame cutting?

36-6. Does a cutting flame resemble a welding flame in appearance? Explain.

36-7. What are preheating flames?

36-8. How does an improper gas mixture affect preheating flames?

36-9. Where is the necessary oxygen required for secondary combustion obtained?

36-10. List some fuel gases that are used for flame cutting.

36-11. Wherein are the cutting tips for the different fuel gases at variance?

36-12. Why is it possible to develop carbon pickup in flame-cut plate edges?

36-13. How can cutting torches be distinguished visually from welding ones?

36-14. What is needed to convert a welding torch into a cutting one?

36-15. Wherein does a machine cutting torch differ from a manual design?

36-16. How is the term "kerf" applied to flame cutting?

36-17. To what extent can dimensional accuracy be developed in flame cutting?

36-18. What type of materials lend themselves best to flame cutting?

36-19. What must be done in order to cut cast iron effectively?

36-20. How is it possible to sever cast iron rapidly with a gas torch?

36-21. Mention some problems encountered when cutting steel plate.

36-22. What equipment is necessary for contouring steel plate accurately?

36-23. If templates can be eliminated from flame-shaping steel plate, outline the requisite procedure.

36-24. What type equipment is needed for straight-line cutting with a torch?

36-25. Describe any equipment that can cut both straight and contour without making basic adjustments or additions.

36-26. If it is possible to flame-cut stainless steel, explain the needed procedure.

36-27. What are some advantages of arc cutting?

36-28. With what services must a shop be equipped that contemplates the installation of arcair cutting equipment?

36-29. Give an example of underwater cutting in connection with a construction job such as a dam.

36-30. How is the flame lighted for underwater cutting?

36-31. What can be done to prolong the life of a road-grader blade?

36-32. Specify an overlay material that will combat extreme abrasion.

36-33. How is it possible to reclaim a shaft journal that is worn 0.010 in. undersize?

36-34. What is the purpose of metalizing symbols?

36-35. Describe an application for a ceramic sprayed coating.

36-36. What is the basic principle of heat bending?

36-37. What type material lends itself best to heat bending?

36-38. What possibility exists for changing the chemistry of a member undergoing heat bending or straightening?

36-39. Discuss the application of heat bending to the straightening of a bent automobile frame.

REFERENCES FOR WELDING SECTION

Chaps. 30–36

"Adhesion and Adhesives," 1951, by DeBruyne-Houwink, Elsevier Publishing Company, Amsterdam.

"Adhesive Bonding of Metals," 1954, by Epstein, Reinhold Publishing Corporation, New York.

"Arcs in Inert Atmospheres," 1957, by Kuhn, John Wiley & Sons, Inc., New York.

"Brazing Manual," 1955, American Welding Society, New York.

"Codes, Standards, and Specifications," American Welding Society, New York.

"Electric Arc Manual," I & II, n.d., Murex Company, Waltham Cross, England.

"Handbook of Fastening and Joining Metal Parts," 1956, by Laughner and Hargen, McGraw-Hill Book Company, Inc., New York.

"The Oxy-Acetylene Handbook," 1947, The Linde Air Products Company, New York.

"Procedure Handbook of Arc Welding Design and Practice," 11th ed., 1957, Lincoln Electric Company, Cleveland.

"Thermal Stresses," 1957, by Gatewood, McGraw-Hill Book Company, Inc., New York.

"The Welding Encyclopedia," 13th ed., 1955, by Jefferson (ed.), McGraw-Hill Book Company, Inc., New York.

"The Welding Handbook," 1958, American Welding Society, New York.

"Welding Engineering," 1954, by Rossi, McGraw-Hill Book Company, Inc., New York.

"Welding Metallurgy," 2nd ed., 1949, by Henry and Claussen, American Welding Society, New York.

INDEX

Abrasives, artificial, 466
  grains, 467
  natural, 467
Acetone, 583
Acetylene, 581
  compressed, 582
  cylinders, 583
  generator, 582
  manifolds, 592
  regulators, 586
Adhesive bonding, 559
Alternating current, 567
  welding, 568
Aluminum alloys, 32, 211
  casting, 35
  designations, 34
  heat-treatment, 259
  wrought, 34
American Foundrymens Society (AFS), 14
American Iron and Steel Institute (AISI), designations, 22
American Railroad Association (ARA), 23
American Society for Testing Materials (ASTM), 22
American Welding Society (AWS), 551
Annealing, 250
Arc cutting, 658
Arc striking, 575
Arcair process, 660
Argon, 637
Armor-plated dies, 667
Atmosphere, controlled, 225
Atomic pile, 546
Austenite, 235
Automatic arc welding, 561, 627
  shielding, 628
Automatic screw machines, 314
  camless, 323
  disk-cam, 315
  drum-cam, 317

Automatic screw machines, multiple-spindle, 319
  single-spindle, 315
  Swiss, 318
Automation, 3
  cold-forming, 202
  molding, 126
  sectionized, 502

Bainite, 243
Benardos, N., 569
Bentonite, 89
Beryllium, 44
Blast cleaning, 171
  air, 172
  airless, 174
  mud, 173
  water, 173
Blowpipe, 580
Bolton, John, 13
Bonding agents, 89, 467, 559
Borides, 58
Boring, 279, 359
  bars, 365
  deep hole, 370
  precision, 366
Bournonville, Eugéne, 549
Brakes, 188
Braze joint design, 597
Braze welding, 594, 601
Brazing, 594
  alloys, 596
  bond, 595
  dip, 601
  flux, 597
  induction, 600
  metals, 595
  paste, 596
  torch, 598
  wire, 599
Brinell (Bhn), 239

Broaches, 431
  construction, 433
  pitch, 432
  shanks, 435
  surface, 434
Broaching fixtures, 438
Broaching machines, 435
  horizontal, 436
  vertical, 436
Buffing, 498
Burn-off, 575, 633
Byers process, 17

C process, 123
Calcium carbide, 580
Calipers, 533
  inside, 534
  micrometer, 534
  outside, 533
  vernier, 537
Can making, 197
Capitol, 14
Carbon dioxide gas, 634, 637
Carbon dioxide process, 95
Carbonitriding, 246
Carburizing, gas, 245
  liquid, 246
  pack, 245
Case hardening, 245
Cast alloys, 520
Cast iron, 11
  chilled, 12
  ductile, 15
  gray, 10, 13
  malleable, 15
    pearlitic, 16
Castings, 62
  centrifugal, 129
  continuous, 135
  die, 136
    air injection, 139
    cold-chamber, 137
    plunger-type, 137
    vacuum, 140
  distorted, 671
  permanent-mold, 131
  precision, 143
  plaster, 147
Cellini, Benvenuto, 143
Cemented carbides, 29, 520
Ceramic coatings, 60, 668
Ceramic oxide tools, 524
Cerium, 14
Cermets, 57
Chamfering, 282
Cheeks, 113

Chemical milling, 428
Chip formation, 514
Choke gate, 104
Chucking machine, 312
Clad sheet, 33, 210
Cobalt, 44
Coke, metallurgical, 153
Cold strip mill, 19
Cold weld, 553
Cold working, 179
  drawing, 181
  extrusion, 182
  forming, 184
  rolling, 180
Combination head, 533
Computers, 329, 655
Contraction, 73, 688
Converter, 155
Copper, 29
  casting alloys, 30
  wrought, 31, 211
Core baking, 95
Core blowers, 94
Cores, 74
  binders, 94
    gasless, 98
  box, 75
  dry-sand, 74
  foundry, 93
  metal, 133
  print, 75
Counterbores, 379
Countersinks, 379
Croning, Johannes, 123
Cupola, 152
  basic, 154
Cutting fluids, 513
Cutting torches, 650
Cybernetics, 5

D process, 125
Davy, Sir Humphry, 549
Delhi, 548
Dial gages, 537
Die heads, chasers, 348
  rotating, 348
  self-opening, 347
  solid, 350
  stationary, 348
Dies, 141, 202
  forging, 225
Dietert, H. W., 125
Dip brazing, 601
Distorted castings, 671
Distortion, 74, 252
Dividers, 534

Dividing head, 418
Draft, 66, 213
Drag, 653
Draw bench, 186, 556
Drilling, 372
Drilling machines, 380
  heavy-duty, 386
  multiple-spindle, 385
  radial, 385
  types, 381
  (*See also* Twist drills)
Drilling rates, 377
Drop-hammer forming, 194
Drop-hammer types, 215
Dura, 548
Duty cycle, 566

Electric arc stud weld, 641
Electric eye, 654
Electrodes, carbon, 569
  classification, 572
  coatings, 573
  color code, 574
  flux-coated, 634
  resistance type, 614
  shielded, 569, 572
  wire, 633
Electrolimit measuring, 368
Electronic control, 610
  slope, 611
End cutting edge angle, 518
Endothermic, 589
Epoxy resins, 80
Ernst, Hans, 512
Explosive forming, 204
Extrusion, 222
  cold, 182
  hot, 224

Facing, 277
  sand, 90
Feedback, 331
Ferrule, 641
Fiberglass, 46
Finishes, 491
Firecracker welding, 642
Flagging, 538
Flame hardening, 257
Flame shaping, 646, 654
Flash-back arresters, 592
Flash welding, 623
Flaws, 492
Floturn, 193
Follow board, 67
Forging, 212

Forging, closed die, 216
  drop, 213
  extrusion, 221
  hammer, 212
  impact die, 212
  no-draft, 217
  precision, 221
  press, 216
    massive, 217
  roll, 219
  upset, 220
Fouché, Edmond, 549
Foundry patterns, 63
  draft, 66
  fillets, 65
  mounted, 69
  parting, 66
  plastic, 78
  ribs, 64
Fuel gases, 649
Fuels, 151
Furnace, air, 156
  brazing, 600
  crucible, 158
  cupola, 152
  electric arc, 159
  induction, 162
    low-frequency, 164
  open-flame, 159
  resistance, 165
  reverberatory, 157

Gage blocks, 539
Gages, air, 543
  dial, 537
  multi-reading, 543
  plug, 540, 545
  ring, 540
  snap, 541
  visual, 542
Gaging, 538
  in-process, 538
  post-process, 538
  pre-process, 538
Gamma ray, 6
Gated patterns, 112
Gating system, 101
Gear checking, 461
Gear finishing, 458
  grinding, 460
  honing, 460
  lapping, 460
  pointing, 461
  shaving, 458, 460
    rack, 461
    rotary, 458

Gear shaping, 452
  generators, 452
  shear speed, 454
Gearing, accurate, 463
  fine pitch, 462
Gears, 443
  bevel, 446
    spiral, 456
    straight, 455
  fabricated, 457
  helical, 444
  herringbone, 444
  hobbing, 449
    machines, 451
  hypoid, 446
  milling, 448
  rack, 447
  spiroid, 444
  spur, 444
  square, 445
  worm, 446
    cone drive, 446
  zerol, 446
Glascast, 149
Goldschmidt, Hans, 551
Graduations, 532
Granular flux, 629, 631
Green compression, 87
Grinding, 471
  abrasive belt, 489
  cemented carbide, 475
  centerless, 482
  cutter, 474
  cylindrical, 477
    machines, 479
  disk, 487
  dry, 473
  face, 486
  fluids, 472
Grinding wheels, abrasives, 467
    bond, 467
    resinoid, 468
    rubber, 468
    silicate, 468
    vitrified, 468
  dressing, 471
  grades, 469
    designations, 470
  structure, 468
Grindstones, 465
Guerin forming, 194
Gypsum, 78

H-iron, 20
H-steels, 24
Hard facing, 661

Hardening, 233
  flame, 257
Hastelloy, 29, 262
Heat bending, 668
  straightening, 670
Heat-resisting alloys, 29
Heat-treatment, 231
  precipitation, 260
  solution, 259
Heating, induction, 256
  speed, 256
Helium, 637
Hess, Albert, 583
High-pressure molding, 119
Holslag, C. J., 567
Holt, Joseph, 668
Honing, 494
Hot spots, 72
Huntsman, Benjamin, 18
Hydroform, 196
Hydrogen, 639
Hydrospin, 192

Impact extrusion, 197
Indexing, 419
Induction brazing, 600
Inert-gas arc, 635
Ingot, 206
  iron, 21
Integrated-interlocked line, 509
Interferometer, 546
Interstate Commerce Commission, 585
Isothermal transformation, 239, 244
Isotopes, 7

Jig borer, 367
  tooling, 369
Jigs, 578
Jo-blocks, 539
Johansson, C. E., 539
Jolter, 115

Knurling, 282

Laminated products, 48
Lapping, 495
Lathe, automatic, 306
  bed, 282
  bench, 266
  carriage, 286
  centers, 272
  change gear train, 285
  chuck, 270

Lathe, chuck, collet, 271
  independent, 270
  universal, 270
  engine, 265
  headstock, 284
    spindle, 284
  lead screw, 286
  specialized, 289
  tail stock, 275, 287
  thread-cutting, 345
  turret (see Turret lathes)
Lay, definition, 492
Le Châtelier, H., 580
Light rays, 544
Lithium, 45
Low-pressure torch, 588

M-g (motor-generator) sets, 561
Machine oxygen cutting, 654
Magnesite, 160
Magnesium alloys, 36
  castings, 39, 41
  designations, 37
  pellets, 38
  wrought, 38, 211
MAGS, 639
Malcomizing, 249
Mandrels, 274
Manifolds, 592
Martempering, 253
Martensite, 236, 238, 241
Match plate, 68, 112
Mercury, 145
  pattern, 148
Metal ceramic, 59
  powders, 54
Metal electrode, 569
Microinch (μin.), 492
Micrometer calipers, 534
  direct reading, 537
  outside, 534
  thread, 536
Mig, 638
Milling, automatic cycle, 414
  carbide, 411
  down, 406
  face, 403
  peripheral, 403
  up, 405
Milling cutters, 407
  arbor mounting, 408
    angle, 409
    fly, 409
    formed, 409
    inserted tooth, 409
    plain, 408

Milling cutters, arbor mounting, side, 408
    slitting saw, 409
    staggered-tooth, 408
  shank mounting, 410
    end, 410
    shell, 411
    T-slot, 411
    Woodruff, 411
Milling machines, arbors, 419
  bed-type, 426
  column and knee, 412
  duplex, 421
  plain, 412
  planer, 422
  ram-type, 417
  rotary head, 426
  tracer, 424
  universal, 413
    head, 417
  vertical, 417
Mills, blooming, 208
  broach, 438
  continuous, 208
  reversing, 209
  three-high, 209
  Yoder, 187
Moldenke, Richard, 14
Molding sand, 82
  conditioning, 88
  grains, 84
  olivine, 83
  silica, 83
  specifications, 88
  synthetic, 83
  zircon, 84
Molds, CO_2, 95
  frozen, 126
  permanent, 131
  pit, 113
  semipermanent, 134
Monel, 43, 262
Ms temperature, 241
Muller, sand, 91

Natural aging, 261
NEMA code, 574
Nickel, 43
Nitralloy, 248
Nitriding, 246
  Floxe Process, 248
  glow discharge, 249
  liquid, 249
Nitrogen, 248, 638
Normalizing, 250
Nose, 518

Nucleonics, 5
  gages, 7
Numerical control, 8, 325, 327
  transfer line, 337

Olivine, 83
Optical measurements, 545
Oxyacetylene, 580
  welding flames, 589
Oxygen, 584
  cutting, 646
  cylinders, 585
  regulators, 586
Oxyhydrogen, 592

Parlanti molds, 132
Pattern, 62
  loose, 64
  parting line, 66
Percussion welding, 624
Perlite, 107
Permeability, 86
Picard Émile, 549
Pig iron, 11
Pin lift, 117
Pit molds, 113
Planers, 391
  double-cutting, 395
  openside, 392
Plaster, 77
Plastics, 45
  molding, 46
  types, 45
Platen, 196
Plywood, resin, 49
Polarity, 566
Polymers, 50
Powder cutting, 658
  metallurgy, 52
Power factor, 565
  line-load, 609
  supply, 608
Precision, 531
Preheating flames, 648
Press forming, 198
  hot, 221
  hydraulic, 200
  mechanical, 200
  transfer, 201
Pressure controls, 613
Process machines, 502
Process tape, 332
Profiler, 426
Programming, 337, 426
Projection welding, 622
Pulsation welding, 619

Quality control, 4
  gaging, 538
Quenching, 251

Radioactive isotopes, 7
Radioisotopes, 6, 546
Rake angles, 517
Raynham Hall, 548
Reaming, 281, 379
Rectifier direct current, 564
Relief angles, 517
Resistance welding, 606
  electrodes, 614
    composite, 615
  pressure controls, 613
Reynolds number, 110
Riser, 106
  blind, 108
  insulating, 106
Roll-over, 118
Rolling, cold, 180
  forming, 186
  hot, 206
Rms, 492
Rules, 532
Runner box, 103

S curves, 240
SAE-AISI steels, 23
Salt baths, 255
Sand muller, 91
Sand reclamation, 92
Sand slinger, 118
Screw threads, 341
  American Standard, 344
  forms, 345
  series, 343
Seam welding, 621
Selenium rectifiers, 564
Semiautomatic arc, 633
Shapers, 396
  draw cut, 400
  horizontal, 396
  vertical, 400
Shell cores, 98
Shell molds, 124
Shewhart, Walter, 4
Shot peening, 183
  forming, 184
Shrinkage, 73
Skelp, 556
Skim gate, 103
Slavianov, N., 549
Slotters, 401
Slush casting, 71, 134

Snap molds, 112
Snyder, W. A., 126
Society of Automotive Engineers
   (SAE), 22
Soft facing, 664
Solidification, 69, 105
   directional, 72, 103
Sowter, Anthony, 553
Spark drilling, 388
Spectrography, 545
Spinning, 189
   hot, 229
Spinning lathes, 190
Spot facer, 380
Spot welding, 617
   cycle, 618
   gun-type, 619
Sprayed metal coating, 664
Sprue, 101
Sprue cutter, 169
Squeezer, 114
   jolt, 116
   plain, 114
Stabilizing, 262
Stack cutting, 658
Steam treating, 249
Steel, 18, 231
   alloy, 21, 22, 27
   cementation, 18
   crucible, 18
   high-speed tools, 519
   low-alloy high-strength, 24
   methods, 19
   NE, 10
   plain carbon, 21, 235
   selection, 22
   stainless and heat resisting, 25
      precipitation hardening, 26
Steel making, 18
   Bessemer, 20
   electric, 19
   open-hearth, 18
   Stora, 20
Stirling iron works, 548
Stretch forming, 189
Stud welding, 641
Submerged melt weld, 629
Superfinish, 495
Supermicrometer, 541
Surface, 491
   nominal, 491
   quality, 492
   roughness, 492
      measurement, 493
      number, 492
Surfacing, 661
System sand, 90

TAGS, 639
Taps, 351
Taylor, Frederick, W., 511
Taylor-White Process, 511
Temperature control, 254
Temperature gradient, 607
Tempering, 237
Thomson, Elihu, 549
Threading, 280
   chasing, 346
   grinding, 335
   machines, 352
   milling, 356
   multiple-start, 345
   rolling, 354
TIG, 638
Time controls, 612
Titanium, 42
Tool blocks, 307, 309
   universal, 311
Tool cutting action, 512
Toolometer, 503
Tools, 516
   diamond-tipped, 526
   single-point, 516
   types, 518
Townsend, Peter, 548
Transfer machines, 501
Transfermatics, 502
Trepanning, 278
Tube-in-strip, 229
Tubing, seamless, 211
Tumbling mills, 170
Tungsten inert gas, 638
Turning, form, 277, 288
   straight, 274
   taper, 275
      attachment, 276
Turret lathes, 292
   automatic, 297
   drum-type, 305
   horizontal, 292
      ram-type, 295
      saddle-type, 293
      tooling, 300, 364
   vertical, 298
      automatic, 300
Twist drills, 373
   helix angles, 374
   lips, 376, 377
   points, 374
   sharpening, 375
   types, 378

Ultrasonics, 256
   machining, 526
   tooling, 527

Under-water cutting, 659
Upset welding, 624

VA curves, 563
Vacuum melting, 166
Van Horn, Kent R., 185
Vapor blast, 497
Variability, 531

Waviness, 492
Wax, 145
Weiner, Norbert, 5
Weld, cold, 553
Weld positioners, 577
Weld rods, 591
Welder, 553
Welding, 548
  a-c, 568
  arc, automatic, 561, 627, 628
    contact, 576
  braze, 594, 601
  electrodes, 608
    bare, 570
    shielded, 569
      iron powder, 573
      low-hydrogen, 573
  firecracker, 642
  flash, 623

Welding, flow, 554
  forge, 556
  induction, 557
  percussion, 624
  projection, 622
  pulsation, 619
  resistance (see Resistance welding)
  spot, 617–619
  stud, 641
  submerged melt, 629
  symbols, 558
  Thermit, 557
  transformers, 567
Welding hose, 587
Welding torches, 587
  design, 588
Weldor, 553, 591
West Point, 548
Willson, Thomas L., 580
Wrought iron, 17
Wrought-iron products, 62

Yoder mill, 187

Ziegler, Professor, 50
Zinc, 42
Zinc alloy castings, 42
Zircon, 34
Zirconium, 44